C0-AZS-505

The
Cell Biology
of
Sponges

Tracy L. Simpson

The
Cell Biology
of
Sponges

With 221 Figures

Springer-Verlag

New York   Berlin   Heidelberg   Tokyo

Tracy L. Simpson
Department of Biology and Health Science
University of Hartford
West Hartford, Connecticut 06117

Library of Congress Cataloging in Publication Data
Simpson, Tracy L., 1937–
   The cell biology of sponges.
   Bibliography : p.
   Includes index.
   1. Sponges—Cytology. 2. Porifera—Cytology.
I. Title.
QL371.S55 1984   593.4'0487   83-14611

© 1984 by Springer-Verlag New York Inc.
All rights reserved. No part of this book may be translated or reproduced in any form without written permission from Springer-Verlag, 175 Fifth Avenue, New York, New York 10010, U.S.A.
The use of general descriptive names, trade names, trademarks, etc., in this publication, even if the former are not especially identified, is not to be taken as a sign that such names, as understood by the Trade Marks and Merchandise Marks Act, may accordingly be used freely by anyone.

Typeset by BiComp, Inc., York, Pennsylvania.
Printed and bound by Halliday Lithograph, West Hanover, Massachusetts.
Printed in the United States of America.

9 8 7 6 5 4 3 2 1

ISBN 0-387-90893-5   Springer-Verlag New York Berlin Heidelberg Tokyo
ISBN 3-540-90893-5   Springer-Verlag Berlin Heidelberg New York Tokyo

In Memory of Rebecca (Rita) Simpson,

Whose spontaneous magnetism for and joy in
Nature will always be with those who knew her.

Foreword

Modern biology owes much to the study of favorable model systems which facilitates the realization of critical experiments and results in the introduction of new concepts. Examples of such systems are numerous and studies of them are regularly recognized by the scientific community. The 1983 Nobel Prize in Medicine and Physiology is a magnificent example in which corn plants served as the experimental model. In a manner somewhat more modest, other biological systems have attracted recognition due to their critical phylogenetic position, or indeed because of their uniqueness which distinguishes them from all other organisms. Assuredly, among the whole assemblage of living organisms, sponges stand out as worthy of interest by scientists: they are simultaneously models, an important group in evolution, and animals unlike others.

As early as the beginning of this century, sponges appeared as exceptional models for the study of phenomena of cell recognition. Innumerable works have been dedicated to understanding the mechanisms which assure the reaggregation of dissociated cells and the reconstitution of a functional individual. Today, research on these phenomena is at the ultimate, molecular level. Through an assemblage of characteristics the sponges are, based upon all available evidence, the most primitive Metazoans. Their tissues—perhaps one can say their cell groups—are loosely assembled (they possess no tight or gap junctions), cell differentiation appears highly labile, and they do not develop any true organs. But, they are most certainly Metazoans. They contain an intercellular milieu rich in collagen and are capable of coordinating their cellular activities in order to attain a significant degree of integration. However, the sponges are *des animaux à part*. They are able to accumulate silica, to form gametes from somatic cells with digestive function, and to realize fantastic potentialities for asexual reproduction; one group even includes individuals which are syncytial! Most of these aspects of sponges generate interest among biologists, whether they are specialists in evolution, cell biologists, or molecular biologists.

The goal which Tracy L. Simpson has wished to accomplish during his labors for the past nine years is to offer a comprehensive work on the structure and function of sponge cells which is for all scientists and at the same time completely up-to-date. In order to understand the originality of this work, perhaps it is necessary to consider two questions: what need does this book fulfill and how does it do so? There exist few reviews on sponges even though the literature is abundant—the author annotates almost 900 references. In some reviews, different research groups ignore the work of other groups (in particular in the field of cell aggregation) and literature citations are often incomplete. In certain general works, previous research is reviewed, but without critique, and some of this data is even obsolete. Too many syntheses of specific areas are only bibliographic compilations without a true perspective. Finally, some excellent works are either focused only on a very specific subject or are published volumes based upon symposia. What is required, then, is a "critical synthesis" which is both broadly based and current. This need is becoming more acute as sponges begin to be considered as models, attracting, for example, molecular biologists whom, among others, need objective synthetic information.

To respond to such a need has not been easy. T. L. Simpson has adopted an approach to each chapter which is most rewarding. He presents very complete analyses and I am sure that few papers have escaped his attention. But, he also presents a personal synthesis which makes the work highly interesting since for the most part this has not previously been accomplished. This synthesis is artfully supported by numerous tables which serve as mini-reviews. For example, one of the strong points of the book is a detailed consideration of the kinds of sponge cells. The published data permit the grouping of certain diverse cell types within one assemblage—"special cells." Each type is reviewed in the text and then all of the special cells are treated in a table which is extremely detailed, including numerous references. One will equally note numerous review tables, particularly in the chapters on mineralization and reproduction. Furthermore, this book is rendered unusual in the number and quality of its illustrations: almost 600 illustrations, of which more than 500 are photographs, the vast majority being electron micrographs. The tables and illustrations make this work very convenient to consult and give to it an exceptional, informative quality.

While this book is most assuredly not a general presentation on the sponges, it permits the nonspecialist to grasp the nature of these primitive animals. Although it encompasses data corresponding to more than a century of literature, this volume is not a treatise; it presents numerous synthetic views which carry the mark of their author. The truth is that this work is unique and that it does not correspond even slightly to any other existent work.

The basic morphological data which introduce this book will be very useful for all those who have an interest in sponges, both in research and teaching. The following chapters focus on the definition, the structure and—where known—the function of sponge cells. It has not been easy to clarify the diverse terminologies employed in the literature when reconsidering older views in light of the most recently available data. The result is, however, most satisfactory and extremely informative. A large place is given to biomineralization—it is without doubt due to a visible concern of the author for a subject which is dear to him. Beyond descriptions, sometimes complex, of diverse mineral forms encountered among the sponges, discussions are presented of general problems of the concentration or dissolution of minerals. A complete chapter is devoted to the aquiferous system—its organisation and its activities. At first sight this material appears to be of specific interest for spongologists, who will find there all of the detailed anatomical terminology. The fundamental analysis which is presented supports the view that sponges are animals capable of behavioral integration. This view is substantiated by observations on the water current which traverses these animals, on the effects of different factors on the current, and on studies of the anatomy and cellular structures which assure its regulation. There is no other equivalent synthesis of these data; such is essential for all researchers who are concerned with the evolutionary emergence of neuroid and muscular functions. The last sections of the volume deal with the developmental biology of sponges: gametogenesis and sexual reproduction, asexual reproduction, regeneration, cell recognition, and cell differentiation. A comprehensive view of this field has been needed for some time.

Finally, I further like this book because more than assembling information, more than offering a focus on subjects of much interest, the book very often emphasizes the uncertainties and the obscurities; and it indicates possible paths which might be taken. What could be more stimulating when one has an interest in a discipline than to note that all is not known and that the questions which remain unanswered are still more passionate than those for which there have been—provisionally—a response?

November, 1983   ROBERT GARRONE
Villeurbanne, France   Maître de la Recherche, C.N.R.S.
                                                    Laboratoire D'Histologie et
                                                       Biologie Tissulaire
                                                    Université Claude Bernard

Preface

The writing of this work was stimulated by discussions with colleagues in the fields of biochemistry, developmental biology, and physiology who expressed their, and other's, need for a current, critical review and analysis of sponge cell biology, and secondly by my own conviction that the field of sponge biology in general could benefit from such a synthesis and evaluation of the data. The major problem faced in writing this book was that of balancing the text relative to presenting, on the one hand, a review of the data and, on the other hand, a synthesis of it. A vigorous attempt has been made to be as uniform as possible in reviewing data but this, of course, is not always possible because some papers stand out as key advances in one or more areas. To the extent that it has been feasible to synthesize specific perspectives or to emphasize deficiencies in knowledge, these have been done. A major effort is made to review cellular structure *per se* since this has not previously been attempted. Some speculations are also to be found and these, hopefully, will not only stimulate new investigations but will also serve as respites from the unavoidable rigidity of data review. Much effort has been expended to avoid errors, although it is probably not possible in an undertaking of this scope to finally arrive at an error-free state. For such of those that do occur by omission or otherwise, I take full and sole responsibility.

There are a number of important, recent monographs and symposial volumes which contain much information on sponge cell biology as well as other topics. Outstanding among them is *Biologie des Spongiaires* (C. Lévi and N. Boury-Esnault, Eds., 1979. Editions de CNRS, Paris). Others include *Biology of the Porifera* (W. G. Fry, Ed., 1970. Acad. Press), *Aspects of Sponge Biology* (F. W. Harrison and R. R. Cowden, Eds., 1976. Acad. Press), *Phylogenesis of Connective Tissue. Morphological Aspects and Biosynthesis of Sponge Intercellular Matrix* (by R. Garrone, 1978. S. Karger), *Sponges* (by P. R. Berquist, 1978. Univ. Calif. Press), *Spongiaires* (P-P. Grassé, Ed., 1973. Traité de Zoologie, Tome III, Fasc. I, Masson et Cie, Paris), and *Living and Fossil Sponges* (by W. D. Hartman, J. W. Wendt, and F. Wiedenmayer, 1980. Univ. Miami). Furthermore, there are numerous recent symposial volumes which include important contributions such as *Nutrition in the Lower Metazoa, Phylogeny of Immunological Memory, Silicon and Siliceous Structures in Biological Systems, Cell–Cell Recognition, Biology and Systematics of Colonial Organisms,* and *Fourth European Marine Biology Symposium,* among others. The demanding reader will doubtless want to refer to some of the above works as well as to the original literature for further details, particularly as concerns experimental technique.

A decision was made that one effective, useful, and accurate means of reviewing data is to include original illustrations contributed directly by researchers and this has been done extensively. In this way and textually throughout the volume an effort is made to convey appropriate recognition of the endeavors and dedication of all those who strive to more fully comprehend sponge cell structure and function.

September, 1983   TRACY L. SIMPSON

Acknowledgments

Numerous individuals have aided in this labor and for their help, assistance, and encouragement I am most grateful. Lynn D. Simpson, my wife, has freely and generously given of her time and efforts for typing substantial portions of the manuscript and for aiding in numerous technical problems and details. Fran Libbey, science librarian, has in many instances been instrumental in securing essential literature; Paula Stein has meticulously assisted with the compilation of the bibliography. Emily Barrett, department secretary, has been exceedingly helpful and offered assistance in numerous instances. Furthermore, I am very appreciative of the interest, tolerance, and support offered me during the preparation of this work by my colleagues in the Department of Biology and Health Sciences.

I express my gratitude and thanks to the following researchers of sponges whose interest in this book is exemplified by the original photographic materials which they have generously provided: Roland M. Bagby, Nicole Boury-Esnault, Hagen Bretting, Max M. Burger, Marco Buscema, Dominique Carriere, Robert Connes, A. S. G. Curtis, Danielle DeSutter, Louis De Vos, Jean-Pierre Diaz, Claude Donadey, Ryan W. Drum, Clive W. Evans, Paul E. Fell, Marie-France Gallissian, Robert Garrone, John J. Gilbert, Willard D. Hartman, William H. Hildemann, Doris Hohr, Susie Humphreys, Tom Humphreys, M. Fischel Johnson, W. Clifford Jones, Ernest F. Kilian, Paul-Friedrich Langenbruch, Philip W. Ledger, Claude Levi, Hideo Mukai, W. E. G. Müller, Max Pavans de Ceccatty, Shirley A. Pomponi, Jacqueline Pottu-Boumendil, Henry M. Reiswig, Francine Rozenfeld, Klaus Rutzler, Michele Sara, Lidia Scalera-Liaci, Ilse Schmidt, Van Elliot Smith, Ole S. Tendal, Kenneth M. Towe, Jean Vacelet, Gysele Van de Vyver, Yoko Watanabe, Norbert Weissenfels, Clive R. Wilkinson, Craig E. Williamson, and Phillipe Willenz. I sincerely hope that their expectations are fulfilled.

Aspects of this work have been discussed with numerous individuals. Most especially, Willard D. Hartman has taken a constant interest in its progress and revisions by offering his seemingly endless knowledge of sponges. I am indebted to Robert Garrone who has conscientiously and thoroughly read the manuscript and has suggested important revisions. In addition, I am particularly appreciative for discussions with Max Pavans de Ceccatty, Gysele Van de Vyver, Louis De Vos, Max M. Burger, Norbert Weissenfels, Philip W. Ledger, John J. Gilbert, William H. Kuhns, Robert S. Turner, and Paul Langenbruch, and Gideon A. Rodan. The University of Hartford generously provided support through its facilities and a small grant was made available through the Vincent Coffin Fund to aid in the final preparation of the bibliography. The final revisions and editing of this work were accomplished during a sabbatical leave from the University of

Hartford and an extended leave of absence as a Foreign Exchange Scientist in the U.S.–France Cooperation in Science Program sponsored jointly by the Centre National de la Recherche Scientifique (France) and the National Science Foundation (U.S.A.). Finally, to my father, George Simpson, I am indebted for his enthusiastic interest, suggestions, and most especially for his professional expertise in matters pertaining to book publication.

September 1983   T. L. S.

Contents

Morphology

Cellular Structure

Cellular Functions

Development

Contents xix

CHAPTER ONE

Functional Morphology and Morphological Variation

General Features

The apparent simplicity of the cellular structure of sponges has generated much interest in this phylum of primitive metazoans, particularly the capacity of some types of adult cells to act in a seemingly embryonic fashion. In at least some species, nonepithelial cells differentiate into a number of functional cell types including spicule-secreting cells (sclerocytes), collagen-secreting cells (spongocytes), and others. Indeed, it is in part this quality which conveys to these multicellular animals their evolutionary uniqueness. Sponges lack reproductive, nervous, muscular, endocrine, circulatory, digestive, excretory, and respiratory systems, and with the exception of epithelial cells they lack anatomically discrete tissues. All sponges, except the Hexactinellida, possess two well-defined types of epithelial tissue: pinacocytes and choanocytes (Lévi, 1970); although present among the hexactinellids (glass sponges) both of these tissues have been recently confirmed as syncytial (Reiswig, 1979; Mackie and Singula, 1983). It is possible both structurally and physiologically for a sponge to consist solely of these two cell types and a few approach this condition (*Clathrina, Oscarella*) (Herlant-Meewis, 1948a; Lévi and Porte, 1962; Tuzet and Paris, 1963a).

As a phylum of animals, the Porifera is a relatively small one containing some 5,000 to 5,500 described species and an unknown number, certainly large, of undescribed animals. An indication of the number of undescribed sponges is the recent establishment of a new class of sponges, the Sclerospongiae (Hartman and Goreau, 1970). The structure of these sponges suggests a close evolutionary relationship with an extinct group of marine animals, the Stromatoporoida, which are now considered as a group within the Porifera.

Sponges are aquatic animals occurring in all of the oceans; there are also a small number of freshwater species inhabiting ponds, lakes, and streams in most areas of the world. One class, the Hexactinellida, is found almost exclusively at great depths in the oceans and, partly because of their inaccessibility, little is known about them. Thorough ecological investigations, such as those of Hartman (1958a), have been few, although recently Sara (1970), Wilkinson and Vacelet (1979), Reiswig (1973, 1974), Frost (1978a), and others have published important papers in this field. Many questions dealing with the mechanisms of distribution of sponges and their interactions with other organisms and the environment remain largely unanswered, however. A very important and fertile area of research involving the relationship of environmental factors to reproduction is just now coming under scrutiny (see for example Storr, 1964; Liaci and Sciscioli, 1970; Simpson, 1968b, in press; Fell *et al.*, 1979; Bergquist *et al.*, 1970; Reiswig, 1976; Simpson and Gilbert, 1973, 1974; Van de Vyver and Willenz, 1975; Diaz, 1973, 1979a). An excellent, detailed review of the ecology and ecological relationships of sponges has been compiled by Sara and Vacelet (1973) and reference should be made to it. Partly because of the thoroughness of their review but also because structure and acitivty on the cellular level are the main thrust of this book, ecology *per se* is not treated herein.

During the nineteenth century, research on sponges, as was the case with most other lower invertebrate phyla, was primarily taxonomic and histological (Minchin, 1900; Sollas, 1909; Hyman, 1940). H. V. Wilson's discovery in 1907 that suspended adult sponge cells will settle out, form cell—cell adhesions, and eventually reform a whole, viable animal focused attention on the developmental physiology and cell biology of the Porifera. Currently, the mechanism of sponge cell adhesions, which is a model system, has generated much interest among developmental biologists (Humphreys, 1963, 1965, 1970; Burger *et al.*, 1975; Müller *et al.*, 1976; Curtis, 1970; Henkart *et al.*, 1973; Cauldwell *et al.*, 1973; McClay, 1974; Kuhns *et al.*, 1973, 1974, 1980; Burger and Jumblatt, 1977; Turner, 1978; Müller, 1982).

Most sponges form microscopic, inorganic concretions (spicules) that are either calcareous or siliceous, and collagenous fibrils and fibers, the latter referred to as spongin (Garrone, 1978). The Sclerospongiae (coralline sponges) are a special group, in actuality among all animal species, since they deposit a skeleton which is both calcareous and siliceous. Some species of marine sponges (horny sponges) elaborate relatively enormous quantities of spongin, and the skeleton of some of these animals (bath sponges) has been used by man for centuries because of its capacity to absorb fluids.

In most sponges there is a high degree of development of the mesohyl[1], which is comprised of matrix and cells, and some of the latter may possess special, cytoplasmic structural differentiation. Some types of mesohyl cells secrete collagen, ground substance, and spicules, may form reproductive cells, are involved in the assimilation and transport of

---

[1]The term *mesohyl* refers to the intercellular compartment in sponges (Borojevic *et al.*, 1967) and is comparable to the mesoglea and mesenchyme of other metazoans.

nutrients, and are responsible for continuing growth concomitant with the production of newly differentiated tissue. The elucidation of the functional and developmental physiology of these cells has, since 1907, been an important area of active study. The deposition of silica (silicification) is a unique phenomenon among organisms (Simpson and Volcani, 1981); silica-secreting sponges, which include the vast majority of the Porifera, are therefore unusual in that this process is commonplace among them. It is puzzling that so little research has been undertaken on silica deposition in these animals. Of late, there has been considerably more interest in the process (Garrone, 1969a; Garrone *et al.,* 1981; Elvin, 1971, 1972; Shore, 1972; Schwab and Shore, 1971a, 1971b; Simpson and Vaccaro, 1974).

Reproduction in sponges involves sexual development of free-swimming larvae (parenchymellae, amphiblastulae, coeloblastulae), which serve as a means of geographic distribution. Although data are not numerous and other views have been expressed (Bergquist *et al.,* 1970), larvae are doubtless produced by a sexual process (Fell, 1974a; Brien, 1973; Gilbert, 1974; Simpson, in press). Growth in many sponges is relatively unlimited and it is therefore clear that these animals contain cell systems capable of morphogenetic replication (Simpson, 1973). Among many freshwater species and a few marine forms, special dormant structures, gemmules, are produced which are capable, under appropriate conditions, of developing asexually into adult animals (Rasmont, 1962; Simpson and Fell, 1974).

One of the amazing attributes of sponges is that given their minimum structural components (pinacocytes, choanocytes, and usually archeocytes) these animals have evolved a vast array of growth forms, some of which are highly regular and the remainder of which are best described as irregular and highly plastic. Growth forms range from thin encrustations, 500 to 1,000 μm in thickness, to relatively thick, subspherical animals measuring a meter in height; and from spherical animals a few centimeters in diameter to vase-shaped species measuring a meter or more in diameter. A small number of marine species have evolved the capacity to excavate (burrow into) calcareous substrata (mollusc shells, coral, limestone) and these sponges are common in oyster beds and on reefs. Although the mechanism of burrowing is not thoroughly understood, there has recently been significant progress in understanding its basis (Cobb, 1969, 1975; Rutzler and Rieger, 1973; Pomponi, 1980). While sponges have evolved an immense diversity of growth forms, none of them have become parasitic.

Although there have been reports of nerve cells in sponges (Pavans de Ceccatty, 1955, 1958) there is no behavioral or physiological evidence to support these conclusions (Jones, 1962; Prosser *et al.,* 1962; Bagby, 1966). Sponges appear to be the only free-living multicellular animals lacking classical nervous tissue; responses to environmental changes are thus a consequence of direct irritability on the cellular level, which, however, does involve communication along cell processes which function as neuroid tissue (Pavans de Ceccatty, 1974a).

Functional Morphology

Sponges possess an outer layer of highly flattened epithelial cells, pinacocytes, which cover (exopinacocytes) and, except in special cases, anchor (basopinacocytes) the adult animal. In one class, the hexactinellids, the pinacoderms are syncytial (Reiswig, 1979; Pavans de Ceccatty, 1982; Mackie and Singula, 1983). Flagellated cells, referred to as choanocytes or collar cells, which posses a microvillus collar surrounding the basal portion of each flagellum, are a further, additional, universal feature except in the hexactinellids, which possess a syncytial choanosome. The sessile existence of sponges coupled with their possession of collar cells partially lining an internal water-filled system of canals are exclusive features of the phylum (Table 1-1). A third type of cell that is present in most (possibly all) sponges, including hexactinellids, is an ameboid, mesohyl cell referred to as an archeocyte but early named by Wilson and Penney (1930) a "nucleolate cell." Much more will be said concerning archeocytes in the following chapters since they play a central role in many, if not all, physiological and developmental processes.

Most sponges possess a complex (leuconoid structure) canal system leading to and away from groups of choanocytes which form choanocyte chambers (Reiswig, 1975a). The canals are of two types, incurrent and excurrent, and are lined by a layer of flattened epithelial cells (syncytial in hexactinellids), endopinacocytes. The incurrent canals usually conduct water from the environment to the choanocyte chambers and the excurrent conduct it away from them, back to the environment. At the points of juncture of the canals with the exopinacoderm are incurrent openings, ostia, and excurrent openings, oscules (Table 1-2). The canal system and choanocytes are bathed by a flow of environmental water, which is produced by the active beating of the choanocyte flagella and the passive movement of environmental currents (Van Tright, 1919; Kilian, 1952; Vogel, 1977). This flow of water serves as one means of food gathering and as a transport system (Reiswig, 1975b). In a small number of species (*Leucosolenia, Sycon,* and others) the canal system is relatively simple (Table 1-3). These more simple systems are referred to as asconoid and syconoid in which incurrent and excurrent canals are short or absent and the mesohyl is weakly developed.

In many syconoid and leuconoid sponges, the mesohyl below the exopinacoderm is dense and contains (1) layers or tracts of cells, or (2) groups of spicules, or (3) spongin fibers or exceptionally dense fibrils, or (4) a combination of these. When the outer mesohyl is so constructed, it is referred to as the ectosome when it is thin or as the cortex, when thick. In such species, the more internal tissue is referred to as the endosome, choanosome, or in few cases the medulla.

Variation in Morphology: The New Systematics

Historically, studies of comparative morphology have been those dealing with the systematics of sponges and often have resulted in widely differing taxonomic views and systems (see for example, Lévi, 1956). A major, indispensible reference to the older literature is Vosmaer's *Bibliography of the Sponges* (1928). Taxonomic groups below the level of class have been and continue to be established, merged, or redefined. Indeed, current disagreement even exists on the class level [compare Vacelet (1979b, 1981) with Hartman *et al.* (1980)]. There is little question that the Porifera represent one of the most difficult animal phyla to deal with in terms of comparative morphology and taxonomy. The skeleton of these primitive animals displays a wide range of diversity and morphologists and taxonomists have traditionally studied it rather than cellular, embryological, or biochemical aspects. Recently, however, analyses of the latter have taken on much importance for the development of new insights into comparative morphological relationships and thus for major taxonomic revisions.

The fundamental problem in taxonomy is that sponge skeletons (with the exception of spicule geometry—but see following section) are not always readily defined and a diversity of skeletons is produced by animals lacking organ systems and possessing *generally* similar cellular features. Furthermore, and of much importance, most sponge cells are small (5–15 μm) and thus it is difficult, employing only light microscopy, to establish identity of structure in different animals. Some of these difficulties can be overcome by using cytochemical procedures (Simpson, 1968a), whereas others require ultrastructural information (Lévi, 1965). Just as important, the significance of skeletal differences is not really clear and will not be until insight is gained into the biochemical and genetic systems that give rise to them. Of specific concern in this regard is knowledge of the genetic control of spicule geometry; such information is mandatory for understanding and establishing homologies in skeletal construction. Most nineteenth-century taxonomic studies dealt with skeletal features and more recently these continue to retain importance. Consequently, a description of comparative morphology involves in large measure a survey of the skeleton in the phylum.

Skeletal Morphology

The skeleton of sponges can be an exoskeleton, endoskeleton, or possibly intermediate between them (Chap. 4) and consists of secretory products of two types: mineral deposits, and organic fibers (Table 1-4). A few

Table 1-1 Major Categories of Sponge Cells

Cell Type	Location	General Features[a]	Distribution in the Phylum[b]
Exopinacocytes	Covering outer surface	Highly flattened; usually without a nucleolus; phagosomes often present	In all species except hexactinellids in which the pinacoderms are syncytial
Endopinacocytes	Lining canals		
Basopinacocytes	Attachment epithelium		
Porocytes	Modified exo- and endopinacocytes		
Choanocytes	Line part of canals	Cell and anucleolate nucleus relatively small except in Calcarea and Homoscleromorpha; one flagellum per cell surrounded by collar	In all species except hexactinellids in which multiple flagella and collars occur on the same cell
Archeocytes	Mesohyl	Motile with at least one nucleolus and many phagosomes	In most, possibly all, species
Spongocytes	Mesohyl	Motile; features as in archeocytes; well developed endoplasmic reticulum; secrete spongin fibers	In most demosponges, absent in Calcarea and hexactinellids; probably present in sclerosponges

Megasclerocytes	Mesohyl	Possibly motile; features as in archeocytes; produce organic, axial filament in silica depositing species; secrete megascleres	In most species; information on hexactinellids meagre
Microsclerocytes	Mesohyl and pinacoderms	Possibly motile; nucleus small and usually anucleolate; secrete microscleres	In many demosponges and possibly hexactinellids; probably present in some sclerosponges
Collencytes	Mesohyl	Motile; features as in archeocytes but with a small nucleolus or none; few phagosomes present	In some demosponges and Calcarea
Myocytes	Mesohyl	Usually located around oscules; microfilaments in cytoplasm; features as in collencytes	In some demosponges
Lophocytes	Mesohyl	Features as in archeocytes; secrete collagen fibrils in long trailing tail	In some demosponges
Special cells (Cellules à inclusions)	Mesohyl	Usually motile; usually without a nucleolus; with highly differentiated, special, cytoplasmic inclusions	In most demosponges; rare in Calcarea; present in hexactinellids

[a]The absence of a nucleolus refers to light microscope level observations. Small nucleoli may indeed be visible on an ultrastructural level.
[b]Where known.

Table 1-2 Structural Components of the Canal System[a]

Structure	Cellular Features	Location	Function
Ostium	Incurrent opening formed by one (or more) porocytes	Exopinacoderm	Incurrent water flow
Vestibule	Lined by prosendopinacocytes	Superficial; connect ostia with incurrent canals	Incurrent water conduction
Incurrent canals	Lined by prosendopinacocytes	Connect vestibules to choanocyte chambers	Incurrent water conduction
Pinacocytic prosopyles[b]	Formed by prosendopinacocytes	Opening of incurrent canal to choanocyte chambers	Incurrent water conduction
Choanocytic prosopyles[b]	Formed by spaces between choanocytes	Openings into choanocyte chambers	Incurrent water conduction
Choanocyte chambers	Groups of choanocytes bounded by mesohyl and endopinacocytes	Part of the lining of the canal system	Production of water current
Choanocytic apopyles[b]	Formed by modified choanocytes	Opening out of choanocyte chambers	Excurrent water conduction
Pinacocytic apopyles[b]	Formed by apendopinacocytes	Opening into excurrent canal	Excurrent water conduction
Excurrent canals	Lined by apendopinacocytes	Connect apopyles to atrium	Excurrent water conduction
Atrium	Lined by apendopinacocytes	Connect excurrent canals to oscule	Excurrent water conduction
Oscule	Formed by a number of exo- and apendopinacocytes	Exopinacoderm	Excurrent water flow

[a]Not including hexactinellids and compound leuconoid structures. See Chapter Six.

[b]The term *prosopyle* is used in this work to refer to the whole incurrent structure leading into choanocyte chambers; the term *apopyle* for that leading out. The terms *pinacocytic* and *choanocytic* refer to the *openings* of prosopyles and apopyles which are constructed by these two tissue types. See Chapter Six for further discussion of this important distinction.

Table 1-3   Types of Canal Systems[a]

Type	Description	Distribution in the Phylum
Asconoid	Ostia open directly to a continuous layer of choanocytes which face a single atrium which opens via an oscule	In some Calcarea
Syconoid	(1) Ostia open directly to choanocyte chambers which open via apopyles into a single atrium which opens via an oscule, or	In some Calcarea
	(2) Ostia lead to short incurrent canals which join prosopyles at choanocyte chambers which open via apopyles to a single atrium which opens via an oscule	In some Calcarea; some demosponges and hexactinellids have syconoid-like systems[b]
Leuconoid	Ostia lead to vestibules which connect via incurrent canals to prosopyles which lead to choanocyte chambers which open via apopyles that lead to excurrent canals which open into atria which lead to oscules	Most species
Compound leuconoid	As in leuconoid except oscules open into a spacious excurrent cavity, the secondary atrium which has a single, very large secondary oscule	Some demosponges

[a]See Chapter Six for a detailed discussion of canal components.
[b]Hexactinellid canal structure is poorly known and has a syncytial basis; consequently, comparisons with other sponges are difficult.

species (*Halisarca, Oscarella, Octavella*) do not secrete distinctive skeletal materials.

Mineral deposits are of two kinds: calcareous and siliceous (see for example, Vinogradov, 1953). The former, calcium carbonate deposits, are frequently mixed with small amounts of magnesium carbonate (Jones, 1970) and are either crystalline calcite or aragonite (Hartman and Goreau, 1970; Jones, 1979b), whereas siliceous products are amorphous, hydrated silica (Vinogradov, 1953; Schwab and Shore, 1971b). Calcareous deposits can be in the form of (1) separate spicules deposited in the mesohyl, (2) a network of cemented spicules, or (3) massive, aspicular crystalline deposits, with distinctive microscopic features (Cuif *et al.*, 1979). Siliceous skeletons consist of (1) separate spicules deposited in the mesohyl in

Table 1-4　General Survey of the Skeleton[a]

Component	Chemical Composition	Form
Mineral Deposits		
Spicular		
Calcareous spicules, scales	Calcite (crystalline): primarily $CaCO_3$ but with some $MgCO_3$	Monaxons, diaxons, triaxons, tetraxons
Siliceous spicules	Amorphous, hydrated silica	Monaxons, triaxons, tetraxons, large variety of microscleres including chelas, sigmas, asters
Spicular, enclosed in aspicular deposit	Silica (see above)	Monaxons
Spicular, cemented[c]		
Calcareous	Calcite (see above)	Tetraxons, triaxons
Siliceous	Silica (see above)	Hexactines, desmas
Aspicular		
Calcareous	Calcite (see above)	Massive skeleton with spherulites or lamellae
	Aragonite, orthorhombic crystals	Massive skeleton with "water jet" (pencillate), or spherulites, or microfibrils (=lamellae)
Organic fibers		
Observed with the light microscope		
With or without embedded spicules	Collagen and hexoses	Fibers; abundant or sparse; branching and/or anastomosing; 10–100 μm
Observed with the electron microscope	Collagen and hexoses	Macromolecular fibrils; width: 20 nm; axial period: approx. 625–650 A and 200 A

[a]Detailed information on the skeleton is presented in Chapter Four.
[b]Of living species where known.
[c]Not including the cementing material.

Distribution in the Phylum[b]	Selected References
Calcarea	Jones (1970)
Demospongiae, Hexactinellida, Sclerospongiae	Schwab and Shore (1971b); Vinogradov (1953); Hartman (1981); most taxonomic literature
Sclerospongiae	Hartman and Goreau (1970); Hartman (1979)
Pharetronida	Pouliquen and Vacelet (1970); Vacelet (1981)
Hexactinellida, Lithistida	Schulze (1887); Hyman (1940); Hartman (1981)
Pharetronida, Tabulospongida	Vacelet (1964, 1970a,b); Hartman and Goreau (1975); Mori (1976, 1977); Cuif *et al.* (1979)
Ceratoporellida, Stromatoporoida, Sphinctozoidia	Hartman, (1969); Hartman and Goreau (1970, 1972); Vacelet (1977b, 1979b); Cuif *et al.* (1979)
Demospongiae, Sclerospongiae	Most taxonomic literature; Gross *et al.* (1956); Garrone (1969a, 1978); Florkin (1968)
Calcarea, Demospongiae, Hexactinellida	Florkin (1968); Gross *et al.* (1956); Jones (1967); Vacelet (1971b); Borojevic and Lévi (1967); Lévi and Porte (1962); Tuzet and Connes (1964); Travis *et al.* (1967); Garrone (1978); Ledger (1974); Mackie and Singula (1983)

which the spicules occur either free or bound together with spongin or (2) spicules cemented together which form a network. Few data are available on the question of how calcareous or siliceous spicules are cemented together; namely, whether there is true continuity between the spicules or whether there are minute amounts of cementing material present. This question is fully discussed in Chapter Four. In the present discussion, the term *"cemented spicules"* is employed in a general fashion and refers to structures held together in tracts or in a network by inorganic material, that is, by material not dissolved by chemical treatment which is expected to solubilize organic substances. In many sclerosponges, siliceous spicules become entrapped in (surrounded by) a solid aragonitic skeleton and this arrangement is arbitrarily treated here as a separate category, in addition to cemented spicules (Table 1-4).

Organic fibers consist of collagen (Gross *et al.,* 1956; Garrone, 1969a, 1978; Garrone and Pottu, 1973) and are associated with other matrix substances (Garrone, 1978; Travis *et al.,* 1967). Such fibers can be (1) large ($\sim$100 μm) or small ($\sim$10 μm) and encase siliceous spicules or foreign objects, or (2) large or small and have no embedded spicules, or (3) in the form of fibrils visible only at the ultrastructural level. A generalization arising from recent ultrastructural investigations is that all sponges studied possess collagen fibrils. Table 1-4 summarizes the kinds and distributions of these structures found in sponge skeletons.

Historically, the chemical nature of spicules, their geometry and arrangement, the arrangement of organic fibers, and the morphology, microstructure, and chemical composition of aspicular, mineral deposits have formed the basis of taxonomy in the Porifera.

Spicule Geometry as a Major Morphological Feature

Some discussion of spicule geometry and its (assumed) importance for determining morphological relationships and phylogeny is in order. This subject is very difficult to treat and if done in detail could easily comprise a separate volume. An appreciation of this can be easily gained from a reading of a recently published work dealing with the relationships of fossil and living sponges (Hartman *et al.,* 1980). The basic geometric forms of spicules in the Calcarea and Hexactinellida, although complex, are less varied in comparison to the Demospongiae and Sclerospongiae and consequently are more easily comprehensible since a basic geometry is ascribable in each of these two classes. On the other hand, among the demosponges which possess, as a group, highly varied spicule geometries, it has long been espoused that the tetractine[2] spicule type (with four axes), specifically the caltrops, is primitive and thus pivotal in under-

---

[2]For purposes of this discussion the ending *actine* is used to refer to *both* a ray *and* an axis unless otherwise specified.

standing phylogeny (Reid, 1970; Hartman, 1981). Earlier taxonomies emphasized this and indeed it still imperceptively permeates present views. A discussion of the evolution of demosponge spicules based upon this point of view has recently been presented by Hartman (1981) and the interested reader will find this to be an unusually clear and succinct treatment of the subject. In earlier studies, the conclusion was drawn that all (or most) demosponge spicule geometries are derived, in an evolutionary sense, from the tetractine through reduction, or in one case (spheroid asters) multiplication, of the number of spicule axes. Thus, the siliceous triactine is viewed as a tetractine lacking one axis, the diactine lacking two axes, and the monactine lacking three axes. The diactine is not only difficult to comprehend but also focuses attention on the question of the nature of our understanding of the tetractine as a basis of demosponge spicule evolution. Diactine refers to the possession of two rays while diaxon refers to two axes. Many diactines (called oxeas) have only a single, morphologically recognizable axis, but since they are similar at both ends they are considered to have two rays. Thus, the midpoint of the spicule must be considered equivalent to the point of merger of the rays of tri- and tetractines and consequently diactines can be considered to be tetractines that have lost two rays (axes). However, since in reality the two remaining rays are in the same plane, diactines can also be considered monaxonal. Microscleres are also viewed as being derived from tetractines through the development of three lines: triactinal line, diactinal line, and polyactinal line. The triactinal line of Dendy (1921) has been generally abandoned, but the two remaining lines—asterose microscleres (=polyactinal) and cheloid–sigmoid microscleres (=diactinal) are still considered to be of importance, not withstanding complications. Thus, two major lines of evolution emerge in the demosponges: tetractine–asterose (Tetractinomorpha and Homoscleromorpha) and monactine–cheloid (Ceractinomorpha). Although present views of sponge phylogeny are significantly different from this simplistic scheme, they are still heavily influenced by it. Thus, a further exploration of its basis and associated problems is of importance.

A sequence of reduction in the axes of spicules assumes that each axis is a separate entity joined to its partners only at one point. Thus, it is to be expected that the actual deposition of each of the axes begins at the point of juncture of all axes—namely, that each axis grows away from that point. As a matter of fact there is no evidence to support the older idea that spicules begin as granules (=points) (see Minchin, 1909). When siliceous spicules are first secreted they do not begin "at a center" but rather a short filament appears *in toto* which then grows (Chap. 4). There is no suggestion of its growth from a center, although it is likely that growth does occur at both ends. The presently available data are, to be sure, very limited and thus urgently require extension; however, they are clear. If, indeed, secondary, tertiary, quarternary, etc., axes develop at the *end* (or ends) of a growing filament then new axes are, in reality, added to a preexisting primary (=filament) axis. The primary axis would then appear to be a "primitive" monaxonal spicule. Thus, in demosponges when spicules develop from a single primary axis, as is presently indicated (except possibly in the case of spherical, asterose microscleres), then all additional axes can be viewed as elaborations of one or both ends of that single axis, not as fundamentally different types of spicules. This admittedly unorthodox view can lead to a number of somewhat shocking suggestions: that triaenes, now considered to be tetractines, are monaxonal with one elaborated end; that there is no such entity as a diactinal (=two axes) spicule, all of them are monaxonal with no elaboration of their ends; cheloid and sigmoid microscleres are monaxonal with elaborated ends (cheloid) or without elaborated ends but with a curved axis (sigmas, toaxas, streptasters, sigmaspires); but, spherical asterose microscleres may indeed actually be secreted from a "center" (Rutzler and MacIntyre, 1978) and thus are possibly quite distinct from all other demosponge siliceous spicules. Such arguments are at least worthy of serious consideration. They certainly do not simplify matters, but they do force a reevaluation of an important part of the basis of sponge taxonomy and phylogeny (see for example, Finks, 1970; Hartman, 1981). Interestingly, Wiedenmayer (in Hartman *et al.,* 1980) argues that demosponges evolved from ancestors that possessed monaxonal, siliceous spicules.

The tri- and tetraxons of calcareous sponges are very different entities from their corresponding siliceous counterparts since the former are secreted intercellularly and the latter intracellulary (Chap. 4). The genetic systems controlling a highly specific arrangement of cell–cell contacts in the secretion of calcitic spicules is not likely to be similar to those controlling the intracellular deposition of a membrane-bound, organic, axial filament which lies at the basis of silica deposition in siliceous spicules (Chap. 4). Also, it is clear that the initiation of triaxon, calcitic spicules does involve the simultaneous appearance of all three axes from a single point (Ledger, 1974; Ledger and Jones, 1977). Further, and of much importance, at least some diactinal, calcitic spicules can truly be considered as reduced triaxons because the spicule is secreted in exactly the same manner as two rays of a triaxonal spicule (see, for example, the diactinal spicules of *Lelapiella* in Vacelet (1977a). Other types of so-called diactinal calcitic spicules possessing only one axis should probably be considered as monaxonal—namely, as one ray of a triaxon.

Finally, some mention must be made of siliceous hexactinellid spicules, namely, hexactines (=triaxons). Although literally nothing is known for sure about their secretion it is conceivable that they, too, begin as monaxonal structures. It would be of great interest to have data on this point since if they are secreted differently, that is, the axes all grow from a single point, this would be an additional major difference between them and most other demosponges and sclerosponges. On the other hand, such a method of secretion would be similar to the apparent method of secretion of spherical, asterose demosponge microscleres. Also, if this were the case, their secretion could be considered similar to that of calcitic spicules.

Other Morphological Reproductive, and Biochemical Features

The works of Sollas (1888) and Bidder (1898) represent two of the first attempts to compare sponges on the basis of whole animal morphology. These early workers compared larval morphology, cortex morphology, and the morphological arrangement of choanocyte chambers in addition to skeletal morphology. It is of some note that their decisions have been reinforced and generally accepted (Topsent, 1928; Hartman, 1958b). There is now strong and growing emphasis on this approach to comparative morphology, a few examples of which follow. Two of the subclasses of the Calcarea are distinguished by differences in embryogenesis and developmental pattern and by cytological differences in choanocyte structure, as well as by spicule differences (Hartman, 1958b). The size of choanocytes in these sponges is, in relation to other cells in them, large and this is diagnostic of these subclasses as well as possibly of the pharetronids (Vacelet, 1964) but clearly not of the sphinctozoids (Vacelet, 1979a). The two recently established major subclasses of the Demospongiae differ in that one is mostly oviparous and develops coeloblastulae larvae while the other is viviparous and produces parenchymellae larvae (Lévi, 1956). (see Chap. 7). While the class Hexactinellida is unique in its spiculation it is also unique in its tissue construction (Reiswig, 1979; Mackie and Singula, 1983). The patterns of free amino acids among demosponge orders has suggested taxonomic revisions, some of which have been formally proposed (Bergquist and Hogg, 1969; Bergquist and Hartman, 1969). The pioneering and promising analyses of sponge sterols (Bergmann, 1949, 1962) have proven a very complex story indeed (see, for example, Kanazawa *et al.,* 1979) and consequently no comprehensive synthesis of these data has been attempted other than a recent review of the results (Bergquist, 1979). On the level of family, genus, and species, cytological, other biochemical, serological, and reproductive data have proven, in a number of cases, to be not only useful but also insightful (Brien and Govaert-Mallebranche, 1958; Paris, 1961; Simpson, 1968a; Brien, 1970; Connes *et al.,* 1974a; Pomponi, 1976); many more such comparative investigations are in order.

Morphological Variation in the Phylum

During the past twenty-five years, a new taxonomy of the Porifera has emerged based primarily upon a blending of cellular features, skeletal construction, and patterns of development. This new taxonomy is due in large measure to the work of Lévi (1956, 1957) and Hartman (1958b).

Establishment of the classes of the Porifera originates with the works of Sollas (1888), Schmidt (1870), Vosmaer (1885), Bowerbank (1862), Schulze (1887), and others. Their efforts eventually led to the general acceptance of three classes: the Demospongiae, the Hexactinellida (=Hyalospongiae), and the Calcarea. A major addition is the very recent establishment by Hartman and Goreau (1970), of a new class of sponges, the Sclerospongiae.

Classes can be distinguished on the basis of the chemical composition of the skeleton except in the case of the Hexactinellida, which are characterized by a specific geometric form of siliceous spicule, the hexactine. The following description of morphological variation in the phylum relies upon the work of Hartman (1958b), Hartman et al., (1980), Lévi (1956, 1957), Hartman and Goreau (1970), Vacelet (1970a), and Bergquist (1978). Lévi (1973) and Vacelet (1981) have presented classifications of the Demospongiae and Calcarea which differ in a number of significant aspects from that presented here (see later Table 1-6). Reference should be made to their publications in order to appreciate a different point of view. Vacelet (1981) now considers that the calcification patterns in the pharetronids are secondary to other aspects (reproduction and choanocyte structure) and accordingly disperses them in the Calcaronea and Calcinea. He further views reproduction and cell features of the sphinctozoids and sclerosponges as comparable to the demosponges and moves them both into the latter class, abandoning the class Sclerospongiae. Lévi (1973) places the Sclerospongiae as a subclass of the Demospongiae, based upon their mode of reproduction, cell features, and spicular skeleton.

Class Calcarea.   Among the calcareous sponges are the simplest members of the phylum in terms of canal structure. In some of these sponges the canals are of the asconoid and syconoid types, while the remaining members have the more common leuconoid structure. The Calcarea are distinguished by the fact that they secrete spicules of crystalline calcium carbonate deposited in all cases as calcite; these spicules include triaxons, tetraxons, and monaxons (Figs. 1-1, 1-2). There is rarely a size distinction between large (megascleres) and small (microscleres) spicules, and organic fibers are present only as fibrils. A newly described member of the class does not secrete any spicules but forms a massive, aragonitic skeleton. The Calcarea are mostly small animals with limited growth potential; all of them are marine. In comparison to other classes, they have poorly developed mesohyl and with some exceptions, mesohyl cells form products, spicules and gametes, rather than contributing to a separate category of cells. Furthermore, the choanocyte nucleus and cell body are of about the same size as the pinacocytes and archeocytes (Hyman, 1940; Tuzet, 1973a); in other classes, choanocytes are comparatively small (Lévi, 1956; Hartman, 1969). The class is divided into the following four

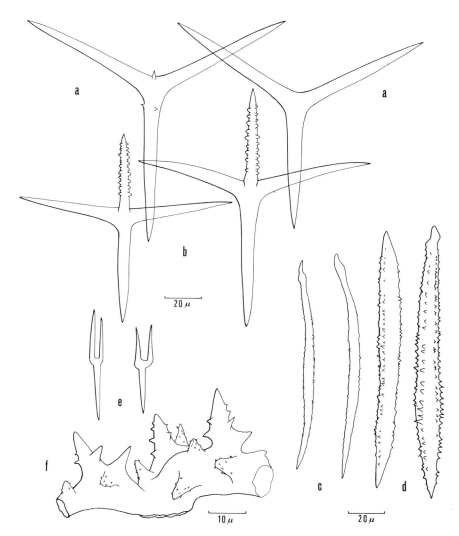

Figure 1-1 Examples of usual (A., C.) and unusual (B., D., E.) calcitic spicules in the pharetronid *Monoplectroninia hispida*. **A**. Triactines. **B**. Tetractines with spiny oscular ray in an unusual plane. These spicules constitute the oscular armour in this species. **C, D**. Monaxons. **E**. Tuning fork triactines (triactines en diapason). **F**. Tetractines cemented together to form the principal skeleton. (Pouliquen and Vacelet, 1970). (Courtesy Dr. J. Vacelet.)

subclasses (Hartman, 1958b; Hartman *et al.*, 1980; Vacelet, 1970a): Calcinea, Calcaronea, Pharetronida, and Sphinctozoidia.

Subclass Calcinea.   The Calcinea are typified by the genus *Clathrina* (Figs. 1-3, 1-4) in which the following features are diagnostic (Hartman,

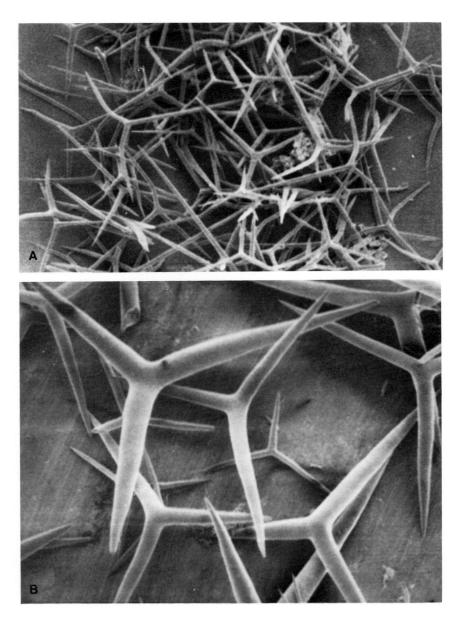

Figure 1-2   Calcitic spicules (SEMs). **A**. *Grantia compressa* (×710) (Jones, unpublished). **B**. *Leucandra nivea* (×380) (Jones, unpubl.). (Courtesy Dr. W. C. Jones.)

1958b): equiangular, triaxon spicules with the optic axis of the spicules perpendicular to the walls of the sponge; the choanocyte nucleus is basal with the flagellum independent of it; coeloblastulae larvae are produced; triaxon spicules appear first in the metamorphosing larva; four cytologically differentiated cells, cellules en croix, are absent during embryogenesis. Most members of the Calcinea also secrete monaxon and tetraxon spicules. According to Hartman (1958b) this subclass includes three orders; however, Vacelet (1970a) removed the order Pharetronida from the Calcinea and has established it as a new subclass (see following discussion). The two orders of the Calcinea include (1) the Clathrinida in which the canal structure is asconoid and there is a single family, the Clathrinidae; and (2) the Leucettida in which the canal system is syconoid or transitional between syconoid and leuconoid; the exopinacoderm is underlain by sufficiently structured mesohyl to produce a cortex and there are two families, the Leucascidae and the Leucaltidae.

Subclass Calcaronea. This subclass is typified by the genus *Leucoso-lenia* in which triaxon spicules are mostly inequiangular and saggital (one ray longer than the remaining two); the optic axes of spicules have variable orientation relative to the walls of the sponge; the choanocyte nucleus is apical and the flagellum arises near its surface; amphiblastulae larvae are produced; monaxons appear first in the larva; and a special quartet of cells, cellules en croix, are produced during embryogenesis. Generally, members of this subclass also secrete tetraxon and monaxon spicules. This group also contains two orders, one of which, the Leucoso-leniida encompasses sponges with asconoid canal structure and the absence of a cortex. The second order, the Sycettida, is constituted of sponges with syconoid or leuconoid canal systems and a cortex except in one family, the Sycettidae. The other families of the Sycettida include the Heteropiidae, Grantiidae, and Amphoriscidae. Hartman (1958b) also included the family Lelapiidae in this order, but Vacelet (1970a) placed this family in his newly proposed subclass, and this decision is followed here.

Subclass Pharetronida. This group includes sponges with leuconoid canals, tetraxon or triaxon spicules, which are frequently cemented together, and sometimes an aspicular calcareous skeleton of calcite. They tend to have a mixture of calcinean and calcaronean features. Most of the living pharetronids have only recently been described (Vacelet and Lévi, 1958; Vacelet, 1964, 1967a, 1970a) and prior to Vacelet's discovery of a number of cryptic, relict species in the grottos of the Mediterranean, we had little detailed data on living forms; in comparison, fossil pharetronids have been known for many years (Zittel, 1878). Due to the importance of this group to our understanding of the phylogenetic significance and relationships of other fossil groups (Sphinctozoidia, Stromatoporoidea, Archeocyathida), a slightly expanded description of this subclass is given. It is truly astonishing that during the same short period (1958 to 1975) living

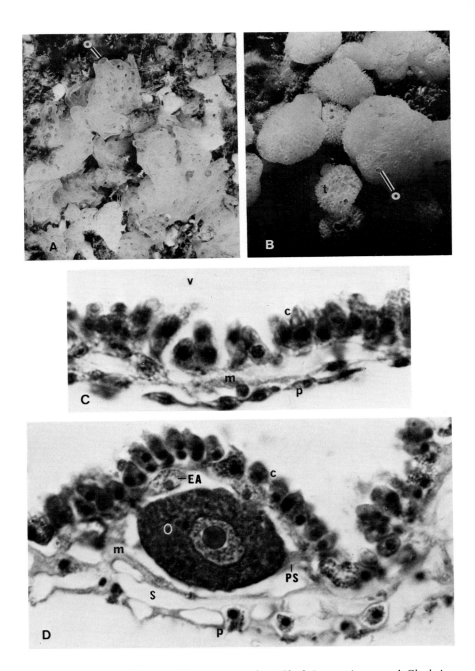

Figure 1-3 The calcinean calcareous species, *Clathrina coriacea* and *Clathrina blanca*. **A**. Underwater photo of a group of *C. coriacea* showing the anastomosing, choanocyte-lined tubes that lead to oscules (*o*) (×1.4) (Johnson, 1978a). **B**. Underwater photo of a number of individuals of *C. blanca* showing the much narrower anastomosing tubes (*t*) and oscules (*o*) (×1.4) (Johnson, 1976). **C**. Longitudinal section of a small portion of the wall of a tube of *C. blanca*. A single layer

relicts of three fossil sponge groups, the pharetronids, sphinctozoids, and stromatoporoids have been rediscovered. These discoveries have and will continue to shed much light on the early history of the Porifera and other related fossil groups.

The Pharetronida display a variety of skeletons; in addition to the above-listed attributes, two skeletal features are of significance and are generally present: (1) a special arrangement around oscules, called oscular armour, of tetraxons occurring in several layers with the oscular rays parallel to the oscule (see Fig. 4-3A); and (2) the presence of tuning fork spicules (triactines en diapason) (Fig. 1-1) which have only been reported outside of the Pharetronida in two cases, *Leucandra pulvinar* and *L. pandora* (Haeckel, 1871, 1872). The subclass includes six families. The Lelapiidae secrete tuning fork spicules, which are present in tracts. This is the only family without cemented spicules or aspicular mineral deposits. Members of the family Minchinellidae, which contains numerous fossil species from the Cretaceous and Eocene, possess tetraxons cemented together to form a network in addition to tuning fork spicules in the mesohyl, sometimes in tracts. The family Elasmostomatidae is known only from fossils and contains species with tetraxons, which are cemented together to form a reticular skeleton. The Murrayonidae is characterized by a skeleton consisting of a network of calcareous, polygonal bodies cemented together. In one of the two living species, *Murrayona phanolepis* (Fig. 1-5), there are calcareous, oval scales occurring in the cortex; in the second species, *Petrobiona massiliana*, oscular armour is present. The family Paramurrayonidae is represented by a single living species, *Paramurrayona corticata*, in which there is a skeleton of calcareous plates in the cortex overlain by oval scales. This sponge also secretes saggital (equal rayed) triaxons. The Lepidoleuconidae is also represented by only a single living species, *Lepidoleucon inflatum*, whose affinities are not well established. The skeleton of this species consists solely of ovoid calcareous scales in the cortex.

Subclass Sphinctozoidia: A Living Sphinctozoid. Vacelet (1977b) has discovered a living species of this subclass, *Neocoelia crypta*, which demonstrates that this ancient, well-known fossil group consists of sponges (Fig. 1-6). *Neocoelia crypta* secretes an aragonitic, aspicular

---

of choanocytes (*c*) lines the cavity (*v*) (=asconoid canal structure). *p*, surface exopinacocytes. Note the very thin, poorly developed mesohyl (*m*) which contains few cells (light micrograph) ($\times 1,350$) (Johnson, 1976). **D**. Longitudinal section of a tube of *C. coriacea* during the reproductive season. The mesohyl (*m*) is expanded and contains a developing oocyte (*o*) with pseudopods (*PS*) and an eosinophilic "amebocyte" (*EA*). *c*, choanocytes; *p*, exopinacocytes; *s*, cavity previously occupied by a calcitic spicule (light micrograph) ($\times 1,080$) (Johnson, 1976). (All courtesy Dr. M. Fischel Johnson.)

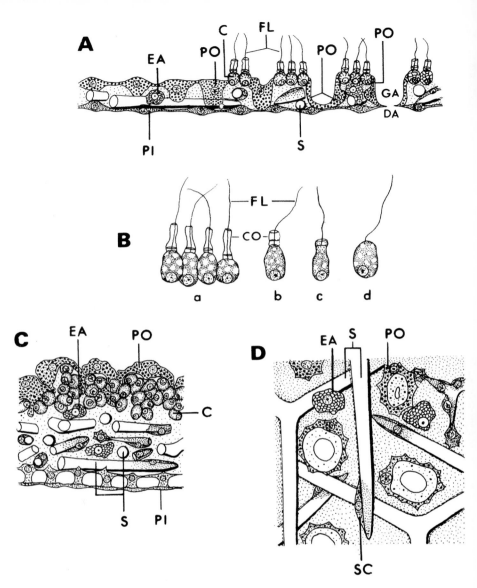

Figure 1-4 Cell features of *Clathrina coriacea* according to Minchin (1900). **A**. Part of a cross section of an expanded tube (×500). **B**. Choanocytes: *a*, fully expanded; *b*, *c*, less expanded; *d*, contracted (×900). **C**. Cross section of a contracted tube showing three or four layers of choanocytes (*c*) with the porocytes (*PO*) pushed over to the choanocytes (×500). **D**. Surface view of porocytes (*PO*) showing various diameters (×500). Key: *C*, choanocytes; *CO*, collar; *DA*, dermal opening of porocyte; *EA*, eosinophilic "amebocyte"; *FL*, flagellum; *GA*, gastral opening of porocyte; *PI*, pinacocyte; *PO*, porocyte; *S*, calcitic spicule; *SC*, sclerocyte (Johnson, 1976, redrawn from Minchin, 1900). (Courtesy Dr. M. Fischel Johnson.)

skeleton laid down in compartments; spicules are absent and the morphology of the skeleton is basically identical to that of many fossil species. The arrangement of canals and choanocytes, and the structure of the larvae, which are parenchymellae (Vacelet, 1979a), are similar to those in demosponges.

Class Sclerospongiae. This unusual group of sponges, which has only recently been established by Hartman and Goreau (1970), is of much significance in a number of contexts. These animals have a unique combination of mineral deposits, aragonite and silica or calcite and silica, unknown in other organisms. Furthermore, they are abundant enough in the waters around Jamaica, West Indies, to be an important contributor to reef formation. In addition, they establish the sponge nature of an extinct group of marine animals, the Stromatoporoida, which was also a major contributor to reef building during the Mesozoic Era and which is now included in this class (Hartman *et al.,* 1980). Living sclerosponges are routinely cryptic in the marine habitat.

The living sclerosponges deposit large quantities of aragonite or calcite and secrete siliceous monaxon spicules, some of which, in the order Ceratoporellida, become entrapped within the aragonitic skeleton. In this order, the aragonite occurs as microscopic units, spherulites, in which crystals radiate out from a center. Organic fibers of unknown composition (but assumed to be spongin) permeate, to a greater or lesser extent, the aragonite and there they invest parts of the siliceous spicules. The aragonite forms box-like compartments which, below the level of the living tissue, usually become filled in and thus solid. The living tissue of the sponge occurs only at the surface and reaches down to the level at which the aragonite begins; the aragonitic skeleton is thus an exoskeleton. The upper surface of the aragonitic skeleton consists of raised processes (*Hispidopetra*) or pits (*Ceratoporella*) and the living sponge tissue covers these features. The cleaned upper surface of the aragonite often contains impressions of surface exhalant canals (astrohize), particularly in *Ceratoporella,* which display a striking resemblance to the upper surface of stromatoporoids. In the order Tabulospongida, the calicular calcareous skeleton is calcitic and microscopically lamellar rather than spherulitic; and, as in *Acanthochaetetes welsi* (Hartman and Goreau, 1975), siliceous spicules only occur in the living tissue (Fig. 1-7). The order Stromatoporoida has been provisionally established by Hartman *et al.* (1980) to receive the fossil species of stromatoporoids as well as the living genera *Astrosclera* and *Calcifibrospongia.* The aragonite of these genera forms a reticulate pattern with vertical "pillars" and horizontal "lamellae," which are typical of fossil stromatoporoids. Their calcareous skeletons are thus more open than that of the ceratoporellids. Siliceous spicules become entrapped in the aragonite and also occur in the tissue, in *Calcifibrospongia* as a reticulated network (Hartman, 1979). Finally, the order

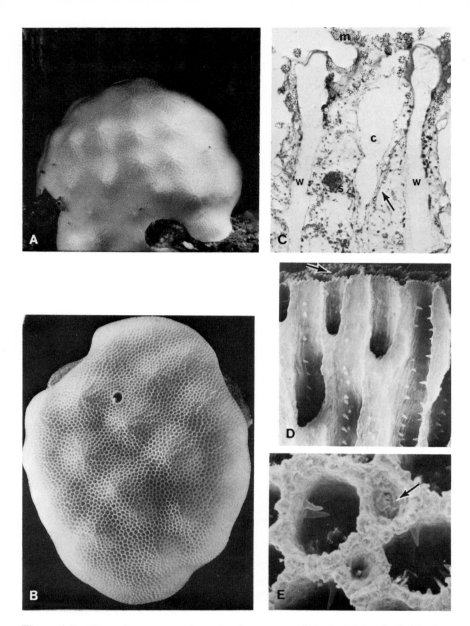

Figure 1-7 The sclerosponge *Acanthochaetetes wellsi*. **A**. Living individual *in situ*. Note prominent astrorhiziae (star bursts) around each oscule (×1.6) (Hartman and Goreau, 1975). **B**. Surface view of cleaned, calcitic skeleton showing the regularly shaped calicles (pits) and the etched pattern of astrorhiziae on the upper surface of the calicles (SEM) (×1.8) (Hartman and Goreau, 1975). **C**. Decalcified section in which the empty spaces (*w*) were occupied by calcite. In the mesohyl is a sperm mass (*s*) and siliceous megascleres (tylostyles) (*arrow*). An incurrent canal (*c*) leads down into the tissue. At the surface is an armor of microscleres (asters) (*m*) (light micrograph) (×105) (Hartman and Goreau, 1975). **D**. Ground section of the calcitic skeleton showing the calicular chambers, short

Merliida contains only the genus *Merlia* whose calcareous skeleton is either calcitic or aragonitic or both and which in some habitats can be absent (Pouliquen, 1972; Vacelet, 1980); siliceous spicules occur only in the mesohyl. Because of the apparent lability of the secretion of the calcareous skeleton, Vacelet (1979b, 1980) suggests placing *Merlia* in an order of its own in the class Demospongiae. Lévi (1973) and Vacelet (1979b, 1981) also both consider that the sclerosponges should be placed in the Demospongiae, and Vacelet (1979b) further has suggested placing the sphinctozoid *Neocoelia* in that class as well as disbanning the subclass Pharetronida and placing its members in the calcinea and calcaronea. Such decisions are derived from the view that hypercalcification (=deposition of massive, calcareous skeletons) occurred in many fossil sponges, which then gave rise to different lines of nonhypercalcified, living species with which the living hypercalcified sponges should be closely associated taxonomically. However, so much of the data are so new that it would be disadvantageous to "bury" these hypercalcareous sponges in existing higher taxa without further insights. In this work a more moderate approach is taken, as put forth by Hartman *et al.* (1980), and these groups are left within their own taxa.

All of the known sclerosponges have leuconoid canal structure and in two cases (*Astrosclera* and *Stromatospongia*) incubated, parenchymellae larvae have been reported (Hartman and Goreau, 1970). The choanocyte chambers and choanocytes in this group are small as is the case among the demosponges (Hartman, 1979). Many entrapped spicules are partially eroded, and this may possibly be related to the deposition of aragonite.

The sclerosponges display similarity to the demosponges in (1) the geometry of their spicules (monaxons), (2) leuconoid canal system with small choanocytes, (3) the secretion of organic fibers, and (4) the formation of parenchymellae larvae. On the other hand, the secretion of a solid calcareous skeleton is a feature that bears resemblance to the pharetronids and sphinctozoids.

Class Hexactinellida. This class of sponges has been little studied and may be one of the least understood groups within any animal phylum. Due to the paucity of definitive investigations on them, it is difficult to generalize on their cellular nature. As reviewed by Hyman (1940), the older literature indicated that the surface epithelium and mesohyl are syncytial. The view put forth by Schulze (1887) and Okada (1928) is that hexactinellids have syncytial pinacoderms; the "choanocytes" are also described

---

spines in the calicle walls, and the calicles visible at the surface (*arrow*) (SEM) (×55) (Hartman and Goreau, 1975). **E.** Surface of the skeleton demonstrating the formation of new calicles (*arrow*) by "budding" rather than by partition of existing ones (SEM) (×20) (Hartman and Goreau, 1975). (From Postilla, Yale Peabody Museum of Natural History, *167*:1–21.) (All micrographs courtesy Prof. W. D. Hartman.)

as syncytial forming a syconoid-like canal structure in which thimble-shaped flagellated chambers[3] open into a central cavity, the spongocoel. In many species, the spongocoel has a single opening. Canals were described simply as channels within the syncytial mesohyl. The syncytial nature of the pinacoderms and choanoderm has been recently confirmed ultrastructurally (Reiswig, 1979; Mackie and Singula, 1983). The syncytia contain special "plugged bridges" not found in other sponges (Pavans de Ceccatty and Mackie, 1982). However, discrete unicellular archeocytes and mesohyl cells with cytoplasmic inclusions are present (see Fig. 1-9C). The hexactinellids include mostly deep-water, exclusively marine sponges in which at least some siliceous triaxon spicules with six rays (hexactines) are secreted. Typically both megascleres and microscleres are secreted; some spicules remain free in the tissue and others are cemented together to form a latticework. Also, in some species there are exceedingly long monactinal spicules emerging from the base of the sponge and anchoring the animals in bottom sediments; these are referred to as root spicules. Of common occurrence also are long monactinal spicules emerging around the oscules (marginal prostals) and on the lateral surfaces (pleural prostals). Incubated, parenchymellae-like larvae are produced. Most hexactinellids have specific growth form and produce vase-, or lamellate-, or funnel-shaped individuals. The spicules secreted by these most unusual animals have a hexactine basis and are either hexactines (Fig. 1-8) or a derivative of the hexactine which results from the absence of one or more rays to produce pentactines, tetractines, diactines (but see previous discussion), and monactines. The Hexactinellida represent a unique and challenging group of animals for future work. Based upon their spicule geometry, arrangement of spicule cementing, and their syncytial nature, a recent suggestion has been made that the hexactinellids possibly belong within a separate subphylum of the Porifera (Reiswig and Mackie, 1983).

The tissue localization of spicule types is very precise and this has served as the basis for the taxonomy of the class. It is important to keep in mind, however, that aspects of this classification are likely to be highly artificial; no significant revisions of the taxonomy of the group have occurred since they were first treated by Schulze (1887). The class is divided into two subclasses.

Subclass Amphidiscophora.   Members of this group never secrete mesohyl microtriaxons which are astral—which have branched tips—but always secrete birotule microscleres; cemented skeletons are also not produced. In the only order, Amphidiscosida, the birotules are either amphidiscs (with similar ends) or hemidiscs (with dissimilar ends). *Hyalonema* is a commonly known genus of the order.

---

[3]Since uniflagellate choanocytes are absent in this class, the chambers are referred to as "flagellated" rather than "choanocyte" (Reiswig, 1979).

Figure 1-8   The diagnostic siliceous spicule type of hexactinellids, the hexactine. This spicule, from *Sympagella nux*, is referred to as a pinnule due to spination of one ray (SEM) (×425) (Hartman, 1981). (Courtesy Prof. W. D. Hartman.)

Subclass Hexasterophora.   This group is characterized by (1) the production of a cemented skeleton (although some members of the order Lyssacinosa have only uncemented skeletons); (2) the secretion of microtriaxons, which are astral (with branched tips); and (3) the absence of birotule microscleres. There are three orders of living species. The order Hexactinosida contains species with a rigid, cemented skeleton of hexactines (see Fig. 4-31A). The hexactines in this latticework (referred to as a dictyonine skeleton) are in parallel array, as in *Farrea*. In the dictyonine-type skeleton, the hexactines are clearly silicified together to produce a *continuous* silica skeleton; consequently, the term *cemented* may be misleading in this instance. The order Lychniscosida is also characterized by a cemented skeleton of hexactines, but in this group the hexactine network has a special structure containing lychnisc spicules ("lantern spicules"), the central part of which has twelve struts. The order Lyssacinosa typically lacks a cemented skeleton, although some species have secondarily cemented spicules (Figs. 1-9A,B). The spicules in these sponges always include diactines and hexactines and their derivatives. The commonly known Venus's flower basket, *Euplectella*, is a member of the lyssacinosids as is *Rhabdocalyptus*.

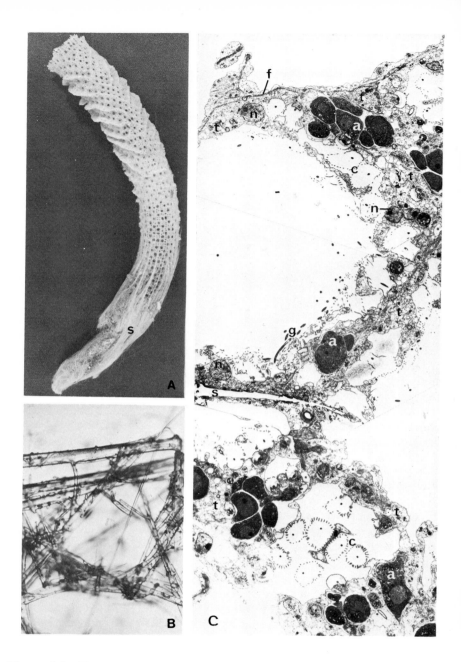

Figure 1-9 Hexactinellid structure. **A**. Whole, dried siliceous skeleton of *Euplectella* sp. showing immensely long root spicules (*s*) (×0.45) (Unpubl., author). **B**. The complex, partially cemented, siliceous lysacchine skeleton of *Euplectella* sp. (light micrograph) (×220) (Unpubl., author). **C**. Reconstruction of the tissue (desilicified) of the hexactinellid *Rhabdocalyptus dawsoni* (TEMs). The principal structural tissue is the trabecular syncytium (*t*) in which are pockets containing collagen fibrils (*f*). There is no defined mesohyl. Archeocyte-type cells

Class Demospongiae. This class is the largest in terms of numbers of species, contains many commonly known genera used as models for developmental studies, and displays a wide variety of morphological and cellular attributes. The demosponges are found worldwide in marine and freshwater environments; in tropical and subtropical marine ecosystems, in particular, exceptionally large species diversity is common. All of them develop leuconoid canal systems, although in a few (*Octavella*) a syconoid-like condition exists. They secrete skeletons of (1) siliceous spicules (megascleres that are monaxonid, triaxonid, or tetraxonid), or (2) spongin fibers, or (3) both spicules and spongin, or (4) no skeleton; many species also secrete microscleres of various geometries. The taxonomy of this group is very difficult and many systems have been proposed. Among those skeletal attributes which are considered important for the delineation of orders are the presence (or absence) of the following: (1) asterose microscleres, (2) tetraxons, (3) meniscoid microscleres (sigmas, chelas), (4) spongin, (5) radiate pattern of spicules. Of these, the following have been used in conjunction to establish three subclasses (Lévi, 1956, 1957): members of the first, the Tetractinomorpha, typically display a radiate pattern of spicules, secrete asterose microscleres (when microscleres are present), lack conspicuous amounts of spongin, secrete tetraxon and/or monaxon megascleres (Fig. 1-10), and develop embryos oviparously. The subclass includes six orders and is quite variable; Bergquist and Hartman (1969) have even suggested its eventual abandonment, but retain it for the present (Hartman *et al.*, 1980; Bergquist, 1978). The second subclass, the Ceractinomorpha, is characterized by nonradiate structure, spongin fibers, monaxon megascleres (Fig. 1-11), meniscoid microscleres (when present) (Fig. 1-12), and viviparity leading to the development of parenchymellae larvae. Seven orders are presently recognized, three of which are characterized by the presence of spongin but the absence of siliceous spicules and are frequently referred to as keratosan (based upon the abandoned order Keratosa) (de Laubenfels, 1936) or horny sponges. These two subclasses were originally established by the pioneering efforts of Lévi (1956) primarily on the basis of embryogenic patterns: among the ceractinomorphs eggs are incubated in the mesohyl and are released following development as free-swimming parenchymellae larvae (solid and

---

(*a*), some in groups, are enveloped by the trabecular syncytium and some of them put out blunt pseudopodial-like extentions at the ends of which are microvillus collars (*c*) and flagella (*g*). At the surface of the trabecular syncytium the latter form flagellated chambers within the spaces bounded by the syncytium. Siliceous spicules are also enveloped by the trabecular syncytium as seen at *s* where a spicule cavity is clearly outlined. The trabecular syncytium which is near the exterior surface contains spicules but not flagellated chambers; the latter occur deeper within the animal. *n,* nuclei of the trabecular syncytium ($\times 1,710$) (Pavans de Ceccatty, unpubl.). (**C**, Courtesy Prof. M. Pavans de Ceccatty.)

Figure 1-10 Some characteristic, siliceous spicule types of tetractinomorph demosponges and of a homoscleromorph (B.) (SEMs). **A**. A tetractine type, referred to as a plagiotriaene from *Geodia gibberosa* (×115) (Hartman, 1981). **B**. Calthrops from *Plakina* sp. Note approximately equal ray lengths and angles (×1,710) (Hartman, 1981). **C**. Microsclere from *Geodia gibberosa*, a spiny oxyaster (×5,400) (Hartman, 1981). **D**. Microsclere, a spiraster, from *Cliona langae* (×3,060) (Hartman, 1981). (All courtesy Prof. W. D. Hartman.)

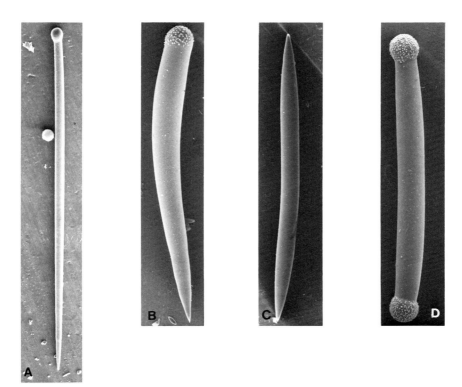

Figure 1-11 Megascleres, monactinal (A., B.) and diactinal (C., D.), from a tetractinomorph (A.) and ceractinomorph (B.–D.) demosponges (SEMs). **A**. Tylostyle from *Spirastrella cocinea* (×290) (Hartman, 1981). **B**. Subtylostyle of *Plocamia karykina* (×450) (Hartman, 1981). **C**. Oxea of *Haliclona* sp. (×720) (Hartman, 1981). **D**. Tylote from *Plocamia karykina* (×340) (Hartman, 1981). (All courtesy Prof. W. D. Hartman.)

flagellated), and among the tetractinomorphs, large eggs are generally released in the sea and develop into coeloblastulae larvae, or more rarely eggs are incubated (as in *Tethya,* but see Chap. 7). In one instance (*Tetilla*) released eggs attach prior to cleavage and no larva is formed (Watanabe, 1978a). This classification appears straightforward until the variability within the two subclasses is considered. The third subclass, the Homoscleromorpha, is small and contains only a single order.

Subclass Homoscleromorpha.   In the order Homosclerophorida there is no differentiation of megascleres and microscleres and no specific localization of spicules occur. The siliceous spicules, when present, are small and are di-, tri-, or tetractinal (Fig. 1-10B). Incubated larvae are of the coeloblastula type (but see Chap. 7). Spongin fibers are not elaborated, the canal system is simple, of the syconoid type as in *Plakina,* and the

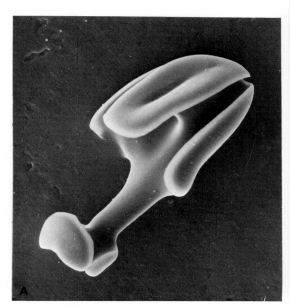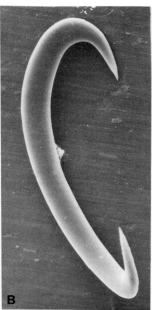

Figure 1-12 Two principal types of microscleres of ceractinomorph demo-sponges (SEMs). **A**. Cheloid type, palmate anisochela, from *Zygomycale parishii* (×1,530) (Hartman, unpubl.). **B**. Sigmoid type, C-sigma, of *Lissodendoryx firma* (×1,650) (Hartman, 1981). (Both courtesy Prof. W. D. Hartman.)

animals are viewed as being primitive demosponges (Lévi, 1957). Some members (*Octavella, Oscarella*) completely lack a skeleton (Fig. 1-13) and are placed within the order because of their incubated, coeloblastulae larvae and their relatively simple canal structure.

Subclass Tetractinomorpha. Although this group is characterized by tetraxons, asterose microscleres, radiate structure, the absence of spongin, and oviparity, some orders possess only one of these features and they are included in the subclass because they can be related to other, more typical forms through the loss of more general features.

The order Astrophorida, also often referred to as Choristida, is charac-terized by species (1) with radiate skeletal structure in which tracts of spicules radiate out to the surface from the center of the animal, (2) with triaene spicules (Fig. 1-10A), (3) without spongin fibers, (4) with asterose microscleres (Fig. 1-10C), and (5) usually with a cortex. The animals are oviparous but larval development has not yet been observed. Examples include *Geodia, Ancorina, Stelleta,* and *Myiastra.*

The order Lithistida (Sollas, 1909), which has recently been reintro-duced by Bergquist (1978) and Hartman *et al.* (1980), includes sponges

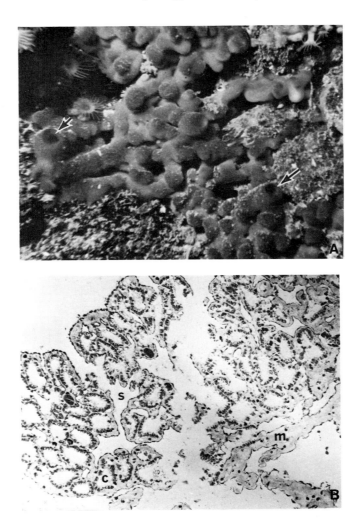

Figure 1-13 *Oscarella lobularis,* a homoscleromorph demosponge that does not produce a skeleton. **A.** Underwater photo showing oscular tubes (*arrow*) (×0.6) (Vacelet, unpubl.). **B.** A section displaying the very low-density mesohyl (*m*), canal spaces (*s*), and the sac-like choanocyte chambers (*c*) (light micrograph) (×150) (Donadey, 1979). (**A,** courtesy Dr. J. Vacelet; **B,** courtesy Dr. C. Donadey.)

with (1) a primary skeleton of special spicules (desmas) cemented together (see Figs. 4-17, 4-31B) and (2) either triaenes or monaxon spicules and asterose microscleres, or none of these. Spongin is absent and sexual reproduction is unknown.

The order Spirophorida has recently been established by Bergquist and

Hogg (1969) and Bergquist and Hartman (1969). It contains members of the family Tetillidae previously placed in the Choristida. Sponges in this new order display astrophorid features except that eggs are reported to develop directly without larval formation into miniature sponges either after their release (*Tetilla serica*) or, supposedly, miniature sponges develop from eggs within the adult and are then released (*Tetilla schmidtii*) (Sollas, 1888; Bergquist *et al.*, 1970). However, some skepticism is clearly in order in considering a sexual, viviparous development of miniature sponges. Stages in embryogenesis of the latter have not been clearly presented and until they are and until the possibility is eliminated that these structures are buds, a neutral position is suggested. Microscleres in this group are sigmaspires, which are historically considered a special class of spicules.

The order Agelasida has been provisionally established by Hartman *et al.* (1980) and contains only the genus *Agelas* in which much spongin is secreted and is echinated by special acanthostyles the latter of which have whorls of spines. Echination involves the partial embedding of spicules at the surface of the spongin fibers in such a manner that they protrude from the fibers, thus producing a spiny appearance of the fiber. The species of the genus are oviparous and biochemically they can be related to the axinellids (Bergquist, 1978). Interestingly, the arrangement of their spongin fibers is strikingly similar to the dictyoceratids (see following sections). Bergquist (1978) places the genus in the order Axinellida.

The order Hadromerida is relatively well delineated and is characterized by sponges which secrete only a single morphological type of megasclere, the tylostyle or subtylostyle (Fig. 1-11A). A cortex is frequently present and some species have radiate structure. Conspicuous amounts of spongin are rare and microscleres, when present, are asterose. The hadromerids are oviparous and where known, produce coeloblastulae larvae. In this group are many, but not all, of the burrowing sponges able to bore into calcareous substrate (Chap. 4). One family, the Chondrosiidae, provisionally placed in this order contains species with only euaster microscleres (*Chondrilla*) or no spicules (*Chondrosia*).

The order Axinellida is characterized by sponges with monactinal (styles) or diactinal (oxeas) spicules (Fig. 1-11) forming tracts that radiate to the surface of the animals from a central area. In distinction to other orders in the subclass (except *Agelas*), spongin fibers are secreted and nonasterose microscleres are formed by some species. The axinellids are oviparous and are separated morphologically from the ceractinomorphs only with great difficulty.

Subclass Ceractinomorpha. This subclass contains sponges in which eggs develop within the mesohyl into parenchymellae larvae; the verongids are a recently discovered exception and their systematic position and relationships have thus been brought into question. The subclass is generally characterized by the secretion of substantial amounts of spongin and monactinal and/or diactinal spicules which do not form a radiate pattern. Three orders, frequently referred to as horny sponges, do not secrete spicules but produce abundant quantities of spongin. While some orders have a simple spiculation, in others numerous types of complex spicules are secreted which are localized fairly precisely within the tissues.

The order Halichondrida is exemplified by animals which secrete one, or a combination of the following types of megascleres: styles, oxeas (Fig. 1-11), strongyles. The spicules occur in tracts or in some cases are randomly distributed in the mesohyl. Spongin is also secreted but is not abundant and microscleres are absent.

The order Haplosclerida contains sponges secreting in most cases only a single type of diactinal megasclere; spongin is abundant and the megascleres form tracts with spongin binding the spicules together. Microscleres are secreted by some members. Among the haplosclerids are the freshwater sponges, most of which produce dormant gemmules (Chap. 8) with distinctive surface spiculation (Penney and Racek, 1968). Most freshwater sponges are in the family Spongillidae, but Brien (1970) has recently described a number of new freshwater animals from Africa which are placed in a new family, the Potamolepididae.

The order Petrosiida (see Hartman, 1982) contains species with diactinal megascleres forming a dense reticulum and thus giving the animals a brittle consistency. Microscleres, when present, are microxeas. The petrosiids have previously been included within the order Haplosclerida.

The order Poecilosclerida is characterized by animals (Fig. 1-14) secreting two types of megascleres with each type localized in specific parts of the animal. The two basic types of localization (not geometry) are (1) "principal spicules," which are embedded in spongin fibers, and (2) "auxiliary spicules," which occur free in the mesohyl or protrude from the spongin fibers in which they are embedded. Cheloid and sigmoid microscleres are usually present and spongin is abundant.

The remaining three orders in the subclass were commonly referred to as keratosan sponges since they were once placed in a single order (de Laubenfels, 1936). Silicification does not occur in these groups and exceedingly large amounts of spongin are routinely secreted. The order Dictyoceratida contains sponges with a meshwork of anastomosing spongin fibers (Fig. 1-15). Two types of fibers can usually be distinguished: primary fibers, which are larger and contain varying amounts of sand grains and detritus; and secondary fibers, which lack foreign material. In the genus *Ircinia,* very small collagenous fibers, called "filaments," are present in the mesohyl (see Fig. 5-5). Primary fibers often form pointed processes at the sponge surface called conules. Among the dictyoceratids are the commercial bath sponges.

The Dendroceratida have nonastomosing spongin fibers which also

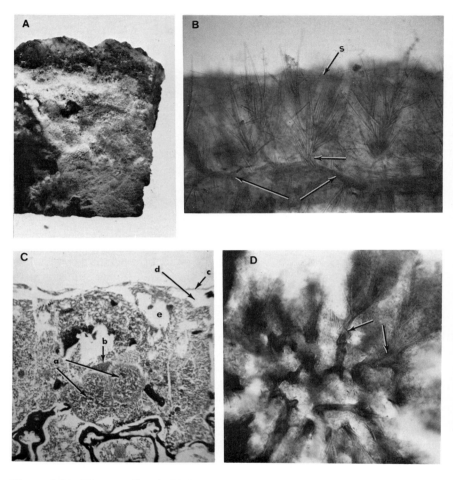

Figure 1-14 The poecilosclerid demosponge, *Microciona prolifera* (light micrographs). **A**. Surface view of an encrusting individual (×1.6) (Simpson, 1968a) **B**. Thick section showing basal and single, upright spiculated spongin fibers (*arrows*) and free spicules (*s*) at the surface (×60) (Simpson, 1968a). **C**. Section showing the dense mesohyl, dermal membrane (*c*), subdermal space (*d*), a canal space (*e*), two maturing larvae (*a*), and a sperm mass (*b*). Darkly stained material is spongin (×45) (Simpson, 1968a). **D**. Thick cross section through an upright branch displaying the reticulation of the spiculated fibers and the single fibers (*arrows*) which course toward the surface (×40) (Simpson, 1968a).

Figure 1-15 Two examples of horny sponges. **A**. The dried collagenous skeleton of *Aplysina* (*Verongia*) *lacunosa* (×0.4) (de Laubenfels, 1948). **B**. Living individual of *Spongia officinalis* which, like many commercial sponges, has a black pigmented ectosome containing melanin (×0.6) (de Laubenfels, 1948).

form conules at the surface. The sponges in this order are generally of small size and one genus, *Halisarca*, lacks a skeleton and is placed in the group because it is viviparous, produces parenchymellae larvae, and has large sack-like choanocyte chambers similar to those of other species in the order. The genus *Darwinella* secretes some spongin in an unusual, pseudospicular shape similar to tetraxon spicules with equal rays.

The order Verongida, only recently established (Bergquist, 1978), contains horny sponges whose spongin fibers contain a central pith of less densely packed fibrils. Usually, but not always, the pith is surrounded by

Table 1-5   A Current Classification of the Phylum as Used in this Volume[a]

Class	Subclass	Order
Calcarea	Calcinea	Clathrinida Leucettida
	Calcaronea	Leucosolenida Sycettida
	Pharetronida	
	Sphinctozoidia	
Sclerospongiae		Ceratoporellida Stromatoporoida Tabulospongida Merliida
Hexactinellida	Amphidiscophora	Amphidiscosida
	Hexasterophora	Hexactinosida Lychniscosida Lyssacinosida Reticulosida (one living species)
Demospongiae	Homoscleromorpha	Homosclerophorida
	Tetractinomorpha	Spirophorida Astrophorida Lithistida Hadromerida Axinellida Agelasida
	Ceractinomorpha	Halichondrida Haplosclerida Petrosiida Poecilosclerida Dictyoceratida Dendroceratida Verongida

[a]Based upon Hartman *et al.* (1980), Hartman (1982), Bergquist (1978).

Table 1-6   Alternative Classifications: Major Suggested Revisions

I. Establishment of two subphyla (after Reiswig and Mackie, 1983)
 Subphylum Cellularia   Subphylum Symplasma
  Classes Calcarea   Class Hexactinellida
         Sclerospongiae
         Demospongiae
II. Elimination of the Pharetronida and Sphinctozoidia as subclasses and the
  Sclerospongiae as a class (after Vacelet, 1981)
  A. Pharetronids placed in two orders as follows:
    Class Calcarea
     Subclass Calcinea
      Order Murrayonida (part of pharetronids)
     Subclass Calcaronea
      Order Lithonida (remaining pharetronids)
  B. Sphinctozoidia and Sclerospongiae placed in orders as follows:
    Class Demospongiae
     Subclass Tetractinomorpha
     Order Merliida (sclerosponges)
     Order Tabulospongida (sclerosponges)
     Subclass Ceractinomorpha
     Order Ceratoporellida (sclerosponges)
     Order Stromatoporoida (sclerosponges)
     Order Sphinctozoidia
III. Elimination of the Sclerospongiae as a class (after Lévi, 1973)
    Class Demospongiae
    Subclass Sclerospongiae

a multilayered cortex (see Fig. 5-4). In distinction to the previous two orders, choanocyte chambers are small (~30 μm) and sexual reproduction is oviparous, a condition unique in the Ceractinomorpha.

Table 1-5 presents a classification of the phylum based upon the new taxonomy briefly reviewed here and used throughout this work. Table 1-6 summarizes the divergent features of the classifications proposed by Lévi (1973), Vacelet (1981), and Reiswig and Mackie (1983).

CHAPTER TWO

The Epithelia

All sponges possess two types of epithelial cells, pinacocytes and choanocytes (collar cells); in the hexactinellids both are syncytial and are discussed in a separate section of this chapter. Choanocytes are a hallmark of the Porifera due to their unique structure. Both types of cells occupy similar positions in adult animals having their distal surface in contact with the environment. Due to their orientation, there is some overlap in their function; in other respects, however, there are important structural and functional differences between them.

Pinacocytes (Excluding Hexactinellids)

The cells forming the external surface, lining most of the surface of canals and attaching the animals to the substratum are present in single, very thin (~ 1 μm) layers and are referred to as pinacocytes. Three types of pinacocytes are recognized on the basis of their position: exopinacocytes cover the outer surface of the animal; endopinacocytes line the canals except in areas where they are replaced by collar cells; and basopinacocytes anchor the sponge to a substratum. Exopinacocytes display structural variation, since some of them contribute to the formation of pores and oscules. Similarly some endopinacocytes have recently been reported to form ostial-like openings in the incurrent canals and some of them are also routinely involved in forming special connections into and out of the choanocyte chambers (see Chap. 6). Among calcareous sponges, exopinacocytes migrate into the mesohyl where they differentiate into sclerocytes (Ledger, 1976; Chap. 4). Until fairly recently the exopinacoderm, indeed all the pinacoderms, in demosponges had been described as syncytial (Wilson, 1910; Wilson and Penney, 1930; Penney, 1933; Hyman, 1940). Phase-contrast and electon microscopy, however, have clearly demonstrated their cellular nature in demosponges (Lévi and Porte, 1962; Borojevic and Lévi, 1967; Simpson, 1968a; Feige, 1969; Bagby, 1970; Pavans de Ceccatty *et al.,* 1970; Boury-Esnault, 1972, 1973, 1974; Harrison, 1972a; Donadey, 1979; De Vos, 1979; Weissenfels, 1980; Garrone, 1978; Pottu-Boumendil, 1975; Diaz, 1979a; Thiney, 1972). Exo- and endopinacocytes in two calcareous sponges (*Leucosolenia complicata* and *Sycon ciliatum*) have now also been shown to be cellular (Jones, 1966; Ledger, 1976). In contradiction to these observations, Reiswig (1979) and Mackie and Singula (1983) have reported that the pinacoderms in hexactinellids are syncytial, thus confirming earlier, nineteenth-century views. Cell and nuclear sizes of exo- and endopinacocytes are similar [see especially Bagby (1970), but also Thiney (1972), Feige (1969), Ledger (1976), Pottu-Boumendil (1975), and Chap. 6 for earlier literature], although Winter-mann-Kilian *et al.* (1969) reported in *Ephydatia fluviatilis* that endopina-cocytes are smaller than exopinacocytes and that the nuclei of the former are about one half the size of the latter. This observation has, however, not been subsequently confirmed. The size of exopinacocytes between different sponge species is also comparable, but their shapes are variable (Table 2-1). Only fragmentary data on basopinacocytes (Fig. 2-1) are available for comparative purposes, but those which are suggest a similar-ity in size to other pinacocytes (Weissenfels, 1974; Pottu-Boumendil, 1975; Bronsted, 1953). The use of the term "exopinacocyte of basal mem-brane" instead of basopinacocyte is highly confusing (Feige, 1969) and implies that exopinacocytes and basopinacocytes are identical, a conclu-sion not borne out by the available data. Two types of endopinacocytes are recognized based upon their position in the canal system: those lining incurrent canals are termed prosendopinacocytes and those lining the excurrent canals, apendopinacocytes. Because of the severe difficulty in distinguishing between these two subcategories in thin and ultrathin sec-tions, no comparative studies have been undertaken, and thus it is not clear if there are fundamental structural differences between them. Much of the data deal with endopinacocytes lining the inner surface of the dermal membrane, and it is not always clear whether apendopinacocytes or pro-sendopinacocytes were studied (Feige, 1969; Garrone and Rozenfeld, 1981; Pottu-Boumendil, 1975). In a very few instances it is clear that apendopinacocytes are described (Thiney, 1972; Bagby, 1970).

Bagby (1970) has published an excellent detailed paper describing ex-opinacocytes and apendopinacocytes (Figs. 2-2, 2-3A) in the marine demosponge, *Microciona prolifera*. Exopinacocytes in this species are sometimes covered by a mat of organic material (25–30 nm) on their outer surface which is secreted by them and may serve as a protective devise and/or an aid in food procurement (Bagby, 1970); it may also have an ionic and osmoregulatory function. This cell coat (glycocalyx) sometimes may be absent, and this appears to be a function of the age of the exopinaco-cytes—younger cells developing in the spring lack it while older, suppos-edly more mature cells possess it (Bagby, 1970). In the dictyoceratid sponge, *Hippospongia communis,* a thin layer of glycoprotein occurs on the external surfaces of both exo- and apendopinacocytes (Thiney, 1972) and Lévi and Porte (1962) have also found a similar, thin layer of amor-phous material covering both of these cell types in *Oscarella lobularis.* A cell coat (approximately 20 nm thick) has further been reported in a num-

Table 2-1 Exopinacocyte Features[a]

Species	Cell Size[b]	Nuclear Size[b]	Cell Thickness[b]		Distance Between Cells[c]	Mitochondrial Size[b]	Reference
			At the Periphery	Within Bulges			
Demospongiae							
Microciona prolifera		2–4 × 4–6	0.5–2.0		100–300	0.4–0.5	Bagby (1970)
Hippospongia communis		5–6	0.15–1.0	11.0	150–200		Pavans de Ceccatty et al. (1970); Thiney (1972)
Haliclona sp.		5–8.5	0.5–2.0	9.5			Pavans de Ceccatty et al. (1970)
Ephydatia fluviatilis		2.5	0.5–1.5		500–1,500	0.35–0.45	Feige (1969)
Hamigera hamigera	18–25 × 2.5–4	1.7–4	0.09–0.4	18–25	200	0.13–0.45	Boury-Esnault (1972)
Polymastia mamillaris	5–30 × 1.4–7	1.3–3 × 1.7–4	0.08–1.9	5–30	100–200	0.17–0.5	Boury-Esnault (1973)
Suberites massa	4 × 15	2.8–3.3	0.3	15–28			Diaz (1979a)
Stylotella incisa	14–28 × 4–7	3.0–3.5	0.3	14–18			Boury-Esnault (1973)
Crambe crambe	9–18 × 2–4	2.0–3.0		14–18			Boury-Esnault (1973)
Acanthella acuta	14–18 × 3–8	3.0–4.0	0.3–0.8	12–21		0.4	Boury-Esnault (1973)
Axinella polypoides	12–21 × 3–5	2.0–4.0					Boury-Esnault (1973)
Oscarella lobularis	7–8	2.0	0.08–0.3 (at edges)	No bulge			Boury-Esnault (1973)
Calcarea							
Sycon ciliatum		2.0–3.5	0.05–1.5	6			Ledger (1976)
Sycon sycandra	4.8–8.5 × 7.3–10.5	2.5–4.0	0.2–0.5	5–9		0.4	Boury-Esnault (1973)

[a] Based to a large extent on Boury-Esnault (1973).

[b] In μm.

[c] In Angstrom units.

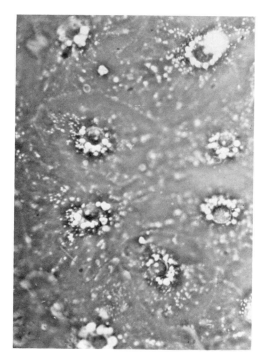

Figure 2-1 Highly flattened, newly developed basopinacocytes of *Microciona atrasanguinea*. Phagosomes are clustered around the nuclei, which are nucleolate due to their recent cytodifferentiation during explant attachment. Outlines of the plasmalemmae are visible in some areas (phase contrast, living cells) (×1,000) (Simpson and Borojevic, unpubl.).

ber of other marine sponges (*Haliclona elegans, Chondrilla nucula, Hippospongia communis*); this coat occurs on all cells including pinacocytes (Garrone *et al.,* 1971). Based upon ruthenium red staining following or not sialase treatment, and periodic acid–thiocarbohydrazide–silver–proteinate staining the coat probably contains glycosaminoglycans as well as glycoprotein. In newly metamorphosed larvae of *Halichondria moorei* exopinacocytes secrete a highly complex coat containing a number of layers (Evans, 1977). In *Sycon ciliatum*, Ledger (1976) has described a similar, but even more complex coat on exopinacocytes, which is also significantly thicker (~130 nm); endopinacocytes in this sponge, in comparison, possess a thinner coat as do porocytes which are, however, an integral part of the exopinacoderm and border other exopinacocytes. There are usually at least two components present in these coats: fibrils (50–70 Å in diameter in *M. prolifera*) and amorphous material. In *Sycon,* the coat has alternating layers of fibrils and amorphous material. A complex glycocalyx on exopinacocytes has recently been observed in *Clath-*

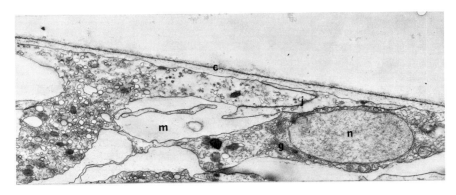

Figure 2-2 Exopinacocytes of *Microciona prolifera* showing the cell coat (*c*), interdigitating junction (*j*), and the positioning of the cell body in the mesohyl (*m*) below the level of the pinacoderm thus producing T-exopinacocytes. Golgi (*g*) and nucleus (*n*) are visible in one of the cells (TEM) (×6,370) (Bagby, unpubl.). (Courtesy Dr. R. M. Bagby.)

rina, Hemimycale, Axinella, and *Crambe;* in the latter two it may have a function in ingestion (Willenz, 1983).

Collagen fibrils are frequently associated with both endopinacocytes and exopinacocytes (see Fig. 5-13B) in the adjoining mesohyl (Boury-Esnault, 1973; Pottu-Boumendil, 1975; Garrone, 1978; Garrone and Rozenfeld, 1981), and it is possible that both cell types contribute to their secretion, although Pottu-Boumendil (1975) has found that exopinacocytes and not endopinacocytes incorporate [^{3}H]proline suggesting that, at least in the thin dermal membrane of *Ephydatia mulleri,* the fibrils originate from the exopinacocytes only. Considerably more study of this question is necessary, since in disorganized tissue of *Suberites,* endopinacocytes appear to develop fibrilogenic activity (Diaz, 1979a) (Chap. 9). Basopinacocytes have been reported to secrete collagen (see Fig. 5-13A) upon the substratum (Borojevic and Lévi, 1967; Bronsted and Carlsen, 1951; Bronsted, 1962; Feige, 1969; Garrone and Pottu, 1973; Bergquist and Green, 1977a; Evans, 1977; Connes *et al.,* 1978; Garrone and Rozenfeld, 1981). In the marine sponge, *Mycale contarenii* the fibrils so secreted are of two sizes in distinction to those in the mesohyl which are of a single size (Borojevic and Lévi, 1967). Bronsted and Carlsen (1951) very early observed two sizes of fibrils between basopinacocytes and the substratum in *Spongilla.* Mazzorana (1982) has recently shown that this layer of collagen contains both spongin microfibrils and collagen fibrils (see Chap. 5). This collagen and undoubtedly other matrix substances are responsible for anchoring, in an unknown fashion, the cells to the substratum. In *Ephydatia,* so-called attachment plaques have been identified (Figs. 2-3B,C) at and near the attachment points of basopinacocytes (Pavans de Ceccatty, 1981). Although much additional work must be undertaken, it seems possible that all pinacocytes may contribute collagen fibrils to the mesohyl and that all of them are able to secrete fibrils on both of their free surfaces; hard data on the latter point would be most reassuring. Feige (1969) and Diaz (1979a) have observed bundles of collagen fibrils in the mesohyl within indentations of the plasmalemma of exopinacocytes, thus providing reasonably good evidence of their collagen biosynthetic capabilities. The exopinacocytes and basopinacocytes of *Ephydatia fluviatilis* have recently been shown, under experimental conditions (hydroxyurea treatment), to contain augmented rough endoplasmic reticulum, numerous microfilaments, and increased numbers of dense inclusions with closely packed, wavy fibrils typical of fibrilogenesis in other collagen-secreting cells (Chap. 5) which may be precursors of collagen fibrils (Garrone and Rozenfeld, 1981). The presence of this characteristic assemblage of structures leaves no doubt of the collagen-secreting ability of these pinacocytes and of their structural similarity to other collagen-secreting cells in the mesohyl (Chap. 5).

Three unusual conditions can exist relative to the pinacoderms and only one is commonly considered. The first involves particularly tetractino-morph, hexactinellid, and sclerosponges in which there appears to be no true basopinacoderm present and about which there is literally no information. In sponges in the first two groups, usually long, and sometimes robust spicules can emerge from the base of the animals and anchor them in bottom sediments. In sclerosponges the massive, crystalline, calcareous exoskeleton anchors the animals. Details of these unique attachments are unknown as are details of their morphogenesis. The second condition involves the absence of the exopinacoderm at least in some areas of the surface (Fig. 2-4). This has been reported in two species of *Aplysina (Verongia)* in which an acellular "cuticle", neither covered by nor underlain by exopinacocytes, occurs at the surface and can be quite thick (1.0–1.5 μm), although it is sometimes considerably thinner (Vacelet, 1971b). Differences in thickness are ascribed to the age of the surface, but this is only conjectural. In some cases, areas of the surface were found in which there was neither a cuticle nor an exopinacoderm present (Vacelet, 1971b). In two additional genera of horny sponges, *Ircinia* and *Cacospongia*, a similar but thinner (0.1 to 0.2 μm) structure has been described which is also not at all associated with an exopinacoderm (Garrone, 1978); in *Cacospongia* the cuticle can become detached exposing collagen fibrils (Donadey, 1982). A cuticle has also been observed in the sphinctozoid, *Neocoelia crypta,* but its structure is not known (Vacelet, 1979b). In *Suberites massa* there is rarely an exopinacoderm present; a layer of collagen fibrils forms an external covering (Connes *et al.,* 1972; Diaz, 1979a) and this has also been reported in *Polymastia mamillaris* (Boury-Esnault, 1973) and *Hamigera hamigera* (Boury-Esnault, 1972). Although it is possible that the latter structures are the result of desquamatization prior to or during preparation of the tissue, a possibility which must be

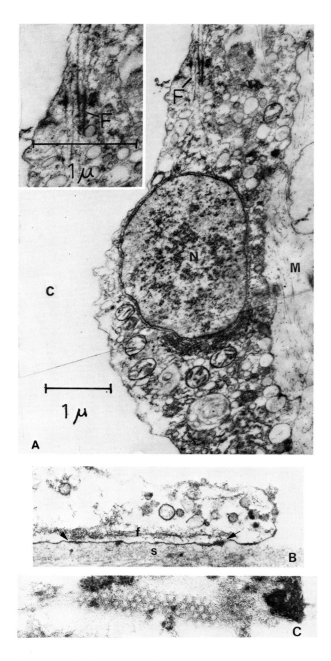

Figure 2-3 **A**. An endopinacocyte of *Halichondria melanodocia* (TEM). Note that the cell is flattened with an anucleolate nucleus (*n*) and is not in a T configuration. Filaments (*F*), possibly contractile, occur in the cytoplasm and the cell is anchored in the mesohyl (*M*) in collagen fibrils. *c,* canal space (×16,815). **Inset:** An enlargement of the filaments (*F*) (×27,015) (Bagby, unpubl.). **B**. A basopinacocyte of *Ephydatia mulleri* cut perpendicular to the substratum (*s*) on which

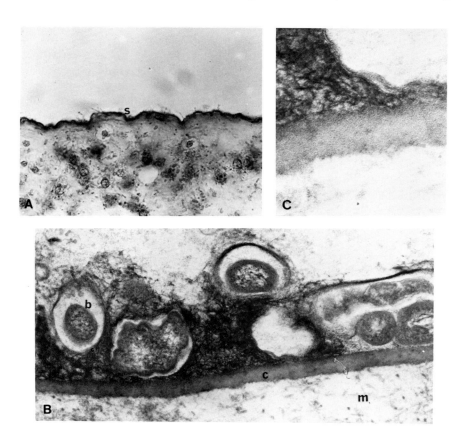

Figure 2-4 The cuticle of *Aplysina (Verongia) cavernicola*. **A**. The surface (s) of the animal is limited by a dense border (light micrograph) (×655) (Vacelet, 1971b). **B**. At higher magnification, the cuticle (c) is clearly bordering the mesohyl (m) in which collagen fibrils are visible. The outer surface of the cuticle is bound to complex materials which entrap bacteria (b) (TEM) (×45,000) (Vacelet, 1971b). **C**. At very high magnification, the cuticle does not appear to contain ordered structure (TEM) (×135,000) (Vacelet, 1971b). (All courtesy Dr. J. Vacelet.)

---

spongin microfibrils have been deposited by the cell. The preparation has been treated with glycerol in order to visualize the cytoskeleton. A long bundle of microfilaments (*f*) is seen and at two points (arrows) they join the plasmalemma to form attachment plaques. The empty look of the cell is due to glycerination (TEM) (×54,200) (Pavans de Ceccatty, 1981). **C**. A tangentially sectioned plaque showing a regularly arranged structure to which microfilaments attach; glycerinated preparation (TEM) (×135,510) (Pavans de Ceccatty, 1981). (**A**, courtesy Dr. R. Bagby; **B**, **C**, courtesy Prof. M. Pavans de Ceccatty.)

explored in all of the above cases, it does not seem a likely event in the case of *Ircinia* and *Cacospongia*. The third condition involves some demosponges in which pinacocytes (=attachment cells) are able to etch and thus "burrow" into calcareous substrata. This special ability of pinacocytes is well documented and important new data have recently been published substantially increasing our understanding of this phenomenon. Details of the process of burrowing are discussed in Chapter Four.

In *Microciona prolifera* the nuclei of exopinacocytes occur in bulges below the level of the exopinacoderm (T-shaped cells) while in endopinacocytes nuclei are at the same level (fusiform cell shape) as the rest of the cell body (see Figs. 2-2, 2-3). Boury-Esnault (1973) has published an important study of exopinacocytes in an impressive number of species and has found that these cells are fusiform in the Homosclerophorida and in the family Spongillidae among the ceractinomorph demosponges. Among the large number of other ceractinomorph and tetractinomorph species examined in that study, exopinacocytes were found to possess a T shape. In the Calcarea both fusiform and T-shaped exopinacocytes occur even within the same animal (Ledger, 1976). It is not clear what functional significance the T shape has, but this morphology could be related to contraction of the exopinacoderm; alternatively, exopinacocytes in some species may require a more secure anchorage in the mesohyl. Boury-Esnault (1973) has reported that the exopinacoderm of at least some sponges (*Polymastia mamillaris*) is quite fragile and in some areas cells may sink into the mesohyl in a teardrop shape leaving the sponge matrix in contact with the environment. Such an event may lie at the basis of the mistaken nineteenth-century view that there are flask-shaped "gland" cells (Fig. 2-5A) associated with the exopinacoderm [see Boury-Esnault (1973) for a very useful although brief review of this subject]. In calcareous sponges it is clear that exopinacocytes can migrate into the mesohyl where they form sclerocytes (Chap. 4) and thus the T shape in some of these cells may be a preparatory stage in cell migration (Ledger, 1976).

The junctions of exopinacocytes in *Microciona prolifera* appear tighter than those of the apendopinacocytes but in neither pinacoderm have specialized junctions been routinely observed (Bagby, 1970); a gap of 10 to 20 nm occurs between opposing membranes of exopinacocytes in many species (Boury-Esnault, 1973; Feige, 1969; Bagby, 1970). On the other hand, in *Ephydatia fluviatilis* and *mulleri* and in *Hippospongia communis,* desmosome-like differentiations of the cell membranes do occur between some exopinacocytes (Fig. 2-5B) (Feige, 1969; Pottu-Boumendil, 1975; Pavans de Ceccatty *et al.,* 1970). Specialized cell junctions between pinacocytes (indeed between all sponge cell types) have been observed only infrequently (except in hexactinellids, see later section) and this may lie at the basis of the supposed "leaky" nature of sponge epithelia. However, it should be borne in mind that few investigations have attempted a system-

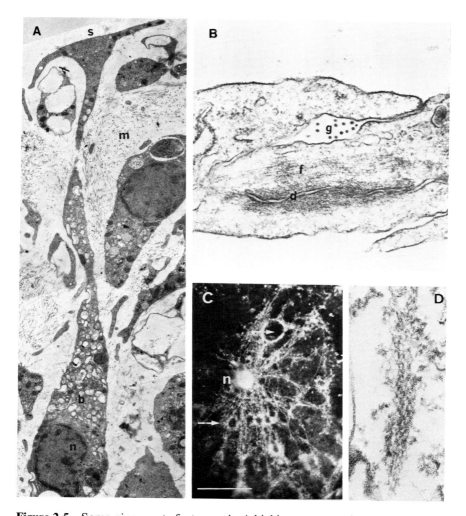

Figure 2-5 Some pinacocyte features. **A.** A highly accentuated T-exopinacocyte of *Hamigera hamigera*. The cell body (*b*) and nucleus (*n*) lie well below the surface (*s*) of the animal giving the cell a flask shape, which led early workers to consider such cells as "gland cells," a mistaken notion. *m*, mesohyl (TEM) (×6,600) (Boury-Esnault, 1972). **B.** A desmosome-like junction (*d*) between two exopinacocytes in *Ephydatia mulleri*. Around the junction are cytoplasmic filaments (*f*). Between the cells are cross-sectioned collagen fibrils (*g*) suggesting fibrilogenic activity of these cells (TEM) (×37,800) (Pottu-Boumendil, 1975). **C.** Immunofluorescent demonstration of actin filaments in a basopinacocyte of *Ephydatia mulleri* extracted with 0.05% Triton. Actin filaments radiate out from the nucleus (*n*) and form a diffuse pattern around contractile vacuoles (arrows) (fluorescence microscopy) (×675, scale bar: 20.0 μm) (Pavans de Ceccatty, 1981). **D.** Demonstration of actin filaments in the cytoplasm of a basopinacocyte of *E. mulleri* showing an arrowhead pattern following treatment with rabbit heavy meromyosin (TEM) (×99,000) (Pavans de Ceccatty, 1981). (**A**, courtesy D. N. Boury-Esnault; **B**, courtesy Dr. J. Pottu-Boumendil; **C, D**, courtesy Prof. M. Pavans de Ceccatty.)

atic search for such junctions and until such a survey is undertaken the available data should be viewed as incomplete.

Harrison (1972a) and Simpson (1963) have directly observed that baso-pinacocytes function in food ingestion, and based upon the presence of phagosomes, there appears to be little difference among pinacocytes in this regard (see Chap. 6), although Harrison (1974b) reports few phago-somes and little acid phosphatase in exopinacocytes. Van Weel (1949) and Kilian (1952) have also reported particulate ingestion by pinacocytes. The presence of acid phosphatase within primary and secondary lysosomes in all three types of pinacocytes attests to their probable involvement in nutritive processing (Harrison, 1972a, 1974b; Diaz, 1979a; Thiney, 1972) as do reports of the presence of phagosomes in them (Bagby, 1970; Thi-ney, 1972; Ledger, 1976). Detailed, comparative, ultrastructural, and cy-tochemical studies of all three types of pinacocytes have not been re-ported and would be most useful. In *Sycon ciliatum,* Ledger (1976) reports fewer phagosomes in endopinacocytes than in exopinacocytes.

Exopinacocytes and endopinacocytes contain few microtubules and more abundant microfilaments (Figs. 2-3, 2-5), which are correlated with their contractile properties (Pottu-Boumendil, 1975; Pavans de Ceccatty *et al.,* 1970; Pavans de Ceccatty, 1981; Thiney, 1972; Feige, 1969); both types of organelles tend to lie parallel to the cell surface. In demosponges these structures are considered to lie at the basis of contractile events in the exopinacoderm and in the canals (Chap. 6). In calcareous sponges, exopinacocytes have been observed during their migration from the ex-opinacoderm into the mesohyl, thus establishing their ability to become ameboid (Ledger, 1976); possibly all pinacocytes given appropriate sig-nals are able to become freely mobile. However, such an idea stands in direct opposition to the commonly accepted role of the pinacoderms as forming a barrier at the environmental interface (Bagby, 1970). Pavans de Ceccatty (1981) has recently demonstrated that microfilaments in baso-pinacocytes contain actin (Figs. 2-5C,D).

There is a general absence of specific structural specialization in most pinacocytes, and Bagby (1970) has suggested that the pinacoderms proba-bly function by permitting the diffusion of small molecules while acting as a barrier for large ones and for mesohyl cells. In this respect they are similar to the endothelium of capillaries among vertebrates. Surprisingly, in a few demosponges, a small number of endopinacocytes possess a flagellum: in *Tethya lyncurium* (Pavans de Ceccatty, 1966), *Hippospongia communis* (Thiney, 1972), *Plakina trilopha* (Donadey, 1979), *Cacospon-gia scalaris* (Donadey, 1982), *Oscarella lobularis* (Lévi and Porte, 1962; Donadey, 1979), and *Corticium* (De Vos, person. comm.). The signifi-cance of this is not clear but signals an unsuspected similarity to choano-cytes in the potential to develop flagella.

In addition to the above-discussed organelles, pinacocytes in demo-sponges contain few mitochondria, small quantities of endoplasmic retic-ulum and ribosomes, both of which are augmented in cells actively secreting collagen (Garrone and Rozenfeld, 1981), anucleolate (light microscope level) nuclei in most cases except in recently differentiated cells (Chap. 9), Golgi membranes, and in some instances glycogen (Connes *et al.*, 1972; Boury-Esnault, 1973; Thiney, 1972, Bagby, 1970; Diaz, 1979a) and lipid (Feige, 1969; Thiney, 1972). Structural specialization in these cells involves contractile vacuoles in freshwater species (discussed in a later section of this chapter), lysosomes and phagosomes, microfilaments, and electron-dense inclusions associated with collagen fibrilogenesis. In the only study available on exo- and endopinacocytes in calcareous species (Fig. 2-6), the cells in *Sycon ciliatum* are described as possessing the same general features as those in demosponges except that microtubules and microfilaments are not described and neither are organelles associated with collagen secretion (Ledger, 1976). Interestingly, Ledger found that exopinacocytes are characterized by more numerous phagosomes and dense inclusions, the latter of which may be the final stages of digestive vacuoles. Endopinacocytes in this species contain large ($\sim$1.0 μm) electron-lucent vesicles, which are absent in exopinacocytes. Of much developmental significance is the finding that both types of pinacocytes are clearly nucleolated and are thus similar to archeocytes, which are generally absent or few in number in this and other calcareous sponges with asconoid and syconoid canal systems.

With the important exception of calcinean and calcaronean sponges, pinacocytes have no apparent role in the formation of new tissue during growth and development, although in demosponges they possibly contribute to the formation of microscleres (Chap. 4). In calcareous species exopinacocytes act as a stock of sclerocytes, which migrate into the mesohyl where they secrete calcitic spicules. During growth and development in demosponges, pinacocytes have not been observed to undergo cell division (see for example, Simpson, 1963, 1968a; Thiney, 1972; Harrison, 1972a) with the exception of one unconfirmed report in which a very low level of mitosis was described in porocytes (Wintermann-Kilian *et al.*, 1969). The question of the origin of new pinacocytes is dealt with in a number of contexts in Chapters Six, Eight, and Nine.

Part of the exopinacoderm is involved in forming openings which connect the canal system to the environment and certain endopinacocytes form special junctions with choanocyte chambers. These structurally specialized pinacocytes are fully described and discussed in Chapter Six.

Choanocytes (Excluding Hexactinellids)

The fine structure of choanocytes was first described by Kilian (1954) and Rasmont (1959). Since their early observations, a number of more complete descriptions have appeared (Fjerdingstad, 1961; Brill, 1973; Watanabe, 1978b). These cells are structurally complex and their flagellar activity functions in the production of a current of water through the canal

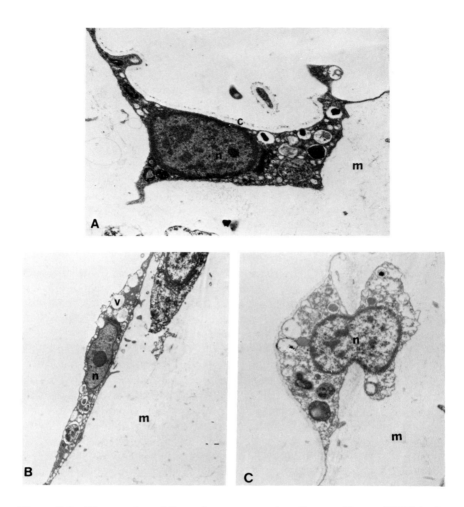

Figure 2-6 Pinacocytes of the calcareous species, *Sycon ciliatum* (TEMs). **A**. Exopinacocyte that displays an intermediate morphology to the fusiform and T shapes. *c*, cell coat; *n*, nucleus; *m*, mesohyl. Note the nucleolate nucleus which is rare in demosponge exopinacocytes and the presence of phagosomes which is not (×9,000) (Ledger, 1976). **B**. An endopinacocyte that borders the atrial cavity and possesses a nucleolate nucleus (*n*) and, in distinction to exopinacocytes in this species, lucent vacuoles (*v*). *m*, mesohyl (×3,150) (Ledger, 1976). **C**. Exopinacocyte in the process of migrating into the mesohyl (*m*). Note the shape of the nucleus (*n*). Such a configuration is also intermediate between fusiform and T shapes. These cells are known to leave the exopinacoderm and to differentiate into sclerocytes (×7,020) (Ledger, 1976). (All courtesy Dr. P. W. Ledger.)

system. Their structure further suggests, and observations substantiate, a specialization for the entrapment of small particulate or colloidal material (Chap. 6). In sponges with syconoid and leuconoid structures, choanocytes occur in spherical clusters (choanocyte chambers) with their flagella directed into a water-filled lumen. Only in a few calcareous species do they form a continuous layer (choanoderm) lining a single cavity. Choanocyte chambers are ultimately bounded by endopinacocytes with two types of openings occurring as part of the chambers themselves: choanocytic prosopyles, which open on the incurrent side of the chamber, and choanocytic apopyles, which are on the excurrent side. Both types of specialization are described in Chapter Six. In asconoid and some syconoid species, ostial openings lead directly to the choanocytes; thus, pinacocytic prosopyles, and in asconoids choanocytic and pinacocytic apopyles are absent (see Table 1-3).

Two structural features distinguish each choanocyte: (1) a single flagellum and (2) long, microvillus extentions of the plasmalemma which form an upright tube (collar) around the lower portion of the flagellum (Fig. 2-7). With the exception of calcareous sponges (but *not* sphinctozoids) and possibly homoscleromorphan demosponges, the cell size of choanocytes is roughly one half that of archeocytes (Lévi, 1965; Simpson, 1968a; Reiswig, 1975b; Vacelet, 1979b). The nuclear size of these smaller choanocytes is also correspondingly small (Fig. 2-8). Using Feulgen microspectophotometric analyses, Harrison and Cowden (1975c, 1976) have found that choanocyte nuclei yield 64%, on average, the extinctions of other cells (archeocytes). While these researchers attribute this difference to the organization of the DNA–protein complex and its effect on staining, it appears possible that these cells could also be haploid, a condition in good agreement with their differentiation into sperm cells (Chap. 7). The nuclei of the larval flagellated epithelial cells (Chap. 7) similarly possessed lower extinctions.

The ultrastructure of choanocytes has been well elucidated in two freshwater species, *Spongilla lacustris* (Fjerdingstad, 1961) and *Ephydatia fluviatilis* (Brill, 1973), and in *Sycon ciliatum* (Ledger, 1976) (Fig. 2-9). These cells have a similar ultrastructure in marine demosponges (Lévi and Porte, 1962; Connes, 1968; Borojevic, 1966; Diaz, 1979a; Watanabe, 1978b) and where documented in other calcareous species (Ledger, 1976; Vacelet, 1979b). The flagellum is bounded by the cell membrane and a small amount of cytoplasm; in freshwater species this membrane forms two crests oriented at approximately 180° to each other; occassionally more than two crests are present (Brill, 1973). In the marine demosponge, *Suberites massa* (Diaz, 1979a), and the calcareous species, *Sycon ciliatum* (Ledger, 1976), crests are apparently absent and it may be that they occur only in freshwater forms. A necklace of three rows of membrane particles occurs in the plasmalemma at the base of the flagellum (Garrone *et al.*, 1980; Lethias *et al.*, 1983). Internally, in the flagellum are

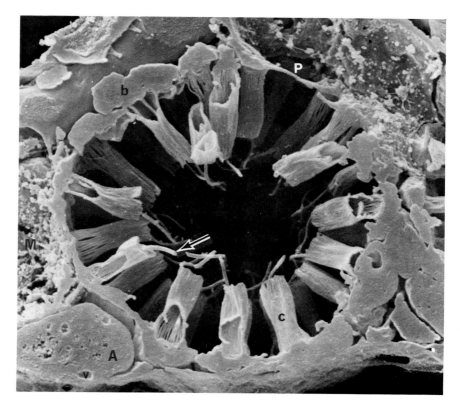

Figure 2-7 A choanocyte chamber and surrounding mesohyl (*M*) in *Ephydatia fluviatilis* displaying choanocyte collars (*c*), flagella (*arrow*), and cell bodies (*b*). A prosopyle (*P*) (incurrent channel) is also seen in this preparation. An archeocyte (*A*) in the mesohyl displays the presence of contractile vacuoles (*v*) in the cytoplasm. The preparation of this material involved a new technique consisting of fixation, dehydration, embedding, cutting a face view of the tissue, removal of the embedding medium, critical point drying, and visualization by scanning electron microscopy (×2,565) (Weissenfels, 1982). (Courtesy of Prof. N. Weissenfels.)

nine sets of double peripheral tubules and a central pair. The peripheral tubules in the basal body have arms and thus are similar to centrioles. Microtubules connect the basal body to the plasmalemma (Garrone, 1969b). A single centriole is present close to the basal portion of the flagellum and lies at right angles to it. The collar consists of 30 to 40 microvilli, each 100–200 nm in diameter. Each microvillus contains longitudinally oriented microfilaments (Garrone, 1969b; Pottu-Boumendil, 1975). The distance between villi is somewhat variable, but within the range of 30–100 nm. The villi are often connected by thin (4 nm) filamentous material. The plasma lemma of each microvillus contains two longi-

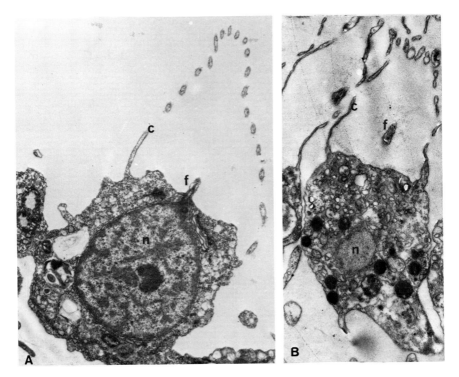

Figure 2-8 Choanocytes (TEMs). **A**. In the calcareous species *Sycon ciliatum* (×8,100) (Ledger, 1976). **B**. In the demosponge *Microciona prolifera* (×6,120) (Bagby, unpubl.). Despite the difference in magnification, the nuclear (*n*) and cell sizes in *S. ciliatum* are about twice that in *M. prolifera*. Both cells, however, possess typical collars (*c*) and single flagella (*f*), which in *S. ciliatum* arise from the nucleus. Note also the well-developed nucleolus in the latter species, which is rarely reported in demosponges. (**A**, courtesy Dr. P. W. Ledger; **B**, courtesy Dr. R. M. Bagby.)

tudinal rows of particles acting as attachment points for the filamentous connections between microvilli (Garrone *et al.*, 1980; Lethias *et al.*, 1983). In *Callyspongia diffusa* the tip of each microvillus is swollen forming a distal bulb (Johnston and Hildemann, 1982). Such a condition has only been reported in this species and may, according to these authors, be artifactual. At the base of the collar, there is a mat of fibrils referred to by Fjerdingstad as "mucous." Brill also found this type of cell coat material connecting the microvilli of neighboring choanocytes. All of these fibrils probably act as a means of holding the microvilli somewhat rigid and thus convey integrity of the collars. In *Clathrina* there is a prominent, continuous "mat" of material connecting neighboring collars; this effectively

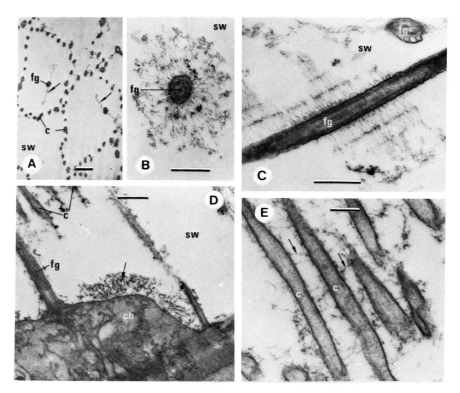

Figure 2-9 Features of choanocytes in *Sycon ciliatum*, which are also reported in other species (see text) (TEMs). **A**. Cross section through distal collars (*c*) and flagella (*fg*) showing the presence of two strands of amorphous cell coat material (*arrows*) on the flagella. *sw*, seawater. Scale bar: 1.0 μm (×4,500) (Ledger, 1976). **B**. Unusual presence of large amounts of cell coat material surrounding the flagellum (*fg*). *sw*, seawater. Scale bar: 0.5 μm (×19,800) (Ledger, 1976). **C**. Longitudinal section of the flagellum (*fg*) showing the somewhat regular arrangement of the amorphous material. *sw*, seawater. Scale bar: 0.5 μm (×25,200) (Ledger, 1976). **D**. Cell coat material (*arrow*) at the base of the collar (*c*). *fg*, flagellum; *sw*, seawater; *cb*, cell body. Scale bar: 0.5 μm (×16,200) (Ledger, 1976). **E**. Amorphous material forming crosslinks (*arrows*) between the collar microvilli (*c*). Scale bar: 0.2 μm (×40,500) (Ledger, 1976). (All courtesy Dr. P. W. Ledger.)

seals off the distal collar from the cell base thus possibly increasing the efficiency of water pumping (De Vos, personal communication). The plasmalemma surrounding the flagellum in some cells has two thread-like processes (vanes) consisting of filaments merging with those between the microvilli of the collar (Brill, 1973). Afzelius (1961) reported the presence of two rows of hairs on flagella in both *Microciona* and *Grantia* which do not occur above the level of the collar. He thus concluded that these are "flimmer" (tinsel) flagella similar to those in choanoflagellates. This condition has not been reported since, and it appears possible that the hairs referred to are actually fibrils, but further reevaluation of this question is warranted. In *Suberites massa,* choanocytes possess a short, tubular extention of the cell (a sleeve) which surrounds the base of the flagellum (Figs. 2-10, 2-11) and is situated internally to the collar (Connes *et al.,* 1971a); this structure has been referred to as a "manchon periflagellaire," and its presence has been confirmed using scanning electron microscopy by De Vos (personal communication).

Choanocytes possess few mitochondria; characteristically, single cisternae of the endoplasmic reticulum occur close to the lateral and basal cell membrane; ribosomes are not numerous suggesting low levels of protein synthetic activity (Harrison, 1974b). At the base of the collar, cytoplasmic contractile vacuoles are present in freshwater species (see later). Phagosomes are also a constituent of the choanocyte cytoplasm (Brill, 1973; Connes *et al.,* 1972; Pottu-Boumendil, 1975; Weissenfels, 1976; Ledger, 1976; Willenz, 1980) and acid phosphatase activity has been demonstrated in them in *Corvomeyenia carolinensis* (Harrison, 1974b). The choanocyte nucleus is generally anucleolate (light microscope level) except in nonsphinctozoid calcareous species (Ledger, 1976), in homoscleromorphs (Donadey, 1978, 1979), in hexactinellids (Reiswig, 1979), and under special conditions in other demosponges (Chaps. 7, 9). Golgi bodies are present apically (Gatenby *et al.,* 1955; Ledger, 1976; Brill, 1973), but glycogen has not been reported in any collar cell (Lufty, 1960; Boury-Esnault and Doumenc, 1979). The bases of choanocytes border the mesohyl, which generally contains collagen fibrils (Connes *et al.,* 1972), but there is absolutely no indication that these cells are, or become, involved in collagen biosynthesis in clear distinction to pinacocytes and some types of mesohyl cells (Chap. 5). Also, in distinction to pinacocytes, choanocytes undergo mitoses (Shore, 1971) and are the only fixed tissue type in sponges which do so. In collar cells of the marine demosponge, *Haliclona rosea,* Garrone (1969b) has described an intranuclear rod which appears to be RNA; its significance is not clear. A number of marine species possess, on the light microscope level, choanocytes with readily detectable cytoplasmic RNA (Simpson, 1968a) and this appears to be a static characteristic of these cells shared in common with pinacocytes and some types of mesohyl cells (archeocytes, collencytes, lophocytes, myocytes).

Choanocytes have been discovered in free-floating buds of a clionid species (Garrone, 1974) and reports of their presence *internally* within mature demosponge larvae have appeared (Harrison and Cowden, 1975b; Meewis, 1941). The flagellated surface cells of sponge larvae (Chap. 7) should not be confused with choanocytes; the former lack microvilli (collars) and are, in many demosponges, cone shaped and small (see Fig. 7-16C).

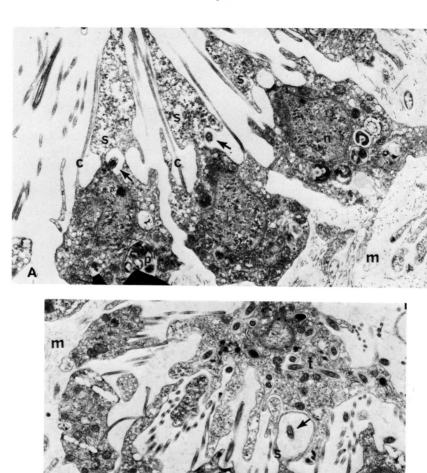

Figure 2-10   The periflagellar sleeve (manchon périflagellaire) of *Suberites massa* (TEMs). **A**. Each of the choanocytes possess a sleeve (*s*) that surrounds the basal portion of the flagellum (*arrows*) and lies internal to the collar microvilli (*c*). The choanocytes are anchored in the mesohyl (*m*), which contains abundant collagen fibrils. A number of phagosomes (*p*) are seen in the choanocyte cytoplasm. *n*, nucleus. (×8,200) (Diaz, 1979a). **B**. A sleeve (*s*) seen in cross section with the flagellum (*arrow*) centrally located. Portions of the sleeves in other cells are also visible. *m*, mesohyl; *t*, cellule centrale (×7,050) (Diaz, 1979a). (Both courtesy Dr. J. P. Diaz.)

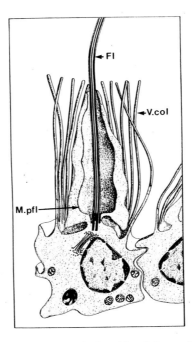

Figure 2-11   Reconstruction of the relationship of the periflagellar sleeve (*M. pfl*) to the collar microvilli (*V. col*) and flagellum (*Fl*) in *Suberites massa* (Connes *et al.*, 1971a). (Copyright Archives de l'Académe des Sciences de Paris.) (Courtesy Dr. R. Connes.)

Variation in Cell Shape

Choanocytes Vespiform and En Sablier.   In the earlier literature, choanocytes of calcareous sponges (*Sycon, Grantia*) were described with abnormal morphology, referred to as "choanocytes vespiformes." Vacelet (1964) has more recently described the same type of choanocytes in the pharetronid, *Petrobiona,* and he presents a very useful review of the early literature. Vespiform choanocytes are dumbell shaped and occur in chambers that have contracted such that the basal choanocyte surface is connected to the mesohyl via long, very thin, filopods appearing in the light microscope as thin strands of material. The vespiform morphology is taken on by all of the choanocytes of a chamber, but all chambers are not necessarily constituted of these cells. The nucleus of these cells occurs in the distal portion of the cell and the collar and/or flagellum may be lost (Duboscq and Tuzet, 1939; Bidder, 1892). Bidder has referred to the basal portion as the "plinthe" and the distal portion as the "colonne". While Vacelet (1964) considers that this condition is likely a sign of cellular degeneration, Duboscq and Tuzet (1939) have suggested that it is due to the presence of central cells in the chambers (see Chap. 6). They hypothesized that the central cells cut off the flow of water by attaching to flagella, thus stopping flagellar beating and leading to asphyxiation, a view rejected by Reiswig and Brown (1977) and questioned by Vacelet (1964). Bidder (1892) suggested that the plinthe is phagocytized by other cells and thus serves as a nutrient source. Duboscq and Tuzet (1939) suggest that the plinthe contains excretory products and is shed as a means of excretion. The significance of vespiform choanocytes as pointed out by Vacelet (1964) is still obscure. Detailed ultrastructural studies would add much to our knowledge of their formation and function.

A morphological abnormality of choanocytes referred to as "choanocytes en sablier," which is similar to the vespiform morphology, has been described by Vacelet (1964) in *Petrobiona* and by Donadey (1979) in *Oscarella* (Fig. 2-12). Apparently not all of the choanocytes of a chamber are simultaneously transformed into this morphology. Further, in these "hourglass" choanocytes the basal surface becomes highly flattened and does not put out filopodia, and the flagellum is not usually lost although the collar may be. Vacelet (1964) has shown that insufficient oxygen and warming can rapidly cause choanocytes to transform into an hourglass morphology. This transformation appears to be reversible, but more extensive experimental work is required to extend these preliminary observations. Some types of fixatives may also cause morphological changes in choanocytes (Sara, 1963; Boury Esnault *et al.*, in press).

Other Shapes. De Vos *et al.* (1981) and Boury-Esnault *et al.* (in press) have recently studied the choanocytes of a variety of species by scanning

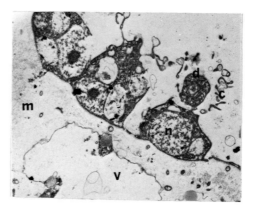

Figure 2-12 An example of an hourglass choanocyte (choanocyte en sablier) of *Oscarella lobularis* (TEM). The hourglass cell possesses a proximal portion of the cell body containing the nucleus (*n*) and a distal portion (*d*) that appears partially surrounded by the collar (*c*). *m*, mesohyl; *v*, a portion of a large vacuolar cell showing the vacuole and limiting plasmalemma. (×5,300) (Donadey, 1979). (Courtesy Dr. C. Donadey.)

electron microscopy and have established broad morphological categories based upon cell shape. In *Clathrina* and *Ephydatia* the cell body is spherical (Fig. 2-13) while in *Cacospongia, Oscarella, Corticium,* and *Petrobiona* it is trunkate (Fig. 2-14), that is, slightly ellipsoidal. In *Geodia, Suberites, Agelas,* and *Ceratoporella* the basal portion of the cell is highly flattened and broad and the more distal portion arises out of it in the form of a column, on the top of which is the collar. Finally, in *Spheciospongia* the cells are considered to be en sablier with the collar highly flared. The latter condition is considered normal in this species which suggests that the en sablier configuration may indeed not be an artifact or the result of environmental conditions.

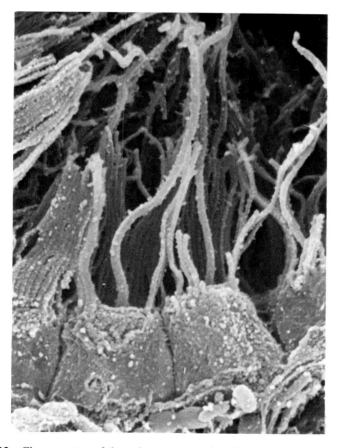

Figure 2-13 Choanocytes of the calcareous species, *Clathrina contorta*. The cell shape is spherical and is considered as one morphological type. Compare cell size with that in a demosponge (Fig. 2-14) (SEM) (×3800) (De Vos *et al.,* unpubl.). (Courtesy Drs. L. De Vos, N. Boury-Esnault, J. Vacelet, and C. Donadey.)

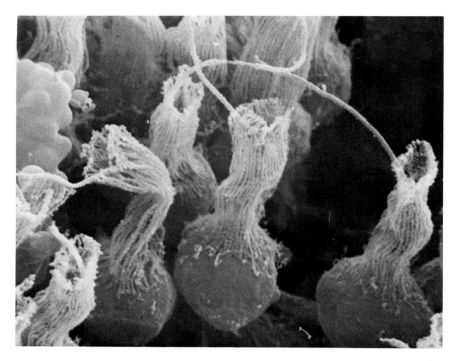

Figure 2-14 Choanocytes in the demosponge *Corticium candelabrum* showing the trunkate shape of the cell body, which is considered as a specific morphological type. Compare the cell size in this demosponge with that in a calcareous species in Fig. 2-13 (SEM) (×5,690) (De Vos *et al.,* unpubl.). (Courtesy Drs. L. De Vos, N. Boury-Esnault, J. Vacelet, and C. Donadey.)

Pinacoderm and Choanoderm in Hexactinellida

In hexactinellids, choanocytes *per se* do not exist; instead a choanosyncytium (syncytial choanoderm) has been described (Fig. 2-15). In the syncytium there are approximately ten flagella for each nucleus (Reiswig, 1979). A point of some potential importance is the presence within the choanosyncytial nuclei of well-developed nucleoli, a condition occurring infrequently in choanocytes of other sponges. The collars and flagella appear completely comparable to other sponges, 38 microvilli per collar with a 100 nm spacing; a basal body is present at the point of origin of the flagellum (Reiswig, 1979). The choanosyncytium is enveloped by the trabecular syncytium and the latter also forms the epithelial lining of canals as well as a secondary, very thin, syncytium lying at the level of the collars (Mackie and Singula, 1983). Although the choanosyncytium is embedded in parts of the trabecular syncytium, the two are easily recognizeable as separate entities on an ultrastructural level. The cytoplasm at the base of each collar–flagellum unit is somewhat more voluminous and has been called a "nodal body"; the whole structure (collar, flagellum, nodal body) is referred to as a "collar body" (Mackie and Singula, 1983).

The exopinacoderm is also syncytial and forms ostial openings which appear to be noncontractile (Mackie et al., 1983). This syncytium forms a very thin, surface dermal membrane which produces collagen fibrils within spacious indentations of the syncytium. The internal trabecular syncytium is directly continuous with the dermal membrane and the two are actually part of the same very large syncytial network forming the basis of the structure of these highly unique metazoans. The canal spaces are lined by the trabecular syncytium, which is thus positionally comparable to the endopinacoderm in other sponges. This syncytium elaborates collagen fibrils within indentations, some extensive, as in the dermal membrane. The trabecular syncytium forms a kind of "scaffold" into which the choanosyncytium is inserted and possibly the former acts as a primary support system for the latter. The siliceous skeleton is enveloped by the trabecular syncytium and the former is probably crucial for the integrity of the trabeculum (Pavans de Ceccatty, personal communication) (see also Fig. 1-9).

The choanosyncytium consists of collar bodies and choanoblasts. Each of the latter contains a nucleus and puts out numerous cell processess ending as collar bodies at the surface of the trabecular syncytium thus forming localized groups of collar bodies, flagellated chambers. Between the choanoblast and its collar bodies are disk-shaped plugs—junctional plugs—which separate the cytoplasm of the two but which are perforate and thus allow limited exchange (Pavans de Ceccatty and Mackie, 1982). Such plugs also occur between the trabecular syncytium and the collar bodies as well as between the latter and the choanoblasts. These disk-shaped, plugged junctions are unique organelles shown to be derived from the Golgi and to interact with the plasmalemma forming special barriers (Pavans de Ceccatty and Mackie, 1982). The presence of such perforate barriers between the syncytia in hexactinellids produces a condition intermediate between that of a true syncytium and that of cellularity (Pavans de Ceccatty, personal communication). Phagosomes occur within both choano- and trabecular syncytia. In the flagellated chambers, the trabeculum puts out thin processes which form a secondary syncytium at the level of the collars (Mackie and Singula, 1983). Although this secondary trabeculum was mistakenly identified as part of the choanosyncytium, its structural relationship to the latter was correctly deduced (Reiswig, 1979) (see Fig. 6-8). Discrete uninucleate cells—archeocytes, granular cells—occur in the trabecluar syncytium and plugged junctions are also found between them and the syncytium (Chap. 3).

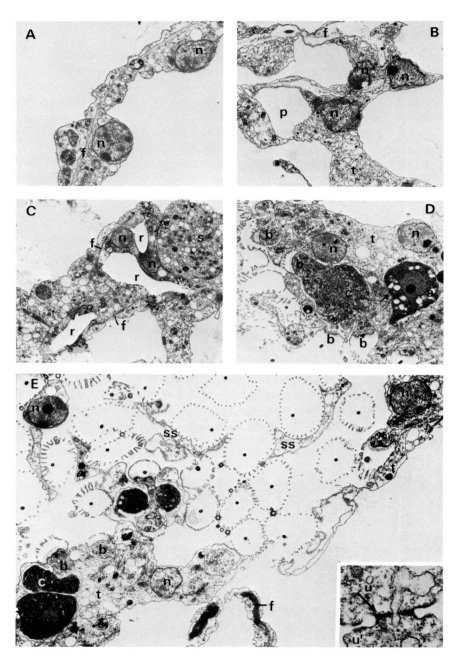

Figure 2-15 Pinacoderms, choanoderm, and tissue in the hexactinellid *Rhabdo-calyptus dawsoni* (TEMs). Magnification for all figures, ×3,600 except inset in E, ×36,000. **A**. Cross section of the exceedingly thin, syncytial "dermal membrane" which forms the surface of the animal. Typically, there is a thin layer of collagen fibrils (*f*) within elongate pockets of the syncytium. Note the continuous cytoplasmic compartment. *n*, nuclei. **B**. Tangential section of the dermal membrane

Contractile Vacuoles and Water Balance

Contractile vacuoles have now been clearly demonstrated in the pinaco-cytes of freshwater sponges (Feige, 1969; Brauer, 1975; Weissenfels, 1974); both exo- and endopinacocytes possess them (Weissenfels, 1975, 1980). Similar contractile vacuoles have also been described in freshwater sponge choanocytes (see Fig. 6-23B) (Jepps, 1947; Weissenfels, 1976; Brill, 1973; Lufty, 1956), in porocytes (Harrison, 1972b), in archeocytes (see Fig. 2-7) (Weissenfels, 1976; Jepps, 1947), and in sclerocytes (Weis-senfels and Landschoff, 1977; Jepps, 1947). Indeed, Weissenfels (1975) finds that all cell types in *Ephydatia fluviatilis* possess them. In basopina-cocytes, at least, the vacuoles and cytoplasmic nephridial system are arranged radially around the nucleus (Fig. 2-16); in choanocytes they are found apically near the basal body of the flagellum. Early studies of them in choanocytes initially suggested they were Golgi related and that they might also be present in the marine species *Grantia compressa* (Gatenby *et al.,* 1955). Although such Golgi-related vacuoles in this species can be caused to swell in hypotonic seawater, there is no clear indication that they are osmoregulatory (Lufty, 1956) and, as expected, Jepps (1947) did

---

(above) showing its continuity with the trabecular syncytium (*t*). The syncytia are continuous but differ in their position in the animal. *f*, collagen fibrils; *n*, nuclei; *p*, pore-like structure in the syncytium. **C.** Internal to the dermal membrane the trabecular syncytium enrobes siliceous spicules and in some areas it appears different and is referred to as the trabecular cord syncytium (*s*). In this desilicified section, the cavities of three rays (*r*) of a siliceous spicule are seen within an ill-defined, probably syncytial, sclerocyte that is bounded by a very thin layer of collagen fibrils (*f*). *n*, sclerocyte nuclei in the same cytoplasm. **D.** Still more internally the trabecular syncytium (*t*) continues within the animal where archeo-cytes (*a*) and choanoblasts (*c*) occur embedded in it. Choanoblasts produce cell extentions which form collar bodies (*b*) at the surface of the trabeculum. The choanoblast shown here is connected to three collar bodies—a fourth is also seen above. Each collar body consists of a microvillus collar, flagellum, and a "bulb" of choanoblast cytoplasm separated (not shown here) from the choanoblast by a plugged junction. *n*, trabecular nuclei. A plugged junction is seen between the archeocyte and the trabeculum (arrow). **E.** The flagellated chamber shown here consists of trabecular syncytium (*t*) enclosing collar bodies (*b*) and choanoblasts (*c*) and also forming thin extentions upward, between the collars. This latter structure is referred to as the secondary syncytium (*ss*) (see also Figure 6-8). Part of the trabeculum contains enclosed tracts of collagen fibrils (*f*). *n*, trabecular nuclei. Inset: A plugged junction (arrow) between two "units" within the trabecu-lar syncytium. These junctions are perforate and in this example smooth reticu-lum bridges the two units (*u* and *u'*) which have a common plasmalemma. See also plugged junctions in Figures 3-1E and 3-11E. All electron micrographs courtesy Prof. M. Pavans de Ceccatty (unpubl.). (Inset in **E**, Pavans de Ceccatty, 1982.)

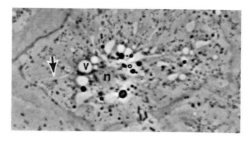

Figure 2-16 A living basopinacocyte of the freshwater demosponge *Ephydatia fluviatilis* demonstrating the occurrence of prominent contractile vacuoles (*v*) clustered around the nucleus (*n*). Very thin nephridial tubules (*arrow*) radiate outward in the cytoplasm (phase-contrast micrograph) (×1,050) (Weissenfels, 1975). (Courtesy Prof. N. Weissenfels.)

not even find them in a substantial number of marine demosponges and calcareous species. Based upon the molarity of sponge tissue relative to seawater (Table 2-2) (Prosser, 1967), there is no compelling reason to consider that such vacuoles in marine species are indeed contractile vacu-

Table 2-2 Ionic content of marine species[a]

Species Analyzed	Millimolar			
	Na	K	Ca	Cl
I. At Naples, Italy				
Average values, whole animal				
Hymedesmia vesicolor				
Dysidea avara				
Chondrosia reniformis	374	31.6	—[b]	—
Halichondria panicea				
Tethya aurantium				
Crambe crambe				
Calculated intracellular				
(Averages)	195	58.5	—	—
Seawater	507	11.7	—	—
II. At Woods Hole, Massachusetts				
Average values, whole animal				
Microciona prolifera	300	66	8.4	225
Calculated intracellular				
(Averages)	216	104.5	7.8	45
Seawater	426	9	9.3	495

[a]Taken from Prosser (1967).
[b]No data.

oles. In fact, based upon the concentration differences, osmotic water *loss* is to be expected.

In freshwater sponges, both the rate and the volume of output of the vacuoles can be directly affected by the osmolarity of the medium (Brauer, 1975). At 12–15 mosmolar no output occurs and at decreasing solute concentration there is a strictly linear relationship between output and osmolarity of the medium: the lower the osmolarity of the medium the higher the output. Weissenfels (1974) has also shown that with increasing osmolarity the activity of these vacuoles decreases in basopinacocytes. The output response has been shown to be related to osmolarity not ionic strength and the vacuole contents appear isotonic with the medium. While these data indicate that intracellular K^+ is probably regulated independently of the contractile vacuoles, it seems probable that much of the intracellular Na^+ is contained within them and they thus may act as a reservoir for this ion (Brauer, 1975).

The nephridial system in basopinacocytes, where it has been best studied, is complex and consists of vacuoles, lacunae, and thin channels (Fig. 2-16) (Weissenfels, 1974). The vacuoles may even contain membranous material suggesting that they possibly also function in some non-osmoregulatory capacity. While it seems appropriate to consider that the contractile vacuoles in the epithelia are the primary ones involved in osmoregulation, those in other cells may be also, but there are no data on the point. Alternatively, and of much potential significance is the possibility that these vacuoles in mesohyl cells may perform dual roles being involved in osmoregulation as well as in digestion and elimination (archeocytes) and selective ion transport (sclerocytes).

The presence of contractile vacuoles in freshwater larvae has not been reported and the question of how osmoregulation occurs in them is a fertile area for future investigations. Water balance in dormant, freshwater gemmules is discussed in Chapter Eight.

CHAPTER THREE

Cellular Components of the Mesohyl

The mesohyl, which comprises all of the tissue bounded by and lying internal to the pinacoderms and collar cells, is highly variable in terms of the degree of its development and the kinds of cells present in it. This variability cannot be emphasized too strongly in view of the confusion resulting from many general descriptions of mesohyl cells. The activities of these cells result in the formation of major portions of the skeleton including ground substance, mineral elements, and collagen. The specific role of many types of mesohyl cells has yet to be determined (Lévi, 1970), and such determinations are of great importance for any future understanding of cell interactions.

The noncellular components of the mesohyl are mineral deposits, spongin fibers, collagen fibrils, and unstructured ground substance (Chaps. 4, 5). All sponges elaborate ground substance and, in addition, it can now be stated that collagen fibrils are universally formed. Based upon ultrastructural studies this is even the case in hexactinellids, *Euplectella* (Travis *et al.,* 1967) and *Rhabdocalyptus* (Mackie and Singula, 1983); in the calcareous sponges *Clathrina* and *Leucosolenia* (Jones, 1967), *Sycon* (Tuzet and Connes, 1964; Ledger, 1974, 1976) and *Leucandra* (Ledger, 1974); in the sphinctozoid *Neocoelia* (Vacelet, 1979b); and in the homoscleromorph demosponges *Oscarella* (Lévi and Porte, 1962; Donadey, 1979) and *Plakina* (Donadey, 1979). Regardless of the presence or absence of mineralization or spongin fibers or of the types of spicules secreted or the types of mesohyl cells present, similar matrix materials, ground substance and collagen fibrils, are elaborated. Such a generalization suggests that *part* of the basis for the diversity in mesohyl cell structure is due to modulations in biosynthetic pathways for matrix materials which result in the stabilization, or not, of intermediate stages thus producing diverse cytoplasmic architecture, a view supported at least to some extent by the following discussion. The balance of cell diversity can be accounted for, with admittedly very little supporting data, by differences in secretory products formed (i.e., different spicule types) and by cell transformations in which intervening stages become temporarily stable. Such views emphasize the fluidity of mesohyl cells in distinction to epithelial cells which appear, in a comparative sense, to be more stable. However, even this very general distinction breaks down to some extent when dynamic developmental processes are considered (Chaps. 7, 9).

Cell Types and Structure

Mesohyl cells can be treated on the basis of the presence and relative amounts of nuclear and cytoplasmic RNA; their potential for mitosis; the possession of phagosomes; their function; and the presence and structure of complex, special cytoplasmic organelles whose function is still, in many cases, obscure. These features in combination can be used to outline the following categories of mesohyl cells (see also Table 1-1): archeocytes, polyblasts, thesocytes, spongocytes, gemmular epithelium, lophocytes, trophocytes, megasclerocytes, histoblasts, collencytes, fiber cells, myocytes, neuroid cells, microsclerocytes, special cells, and gametes. The latter, gametes, are dealt with later in Chapter Seven. Other groupings of mesohyl cells have been proposed (Table 3-1) (Lévi, 1965, 1970; see also, Webb, 1935); that adopted here emphasizes ultrastructural, cytochemical, and cytological features. Webb (1935) has suggested grouping cell types according to whether their function is known or unknown, and this serves as a further, partial basis for the present discussion. The terminology adopted here is *not* proposed as a definitive revision of terminology but rather as a working basis for review and discussion.

In most cases, cell types require additional investigations in order to further characterize them. Such characterization is not simply an exercise in cataloguing; the establishment of cell categories in sponges implies a degree of understanding of their developmental physiology. In many cases such understanding is quite limited and consequently significant difficulties emerge in establishing meaningful insights and comparisons. This will become obvious from the following discussion, particularly as concerns the group collencytes. A fundamental obstacle in establishing identity (homology) of cell types lies, of course, in our ignorance of the functional roles of many of them. However, it is significant that it is at all possible to establish mesohyl cell categories. The fact that these cells fall into more or less definable groups strongly implies that each type represents a specific tissue type despite the fact that there is little or no anatomical discreteness. This is in strong contrast to the epithelia which occur morphologically, at least, as discrete tissue types. The idea of mesohyl tissue types can serve as a basis for further understanding of the almost unlimited growth potential of many sponges: the mesohyl "tissues" are able to freely migrate into new growth areas without the requirements for a highly coordinated, morphological sequence of events otherwise needed for the formation of anatomically discrete tissues. This in turn permits (or requires) constant morphogenetic remodeling rather than a step-by-step series of interlocking processes typical of most metazoan development. Indeed, there are now well-documented cases of such remodeling (Chap. 9) which, as expected in the absence of highly programmed morphogenesis, is a slow process.

Table 3-1 Two Examples of the Categorization of Cell Types

Minchin (1900)

Tissue-forming cells: Histocytes ......

- Dermal layer
  - I. Epithelial stratum ......
    1. Pinacocytes (epithelial cells)
    2. Myocytes (contractile cells)
    3. Gland cells
    4. Spongoblasts
  - II. Porocytes ......
    5. Pore cells
- Gastral layer
  - III. Skeletogenous stratum ......
    6. Scleroblasts
    7. Collencytes (stellate cells)
    8. Desmacytes (fiber cells)
    9. Cystencytes (bladder cells)
  - IV. Gastral epithelium
    10. Choanocytes (collar cells)

Archeocytes (primordial cells)

- V. Amebocytes (wandering cells) ......
  11. Phagocytes (ingestive cells)
  12. Trophocytes (nutritive cells)
  13. Thesocytes (storage cells)
- VI. Tokocytes (reproductive cells)
  14. Statocytes (gemmule cells)
  15. Gonocytes (sexual cells)

Epithelium stratum (cellules limitant la surface, les canaux et les espaces aquifères)	Pinacocytes	
	Myocytes contractiles	
	Cellules glandulaires	
	Porocytes	
	Cellules sensorielles	
Skeletogenous stratum	Collencytes—cellules étoilées	
	Desmacytes—cellules fusiformes	
	Lophocytes—cellules à pinceau	
	Cystencytes—cellules vésiculaires	
	Scleroblasts	
	Silicoblasts	
	Calcoblasts	
	Spongoblasts	
Gastral epithelium	Choanocytes	
Wandering cells amebocytes et dérivés	Phagocytes	Cellules spheruleuses
	Archeocytes	Cellules Globofères
	Trophocytes	Cellules Rhabdifères
	Thesocytes	Cellules Eosinophiles
		Cellules Vacuolaires
		Cellules Granuleuses
		Cellules Grises
Cellules reproductrices	Gonocytes	
	Archeocytes gemmulaires	
	Cellules nerveuses?	

Archeocytes, Polyblasts, Thesocytes

These cells (Fig. 3-1) have in common the following features (see for example, among numerous other studies: Borojevic, 1966; Simpson, 1963, 1968a; Fell, 1969; Connes, 1968; Rasmont, 1956; Thiney, 1972; Simpson and Fell, 1974; De Vos, 1971; Pottu-Boumendil, 1975; Diaz,

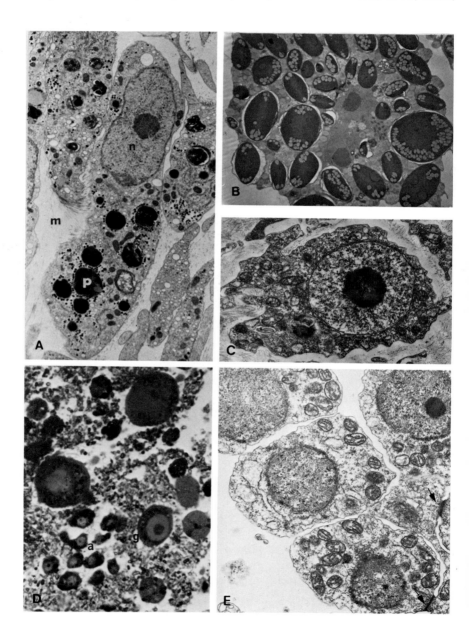

1979a; Connes *et al.*, 1972): a nucleolate nucleus, large (~4 μm) in comparison to other cells (except in some calcareous species and homoscleromorphs) and routinely containing a single nucleolus; moderate to well-developed rough endoplasmic reticulum; numerous ribosomes; numerous mitochondria; well-developed Golgi bodies; phagosomes; lysosomes and small vesicles; sparse microfilaments and microtubules.

Archeocytes (Figs. 3-1A,E; 3-2D).   These cells are typical constituents of the mesohyl of demosponges (Lévi, 1970) and hexactinellids (Mackie and Singula, 1983). In addition, in the pharetronid *Petrobiona,* Vacelet (1964) has described cells resembling archeocytes although his terminology is not adopted here. Further, *Petrobiona* possesses specialized tracts—"cordon trabeculaire"—which contain cells with archeocyte features. Vacelet (1964) has referred to these cells as "thesocytes" because they contain, as with gemmular thesocytes, substantial quantities of storage products, some of which in the former include DNA (Vacelet, 1962, 1964) (see following discussion of Thesocytes for a suggested resolution of this important problem). In *Merlia normandi,* Vacelet (1980) has described groups of cells lodged within the base of the skeleton which contain abundant reserve material in a form much like that of the gemmular thesocytes of *Suberites* (Chap. 8). These cells, however, possess typical archeocyte features. In most calcareous sponges and homoscleromorphs, on the other hand, the mesohyl is relatively noncellular except for the presence of sclerocytes (Ledger, 1976) and, during certain periods, sexual reproductive cells (see Fig. 1-3D) (Chap. 4). In at least one case, *Sycon raphanus,* Tuzet and Paris (1963b) have described "amebocytes," which appear to be typical archeocytes. Reference should be made to Pavans de

---

Figure 3-1   Cells with archeocyte features (see further Fig. 3-2). **A.** A typical mesohyl (*m*) archeocyte in *Cliona lampa* showing the nucleolate nucleus (*n*) and prominent phagosomes (*p*) (TEM) (×4,590) (Rutzler and Rieger, 1973). **B.** A thesocyte of *Ephydatia fluviatilis* with binucleate condition and the cytoplasm packed with vitelline platelets (TEM) (×2,700) (De Vos, unpubl.). **C.** A polyblast of *Suberites massa* displaying high nuclear:cytoplasmic volume. Such cells are considered by some workers as choanocyte-derived (TEM) (×7,830) (Connes *et al.*, 1972). **D.** Megacytes (*g*) spontaneously formed by *Aplysina (Verongia) cavernicola* in apparent response to a virus invasion. For comparison, smaller archeocytes (*a*) are seen in the mesohyl, which is crowded with symbiotic bacteria (light micrograph) (×855) (Vacelet and Gallissian, 1978). **E.** A group of archeocytes in the hexactinellid *Rhabdocalyptus dawsoni.* Note the numerous mitochondria but the absence of phagosomes, which are generally not found in hexactinellid archeocytes. Nucleoli are not in the plane of sectioning in three of the cells. Although these cells are "discrete," they communicate via plugged junctions (*arrows*) with other cells (TEM) (×9,720) (Pavans de Ceccatty, unpubl.). (**A,** courtesy Dr. K. Rutzler; **B,** courtesy Dr. L. De Vos; **C,** courtesy Dr. R. Connes; **D,** courtesy Dr. J. Vacelet; **E,** courtesy Prof. M. Pavans de Ceccatty.)

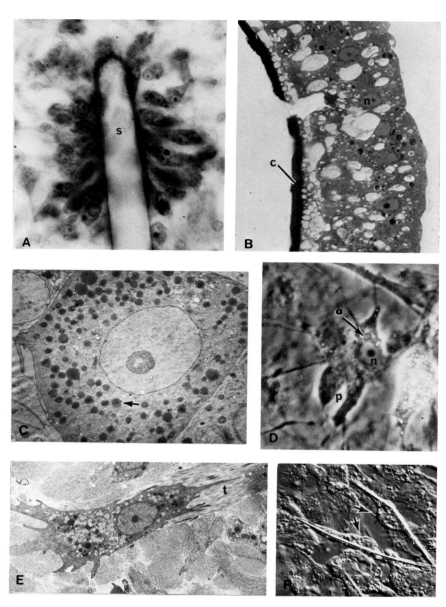

Figure 3-2 Cells with archeocyte features. **A**. Whole mount of spongocytes surrounding and secreting spongin on one extremity of a siliceous spicule (*s*) of *Microciona prolifera* (light micrograph) (×990) (Simpson, 1963). **B**. The gemmular epithelium of *Ephydatia fluviatilis* consisting of columnar spongocytes in the process of secreting the gemmule coat (*c*). *n*, nucleus (light micrograph, semithin section) (×1,080) (De Vos, 1977). **C**. Trophocyte of *Ephydatia fluviatilis* with numerous cytoplasmic lipid inclusions (*arrow*) (TEM) (×4,500) (De Vos, unpubl.). **D**. For comparison, an archeocyte in the mesohyl of *Microciona prolifera* with nucleolate nucleus (*n*), phagosomes (*a*), and pseudopods (*p*) (phase-contrast micrograph, living cell) (×990) (Simpson, 1963). **E**. Lophocyte of *Chondrosia*

Ceccatty (1955), who has presented a useful, brief review of the older literature dealing with mesohyl cells in calcaronean and calcinean sponges. In hexactinellids (Fig. 3-1E), archeocytes are normal constituents of the mesohyl (Reiswig, 1979) and appear cellular, not syncytial, but generally do not possess phagosomes (Mackie and Singula, 1983). Archeocytes also are present in the mesohyl of the sphinctozoid, *Neocoelia* (Vacelet, 1979b). Sclerosponges, which have similar histology to demosponges, doubtless also possess archeocytes (as in *Merlia*, above) although there are no detailed data for this new group.

Archeocytes are mitotically active, are motile with the formation of well-developed pseudopodia, and are usually found in all areas of the mesohyl, although their numbers may be limited in specialized regions such as the cortex. Hexactinellid archeocytes, however, appear to have little or no capacity for movement (Pavans de Ceccatty, 1982). There are few hard data on mitotic activity in these cells other than the well-known case of their divisions that occur following the hatching of freshwater sponge gemmules (Rozenfeld and Rasmont, 1976; Garrone and Rozenfeld, 1981). However, in this specific case the products of division differentiate into choanocytes (Chap. 8). It would be most useful to have additional studies of the uptake of [3H]thymidine as has been reported for choanocytes (Shore, 1971). Archeocytes typically display phagocytic activity (Chap. 6), an attribute distinguishing them from polyblasts and thesocytes.

Two separate reports have appeared describing the development of very large (giant) archeocytes; interestingly the stimulus in one case was mechanical disturbance to the mesohyl (Diaz, 1977); in the other it was related to the presence of virus-like particles (Vacelet and Gallissian, 1978). These giant archeocytes may be comparable to young oocytes since in one of the studies [with *Aplysina (Verongia)*, Vacelet and Gallissian (1978)] the sponge was reproductively active; in this case they were referred to as "megacytes" (Fig. 3-1D). In *Suberites massa*, Diaz (1977) has referred to them as "archeocytes hyalins" which also appeared to him as young oocytes. Archeocytes have been referred to as "phagocytes" in *Petrobiona* (Vacclet, 1964) and in *Spongilla* (Van Weel, 1949), and in *Petrobiona, Sycon,* and *Grantia* they have been called "amoebocytes hyalins" (see Pavans de Ceccatty, 1955). Meewis (1936) has used the terms "ameobocytes et cellules spheruleuses" to refer to them in *Spongilla lacustris*. Some archeocyte-type cells may develop abundant cytoplasmic glycogen; in *Ephydatia mulleri* such cells have been referred

---

reniformis with a prominent trailing tuft (*t*) of secreted collagen fibrils (TEM) (×2,880) (Garrone, 1971). (Copyright Archives de l'Académie des Sciences de Paris.) **F**. Living megasclerocytes (*arrows*) of *Ephydatia fluviatilis* (Nomarski interference micrograph) (×360) (Garrone *et al.*, 1981). (**B, C,** courtesy Dr. L. De Vos; **E, F,** courtesy Dr. R. Garrone.)

to as "dark amebocytes" (amoebocytes sombre) (Pottu-Boumendil, 1975) and possibly should be categorized as special cell types (Garrone, personal communication).

Polyblasts (Fig. 3-1C). The term "polyblaste" as introduced by Tuzet and Pavans de Ceccatty (1955) has recently been employed by a number of workers to refer to archeocyte-type cells, which are distinguished by the general absence of phagosomes and by their relatively small volume of cytoplasm in relation to nuclear volume (Connes, 1968; Thiney, 1972; Connes et al., 1972, 1974b). The significance of these cells, although originally viewed by these workers as crucial stages in developmental processes (Chap. 9), is not really clear. Some reports suggest that polyblasts are an intermediate stage between choanocytes and archeocytes, with the latter considered to be derived from the former (Connes et al., 1972). In that study, polyblasts were observed as constituents of choanocyte chambers. Diaz (1977) has further observed polyblasts, which he refers to as "archeocytes hyalins", originating from endopinacocytes and from choanocytes following mechanical trauma. Thiney (1972) has found that following tissue removal from the oscular diaphragm of *Hippospongia communis* most of the cells (choanocytes are not present in this tissue) tend to take on similar morphology, that of archeocytes and polyblasts. Although polyblasts are definable morphologically on the basis of a high ratio of nuclear to cytoplasmic volume, their specific role in development has not been fully documented. Thiney (1972) has suggested that they may be division products of archeocytes rather than a separate cell category, which, however, does not lessen their potential importance in morphogenesis (Chap. 9).

Thesocytes (Fig. 3-1B). These cells constitute gemmules and are derived from archeocytes (Chap. 8); they are structurally similar to the latter except they lack phagosomes and contain numerous complex vitelline platelets (in freshwater sponges) or similarly complex storage granules (in marine species). In spongillid gemmules two nuclei are present in each cell while in marine thesocytes and presumably some other freshwater gemmules they are uninucleate (Rasmont, 1956; Simpson and Fell, 1974; Carriere et al., 1974; Brien, 1973). However, in the latter group (family Potamolepididae) further confirmation of their uninucleate state is required (Van de Vyver, personal communication). During gemmule germination in freshwater sponges, the binucleate thesocytes undergo division to produce mononucleate archeocytes; the situation in marine sponges appears complex and is discussed in detail in Chapter Eight although it seems clear here also that the thesocytes do give rise to archeocytes (Connes et al., 1978). Vacelet (1980) has described groups of apparently nutrient-laden cells in *Merlia normandi;* these cells form basal aggregates in the thin encrusting animal and are referred to as thesocytes. Their other cytoplasmic and nuclear characteristics are not well established. As intimated above for *Petrobiona,* the term thesocyte is really inappropriate for these cells since they are not constituents of gemmules. In particular, in both cases, what is not clear is whether the nutrients serve as an energy and synthetic source for cell division as is the case with gemmules or whether they serve, for example, as a basis for specific cell activity such as secretion. Until this is clarified these cells should not be confused with or referred to as thesocytes. An alternative suggestion in both cases is to simply refer to them as "storage cells," which appropriately leaves open the question of whether they indeed can be placed in an existent cell category.

Reiswig (1979) and Mackie and Singula (1983) have described a type of hexactinellid mesohyl cell (not syncytial) which they refer to as a thesocyte. These cells are strikingly different from demosponge thesocytes, should not be confused with them, and are further described in a following section (Special Cells).

Summary.   These three categories of cells—archeocytes, polyblasts, and thesocytes—although characterized by similar organelle structure also have in common a negative attribute; in static, histological, and ultrastructural observations, none of them can be reliably identified as performing a specific function other than storage of nutrients (thesocytes) or nutrient (phagocytosis) processing (archeocytes). Since a number of cells (primary oocytes, spongocytes, lophocytes, megasclerocytes), which are clearly involved in specific functions possess similar cytological features (usually referred to as archeocyte features) (see following section and Chaps. 4, 5), and since the thesocytes of gemmules and their archeocyte products are able to provide the sole cellular basis for development of a whole animal, all three cell types are generally considered to be pluripotent or embryonic in nature (other data relevant to this view are discussed in Chap. 9). On the basis of their cytochemistry alone (Harrison, 1974b) they have been considered comparable to "stem cells" in other animal systems.

Spongocytes, Gemmular Epithelium, Lophocytes, Trophocytes, Megasclerocytes

These cells (Fig. 3-2) all have basic archeocyte features and are in addition recognizably functionally differentiated.

Spongocytes, Gemmular Epithelium[1].   Spongocytes (Fig. 3-2A) and the cells that secrete the gemmule coat and constitute the gemmular epithelium (Fig. 3-2B) are active in collagen biosynthesis, which is recognizable on a light microscope level. The cells comprising the gemmular epithelium can actually be considered a type of spongocyte (De Vos, 1977; Connes

[1]There is no present terminology for this epithelium. The term "gemmular epithelium" is only suggested here as a possibility.

and Artiges, 1980) but are separately considered here because they form a classical, secretory, columnar epithelium around developing gemmules—the only known case of the formation of such a columnar epithelium in the phylum. Interestingly septate-like junctions have been observed between these cells (De Vos, 1977).

Spongocytes and the cells in the gemmular epithelium function in the synthesis and secretion of large amounts of collagen in the form of spongin (Chap. 5). During growth, larval metamorphosis, regeneration, and gemmule formation, spongocytes form discrete groups of cells which elaborate the developing fibers (Simpson, 1963; Lévi, 1960; Connes, 1968; Rasmont, 1956; Garrone and Pottu, 1973; Harrison and Cowden, 1975a; De Vos, 1977; Garrone, 1978; Connes and Artiges, 1980). Following the secretion of the collagenous gemmule coat, the cells of the gemmular epithelium undergo disintegration (Rasmont, 1956) and this is presumably also true of spongocytes in general, but the fate of the latter cells requires further elucidation (Garrone, 1978). Both types of cells are characterized by exceptionally well-developed rough endoplasmic reticulum, nucleoli, Golgi bodies, and the presence of dense inclusions and smooth membrane vesicles, all of which typify collagen-secreting cells in sponges (Table 3-2) (Chap. 5).

Lophocytes. In a substantial number of species (see Table 5-3), cells with archeocyte features have been observed in which long fibrillar extentions of the cell are involved in collagen fibril secretion (Fig. 3-2E). These cells have been given a special name, lophocyte, and are more fully described in Chapter Five. In regenerating tissue of *Tethya* they form tracts and may, in this case, be terminally differentiated (Connes, 1968).

Individual archeocytes in the mesohyl have also been reported to secrete collagen fibrils (Borojevic and Lévi, 1964b; Connes *et al.*, 1972, 1978; Feige, 1969) and while they can be considered as possessing collagen biosynthetic activity there is no agreement as to whether these cells should be called archeocytes or lophocytes (see Garrone, 1978). Such individual archeocytes that secrete fibrils *apparently* are able to function in other capacities and there is no suggestion that they are terminally differentiated for collagen secretion. Feige (1969) maintains that lophocytes are actually archeocytes engaged in a high level of collagen biosynthesis, and Efremova (1967) has followed individual archeocytes in hatching gemmules of *Ephydatia fluviatilis* and has observed the same cell both developing and losing typical lophocyte morphology; he thus also considers lophocytes as a transient stage of archeocytes. There is currently no resolution of this problem, but it is possible that the stability of the lophocyte morphology varies in different species.

Trophocytes. Cells with archeocyte features (Harrison and Cowden, 1975a) are present in initial cell aggregates in the mesohyl during gemmule formation in freshwater sponges (Chap. 8); they contain few or no phago-

Table 3-2 Comparative Cytological Features of Spongocytes[a]

	Nucleolus	Rough Endoplasmic Reticulum	Phagosomes	Dense Inclusions	Golgi Apparatus	Smooth Membraned Vesicles
Haliclona elegans	Large	Highly developed	Few	Very numerous	Active	Numerous
Ephydatia mulleri	Small	Highly developed	Few	Scarce	Not clearly visible	Few
Aplysina (Verongia)[b]	Small	Highly developed	Few	Numerous	Not clearly visible	Numerous
Ephydatia fluviatilis[c]	Large	Highly developed	Few	Some	Active	Apparently present
Suberites domuncula[d]	Small	Well developed	Few	Some	?	Yes

[a]Based upon Garrone and Pottu (1973).
[b]From Vacelet (1971a).
[c]Gemmular epithelium. From De Vos (1971, 1977).
[d]Gemmular epithelium. From Connes and Artiges (1980).

somes but have large amounts of cytoplasmic glycogen and numerous small lipid droplets (Fig. 3-2C) (De Vos, 1971; Tessenow, 1969; Ruthmann, 1965). Trophocytes function as a nutrient source for gemmule formation and are engulfed by archeocytes as the latter are developing into thesocytes. In marine gemmule formation no single class of cells appears to act as trophocytes (Connes, 1977). The term trophocyte has also been used to refer to cells providing, or suspected of providing, nutrients to developing oocytes. In some cases these cells appear similar to gemmular trophocytes (Simpson and Gilbert, 1973; Gilbert, 1974), but in others there are clear differences (Johnson, 1979a; Fell, 1969; Diaz et al., 1975; Diaz, 1979a; Lufty, 1957a,b). In order to avoid further confusion, it seems advisable to refer to cells involved in, or suspected of involvement in, furnishing nutrients to developing egg cells as "nurse cells" rather than as trophocytes (Fell, 1969). In their review of the terminology used for sponge cells, Borojevic et al. (1967) suggested using the term trophocyte for both gemmular trophocytes and for nurse cells; at that time, however, the wide morphological diversity of nurse cells was not fully appreciated (see Table 7-2). Nurse cells are a highly heterogeneous morphological group and are discussed in detail in Chapter Seven. It should be kept in mind that some nurse cells may, indeed, be morphologically comparable to gemmular trophocytes, but until more is known concerning nutrition during both gemmule formation and oogenesis, it seems advisable to emphasize possible differences rather than submerge them in terminology.

Megasclerocytes. Among demosponges and a few calcareous species, the structure of megasclerocytes (which secrete megascleres, either siliceous or calcitic) is known and is like that of archeocytes (Fig. 3-2F) with especially numerous mitochondria, but few phagosomes (Herlant-Meewis, 1948a; Simpson, 1963, 1968a; Wintermann, 1951; Schröeder, 1936; Jorgensen, 1947; Pottu-Boumendil, 1975; Simpson and Vaccaro, 1974; Garrone, 1969a; Connes et al., 1972; Ledger, 1976; Boury-Esnault, 1976a; Garrone et al., 1981). No really reliable information is available on the intriguing question of the structure of silica-secreting cells in hexactinellids although silicification has been stated to occur within a syncytium (Okada, 1928). Although no data are available on the deposition of megascleres in sclerosponges, their spicule morphology implies a cellular basis similar to that in demosponges. In both calcareous sponges and demosponges, megasclerocytes become fusiform and the similarity ends there. In the former, calcite is secreted intercellularly without the intervention of a morphologically recognizable matrix and, in the latter, the megasclerocyte forms an intracellular organic filament around which silica is deposited (Chap. 4). As spicule growth comes to an end, megasclerocytes have been reported to undergo degeneration, but this is not at all certain.

Histoblasts, Collencytes, Fiber Cells, Myocytes, Neuroid Cells
Histoblasts, Collencytes (Fig. 3-3)   When freshwater gemmules hatch, motile histoblasts form the new pinacoderms (Wintermann, 1951). These cells are anucleolate, or rarely contain a small nucleolus, and possess a finely granular cytoplasm usually devoid of inclusions but sometimes with remnants of digested nutrients in the form of phagosomes (Fig. 3-3C). Although histochemical and ultrastructural information is not yet available for them, since they are derived directly from thesocytes during gemmule germination (Berthold, 1969; Rozenfeld, 1970; Höhr, 1977) (Chap. 8), it is likely that they at least possess moderate numbers of mitochondria and ribosomes, as well as Golgi membranes. In the newly hatched sponge, those histoblasts remaining in the mesohyl are referred to as collencytes and are typically fusiform (Wintermann, 1951). During and following germination of gemmules of the marine sponge, *Suberites domuncula,* histoblasts are also formed and have been observed ultrastructurally in a preliminary manner (Connes *et al.,* 1978). In this sponge, they do, indeed, contain Golgi membranes, remnants of phagosomes, mitochondria, small vesicles, ribosomes, and anucleate nuclei, and are actively motile. Motile, mesohyl cells conforming to these descriptions are also present in *some* adult sponges: *Neocoelia crypta* (Vacelet, 1979b); *Suberites massa* (Fig. 3-2A) (Connes *et al.,* 1972; Diaz, 1977); *Tethya lyncurium* (Connes, 1968); *Microciona spinosa, Thalysias juniperina, T. schoenus, Tedania ignis* (Simpson, 1968a); *Corvomeyenia carolinensis* (Harrison, 1974b); and in the mature larvae of *Mycale contarenii* (Lévi, 1964; Borojevic, 1966) and *Hamigera hamigera* (Boury-Esnault, 1976a). Borojevic (1966) uses the term collencyte in the following, very specific, manner: mesohyl cells which are presumptive pinacocytes [which, according to Lévi, (1964), are also capable of secreting collagen fibrils]. In *Mycale* larvae and in reaggregation masses of *Ophlitaspongia seriata,* collencytes contain Golgi membranes, ribosomes, and mitochondria (Lévi, 1964; Borojevic and Lévi, 1964b). In *Suberites massa,* they occasionally contain small nucleoli as well as numerous small, vesicular, cytoplasmic inclusions, and they apparently secrete collagen fibrils in this species thus making it very difficult to cytologically separate them from archeocytes. In *Corvomeyenia carolinensis,* collencytes contain cytoplasmic acid phosphatase (Harrison, 1974b). Some workers (De Vos, personal communication) have abandoned the term collencyte due to the difficulties encountered in defining it.

Fiber and "Other" Cells.   The designation collencyte, as well as fibroblast, spindle cell, fusiform cell, fiber cell, have also been used to refer to fusiform (Fig. 3-2B) and stellate cells in the mesohyl, which represent a heterogeneous, and at times confusing, group including (1) terminal stages

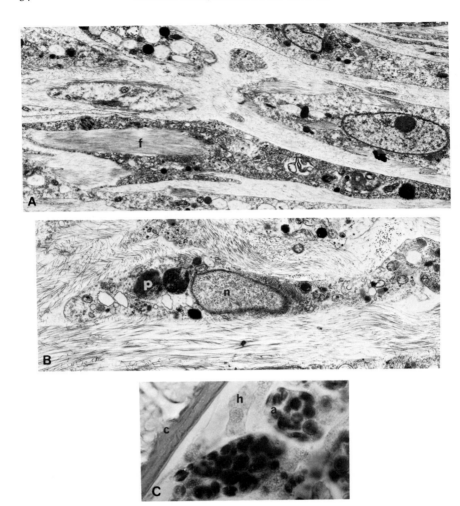

Figure 3-3 Collencytes, fiber cell, and histoblast. **A**. Collencytes of *Suberites massa* displaying fibrilogenesis (*f*). These elongate cells are difficult to define and to distinguish from other cell types (see text) (TEM) (×4,635) (Diaz, 1979a). **B**. "Fiber cell" of *Suberites massa* which is probably a terminal stage of an unknown cell type, possibly a lophocyte or collencyte. The elongate shape gives to these cells the appearance of a "fiber" in light micrographs. Note the presence of phagosomes (*p*) and an anucleolate nucleus (*n*). The surrounding mesohyl is packed with collagen fibrils (TEM) (×6,840) (Connes *et al.*, 1972). **C**. Histoblast (*h*) of *Ephydatia fluviatilis* which has differentiated within the gemmule coat (*c*) of a germinating gemmule. Note the absence of any prominent features and compare with the developing archeocytes (*a*) which are packed with vitelline platelets. Histoblasts have not been investigated ultrastructurally (light micrograph) (×900) (Rozenfeld, 1970). (**A**, courtesy Dr. J. P. Diaz; **B**, courtesy Dr. R. Connes; **C**, courtesy Dr. F. Rozenfeld.)

of spongocytes and lophocytes (Connes, 1968; Tuzet and Paris, 1957, 1966), (2) degenerative stages of cells (Vacelet, 1964; Tuzet and Paris, 1966), and (3) a network of cells in the ground substance (Paris, 1961). Wilson and Penney (1930) have referred to a fusiform cell type in the marine species *Microciona prolifera* as a fiber cell; in adult tissue of this sponge such fiber cells form parallel tracts below the exopinacoderm in some areas (Simpson, 1968a). Superficial fiber cell tracts are also present in other poecilosclerid demosponges and are associated with megascleres (Simpson, 1968a). Fiber cells, in some cases organized into tracts, are present also among haplosclerid species where they too possibly contribute to the skeleton (Pomponi, 1974). Fiber cells are likely terminal stages of megasclerocytes, spongocytes, and/or lophocyte activity (Table 3-3). "Collencytes" have also been reported in regenerating tissue of *Sycon raphanus* (Tuzet and Paris, 1963b). Thus, technically, two "types" of collencytes can be recognized—the first is motile, functions as presumptive pinacocytes, and is possibly involved in collagen fibrilogenesis. The second is ill-defined, probably nonmotile, and possibly terminally differentiated. For the latter, some term (or terms) other than "collencyte" should be employed, but it is not possible at present to even consider suggesting new terminology without producing further confusion. The *restrictive* use of the term *collencyte* as suggested by Borojevic (1966) will at least begin to clarify an otherwise difficult problem in determining cell function.

Myocytes, Neuroid Cells. Two other types of cells, which are discussed in more detail in Chapter Six have the same general shape and characteristics as collencytes; these are myocytes (Fig. 3-4) and neuroid cells. The former are characterized by fusiform shape, mitochondria, ribosomes, small vesicles, small or no nucleoli and, most importantly, the presence of cytoplasmic myofilaments. The position of myocytes within the mesohyl is also characteristic; these contractile elements frequently occur in the mesohyl of oscules, in the dermal membrane overlying excurrent canal spaces, and in the mesohyl surrounding the highly differentiated sieve plates of some tetractinomorphs (see Chap. 6). Such myocytes have been well described in *Tedania ignis* and *Microciona prolifera* (Bagby, 1966), in *Aplysina (Verongia) cavernicola* (Vacelet, 1966), in *Tethya lyncrium* (Pavans de Ceccatty, 1966; Connes, 1968), in *Hippospongia communis* (Thiney, 1972), and in *Euspongia officinalis* (Pavans de Ceccatty *et al.*, 1970). In each of these cases, they have been identified ultrastructurally on the basis of myofilaments and position. In the absence of electron microscopic observations, these cells would probably have been described as "collencytes." Neuroid cells, which generally have a fusiform or stellate shape, are also similar to collencytes (in the restrictive sense, see above) except they may possess nucleoli (Pavans de Ceccatty, 1955) and thus are also similar to archeocytes. They have been described in a

Table 3-3   Characteristics of Collencytes and Cells Resembling Collencytes

Cell Type	Nucleus	Cytoplasm	Shape	Presumed Motility	Special Features
Myocytes	Anucleolate	Few inclusions; myofilaments	Fusiform	–	Present in oscules and dermal membrane
Fiber cells	Anucleolate	Very reduced	Fusiform	–	Present in tracts and associated with spicules; probably terminal stages of spongocytes, lophocytes, megasclerocytes
Histoblasts	Anucleolate	Few inclusions	Fusiform to ameboid	+	Present in hatching gemmules
Collencytes, specific useage, (as per Borojević, 1966)	Anucleolate	Few inclusions	Fusiform to ameboid	+	Present in adult mesohyl and larva; presumptive pinacocytes
Collencytes (generalized useage) fibroblasts, spindle cells, fusiform cells, fiber cells	Anucleolate	Reduced; rarely with inclusions	Fusiform	–	Poorly understood cell type; possibly terminal stage of lophocytes or degenerative stage of other cells, or synonomous with myocytes or neuroid cells
Neuroid cells	Occasionally with a nucleolus	Few inclusions	Fusiform to stellate	–	Silver staining, Nissil granules, nuclear to cytoplasmic volume low

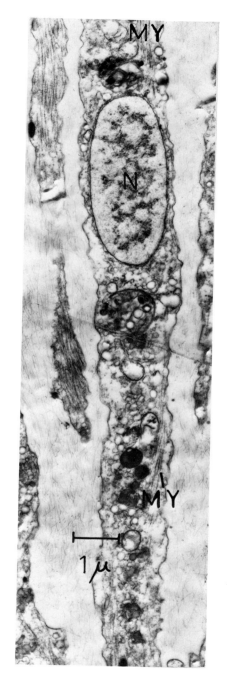

Figure 3-4 Myocyte of *Tedania ignis* displaying an anucleolate nucleus (*N*) elongate shape, and cytoplasmic myofilaments (*MY*) (TEM) (×12,000) (Bagby, 1966). (Courtesy Dr. R. M. Bagby.)

number of calcareous and demosponge species and are characterized on the basis of their staining features and on the contacts they form with other cells (Pavans de Ceccatty *et al.*, 1970). These cells are not homologous to neurons in other metazoans (Pavans de Ceccatty, 1974a,b), and Jones (1962) originally questioned whether they possessed any coordination or communication function at all. It is now clear that these cells do, indeed, play an important role in coordination of "complex" behavior in some species (Chap. 6). The term neuroid cells in essence refers to the functional capacity of cells to transmit information, not to a specific morphological cell type. Neuroid cells thus include myocytes, archeocytes, "collencytes," and possibly other mesohyl cells (some types of fiber cells), which, due to their position and contacts, are able to function in communication and coordination (Pavans de Ceccatty, 1974a). Indeed, exo- and endopinacocytes are considered to function as neuroid cells in a number of interesting cases and the giant syncytia in hexactinellids which form the pinacoderms are able to propagate signals (Mackie *et al.*, 1983). Both myocytes and neuroid cells can be considered to be fixed archeocytes with, respectively, contractile or transmittive functions. The critical question is whether these two functionally defined cell types are also developmentally fixed types or whether they are modulated states of other cell types (Chap. 9). Since a definitive answer to this question is not possible at present, they are considered here as separate cell types. Hexactinellids appear not to possess myocytes (Mackie and Singula, 1983).

Summary.   As is obvious, it is difficult to deal with this assemblage of cells. All of them possess the following basic features: frequently an anucleolate nucleus and fusiform cell shape, the presence of moderate numbers of ribosomes (or, on a light microscope level, positive, cytochemical staining for RNA in the cytoplasm), mitochondria, Golgi bodies, but the general absence of cytoplasmic inclusions and phagosomes. Thus, they have basic pinacocyte features (Chap. 2) but are mesohyl in position. Furthermore, some are doubtless involved in dynamic transitions and thus can be defined only with difficulty. An additional feature of importance and assistance is motility. Only histoblasts and collencytes (*sensu strictu* as per Borojevic, 1966) are motile, whereas myocytes, fiber cells, collencytes (generalized useage), and neuroid cells are more or less fixed elements which are structural in nature. Unfortunately, information on motility is scarce and this attribute is of more conceptual than practical value. In a review of sponge "nerve" cells, Jones (1962) has compiled an impressive array of classical information on collencytes, myocytes, spindle cells, and other morphologically similar cells. This excellent review should be consulted especially for references to the older literature.

Microsclerocytes

The only clearly established feature known to distinguish these mesohyl cells from others is their actual secretion of microscleres. Microsclerocytes are not present in most sclerosponges or calcareous species and there are few descriptions of them in any species. Connes (1968) obtained preliminary electron micrographs of them in the demosponge, *Tethya lyncurium*, establishing that they contain mitochondria, small vesicles, and small (1.5 to 2.0 μm) anucleolate nuclei; the young, intracellular microsclere (strongylaster) is bounded by a membrane. In a number of poecilosclerid demosponges (Simpson, 1968a) microscleres are secreted by cells with small, anucleolate nuclei (Fig. 3-5), but the secretion of one type (toxas) was found to be highly unusual in that two modes of deposition were observed, one of which involves cells with similarly small nuclei (see Fig. 4-26) (Chap. 4). Leveaux (1939) reported that the microsclerocytes responsible for the secretion of spicules that are incorporated into the gemmule coat of *Spongilla* and *Ephydatia* begin as nucleolate cells which then lose their nucleoli when the silica is deposited. This appears to be the only documented instance of a nucleolate microsclerocyte; however, in this case, the nucleus and nucleolus are small in comparison to archeocytes and thus similar to other microsclerocytes. Wilkinson and Garrone (1980a) have found that the microsclerocytes of *Neofibularia*

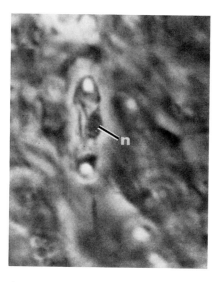

Figure 3-5 Living microsclerocyte of *Microciona prolifera* secreting a chela (front view). The nucleus (*n*) is small and anucleolate and the cell size is also small. Compare with megasclerocytes in Fig. 3-2F (phase-contrast micrograph) (×2,200) (Simpson, 1978).

irata which secrete raphides and those which secrete microxeas possess small anucleolate nuclei and especially abundant mitochondria. In the case of microxeas uniquely, many spicules possibly are elaborated by a single cell (see Fig. 4-21); this is the first ultrastructural observation of possible multiple spiculogenesis in a single cell. In *Neofibularia*, raphides and C-sigmas are secreted one per cell (see Fig. 4-20B,C). In her recent volume on sponges, Bergquist (1978) pictures an anucleolate microsclerocyte (see in that publication Plate 4, Fig. a) and suggests the sclerocyte is secreting two spicules. Such a conclusion arises from the fact that some microscleres (sigmas, chelas, Fig. 1-12) in ultrathin sections, when cut at an appropriate angle (frontal plane) appear as if they are two spicules (see Fig. 4-20C). This has clearly been described in serial sections of sigmas by Wilkinson and Garrone (1980a) and should be taken into consideration in studies of spicules which lie in more than one plane. Additional ultrastructural data on microsclerocyte structure are urgently needed to further support and extend that presently available. However, even it its absence, it is clear that demosponge microsclerocytes are quite different from megasclerocytes and can be considered to represent a separate cell category. Their small nuclear size and absence of a nucleolus are points of similarity to the special cells (see following section) of the mesohyl although microsclerocytes do not contain an array of complex, special, cytoplasmic inclusions, at least not at the time when silica is being deposited.

Special Cells—Cellules à Inclusions

This group of cells is distinguished by a reduction of features characterizing archeocytes; notably they have fewer mitochondria and ribosomes (usually weak or negative light microscopical, cytochemical staining for RNA), reduced rough endoplasmic reticulum or only patches of it, anucleolate nuclei (with, however, some exceptions), no phagosomes, and as far as is known no mitotic activity. In demosponges, their nuclei are routinely intermediate in size (2.5–3.0 μm) between those archeocytes (4.5 μm) and choanocytes (2.0 μm) (Simpson, 1968a). Golgi bodies are sometimes present and there are always present special (and usually structurally complex) membrane-bound cytoplasmic inclusions. Special cells are found in most demosponges but in only a few calcareous species. In *Sycon ciliatum*, for example, a thorough ultrastructural investigation did not reveal their presence (Ledger, 1976). On the other hand, in some species "amoebocytes granuleux et eosinophiles" have been described which may be comparable to special cells in the demosponges (Pavans de Ceccatty, 1955; Sara, 1955a; Vacelet, 1964). The sclerosponges have not yet been investigated in terms of their cell structure. The hexactinellids have recently been found to possess special cells (Mackie and Singula, 1983). There are, in demosponges, numerous different kinds of special cells which have been described; a listing is given in Table 3-4. The terminology employed for these cells is diverse and it is too soon to suggest a unifying system. Despite the need for additional comparative cytological, cytochemical, and ultrastructural data aimed at establishing homologies within this group of cells, two very broad, morphological categories of special cells can be recognized: (1) cells which contain numerous (~30) small granules (~0.1–1.0 μm) which are homogeneous and (2) cells with a smaller number (1–10) of somewhat larger inclusions (~2.0–2.5 μm) which are *not* phagosomes and which usually have internal structure. The function of many of these cells is poorly documented although some important, new information is available.

Special Cells with Larger Inclusions (Figs. 3-6 to 3-9). There is now good evidence that many special cells in this broadly descriptive category are functionally homologous; these include rhabdiferous cells (Fig. 3-7A), spherulous cells (cellules spheruleuses) (Figs. 3-6A–C), sacculiferous cells (Fig. 3-9), and spumeuse cells (Fig. 3-6D) all of which have been reported to release the contents of thei. inclusions into the mesohyl. Donadey (1982) considers whole cell rupture (as in the spumeuse cells of *Reniera mucosa*) as holocrine secretion and the release of the contents of single inclusions (as in spherulous cells of *Cacospongia scalaris*) as merocrine secretion. This distinction may eventually turn out to be an important one. Interestingly, the presence of calcium ions stabilizes the inclusions of spherulous cells and its absence leads to their rupture in *Axinella* (Bretting and Konigsmann, 1979). Part of the materials released are lectins that possibly have an important role in cell–cell interactions and in matrix elaboration during growth and development (Bretting *et al.*, 1983). The naturally released material from rhabdiferous cells in *Cyamon* is the probable origin of the plentiful mucous produced by this species (Smith, 1968). Rhabdiferous cells in *Microciona* and some related genera have been found to spontaneously release their contents *in vivo* in the mesohyl thus acting as a source for a type of glycosaminoglycan (Simpson, 1963, 1968a). These cells have also been observed *in vitro* to release their inclusions with explosive force (Burger *et al.*, 1978). In *Reniera mucosa*, spumeuse cells appear to be the origin of released mucous (Donadey, 1982).

These secretory cells are, however, a diverse assemblage in terms of their morphology, chemistry, and cytochemistry. The inclusions in them are membrane-bound but the inclusion contents are varied and may be relatively amorphous (some spherulous cells, Bretting and Konigsman, 1979), very dense and stringy [rhabdiferous cells in *Ophlitaspongia seriata* (Borojevic and Lévi, 1964b) and *Microciona prolifera* (Simpson, 1963; Bagby, 1972)], fibrillar [spumeuse cells, Donadey and Vacelet, (1977)], and fibrillar–microtubular [sacculiferous cells, Willenz (1983), Smith and Lauritis, (1969)]. However, even within a single cell type there can be morphological variation. For example, in spherulous cells of *Axinella polypoides*, two sizes (with intermediates) of inclusions are present;

Table 3-4 Features of Special Cells and Their Distribution

Cell types	Features	Distribution	References
I. Cells with larger inclusions Rhabdiferous cells	Anucleolate; numerous rod and spherical inclusions containing glycosaminoglycans; cytoplasmic organelles highly reduced	**Demospongiae** *Cyamon* *Microciona* *Ophlitaspongia* *Plocamilla*	Borojevic and Lévi (1964b), Smith and Lauritis (1969), Smith (1968), Simpson (1968a), Bagby (1972)
Spherulous cells (cellules spheruleuses)	Anucleolate; little cytoplasm; inclusions contain granules, fibrils, or amorphous material; some smaller inclusions may be present	**Demospongiae** *Anthosigmella* *Aplysina (Verongia)* *Axinella* *Cacospongia* *Chondrilla* *Cliona* *Hamigera* (larva) *Hemimycale* *Hippospongia* *Mycale* *Pleraplysilla* *Polymastia* *Siphonodictyon* *Spheciospongia* *Spongia* *Suberites* *Tethya* **Calcarea** *Neocoelia*	Lévi (1965), Vacelet (1967b), Connes (1966b, 1968), Thiney (1972), De Vos (1965), Donadey and Vacelet (1977), Gallissian and Vacelet (1976), Bretting and Konigsmann (1979), Pomponi (1979a), Gaino (1980), Boury-Esnault (1976a,b), Willenz (1983), Donadey (1982), Thompson *et al.* (1983), Bretting *et al.* (1983) Vacelet (1979b)

Cells resembling spherulous cells (see also globoferous cells)	As above but contents of inclusions not thoroughly characterized; sometimes one inclusion is larger	**Demospongiae** *Aaptos* *Alectona*[a] *Axocielita* *Callyspongia* *Haliclona* *Halisarca* *Lissodendoryx* *Plakina*[b] *Rhaphidophlus* *Spongilla*[c] *Suberites* *Tedania* *Thalysias*	Connes *et al.* (1972), Lévi (1956, 1967), Simpson (1968a), Garrone (1974), Herlant-Meewis (1948a), Liaci (1963a), Diaz (1977, 1979a), Pomponi (1974), Boury-Esnault (1970), Donadey (1978, 1979)
Sacculiferous cells	Anucleolate; few mitochondria or ribosomes; large inclusions with reticulating fibers and tubules; some smaller, dense inclusions present	**Demospongiae** *Cyamon* *Hemimycale*	Smith and Lauritis (1969) Willenz (1983)
Cellules vacuolaires à batonnets	Anucleolate; large inclusions contain numerous, short rods; cytoplasm reduced	**Demospongiae** *Mycale* (larva)	Lévi (1964)
Cellules vacuolaires	Anucleolate; large inclusions with fibrils; cytoplasm reduced; some cells with only one large inclusion	**Demospongiae** *Mycale* (larva)	Lévi (1964)
	Small but nucleolate nucleus; voluminous empty vacuole; some other inclusions with fibrils sometimes present	**Demospongiae** *Hamigera* (larva) *Oscarella* **Hexactinellida** *Rhabdocalyptus*[d]	Boury-Esnault (1976a), Donadey (1979), Mackie and Singula (1983)

Table 3-4 Features of Special Cells and Their Distribution (*Continued*)

Cell Types	Features	Distribution	References
I. Cells with larger inclusions (continued)			
Cystencytes	Nucleolate with intranuclear rod; single large inclusion contains glycoprotein and acid phosphatase	**Demospongiae** *Ephydatia*	Tessenow (1969), Pottu-Boumendil (1975)
Cystencytes in hexactinellids	Anucleolate with single large inclusion sometimes with crystals	**Hexactinellida** *Aphrocallistes*[e] *Rhabdocalyptus*[e]	Reiswig (1979), Mackie and Singula (1983)
Stylocytes	Anucleolate; intranuclear rod; one larger inclusion plus a number of smaller ones contain glycosaminoglycans; cytoplasm reduced but with ribosomes	**Demospongiae** *Corvomeyenia*	Harrison *et al.* (1974)
Chromocytes	Anucleolate; large transparent vacuoles surrounded by dense membrane-bound inclusions with pigment	**Demospongiae** *Cyamon*	Smith (1968)
	As above but with only dense inclusions plus glycogen and reasonably well-developed organelles (? = gray cells)	**Demospongiae** *Trikentrion* *Terpios* (no data on glycogen or organelles)	Smith (1968), Cheng *et al.* (1968a)
Cellules spumeuses	Anucleolate; inclusions with fibrils and sulfated glycosaminoglycans; inclusions fuse in older cells; few organelles	**Demospongiae** *Pleraplysilla* *Reniera*	Donadey and Vacelet (1977), Donadey (1982)

Cell type	Description	Taxa	References
Choanocerous cells	Anucleolate; single larger inclusion contains aligned tubules; smaller inclusions (6–8) sometimes absent; few ribosomes and mitochondria	**Demospongiae** *Microciona* *Ophlitaspongia*	Borojevic and Lévi (1964b), Simpson (1968a), Bagby (person. comm.)
	As above but contents of larger inclusion not characterized ultrastructurally	**Demospongiae** *Plocamilla* *Rhaphidophlus* *Reniera* *Thalysias*	Simpson (1968a), Tuzet (1932)
II. **Cells with smaller inclusions** Gray cells	Rarely nucleolate; numerous dense, membrane-bound inclusions; abundant glycogen; Golgi, few mitochondria and ribosomes	**Demospongiae** *Alectona*[a] *Anthosigmella* *Aplysina (Verongia)* *Cliona*[f] *Halichondria* *Hamigera* *Hemimycale* *Hymeniacidon* *Microciona* *Mycale* *Ophlitaspongia* *Pachymatisma* *Plocamilla* *Polymastia* *Siphonodictyon* *Spheciospongia* *Suberites (Ficulina)* *Tethya* *Trikentrion*	Borojevic and Lévi (1964b), Connes (1968), Vacelet (1967b), Connes et al. (1972, 1978), Simpson (1963, 1968a), Lévi (1966), Bagby (1972), Diaz (1979a), Rutzler and Rieger (1973), Smith (1968), Garrone (1974), Boury-Esnault (1977), Pomponi (1979a), Boury-Esnault and Doumenc (1979)

Table 3-4 Features of Special Cells and Their Distribution (*Continued*)

Cell Types	Features	Distribution	References
II. Cells with smaller inclusions (continued)			
Microgranular cells	Anucleolate; many minute granules; moderate numbers of ribosomes	**Demospongiae** *Alectona*[a-g] *Aplysina* (*Verongia*) *Chondrosia* *Clathria* *Microciona* *Ophlitaspongia* *Tedania* *Tethya*	Borojevic and Lévi (1964b), Vacelet (1967b), Simpson (1968a), Lévi and Lévi (1976), Gallissian and Vacelet (1976), Garrone (1974), Connes (1968)
Granular cells	Usually anucleolate; little RNA; granules appear homogeneous; sometimes with a single larger inclusion; generally poorly characterized	**Demospongiae** *Anthosigmella* *Aplysina* (*Verongia*)[k] *Cliona* *Halisarca* *Lissodendoryx*[h] *Mycale* *Siphonodictyon* *Spheciospongia* *Spongilla*[j] *Tedania* *Thalysias* **Hexactinellida** *Rhabdocalyptus*	Lévi (1956), Vacelet (1967b), Simpson (1968a), Williamson (1979), Pomponi (1979a), De Vos (1965) Mackie and Singula (1983)

| Amebocytes eosinophiles et granuleux | Nucleus small and sometimes nucleolate; granules in cytoplasm stain with eosin; poorly characterized | Calcarea *Clathrina* *Grantia* *Leucosolenia* *Petrobiona* *Sycon* | Vacelet (1964), Prenant (1925), Duboscq and Tuzet (1936), Pavans de Ceccatty (1955), Sara (1955a) |

[a]Probable generic placement of bud examined ultrastructurally.

[b]The inclusions in these cells are of four types and ultrastructurally are complex, not homogeneous. These cells are placed in this group tentatively.

[c]Herlant-Meewis has referred to these cells in *Spongilla lacustris* as cellules fuchsinophiles (Meewis, 1936) and as cellules eosinophiles (Herlant-Meewis, 1948a).

[d]Referred to by the authors as "spherulous cells" (Mackie and Singula, 1983).

[e]Referred to by the authors as "thesocytes" (Reiswig, 1979; Mackie and Singula, 1983).

[f]Although Rutzler and Rieger (1973) refer to these cells as gray cells, their inclusions appear different from those in other species.

[g]Microgranular cells of *Alectona* contain much glycogen and are only provisionally placed in this category.

[h]De Vos (1965) refers to these cells as cellules fuchsinophiles.

[j]These cells recently pictured by Williamson (1979) may be the cellules eosinophiles described by Herlant-Meewis (1948a) and are also included under the category "Cells resembling spherulous cells." Williamson (1979) also described a "granular cell," in which the inclusion contents are granular and easily disrupted.

[k]Originally referred to as gray cells.

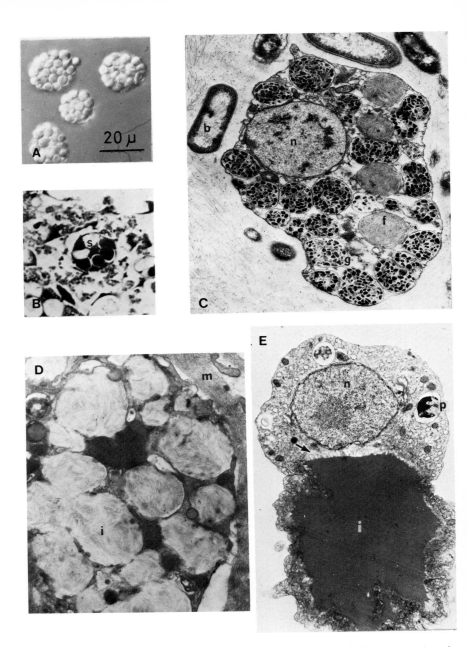

Figure 3-6 Cellules à inclusions (special cells) which contain large cytoplasmic inclusions. **A**. Isolated, whole spherulous cells of *Axinella polypoides* (see Fig. 3-8C) (Nomarski interference micrograph) (×585) (Bretting and Konigsmann, 1979). **B**. A spherulous cell (*s*) in the mesohyl of *Neocoelia crypta* (light micrograph, semithin section) (×605) (Vacelet, 1979b). **C**. Spherulous cell in *Aplysina (Verongia) cavernicola* displaying heterogeneity of the inclusion contents—some are granular (*g*) and others fibrillar (*f*). *n*, nucleus; *b*, bacterium in mesohyl. Note the lack of other usual cytoplasmic organelles in the spherulous cell cytoplasm

the smaller are more dense but the contents of both are relatively amorphous (Fig. 3-8C) whereas in *Aplysina (Verongia) cavernicola* (Vacelet, 1967b) cells referred to by the same name contain inclusions whose contents are highly particulate with the internal "grains" measuring 40–130 nm (Fig. 3-6C). In the latter, the contents of the inclusions were tentatively identified as chromolipid and no release of contents was reported although whole cells were sometimes seen being extruded into excurrent canals. Pigments (lipofuchsin and melanin) have also been reported in spherulous cells of *Aaptos* (Liaci, 1963a). The spherulous cells of *Aplysina (Verongia) fistularis* have recently been shown to contain brominated tyrosine derivatives (aerothionin and homoaerothionin) which are antibiotic (Thompson *et al.*, 1983). These two substances were previously chemically isolated from *Aplysina cavernicola* (D'Ambrosio *et al.*, 1982). Both substances, which may be released into the mesohyl, are possibly involved in regulating the bacterial flora (Thompson *et al.*, 1983); however, not all individuals of *A. fistularis* contain these substances, clearly indicating biochemical variability within the same cell type in the same species. Further, rhabdiferous cells in *Cyamon neon* contain spherical inclusions (Smith, 1968) which appear quite different from those in *Microciona prolifera* (Bagby, 1972), although in both species these cells contain kinds of glycosaminoglycans and the inclusions are released into the mesohyl. Still further, the inclusions of sacculiferous cells do not stain for glycosaminoglycans and their contents are structurally unique (Smith, 1968). The fibrillar inclusions of spumeuse cells fuse together prior to release of their contents (Donadey and Vacelet, 1977). In *Haliclona elegans*, large "segmented fibers" are produced by the alignment of spherulous cells each of which intracellularly produces a segment of the fiber (see Fig. 5-16) (Herlant-Meewis, 1948a; Lévi, 1967). The fiber segments consist of fine fibrils of protein unlike either collagen fibrils or spongin (Garrone, 1978) and the segments remain intracellular in each of the aligned cells.

The morphology of special cells with larger inclusions is further complicated by three additional variables: (1) there usually are a minor number of "other" inclusions present in these cells such as fibrillar inclusions and

---

(TEM) (×18,000) (Vacelet, 1967b). **D**. Spumeuse cell in *Pleraplysilla spinifera*. The inclusions (*i*) are packed with fibrillar material which can be released from the cell. Little cytoplasmic volume in addition to the inclusions remains. *m*, mesohyl (TEM) (×7,830) (Donadey and Vacelet, 1977). **E**. A cystencyte of *Ephydatia mulleri*. The very large inclusion (*i*) is condensed at this stage and at its edges are membranous "feet" (*arrow*). *n*, nucleolate nucleus; *p*, phagosome. This inclusion is clearly *not* a digestive or autophagic vacuole as originally suggested by some workers (TEM) (×6,480) (Pottu-Boumendil, 1975). (**A**, courtesy Dr. N. Bretting; **B**, **C**., courtesy Dr. J. Vacelet; **D**, courtesy Dr. C. Donadey; **E**, courtesy Dr. J. Pottu-Boumendil.)

Figure 3-7 Additional examples of special cells with larger inclusions. **A**. Living rhabdiferous cell (*R*) of *Microciona atrasanguinea* (negative phase-contrast micrograph) (×1,350) (Simpson and Borojevic, unpubl.). **Inset:** A thin extension of a rhabdiferous cell of *Microciona prolifera*. The cytoplasm is packed with spheroid-shaped structures (*s*) seen in cross section (TEM) (×8,550) (Bagby, unpubl.). **B**. Living globoferous cells (*g*) of *Microciona atrasanguinea*. The cells contain many spherical inclusions and a single, larger one (*l*) which is visible in only one of the cells (negative phase-contrast) (×1,350) (Simpson and Borojevic, unpubl.). **C**. A small portion of the peripheral region of the larger inclusion of a globoferous cell in *Microciona prolifera*. The inclusion contains an array of aligned structures (TEM) (×53,100). **Inset:** In cross section the aligned structures are shown to be tubular (TEM) (×98,100) (both Bagby, unpubl.). (**A**, **C**, courtesy Dr. R. M. Bagby.)

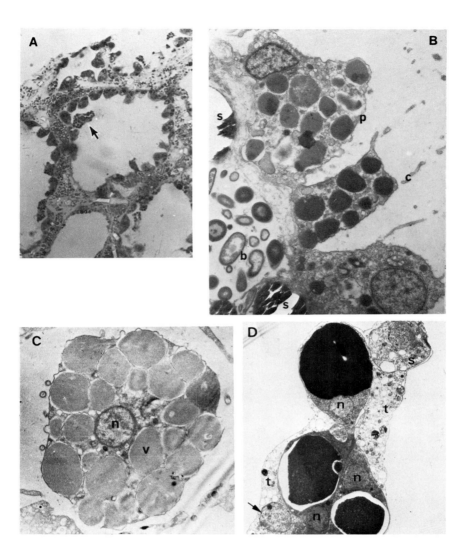

Figure 3-8 Special cells with larger inclusions. **A.** A choanocyte chamber in *Plakina trilopha* in which a cell with inclusions (*arrow*) is present (light micrograph) (×585) (Donadey, 1978). (Copyright Archives de l'Académie des Sciences de Paris.) **B.** These cells with inclusions (*p*) are derived directly from the choanocytes by collar and flagella loss. The inclusions develop, however, while the choanocytes still possess collars (*c*). *b*, bacteria in mesohyl; *s*, fractured siliceous spicules (TEM) (×1,080) (Donadey, 1978). **C.** Spherulous cell of *Axinella polypoides* with the cytoplasm packed with inclusions (*v*). Note superficial resemblance of these inclusions with those in B above; *n*, nucleus (TEM) (×5,220) (Bretting, 1979). **D.** Hexactinellid (*Rhabdocalytus dawsoni*) "thesocytes" here referred to as a type of cystencyte (compare with Fig. 3-6E). Each cell possess one large dense inclusion and a nucleus (*n*). These discrete cells occur within the very thin trabecular syncytium (*t*) in which a nucleus (*arrow*) is seen. An apparently discrete cell (*s*), possibly a sclerocyte, is also present (TEM) (×2,700) (Pavans de Ceccatty, unpubl.). (**A**, **B**, courtesy Dr. C. Donadey; **C**, courtesy Dr. N. Bretting; **D**, courtesy Prof. M. Pavans de Ceccatty.)

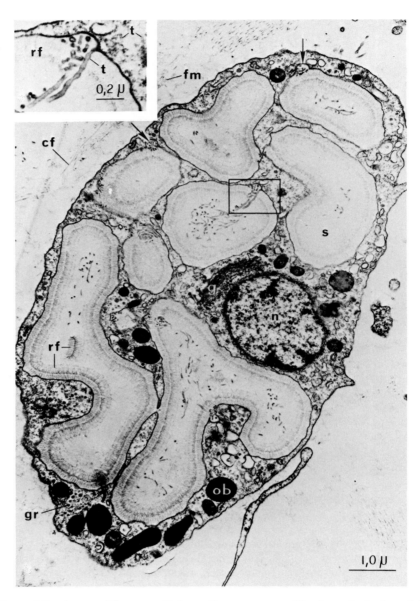

Figure 3-9 A sacculiferous cell from *Cyamon neon*. The large inclusions (*s*) contain reticulating fibers (*rf*); evaginations of the inclusion membranes (*arrows*) contain tubules. In addition, smaller, dense inclusions (*ob*) are present as well as cytoplasmic glycogen (*gr*). *n*, nucleus; *g*, Golgi. In the mesohyl are collagen fibrils (*cf*) some associated with other fibrous material (*fm*) (TEM) (×12,600). **Inset:** Enlargement of boxed area. *rf*, reticulating fibers; *t*, tubule (TEM) (×35,000) (Smith, 1968). (Courtesy Dr. V. E. Smith.)

crystalline arrays in the spherulous cells of *Aplysina (Verongia) caverni-cola* (Fig. 3-6C) (Vacelet, 1967b); (2) the specific morphology of a single cell type is usually somewhat variable even within the same animal as is the case with spumeuse cells in *Pleraplysilla spinifera* (Donadey and Vacelet, 1977) and spherulous cells in *Aplysina (Verongia)* (Vacelet, 1967b); and (3) the chemical constituents present in solutions used for fixation can directly affect the ultrastructural morphology of the inclusions as has been demonstrated in *Trikentrion helium* chromocytes (gray cells?) in which the dense inclusions swell and their contents become vacuolated when fixed in glutaraldehyde–seawater rather than in glutaraldehyde–sucrose (Smith, 1968).

Among other types of this group of special cells with larger inclusions are some in which the release of inclusion contents has not been reported such as vacuolar cells in *Hamigera* larvae, which are reported to contain dissolved pigment (Boury-Esnault, 1976a), a type (cellules vacuolaires à batonnets) resembling sacculiferous cells (Lévi, 1964), and stylocytes which possess a nuclear rod and cytoplasmic inclusions, the latter of which contain a type of glycosaminoglycan (Harrison *et al.*, 1974) (but, stylocytes may actually be cystencytes, see following). Also, inclusions in globoferous cells (Fig. 3-7B) whose staining may be faintly positive for glycosaminoglycans have not been reported to be released (Simpson, 1968a). There is, however, suggestive indirect evidence that the smaller inclusions of these cells are released in *Ophlitaspongia seriata* since many of the cells only contain a single larger one which possesses intriguing internal structure—aligned microtubular elements (Fig. 3-7C) (Borojevic and Lévi, 1964b; Simpson, 1968a). An increasingly large number of mesohyl cells have been described, which possess inclusions like those in spherulous cells. Many of them have not been sufficiently characterized to strictly consider them as spherulous cells (Table 3-4). The "spherulous" cells of the hexactinellid *Rhabdocalytus* are here included as cellules vacuolaires due to their similar structure. In *Plakina trilopha,* cells with larger inclusions have been described and are derived from choanocytes (Fig. 3-8). The inclusions include a heterogeneous array of at least four types, similar ones of which also occur in some collar cells of this species (Donadey, 1978, 1979). It has been conjectured that these cells perform an excretory function since they appear to be released into the lumen of choanocyte chambers. Although they also possess nucleolate nuclei and phagosomes they are here considered as special cells due to their resemblence to spherulous cells.

Other types of special cells which provisionally can be placed in this group are cystencytes, which possess a nuclear inclusion and a large cytoplasmic inclusion (Fig. 3-6E). These nucleolate cells were originally considered to be involved in nutrient processing during gemmule hatching in some freshwater sponges (Tessenow, 1969). This conclusion is no longer tenable since Pottu-Boumendil (1975) has clearly shown that, although the vacuole and its membrane develop significant acid phosphatase activity, these cells are not involved in the digestion of the yolk platelets. The vacuole (inclusion) content is amorphous, undergoes change, contains glycoprotein, and is susceptible to pepsin digestion. Cystencytes contain in addition to the large vacuole, much cytoplasmic glycogen, well-developed Golgi bodies, a few phagosomes, and some rough endoplasmic reticulum. These cells appear involved in the elaboration of ground substance. The structure of cystencytes including the nuclear inclusion is highly suggestive that they and stylocytes are variants of a single cell type in freshwater sponges. When Tessenow (1969) first called attention to cystencytes he considered them specific for newly developing tissue derived from gemmule hatching in freshwater sponges. However, they have now been found in mature tissue where they obviously are not involved in phagocytic activity and nutrient processing (Pottu-Boumendil, 1975). Spongillid cystencytes could also be placed among the archeocyte category since they possess nucleolate nuclei and other typical archeocyte features. Special cells with small anucleolate nuclei and a single large cytoplasmic inclusion are present in at least some hexactinellid sponges (Reiswig, 1979; Mackie and Singula, 1983) (Fig. 3-8D) and are reminiscent of cystencytes; they are provisionally placed in this group although originally referred to as "thesocytes" (see previous discussion of thesocytes). Chromocytes in *Cyamon neon* possess anucleolate nuclei, large lucent vacuoles and membrane-bound inclusions, which contain pigment (Smith, 1968). These inclusions are possibly released suggesting a secretory as well as a pigment function. In *Trikentrion,* chromocytes are similar to both spherulous and gray cells and require further study (see Pigment).

Special Cells with Smaller Inclusions (Figs. 3-10, 3-11).   The primary cell type in this group is the gray cell (Figs. 3-10C,D, 3-11A,B,C) originally described by Wilson and Penney (1930) in *Microciona prolifera* and later further characterized by Simpson (1963) and Bagby (1972). These cells are well characterized, possessing numerous (~20–40), membrane-bound, homogeneous inclusions which are small (~0.2–0.8 μm) and highly osmophilic. Abundant glycogen occurs in the cytoplasm (Simpson, 1963) in the form of alpha rosettes (Borojevic and Lévi, 1964b; Bagby, 1972; Boury-Esnault, 1977). Gray cells sometimes possess small nucleoli and their organelle content (mitochondria, Golgi, ribosomes) is better developed than that in most other special cells. The presence of nucleoli, however, can be variable even within the same species (Borojevic and Simpson, unpub. observ.). The inclusions in *Microciona prolifera* gray cells have recently been found to fluoresce in ultraviolet light (Kuhns *et al.,* 1980), thus yielding an additional marker which, for these cells, has been used to purify them by fluorescence-activated cell sorting (Burkart *et al.,* 1979). The abundance of gray cells has been related to the physio-

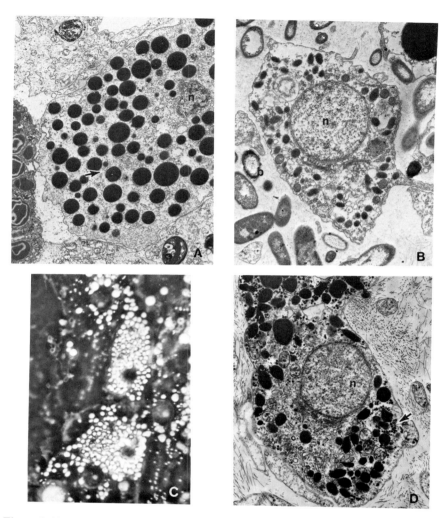

Figure 3-10   Cellules à inclusions (special cells) containing smaller inclusions. **A.** A rare, granular cell in *Spongilla lacustria* which may be comparable to cellules eosinophiles in this species. Each inclusion is membrane bound (*arrow*). *n*, nucleus (TEM) (×3,330) (Williamson, 1979). **B.** A microgranular cell of *Aplysina* (*Verongia*) *cavernicola*. The minute inclusions are membrane bound and the remaining cytoplasmic volume is relatively large. *n*, nucleus; *b*, bacteria in mesohyl (TEM) (×11,250) (Vacelet, 1967b). **C.** Two living gray cells of *Microciona atrasanguinea* showing nuclear area surrounded by numerous refractile granules (negative phase contrast) (×1,350) (Simpson and Borojevic, unpubl.). **D.** A gray cell of *Suberites massa* with anucleolate nucleus (*n*), numerous, uniform dense granules and abundant cytoplasmic glycogen (*arrow*) (TEM) (×6,300) (Connes *et al.*, 1972). (**A**, courtesy Dr. C. E. Williamson; **B**, courtesy Dr. J. Vacelet; **D**, courtesy Dr. R. Connes.)

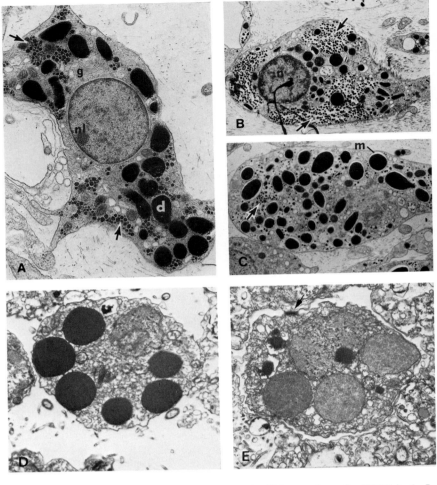

Figure 3-11 Additional gray cells and hexactinellid granular cells (TEMs). **A.** In *Polymastia robusta* gray cells possess a small nucleolus (*nl*) and the cytoplasmic glycogen can form very large aggregates (*arrow*). *g*, Golgi; *d*, dense inclusions (×12,600) (Boury-Esnault, 1977). **B.** Gray cell in *Cliona lampa* with an anucleolate nucleus (*n*) and very abundant glycogen (*arrows*). The dense inclusions are less abundant in this area of the cell. The tuft of collagen fibrils (*f*) at the cell surface suggests a fibrilogenic activity of the cell (×4,590) (Rutzler and Rieger, 1973). **C.** A second example of a gray cell in *Cliona lampa* in which the dense inclusions are more numerous and the cytoplasmic glycogen (*arrow*) less abundant. Note the elliptical shape of the dense inclusions and the discrete membrane (*m*) surrounding each (×4,590) (Rutzler and Rieger, 1973). **D, E.** Granular cells of the hexactinellid *Rhabdocalyptus dawsoni*. In D., the granules are very dense and only a small part of the nucleus is visible. In E., a prominent nucleolus is visible, the granules are less dense and the cell communicates with another cell via a plugged junction (*arrow*) (D, ×8,550; E, ×11,700) (Pavans de Ceccatty, unpubl.). (**A**, courtesy Dr. N. Boury-Esnault; **B, C**, courtesy Dr. K. Rutzler; **D, E**, courtesy Prof. M. Pavans de Ceccatty.)

logical condition of the mesohyl (Boury-Esnault, 1972, 1976b, 1977; Boury-Esnault and Doumenc, 1979; Simpson, 1963). Deprivation of oxygen leads to highly increased levels of glycogen rosettes in them (Boury-Esnault, 1977; Boury-Esnault and Doumenc, 1979). During regeneration, archeocytes are reported to phagocytize gray cells suggesting that the latter act as a nutrient source. During larval metamorphosis, it has been suggested that new gray cells can be derived from the flagellated, larval epithelium (Boury-Esnault, 1976a) and thus they may develop from choanocytes in regenerating adult tissue. Much further investigation of both of these points is required. Since many sponge cell types (but generally not choanocytes—Lufty, 1960) contain some glycogen (Boury-Esnault and Doumenc, 1979), its presence alone is insufficient to characterize gray cells. The gray cells in *Trikentrion* appear also to be chromocytes (pigment cells) with the pigment localized in the inclusions (Smith, 1968). However, the inclusions in these cells subjectively appear different from other gray cells and a reevaluation is called for (see Pigment).

Gray cells have also been observed secreting collagen in the buds of *Alectona* (tentative generic placement) and in *Suberites massa* (Garrone, 1974; Diaz, 1979a). In the latter species, they are considered to be the origin of new lophocytes due to their high fibrillogenic activity (Connes *et al.*, 1972); this conclusion is tentative and requires further substantiation.

A second category of special cell with numerous, small inclusions is the microgranular cell (Fig. 3-10B) containing minute ($\sim$0.09–0.03 μm), osmophilic inclusions which are, in *Ophlitaspongia seriata*, membrane bound. These cells are generally rare, do not contain much, if any, glycogen and have an unknown function. Additional "granular cells" that appear to fall into this general category have also been described (Fig. 3-10A) but are not well characterized (Table 3-4).

Two reports establish that in the marine demosponges, *Suberites* (*Ficulina*) *ficus* and *Suberites domuncula*, "cellules fuchsinophiles" and "cellules eosinophiles" are actually gray cells (Boury-Esnault and Doumenc, 1979). Cellules eosinophiles have been described in a variety of calcareous sponges and their abundance in *Clathrina coriacea* and *Leucosolenia botryoides* can be correlated with oogenesis (Sara, 1955a). In these species, cellules eosinophiles display some phagocytic activity, they can disintegrate in the mesohyl and sometimes are expelled from the tissue by migration into the atrial cavity. They thus may be involved in nutrient cycling but their specific role remains uncertain and no ultrastructural or cytochemical data are available for them. Their structure in these two species does not resemble that of the cellules eosinophiles or fuchsinophiles in *Suberites* and it can be tentatively concluded that in calcareous species these cells are not comparable to gray cells. The hexactinellid, *Rhabdocalyptus dawsoni* possess two types of granular cells (Figs. 3-11D,E) which may be nucleolate and have only recently been described (Mackie and Singula, 1983; Pavans de Ceccatty, unpublished).

Summary of Special Cells

Structure. There still remain very complex problems in establishing homologies among special cells, especially among spherulous cells and other types which are presently poorly characterized. One would have assumed that ultrastructural studies could resolve such questions of structural homology, but this has proven to be the case only in some instances, for example, with both globoferous and gray cells. In others, ultrastructural data add further complication. Indeed, some special cells, such as cystencytes, are sufficiently dynamic in their morphology such that if a strict definition were employed, one would be required to establish a new category for each individual cell described. Thus, it is clear that some combination of structure, cytochemistry, and function is required to effectively delimit a category. Only after appropriate conditions have been established for cell culture will it also be possible to meaningfully compare these cells biochemically.

Possible Functions. Two clearly separate functions can be ascribed to special cells containing larger inclusions: (1) elaboration of matrix (and mucous) substances (2) pigment storage and/or deposition. Among special cells with smaller inclusions, gray cells clearly possess a nutritive–metabolic function and variants of them possibly also act in pigment deposition. Why then are there so many different variant morphologies among special cells? A number of possibilities are of interest. First, some morphological types may actually be intermediate stages of differentiation; namely, one type of special cell may eventually form a second type. This possibility has previously been suggested in microcionid species possessing both globoferous and rhabdiferous cells, the former being considered as a possible precursor of the latter (Simpson, 1968a). There is, however, little hard evidence to support this or other similar views, although they continue to be of much interest. Second, it is possible that during the elaboration of matrix (or pigment) materials, intermediate stages in metabolism accumulate, thus resulting in a particular morphology of the inclusions. Thus, if different intermediate stages accumulate in different species, then the same basic cell type might display variant morphology— different intermediate stages may be accentuated in variants of a particular special cell type resulting in different inclusion morphology. Another possibility is that some special cells are presumptive microsclerocytes; this view is particularly appealing as concerns granular cells since microsclerocytes have not been reported to contain a complex array of special inclusions but possess comparably small, anucleolate nuclei. In microcionid species there is circumstantial evidence that rhabdiferous cells may be involved in the deposition of toxas. Finally, an excretory function has been suggested for some special cells (see for example, Harrison *et al.,* 1974) and there are limited supporting data for this view in *Plakina* and *Aplysina* (*Verongia*) (Donadey, 1978; Vacelet, 1967b); however, excretion (more precisely elimination) is more specifically a function of archeocytes at least as far as is known (Chap. 6). It will be a real challenge to define precisely the specific function and nature of each type of special cell.

Distribution.   A number of studies are sufficiently detailed and complete to present comparative data on the special cell composition in different species (Table 3-5). Such a listing emphasizes that not all sponges

Table 3-5   Special Cell Types in Representative Species

Class Calcarea	**Class Demospongiae** (continued)
Sycon ciliatum (Ledger, 1976)	Subclass Ceractinoporpha
No special cells	*Ephydatia mülleri*
Petrobiona massiliana (Vacelet,	(Pottu-Boumendil, 1975)
1964)	Cystencytes
Amebocytes eosinophiles	Amebocytes sombres[a]
Neocoelia crypta (Vacelet, 1979b)	*Callyspongia plicifera* (Pomponi,
Spherulous cells	1974)
Class Hexactinellida	Cells resembling spherulous cells
Aphrocallistes vastus (Reiswig,	*Haliclona rubens* (Pomponi, 1974)
1979)	No special cells
Cells resembling cystencytes	*Ophlitaspongia seriata* (Borojevic
Rhabdocalyptus dawsoni (Mackie	and Lévi, 1964b)
and Singula, 1983)	Gray cells
Cystencytes (=thesocytes[b])	Microgranular cells
Granular cells	Globoferous cells
Vacuolar cells (=spherulous	Rhabdiferous cells
cells[b])	*Microciona prolifera* (Simpson,
Class Demospongiae	1963)
Subclass Homoscleromorpha	Gray cells
Oscarella lobularis (Donadey, 1979)	Rhabdiferous cells
Vacuolar cells	Globoferous cells
Plakina trilopha (Donadey, 1979)	*Aplysina (Verongia) cavernicola*
Cells resembling spherulous cells	(Vacelet, 1967b)
Subclass Tetractinomorpha	Spherulous cells
Tethya lyncurium (Connes, 1968)	Microgranular cells
Spherulous cells	Granular cells[c]
Microgranular cells	Uncertain subclass placement
Gray cells	*Cyamon neon* (Smith, 1968)
Suberites massa (Diaz, 1979a)	Rhabdiferous cells
Spherulous cells	Sacculiferous cells
Gray cells	Chromocytes

[a]Garrone (person. comm.) considers these to be special cells rather than variants of archeocytes.
[b]Terms used by the authors.
[c]Vacelet originally referred to these cells as gray cells.

possess the same special cell types; that these cells are not prevalent in calcareous species, homoscleromorphs, and haplosclerids; and that there is a tendency for the remaining demosponges to contain a greater diversity of types.

The Cortex

The cortex of sponges, when present, occupies the area immediately below the exopinacoderm and consists of a specialized portion of the mesohyl lacking choanocyte chambers (Fig. 3-12). Its degree of develop-

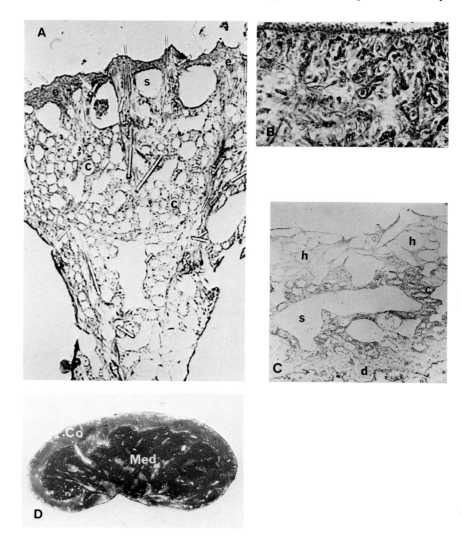

ment is quite variable. Classically, the cortex has been defined on the basis of a specialized portion of the skeleton occurring in the superficial layer of the animal (Sollas, 1888); this area in now also known to contain fibrous elements (collagen, fiber cells, lophocytes) (Garrone, 1978; Cowden, 1970). The cortical region may be pronounced as in astrophorids such as *Stelleta,* or it may only be barely distinguishable from the remainder of the mesohyl. When it is poorly or moderately developed, it is referred to as the ectosome or pseudocortex as in *Suberites* (Fig. 3-12A) (Diaz, 1979a). The presence of a cortex obviously has pronounced effects upon the growth pattern of adult animals since, when present, continued growth has to include the transformation of this specialized area into mesohyl proper and a new overlying cortex must then develop. Studies of the relationship of the cortex to continuing growth patterns would be most enlightening; little work has been conducted in this area. It is also possible in some species that the formation of a highly structured, definitive cortex may completely limit further growth as in *Tethya* (Chap. 9) and thus may further act as a signal for senescence.

The cortex can consist of (1) tracts or a network of fiber cells and/or lophocytes (Paris, 1961); (2) degenerating spongocytes and spongin fibers encasing megascleres (Connes *et al.,* 1972); (3) a layer of high concentration of microscleres or other mineral deposits or collagen fibrils. Reference should be made to Chapter One for general information concerning the distribution of cortex formation. This structure presumably acts as a special supportive devise for openings of the canal system and as a protective layer (Vacelet, 1971b) with the result that superficial injury does not involve the choanocytes. Furthermore, the cortex may in some species serve as a means of establishing a relationship between the sponge and its symbionts (Sara, 1971).

Although it is not practical to fully review cortical structure here, a

---

Figure 3-12 Examples of cortical and ectosomal specialization (light micrographs). **A**. The specialized ectosome (*e*) of *Suberites massa* which contains siliceous spicules, and is partially delimited by subdermal spaces (*s*). Choanocyte chambers are absent in the ectosome; they occur internally in the choanosome (*c*) (×115) (Connes *et al.*, 1972). **B**. The ectosome of *Hamigera hamigera* is similarly devoid of choanocyte chambers and possesses fibrous elements (×495) (Boury-Esnault, 1972). **C**. The cortex of the paretronid *Lelapiella incrustans*. In this decalcified section the holes (*h*) were previously occupied by a cortical layer of calcitic triactines and curved diactine spicules. The choanosome contains canal spaces (*s*) and choanocyte chambers (*c*). The remnants of the basal skeleton of curved, calcitic diactine spicules is also visible (*d*) (×50) (Vacelet, 1977a). **D**. Low-power view of a section of a whole animal of *Chondrosia reniformis*. The cortex (*Co*) has a low cell density but high collagen content and thus stains differentially as compared to the inner medulla (*Med*) which has high cell density (×2.5) (Garrone *et al.*, 1975). (**A,** courtesy Dr. R. Connes; **B,** courtesy Dr. N. Boury-Esnault; **C,** courtesy Dr. J. Vacelet; **D,** courtesy Dr. R. Garrone.)

number of examples are discussed indicating the range of variability. In the astrophorid, *Stelleta grubii,* the cortex consists of mesohyl with well-developed ground substance in which there are relatively few cells (Herlant-Meewis, 1948a). Numerous tracts of fiber cells and erroneously termed "fibres elastiques" (see Garrone, 1978) are present running perpendicular to the exopinacoderm. Many microscleres (asters) are localized here and bundles of megascleres and canals traverse the region. In the hadromerid *Suberites massa,* the cortex (=ectosome) has variable thickness (10–100 μm) and is demarcated from the internal tissue (endosome) by numerous large canal spaces (Fig. 3-12A) (Connes *et al.,* 1972; Diaz, 1979a). Stradling the canals are tracts of megascleres bound together with spongin; some of the distally located spicules protrude from the sponge surface. Collagen is abundant in the ground substance and degenerating, fusiform spongocytes, lying parallel to the surface are common; choanocyte chambers are absent. Gray cells appear to function as lophocytes in this sponge and are abundant in the cortex. In a second hadromerid, *Tethya lyncurium,* the cortex is separated from the endosome by a layer of lophocytes (Paris, 1961) and contains microscleres (spherasters), archeocytes, fiber cells ("collencytes"), and lophocytes. In the hadromerid *Chondrilla,* the cortex consists of more densely packed fibrous elements and more numerous microscleres (asters) than the endosome (Cowden, 1970). In the highly unusual genus *Chondrosia* (Fig. 3-12D) the cortex contains an outer area of loosely arranged bundles of collagen fibrils and an inner one where fibrils are tightly packed and layered (Garrone, 1978) with no mineral skeleton. In *Cacospongia scalaris* the ectosome also contains collagen fibrils as well as pigment containing cells (Donadey, 1982). Among axinellids, such as *Ceratopsis,* the superficial region contains numerous raphides that form a discrete layer (Hoshino, 1976). In the free-floating buds of the hadromerid *Alectona,* very unique *siliceous* scales form a surface armour and make up part of a thin "cortex," which also contains spherulous cells (Garrone, 1974) (see Fig. 8-5).

In the poecilosclerid, *Thalysias schoenus,* the ectosome consists of columns of mesohyl cells surrounding canal spaces. The columns contain spicules, collagen, and fiber cells which are oriented perpendicular to the exopinacoderm and thus laterally surround canals (Simpson, 1968a). At the base of these tracts are small groups of spherulous and granular cells. In a closely related species, *Thalysias juniperina,* many of the cortical columns are oriented obliquely to the exopinacoderm. In *Microciona prolifera* superficial tracts of spicules, collagen, and fiber cells are only sporadically present, and it is difficult to refer to an ectosome or a cortex at all (Simpson, 1968a). In the dictyoceratid, *Thorecta,* a thin cortex is characterized by a densely packed fibrous component, parallel to the exopinacoderm, embedded in a homogeneous matrix (Cowden and Harrison, 1976). Sulfhydryl and disulfide groups and sulfated mucins are significantly more prominent in the fibers than in the matrix suggesting at least a two-component matrix.

Among pharetronids, cortical specialization is the rule. In *Lelapiella incrustans* (Fig. 3-12C) the outer two hundred micrometers of the mesohyl contains calcitic spicules (triactines) curved toward the mesohyl and tracts of curved diactines that course all the way to the basal region of the sponge (Vacelet, 1977a). In *Murrayona phanolepis*, the surface on which oscules occur possesses three or four layers of flat calcitic scales producing a veritable surface armour (see Fig. 1-5C,D) (Vacelet, 1977a). In many pharetronids, special tetractine spicules occur superficially in the mesohyl surrounding oscules and thus produce an oscular armour (see Fig. 4-3A) (Vacelet, 1970a).

In species with a well-developed cortex (or ectosome), incurrent canals are either thin and long as in *Suberites* (Diaz, 1979a) or are organized into highly specialized structures (inhalant organs), which are described in Chapter Six. In both cases a thin dermal membrane, which is typical of many species without cortical differentiation, is absent (see further, Chap. 6).

Histological descriptions of "fibrous elements" that contribute to the cortex are indicative of underlying, specialized cell functions leading to patterns of matrix formation. As pointed out by Garrone (1978), such light microscope descriptions (which are most of them) have limited usefulness in and of themselves, and only detailed ultrastructural investigations are able to pinpoint the relevant processes involving cell–cell and cell–matrix interactions. It is clear that such interactions involve primarily sclerocytes, spongocytes, lophocytes, and special cells, and their undoubtedly complex nature still awaits elucidation. As previously discussed (Chap. 2) pinacocytes are frequently covered by a cell coat (glycocalyx) on their outer surface and in some species an acellular cuticle limits the surface (Chap. 2). Neither of these structures should be confused with a cortex or ectosome the latter of which are multicellular and frequently possess fibrillar or mineral arrays.

Cords of Cells

Thin, elongate groups of mesohyl cells have been described in many species. Generally, their presence is correlated with growth (Brien, 1976), regeneration (Lévi, 1960), or remodeling (Diaz, 1979a). In all three of these cases, cell cords are known to be an early stage of skeleton elaboration. In the taxonomic and descriptive literature, numerous other descriptions of cell cords are to be found such as in *Petrobiona* (Vacelet, 1964). While such groups of cells should not be equated with the cortex or ectosome, it is possible in some cases that they may ultimately be involved in the formation of the latter.

Recent investigations of tissue remodeling in *Suberites* have shown the involvement of cell cords that are *not,* however, involved in skeletono-genesis but that appear to arise due to coordinated cell migration (Diaz, 1979a); consequently, the presence of cell cords is not necessarily indicative of one specific developmental process. There are many interesting and basic questions regarding the structure and function of these cell groups and there are little available data bearing on them.

Symbionts

The occurrence of cyanobacteria, zooxanthellae, and bacteria as symbionts in marine sponges has recently been reported by Vacelet (1979b, 1971c, 1975), Sara (1964, 1971), Sara and Liaci (1964a,b), Wilkinson (1978a,b,c, 1979a,b), and Vacelet and Donadey (1977). Among freshwater species, Gilbert and Allen (1973a,b) and Williamson (1979) have investigated the morphology, pigments, and photosynthetic activity of symbiotic zoochlorellae.

Cyanobacteria

Blue-green algae of the genera *Aphanocapsa* and *Phormidium* have been discovered in a number of marine species (Table 3-6). These small cells (~1.0–5.0 and 6.0–12.0 μm for unicells) occur both extra- and intracellularly, and in both cases some of them undergo disintegration, presumably yielding nutrients to the sponge (Fig. 3-13). In a particular sponge, however, the symbionts are localized in one of the following ways: (1) almost exclusively extracellularly in the mesohyl [*Aplysina* (*Verongia*) *aerophoba*] (Vacelet, 1971c), (2) almost exclusively intracellularly within single large vacuoles (*Siphonochalina tabernacula*) (Wilkinson, 1979b), or (3) a combination of (1) and (2) (*Jaspis stellifera*) (Wilkinson, 1978c).

Symbionts occur in the superficial layer of the host unless the mesohyl is of low density, in which case they may be one or more centimeters deep in the tissue. At the surface, they contribute to a kind of "symbiocortex" and give the host sponge a violet to brown color in well lighted habitats. Sara (1971), Vacelet (1971c), and Wilkinson (1978c) have carried out electron microscopic studies of these symbionts. In *Aplysina* (*Verongia*), they have a different thylakoid structure when they occur deeper in the sponge tissue; in many instances cyanobacteria have been observed dividing. In *Jaspis stellifera, Neofibularia irata,* and *Pericharax heteroraphis* the host only grows under conditions of illumination (Wilkinson, 1978a; Wilkinson and Vacelet, 1979). Transfer of significant amounts of metabolites (glycerol) from symbiont to host has been demonstrated (Wilkinson, 1979a, 1980). Little, if any, extracellular lysis of the symbionts occurs (Wilkinson, 1978c), but their intracellular digestion has been noted in some cases (Vacelet, 1971c). In some host sponges (*Pericharax, Jaspis*) large numbers of cyanobacteria occur intracellularly within large vacuoles of archeocytes; such cells have been termed "cyanocytes" (Wilkinson, 1978c). Some species possess filamentous (multicellular) cyanobacteria in the mesohyl (Wilkinson, 1979a; Castro, 1979).

Zooxanthellae
Sara and Liaci (1964b) and Sara (1964) have described the presence of symbiotic zooxanthellae in two species of *Cliona*. The yellow-green color of these sponges is due to the symbionts occurring extracellularly (in distinction to their localization in anthozoans) and displaying red fluorescence in ultraviolet light. They are most prevalent in the surface layers.

Zoochlorellae
Gilbert and Allen (1973a,b) and Williamson (1979) have recently studied the symbiotic zoochlorellae of *Spongilla lacustris* and of a species of *Heteromeyenia*. The symbionts are intracellular and occur within cytoplasmic vacuoles in archeocytes and choanocytes of vegetative tissue and in the thesocytes (see Fig. 8-11A) of gemmules in the former species; routinely there is only a single alga per vacuole but many algae per cell (Fig. 3-14). Autoradiographic studies indicate that the algae transfer photosyntate to the sponge cells and that only about 1% is lost ("excreted") to the environment. Muscatine *et al.* (1967) report that only a small, but detectable, amount of photosynthate is released from sponge-derived zoochlorellae grown in liquid medium. The bright green color of these and many other freshwater sponges is due to the presence of zoochlorellae; in highly reduced light the sponge is colorless (white) due to the loss of most of the algal symbionts. The growth of these white sponges is accordingly also reduced in comparison to green individuals (Frost, 1978a; Frost and Williamson, 1980). There appears to be little, but some, intracellular digestion of the algae which also are rarely found extracellularly. Algal multiplication occurs in green individuals of *Spongilla lacustris* but not in white ones or within gemmular thesocytes (Williamson, 1979). Algal structure also may differ in white sponges as compared to green ones; in the former the symbionts lack starch and lipid deposits possibly due to the absence of light; algal structure in gemmular thesocytes may also be modified (see Chap. 8).

Bacteria
Vacelet (1970b, 1975), Vacelet and Donadey (1977), and Wilkinson (1978b) have described the occurrence of symbiotic bacteria in a number of demosponges (Table 3-6). The symbionts occur extracellularly and intracellularly within large vacuoles of archeocytes, which are referred to as "bacteriocytes." (Fig. 3-15). In *Aplysina* (*Verongia*) the intracellular bacteria are quite long and initially this raised some question as to whether they were actually bacteria (Vacelet, 1970b): there now is little

Table 3-6 Symbionts

Symbiont	Localization	Color Due to Symbiont	Distribution	Selected References
Cyanobacteria			**Calcarea**	Based upon Wilkinson (1980) taken from Vacelet (1971c), Wilkinson (1978c), Sara (1966), Sara and Liaci (1964a), Rutzler (1981)
Unicellular			Clathrinida	
Aphanocapsa	Intra- and extracellular	Green, violet to brown	*Clathrina*	
			Leucettida	
			Pericharax	
			Sycettida	
			Sycon	
Multicellular	Only extra-	………	**Demospongiae**	
Phormidium	cellular		Homosclerophorida	
			Oscarella	
			Astrophorida	
			Jaspis	
			Lithistida	
			Theonella	
			Hadromerida	
			Chondrilla	
			Cliona	
			Tethya	
			Halichondrida	
			Halichondria	
			Hymeniacidon	
			Ulosa	
			Poecilosclerida	
			Anchinoe	
			Clathria	
			Crambe	
			Hemimycale	
			Neofibularia	
			Haploslerida	
			Callyspongia	
			Calyx	
			Haliclona	
			Pellina	
			Reniera	
			Siphonochalina	
			Petrosiida	
			Petrosia	
			Dictyoceratida	
			Dysidea	
			Ircinia	
			Phyllospongia	
			Spongia	
			Dendroceratida	
			Aplysilla	
			Verongida	
			Aplysina (Verongia)	

Zooxanthellae	Extracellular	Yellow-green		Sara (1964), Sara and Liaci (1964b), Liaci (1964b)
Zoochlorellae	Intracellular	Green	*Cliona* / Many freshwater species	Gilbert and Allen (1973a,b), Williamson (1979)
Bacteria	Intra- and extracellular	Probably none		Vacelet (1975, 1979b), Vacelet and Donadey (1977), Lévi and Lévi (1976), Wilkinson, (1978b), Gallissian and Vacelet (1976), Donadey (1982)

Calcarea
Clathrinida
  Clathrina
Leucettida
  Pericharax
Sycettida
  Grantia
Pharetronida
  Petrobiona
Sphinctozoida
  Neocoelia

Sclerospongiae
Stromatoporoida
  Astrosclera

Demospongiae
Homosclerophorida
  Oscarella
  Plakina
Astrophorida
  Jaspis
  Pachymatisma
  Thenea
Hadromerida
  Chondrosia
Poecilosclerida
  Agelas
  Crambe
  Hamigera
  Neofibularia
Petrosiida
  Petrosia
Haplosclerida
  Reniera
Axinellida
  Acanthella
  Axinella
Dictyoceratida
  Cacospongia
  Halisarca
  Hippospongia
  Ircinia
  Psammaplysilla
  Spongia
Dendroceratida
  Pleraplysilla
Verongida
  Aplysina (Verongia)

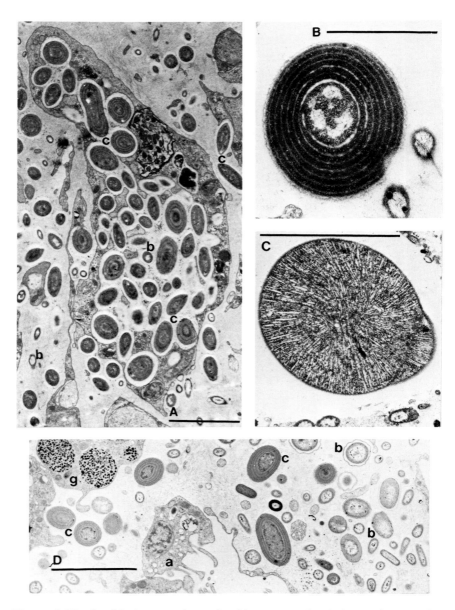

Figure 3-13 Symbiotic cyanobacteria (blue-green algae) in marine species (TEMs). **A**. A large cyanocyte in the mesohyl of *Jaspis stellifera* from the Great Barrier Reef. Cyanocytes are specialized mesohyl cells which contain hundreds of unicellular cyanobacteria (*c*) in a single vacuole with occasional bacteria (*b*) present in the vacuole also. In this species the symbionts occur in cell vacuoles as well as in the mesohyl (see C., this figure). Scale bar: 5.0 μm (×5,490) (Wilkinson, 1978c). **B**. Unicellular cyanobacterium showing central nucleoplasm area surrounded by the distinctive spiral thylakoid. Adjacent are two bacteria for size comparison. Scale bar: 1.0 μm (×37,800) (Wilkinson, 1978c). **C**. Oblique section

doubt that they are. The vacuole may contain little additional material or it may contain a dense mass of relatively amorphous material surrounding the bacteria. In *Aplysina* (*Verongia*), the bacteria-containing vacuole appears to be intranuclear (Vacelet, 1970b), but no further investigation of this strange association has been undertaken. In the absence of ultrastructural information, bacteriocytes could easily be referred to as cellules vacuolaires. Lévi and Porte (1962) have reported the presence of intercellular bacteria in *Oscarella lobularis* and *Halisarca dujardini* and Bertrand and Vacelet (1971) have further found them in *Spongia, Hippospongia, Cacospongia*, and *Ircinia*. Sara *et al.*, (1973) have noted bacteria within the spongocoel of the calcareous sponges *Clathrina cerebrum* and *C. clathrus;* occasionally they are also found in the mesohyl. These authors also report the extracellular presence of bacteria in *Agelas oroides* where they, as is the case with some cyanobacteria in other species, apparently undergo a degree of disintegration possibly providing nutrients to the sponge. Vacelet (1975) has recorded the presence of extracellular bacteria in a number of dictyoceratids as well as in *Petrosia, Chondrosia*, and *Astrosclera* (Vacelet, 1967a), and Vacelet and Donadey (1977) have extended these observations to other demosponge orders (Table 3-6). In *Aplysina* (*Verongia*) some bacteria are apparently ingested by the sponge and utilized as a nutrient source (Vacelet, 1975). In *Chondrosia,* symbiotic bacteria incorporate [^{3}H]proline from the medium and some of them are then phagocytized by mesohyl cells thus acting as a means of uptake of dissolved organic substances for the nutrition of the sponge (Wilkinson and Garrone, 1980b). Lévi and Lévi (1976) have reported that intracellular bacteria are transmitted in the larva to the newly metamorphosing animal, in *Chondrosia reniformis*. These bacteria occur within a vacuole in follicle cells which initially surround the developing egg in the mesohyl. The follicle cells later migrate within the larva and at metamorphosis they are found within the mesohyl releasing the bacteria. In *Aplysina* (*Verongia*), developing eggs ingest mesohyl symbiotic bacteria, which are then carried in the egg cytoplasm for transmittal to newly developing sponges (Gallissian and Vacelet, 1976).

In some species, their facultative, anaerobic bacterial flora is special and is not represented in the ambient water, whereas in others (*Ircinia*) it is (Wilkinson, 1978b). Vacelet and Donadey (1977) have found a correlation between tissue density and bacterial symbionts: in species with a

---

through a multicellular cyanobacterium in *Aplysina* (*Verongia*) *mollis*, a Red Sea species, showing radiating thylokoids and part of the next cell in the chain. These symbionts are not found in cell vacuoles. Scale bar: 5.0 μm (×9,180) (Wilkinson, 1979a). **D**. Mesohyl of Mediterranean species *Aplysina* (*Verongia*) *aerophoba* with both unicellular cyanobacteria (*c*) and bacteria (*b*). *a*, choanocyte; *g*, granular cell. Scale bar: 5.0 μm (×6,300) (Wilkinson, unpubl.). (All courtesy Dr. C. R. Wilkinson.)

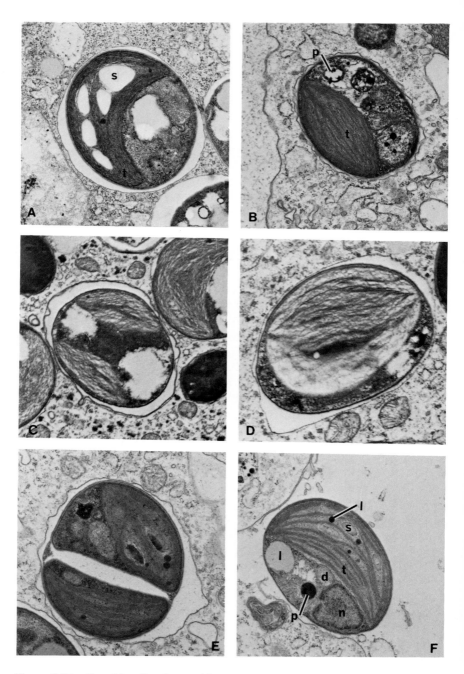

Figure 3-14 Zoochlorellae from white and green *Spongilla lacustris* (TEMs) (all from Williamson, 1979). **A**. Zoochlorella within an archeocyte vacuole of a green sponge. The thylakoid membranes (*t*) are tightly packed and there are many starch (*s*) grains. (×18,450). **B**. An intracellular zoochlorella in a white sponge. Although the thylakoids (*t*) are tightly packed, the polyphosphate granule (*p*) is vesiculated

dense cellular mesohyl, bacterial symbionts are numerous and their morphology is varied, whereas in those with lower tissue density there are few bacteria and only a single morphological type is present. In all cases the bacteria are predominantly extracellular except in *Petrosia*. Some spherulous cells in *Aplysina* (*Verongia*) act as bacteriocytes and their inclusions become compressed due to the presence of large numbers of cytoplasmic bacteria that displace them. In some species, both bacteria and cyanobacteria occur side by side in the mesohyl and even within the same vacuoles of cyanocytes (Wilkinson, 1978c). An astonishing variety of unusual types of bacterial cell walls occurs in symbionts of *Aplysina* (*Verongia*) and the bacteria can occupy as much as one third of the total sponge volume (Vacelet, 1975). In this genus, cyanobacteria are also present in the ectosome and appear to displace the bacteria which only occur in large numbers deeper in the tissue.

Some Problems in Symbiont–Host Relationships

Among the many intriguing questions raised by the presence of sponge symbionts is that of the mechanism of recognition of the symbiont by the host cells. Obviously, some cell surface components are involved in stabilizing the relationship, otherwise the archeocytes would treat them as nutrient material and digest them (Chap. 6). In fact, digestion appears to occur, but only very rarely, suggesting an efficient recognition system. The uptake and retention of bacteria by sponges are well documented (Reiswig, 1971b; Claus *et al.*, 1967; Madri *et al.*, 1967) and have been shown in one case to be sufficient to sustain the nutrient requirements of the animal (Reiswig, 1975b). For the symbiotic association to be established and continued there must be repression or an absence of cell surface interaction which leads to a phagocytic response and eventual digestion. From one point of view one can consider symbiosis as a possible deficiency of appropriate response of archeocytes and choanocytes. Alternatively, there may be a positive symbiont recognition signal that sustains the relationship (Wilkinson, 1980). Also, in sponges with both cyanobacteria and bacteria there may be specific interactions between the symbionts themselves (Vacelet, 1975). The cyanobacterial pigments may

---

(see F., below) (×18,315). **C.** Intracellular alga in a green gemmule with a single coat layer. The thylakoids are loosely packed and there are no starch grains or lipid inclusions present (see F., below) (×16,020). **D.** An alga within a thesocyte of a white gemmule with a single coat layer. The structure is like that in green gemmules (see C.) (×26,100). **E.** A dividing, intracellular alga with two autospores in a green sponge (×29,700). **F.** An intercellular alga in a green sponge showing major structures: *n*, nucleus; *p*, polyphosphate granule; *l*, lipid; *s*, starch grain; *t*, thylakoid membranes; *d*, mitochondrion (×18,900). (All courtesy Dr. C. E. Williamson.)

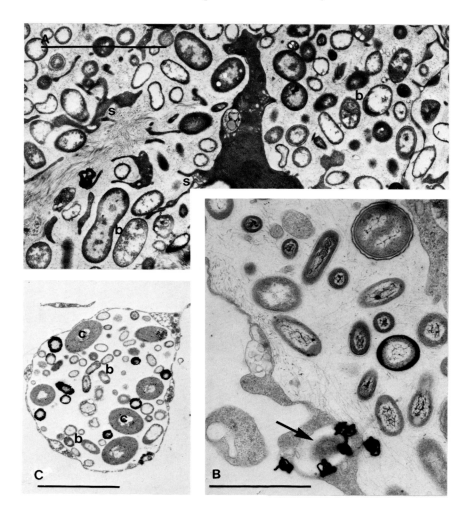

Figure 3-15   Symbiotic bacteria in marine species (TEMs). **A**. Large mixed population of bacteria (*b*) in the collagenous mesohyl of *Chondrosia reniformis*. Note that the bacterial population exceeds the volume occupied by sponge cells (*s*). Scale bar: 5.0 μm (×6,390) (Wilkinson, unpublished). **B**. Morphologically different bacteria in the mesohyl bordering a canal. The endopinacocyte vacuole contains a seawater bacterium (*arrow*) labeled with radioactive tritium which had been fed *in situ* to the sponge, *Aplysina* (*Verongia*) *cavernicola*. The radioactive label shows up as dark tracks in the photographic emulsion superimposed over the thin section. This illustrates the enigma of sponges ingesting seawater bacteria but harboring large populations of symbionts. Scale bar: 2.0 μm (×13,500) (Wilkinson, unpubl.). **C**. A vacuole in a mesohyl cell of *Siphonochalina tabernacula* in which there are large populations of bacteria (*b*) and smaller populations of cyanobacteria (*c*). No symbionts were observed in the mesohyl of this species. Scale bar: 3.0 μm (×16,200) (Wilkinson, unpubl.). (All courtesy Dr. C. R. Wilkinson.)

also play a significant role in shielding the mesohyl cells from solar radiation. Such shielding permits the growth of some sponges in highly illuminated habitats [*Aplysina* (*Verongia*) *aerophoba*] which inhibits the growth of other species not possessing cyanobacteria [*Aplysina* (*Verongia*) *cavernicola*] (Wilkinson and Vacelet, 1979). The means by which cell division of the symbionts is controlled is not known, but it is clear in freshwater species that some mechanism inhibits zoochlorelle division in gemmules but permits it in vegetative tissue (Williamson, 1979). In the case of bacteria, however, there may be little control other than nutrient availability for the symbiont, thus leading to immense populations of the symbiont. These highly significant populations of sponge symbionts in many species should give biochemists some pause before launching extensive extraction procedures for analysis of sponge chemical components.

Pigment

One of the least understood and investigated aspects of the cell biology of the mesohyl is the specific cellular distribution of pigment and the form in which it occurs. The predominant class of substances responsible for pigmentation is carotenoids and, setting aside pigmentation due to symbionts, it appears that carotenoids, with the exception of melanin, are *the* class of pigments in sponges. Earlier reports of porphyrins (MacMunn, 1890; Kennedy and Vevers, 1954) have not been reinvestigated using modern separation and analytical techniques (Kennedy, 1979). Melanin has been reported in a number of sponges (Table 3-7); according to some workers there could also be small quantities of this pigment in species (*Halichondria, Hymeniacidon, Microciona*) that are otherwise known for their carotenoids (Kennedy, 1979). The dramatic blackening of the tissue of *Aplysina* (*Verongia*) *aerophoba* when in contact with the air is due to melanin (Kennedy, 1979). In distinction to many other invertebrates that elaborate carotenoids, xanthophylls are poorly represented in sponges (Goodwin, 1968).

Pigment, either symbiont or sponge derived, probably functions as a protective devise against excessive solar radiation and thus, to some extent, acts as a determinant for habitat distribution of some species as previously discussed. This view is further supported by direct, long-term, *in habitat* experiments; these demonstrate that in *Aplysina* (*Verongia*) *cavervicola,* which does not possess algal symbionts, light inhibits its growth (Wilkinson and Vacelet, 1979). Although no analyses have been carried out, the color of sclerosponges, which ranges from yellow to orange, to red, to pink, and to beige, is probably a result of the presence of carotenoids. Phycoerythrin in a number of species is restricted to those with symbiotic cyanobacteria, which are apparently its source. In symbi-

Table 3-7 Pigments

Pigment	Distribution	References
Carotenoids		
Including but not limited to: carotenes, lycopene, torulene, echinenone, renieratene, isorenieratene, clathriaxanthin, allopurpurin, trikentriorhodin, algelaxanthin, trikentriophidin, tedanin, renierapurpurin	*Agelas schmidtii* *Axinella crista-galli* *Clathria frondifera* *Cyamon neon* *Ectyon oroides* *Ficulina ficus* *Halichondria* *Halma ducklandii* *Hymeniacidon sanguinea* *Leuconia gossei* *Microciona prolifera* *Reniera japonica* *Suberites* *Tedania digitata, muggiana* *Tethya amamensis, lyncurium, aurantium* *Trikentrion helium*	Karrer and Solmssen (1935), Lederer (1938), Drumm *et al.* (1945), Okukado (1975), Liaci (1964c), Smith (1968), Tanaka *et al.* (1978), Goodwin (1968), Buchecker *et al.* (1977), Litchfield and Liaaen-Jansen (1980), Yamaguchi (1957a,b, 1958a,b, 1959, 1960)
Melanin	*Aaptos aaptos* *Aplysina (Verongia) aerophoba* *Cacospongia scalaris* *Cyamon neon* *Halichondria panicea* *Hippospongia communis* *Leucosolenia botryoides* *Pachymatisma johnstonni*	Pavans de Ceccatty (1958), Liaci (1962, 1963a,b), Smith (1968), Kennedy (1979), Willenz (1983)
Chlorophylls Lipofuchsin Chlorophyll	*Aaptos aaptos*	Liaci (1962, 1963a,b)
Lipochromes Chlorophyll	*Haliclona rosea* *Hymeniacidon columella* *Suberites domuncula*	Liaci (1963b)

Table 3-7 Pigments (*Continued*)

Pigment	Distribution	References
Chlorophylls (continued)	*Aplysina (Verongia)*	Liaci (1963c)
Chlorophyll[a] ⎫ Cyanobacteria	*aerophoba*	
Carotenoids ⎬ present	*Calyx nicaeenis*	
Phycoerythrin ⎭	*Ircinia fasiculata*	
	Pellina semitubulosa	
	Petrosia ficiformis	
Chlorophyll[a] ⎧ Zoochlorellae	*Spongilla lacustris*	Gilbert and Allen
Pheopigments[a] ⎩ present	*Heteromeyenia* sp.	(1973a,b)
Chlorophyll[a] ⎧ Zooxanthellae	*Cliona viridis, copiosa*	Sara and Liaci
Carotenoids ⎨ present		(1964b), Sara
⎩		(1964), Liaci (1964b)
? **Porphyrin** ?	*Tethya aurantia*	Kennedy and Vevers
		(1954)

[a]Pigment apparently derived from symbionts.

ont containing species, Liaci (1964b) has found that both the number of symbionts (zooxanthellae and cyanobacteria) and the quantity of pigment are directly related to the amount of available sunlight. In the freshwater sponge, *Spongilla lacustris,* which is normally bright green due to its numerous symbiotic zoochlorellae, a blockage of solar radiation *in habitat* results in almost unpigmented animals (Frost, 1978a; Frost and Williamson, 1980). In *Aplysina (Verongia) aerophoba* with cyanobacteria, dark shields result in a significant paling of color and a corresponding reduction in chlorophyll content of the sponge tissue (Wilkinson and Vacelet, 1979).

A number of reviews of sponge pigments are available (Goodwin, 1968; Fox, 1976; Kennedy, 1979; Minale, 1978) and indicate the complexities of carotenoid pigmentation. A very recent, detailed study of the carotenoids of *Microciona prolifera* serves as an outstanding example of the immensity of the problem of chemically identifying sponge carotenoids (Litchfield and Liaaen-Jansen, 1980). In that study, ten different major carotenoids were reported including three new substances. Even in this analysis, 7% of the total carotenoids were not characterized (Table 3-8). A trace of chlorophyll, doubtless of algal origin, was also noted. Of the total carotenoids, 16% are clearly of algal origin, 70% are specifically sponge, and one substance, allopurpurin (=tedaniaxanthin), is a "hybrid" type having a chemical structure that is a mixture of algal and sponge pigment structure. The major sponge carotenoids of this species contain aromatic rings and the data strongly suggest that this sponge (and probably others) is able to aromatize algal carotenoids, a suggestion also mentioned by Kennedy (1979). Yamaguchi (1957a,b, 1958a,b, 1959, 1960) first described

Table 3-8   Carotenoid Pigments of *Microciona prolifera*[a]

Carotenoid	Percentage of Total Carotenoids
Sponge Type	
Clathriaxanthin	41
Trikentriorhodin	13
Trikentriophidin	14
3,4(2,3)-Didehydro-γ,χ-carotene	2
Algal Type	
β,β-Carotene	8
Alloxanthin	4
β,ε-Carotene	2
Crocoxanthin	1
Allobetaxanthin	1
Hybrid type	
Allopurpurin (=tedaniaxanthin)	7
Uncharacterized	7

[a]Data taken from Litchfield and Liaaen-Jansen (1980).

the novel aromatic carotenoids, renieratene, isorenieratene, and reniera-purpurin. In *Agelas schmidtii,* there are seven major carotenoids, thus rivaling the complexity described in *Microciona prolifera* (Buchecker *et al.,* 1977) and in *Trikentrion helium,* ten or eleven different carotenoids appear to be present (Smith, 1968). Tanaka and his collaborators (1978) have also reported the presence of new carotenoids in a number of demosponges (Table 3-7). It is to be assumed that continuing biochemical studies of pigments will uncover other new carotenoids and that it will take considerable effort to finally arrive at a position permitting meaningful biochemical comparisons.

   Most sponge pigments are clearly intracellular; the best evidence of this is the presence of coloration in the cells, not in the supernatant, of sedimented, dissociated cells (Smith, 1968). Also, light microscopic observations of living cells (Smith, 1968) clearly demonstrate an intracellular position. Using histological and histochemical techniques, Pavans de Ceccatty (1958) also clearly has shown the intracellular localization of melanin in *Pachymatisma johnstoni* and other sponges containing this pigment. On the other hand, there have been few attempts to ascertain whether minor quantities of pigment also occur in the mesohyl. Liaci (1962) identified an extracellular, fluorescent, lipofuchsin in *Aaptos aaptos,* which also occurs intracellularly in some mesohyl cells. If it is generally the case, as has been shown in *Microciona prolifera,* that a small but significant quantity of the total carotenoid pigment is actually algal pigment, then some of the latter in the form of particulate food will certainly be present within phagosomes of pinacocytes, archeocytes, and choanocytes. If indeed, the specific sponge pigments (clathriaxanthin, trikentrionrhodin) are actually produced through aromatization of corresponding algal pigments then they, too, may at some time be present within the primary phagocytic sponge cell types. But, in any case, the algal and sponge pigments may also become concentrated by an unknown mechanism in other cell types, specifically special cells as previously discussed.

The only combined light, electron microscopic, and biochemical study of such localization is that of Smith (1968) (Figs. 3-16 to 3-19). In *Trikentrion helium* a specific cell type, the chromocyte, was found to contain the carotenoid pigments (Fig. 3-16); these are localized within cytoplasmic, membrane-bound inclusions probably in combination with protein. Significantly, archeocytes were also observed containing pigment granules. The chromocytes in this species obviously are to be grouped among the special cells and are reminiscent of spherulous cells except their organelle development and the presence of glycogen are also similar to gray cells (Fig. 3-19). Smith (1968) actually compares them to the latter and suggests that the pigment granules may undergo morphological changes, possibly

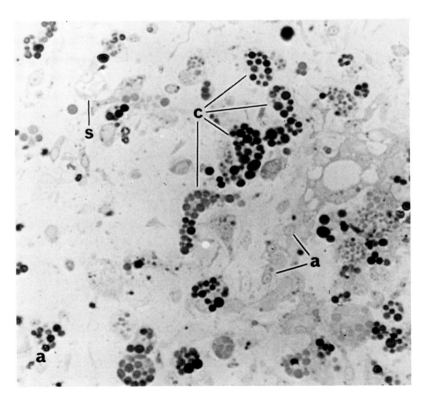

Figure 3-16 Chromocytes (*c*) of *Trikentrion helium*. Also seen in the mesohyl are sacculiferous cells (*s*) and archeocytes (*a*) (light micrograph, semithin section) (×950) (Smith, 1968). (Courtesy Dr. V. E. Smith.)

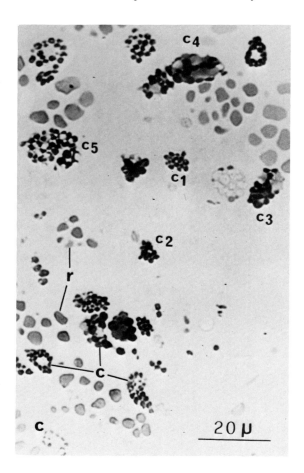

Figure 3-17　Chromocytes (*C* and *C1* to *C5*) of *Cyamon neon*. These chromocytes can contain only granules (*C1* and *C2*) or they can also develop lucent areas within the cytoplasm (*C3* to *c5*). *r*, rhabdiferous cells. (light micrograph, semithin section) (×950) (Smith, 1968). (Courtesy Dr. V. E. Smith.)

degenerative, and that archeocytes may phagocytize some pigment granules released from the chromocytes. Neither of these possibilities is, however, completely documented. In *Cyamon neon*, two types of chromocytes are present, one of them appears to be synonomous with choanocytes since in this case the cell size was very small, 3.0–6.0 μm; in them are small orange-colored granules; no further details were given. In the second type (Figs. 3-17, 3-18) there are dense, membrane-bound inclusions crowded around larger, translucent vacuoles, the pigment apparently being present in the small, more numerous inclusions. Cheng *et al.* (1968a) report the presence of pigment granules in "chromocytes" of

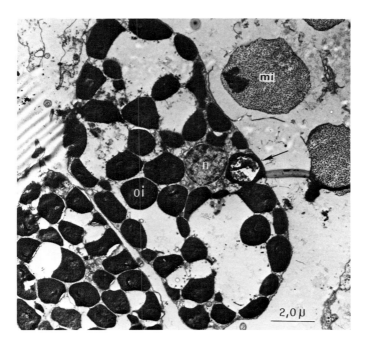

Figure 3-18 Chromocyte of *Cyamon neon*. The cell possesses an anucleolate nucleus (*n*), many dense inclusions (*oi*), a heterogeneous inclusion (*arrow*), and large lucent areas between the dense inclusions. The carotenoid pigments are localized either in the dense inclusions and/or lucent areas. Comparisons with light microscopy of living cells do not permit a more precise conclusion concerning pigment localization in this species. *mi*, an inclusion of a special cell present in this species (TEM) ($\times$5,700) (Smith, 1968). (Courtesy Dr. V. E. Smith.)

Terpios zeteki; some cells contain carotenoids (red granules) and others melanin (black granules).

Wilson and Penney (1930) identified carotenoid pigment within archeocytes of *Microciona prolifera,* whereas Boury-Esnault (1976a) has found that carontenoids in the larva of *Hamigera hamigera* occur within membrane-bound, translucent vacuoles in "cellules à vacuolaires"; in the latter case the pigment was considered to be "in solution" and the cells contain glycogen. The intensity of color in sponge larvae is routinely paler than in the parent, possibly suggesting that little or no pigment may be present within archeocytes which have no source of algal particulates until after metamorphosis when the canal system is functional. In symbiont containing species, this paleness suggests the presence of many fewer symbionts than in the adult cells.

No general statement concerning the intracellular distribution of carotenoid pigments is possible, and this in itself supports the conclusion that

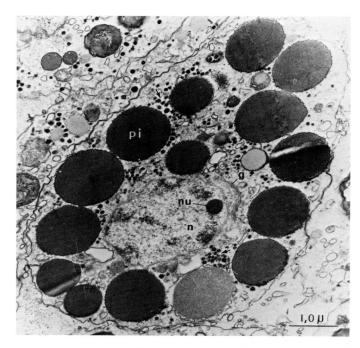

Figure 3-19 A chromocyte of *Trikentrion helium*. The pigment is localized only in the dense inclusions (*pi*). Although these inclusions and the presence of much cytoplasmic glycogen (*arrows*) bear a resemblance to gray cells, the inclusion contents are noticeably less dense and their shape is generally spherical rather than elliptical. *n*, nucleus; *nu*, nucleolus; *g*, Golgi (TEM) (×13,200) (Smith, 1968). (Courtesy Dr. V. E. Smith.)

pigment granules probably occur in a variety of types of cells including archeocytes, choanocytes, and some special cells. It does seem clear that the concept of a specific type of pigment containing cell (chromocyte) can be misleading, since if it is one thing that the data indicate it is that carotenoid distribution is heterogeneous, not uniform, with respect to cell type.

This is also clearly the case with melanin distribution. In *Pachymatisma* and *Hippospongia,* intracellular melanin granules are most abundant in the superficial portions of the mesohyl where they occur within pinacocytes, collencytes (?=archeocytes), and in the former species in lophocytes (Pavans de Ceccatty, 1958); there are no specific melanocytes as such. The development of melanin in these cells is viewed as possibly coupled to their function in elimination since some cells appeared to be released into excurrent canals. In *Halichondria,* melanin granules are not usual, but oocyte development and the presence of foreign organisms or substances stimulate its production in mesohyl cells. In some calcareous species, *Clathrina* and *Leucosolenia,* all of the cells in a part of the tissue can form melanin granules apparently as a response to an unknown, intrinsic, physiological condition (possibly ageing). Neither of these sponges normally produces melanin. Physical disruption (cutting) and exposure to air also are able to stimulate melanogenesis (Kennedy, 1979). The addition of the amino acid tyrosine to the water can induce melanogenesis initially in choanocytes but then in other mesohyl cells (Pavans de Ceccatty, 1958). Thus, in this study, two important conclusions can be drawn: (1) there are no specific melanocytes and (2) melanogenesis can be a labile process, although in some species it is a permanent feature of their cell biology. In *Cyamon neon,* according to Smith (1968), melanin forms *de novo* through oxidation (air or H_2O_2), and in some of the above-cited cases, its presence (especially in superficial areas) may be a result of higher oxygen tension. However, in *C. neon* its formation requires live tissue—boiling of the tissue inhibits its appearance—and consequently the essential involvement of an enzyme is suggested (Smith, 1968).

In *Cacospongia scalaris* and *Spongia officinalis,* melanin containing cells occur in the ectosome (Donadey, 1982). The degree of melanization is related to light availability; individuals in habitats with little available light contain less melanin or sometimes none. The melanin occurs in small (0.6 μm) cytoplasmic vacuoles in "collencytes" in the ectosome. When little melanin is produced, the vacuoles are nevertheless still present. Thus these two species also display a variability in melanogenesis although the type of pigment containing cells appears uniform and does not include pinacocytes or choanocytes. The pigment is unreactive to the DOPA reaction and thus appears different from vertebrate melanin.

CHAPTER FOUR

Calcification, Silicification, Bioerosion

Members of the phylum Porifera constitute an amazing array of species in terms of the kinds and shapes of mineral products they secrete. Depending upon the group, relatively enormous amounts of aragonite, calcite, and silica are secreted by these animals. In viewing sponges from this perspective, one is impressed by the diversity of transport and secretory mechanisms that have evolved in the phylum coupled with the almost total absence of the evolution of discrete tissues involved in these phenomena. In view of the fact that sponges lack an intraorganismal transport system, their capacity to secrete these minerals in large quantities is all the more amazing. The processing of precursors must be highly efficient on a cell to cell basis and may also functionally involve the intercellular matrix, although data on the latter point are not yet available. In a small number of species, the animals are capable of eroding calcareous substrata through a process assumed also to involve transport and secretory processes; these result both in the partial dissolution and the subsequent removal of the substratum.

In a recent scanning electron microscopic study of four coral reef sponges, Wilkinson (1979c) has suggested an interesting and potentially meaningful principle: different skeletal materials may be used by different species to produce similar supporting structures with physically different characteristics. Thus, two species that carry out silicification but lack spongin are ecologically restricted to calmer water (Table 4-1). The remaining two occur in more turbulent habitats and both possess skeletons with greater toughness (resistance to tearing) and more elasticity. Thus, mineral and organic matrix materials are clearly more than supportive; their arrangement and nature may directly influence the entire life-style of a species.

A brief and general review of the skeleton of sponges, which constitutes a major portion of their secretory products, has been presented in Chapter One. Jones (1979b) has recently presented an excellent short review of sponge minerals. Three chemically distinct types of mineral products are deposited: calcareous, siliceous, and iron containing. The present chapter discusses their morphology, chemistry, localization, distribution, secretion, and development.

Table 4-1   Secretory Products of Four Coral Reef Species[a]

Species	Collagen Fibrils	Spongin	Siliceous Spicules[b] (%)	Foreign Matter	Habitat
Pericharax heteroraphis	+	0	52	0	Less turbulent
Jaspis stellifera	+++	0	14	0	Less turbulent
Neofibularia irata	+	+++	7	0	More turbulent
Ircinia wistarii	++	++	0	+++	More turbulent

[a]Data taken from Wilkinson (1979c).
[b]Percentage of dry weight.

Calcareous Deposits: Morphology, Chemistry, Distribution

Calcareous Spicules

The morphology of calcareous spicules is much less varied than that of siliceous spicules. W. Clifford Jones has been responsible, almost single-handedly, for our understanding of the nature of calcareous spicules, and reference should be made to the series of excellent papers published by him (Jones, 1954a,b, 1955a,b, 1967, 1970, 1979a). Types of calcareous spicules are (1) monaxons, with one axis or ray; (2) diactines, with two rays; (3) triactines (=triaxons, triradiates), with three rays lying in differ-ent planes (Fig. 4-1); and (4) tetractines (tetraxons, quadriradiates), with four rays. Triactines can be regular, with three rays that are equal in length all forming the same angle with the principal axis (=principal axis of symmetry) or, they can be sagittal in which one ray lies in the plane of the optic axis and bisects the angle between the two remaining rays. In parasagittal (=primary sagittal) spicules, the angles between each of the three rays is 120° (or close to it) and in sagittal (secondary sagittal) each of a pair of rays (oscular rays) makes the same angle with the third ray (basal ray), and the third angle (between the paired rays) is greater than 120°; thus two of the rays and angles are paired and the third is unpaired. In a variant of the sagittal spicule, the "triactine en diapason" or tuning fork spicule of some pharetronids, the unpaired angle is much less than either of the paired angles. Tetractines can be viewed as triactines to which a fourth ray (apical or gastral ray) has been added.

Monactinal spicules are of two types, one which is completely straight with the optic axis coincident with the spicule axis and a second type, the curved monaxon, in which the optic axis is at right angles to the spicule axis (Jones, 1954a). True diactinal spicules with two rays in different

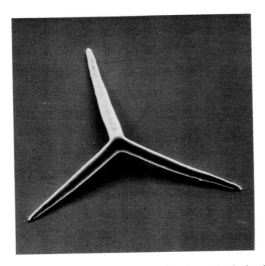

Figure 4-1 A typical calcitic, equiangular, triactine spicule in *Clathrina blanca*. Note that the rays are not in the same plane (SEM) (×600) (Johnson, 1978a). (Courtesy Dr. M. Fischel Johnson.)

planes are rare, although the term is frequently misused to refer to monaxonal spicules. The term monaxon is preferred when it is not clear if the spicule is monactinal or diactinal (Jones, 1970). Some monaxonal spicules have not been thoroughly studied, such as those referred to as "diactinal spicules" in pharetronids (as for example, Vacelet, 1977a). It is probably best to be skeptical about the implied nature of such spicules until appropriate information is available.

Although there is a great deal of regularity in the spicules of many calcareous sponges, there are also examples of spicules with irregular and unusual geometry and features (see Fig. 1-1). Jones (1970) has reviewed the morphology of calcareous spicules, and taxonomic studies such as those of Burton (1963) and Borojevic (1968) contain detailed descriptions. Descriptions of the morphology of more recently discovered morphological variants of calcareous spicules among the pharetronids have been published by Vacelet (1964, 1967a, 1977a), Vacelet and Vasseur (1971) and Pouliquen and Vacelet (1970). As new species of calcareous sponges are discovered, the range of variation in spicule geometry will undoubtedly be extended.

Generally, only a single size range of calcitic spicules is produced by species and these are considered megascleres. However, in some cases such as *Leucandra nivea*, the smallest monaxons (40 μm in length) are referred to as micromonaxons. Only rarely is there a category of calcareous spicules *both* small in size and unique in morphology; such an example are the "microdiactines" of *Tulearinia stylifera* (Vacelet, 1977a however, even in this case it is possible that these "microscleres" are young stages of a larger-size category of "diactines." Most spicules have a smooth surface, but particularly among the newly described species of pharetronids surface spination is present in a variety of patterns such as in *Plectroninia vasseuri* (Vacelet, 1967a). Also in this group many irregularities of normally precise geometric relationships occur.

Calcareous spicules are invested by a thin, organic sheath (Jones, 1955b, 1967) with fibrils (Fig. 4-2A) (Jones, 1967; Travis, 1970). Using corrosion and crystallization techniques, Jones (1955b) has indirectly established that the sheath contains pores. As originally reported in the early literature, calcareous spicules only appear to contain a thin, central, internal, longitudinal core referred to as an axial filament. Jones (1967) and Ledger and Jones (1977) dispute the presence of such an internal organic thread, although Jones (1954a) earlier had suggested that such a structure might act as an orienting axis for the alignment of calcite crystals during their deposition. But Travis (1970), using transmission electron microscopy, has reported the presence of an amorphous intraspicular matrix in very small (0.1 μm in diameter) spicules or an amorphous and fibrillar intraspicular matrix in larger (1.0 μm in diameter) spicules. In the largest spicules examined the matrix has a complex arrangement forming compartments throughout the spicule. The walls of the compartments consist of sheets of matrix as well as of fibrils. Ledger and Jones (1977) and Ledger (1976) convincingly dispute the data of Travis (1970) and consider the isolated fibrils as being derived from the *outer* surface of the spicule sheath; although not eliminating the possibility of the presence of trace amounts of organic material internally, they have found no such matrix during the earliest stages of spicule secretion (Ledger and Jones, 1977). Regardless of the question of the incorporation of an organic matrix into calcareous spicules, it is clear that these spicules do not contain a structure comparable to the relatively large, well-delineated, and characterized axial filament of siliceous spicules (see later sections).

Under the light microscope, larger spicules display longitudinal striping (Fig. 4-2C) and lines of fusion between rays (Jones, 1970). The former are caused by concentric lamination (Fig. 4-2B), which is visible in spicule cross sections following etching with acetic acid (Jones, 1970) or EDTA (Ledger, 1976). The use of tartaric acid for etching followed by examination by scanning electron microscopy demonstrates both primary and secondary concentric bands with, however, varying band widths from section to section (Jones and James, 1972). Employing electron probe microanalysis, Jones and James (1969) found no correlation between the distribution of inorganic constituents (calcium, magnesium, sulfur, strontium) and the presence of concentric rings, fusion lines between spicule rays, and the so-called axial filament. The results suggest that these features are due to crystal imperfections or to traces of organic material (Jones and James, 1969). Based upon the transmission electron micro-

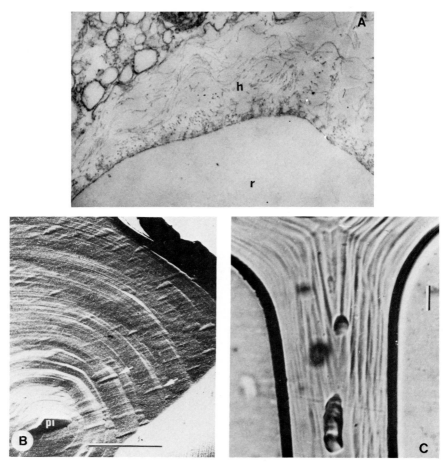

Figure 4-2 Some features of calcitic spicules. **A**. The spicule sheath (*h*) surrounding a decalcified spicule ray (*r*) of *Leucosolenia complicata*. Note the numerous collagen fibrils in the sheath (TEM) (×30,600) (Jones, 1967). (Reprinted by permission from *Nature, 214:*365–368. Copyright © 1967, Macmillan Journals Ltd.) **B**. Second-stage carbon replica of a ground, cross section of a triactine spicule ray of *Leucandra (Leuconia) nivea*. The concentric bands are obvious. Etch marks (*arrow*) and an etch pit (*pi*) are also visible (SEM). Scale bar: 10.0 μm (×1,980) (Ledger, 1976). **C**. First-stage plastic replica of a triactine of *Leucandra (Leuconia) nivea* showing longitudinal striations laid down during the growth of the calcite (light micrograph). Scale bar: 10.0 μm (×720) (Ledger, 1976). (**A**, courtesy Dr. W. C. Jones; **B, C**, courtesy Dr. P. W. Ledger.)

scopic data of Travis (1970), the latter appears a more likely possibility, but the presence of traces of organic material could also secondarily result in crystal imperfections. As suggested by Jones (1979b) consideration should be given to the possibility that varying degrees of hydration may contribute to these features, a situation also reported in siliceous spicules.

Calcareous spicules have been shown to be magnesium calcite (Jones and Jenkins, 1970) containing (by percentage weight) between 1.25 and 3.15% magnesium depending upon the species and the spicule type or size of the spicules (Table 4-2). The calcium carbonate occurs as calcite crystals, which have a highly ordered arrangement such that all crystals in a single spicule have the same orientation and the spicule thus acts like a single crystal of calcite (Jones, 1955a). Thus, the whole spicule has a single optic axis as determined by polarizing microscopy (Jones, 1954a). In addition to calcium and magnesium, these spicules also contain sodium and strontium as minor constituents as well as traces of silicon (as quartz), aluminum, barium, manganese, and lithium; sulfate is also present as a minor constituent (Table 4-3). There is a suggestion in the data on *Sycon ciliatum* that variations in minor and major (Mg) constituents are a result of differences in availability of these elements in different habitats (Table 4-2). Based upon X-ray diffraction and infrared spectroscopy, there are slight indications of the presence of traces of aragonite, but the presence of silicon interferes with these measurements to a large extent (Jones and Jenkins, 1970). There is no suggestion of the presence of vaterite, the third type of crystalline calcium carbonate. The specific

Table 4-2 Minor Elements in Calcareous Spicules[a]

		Percent by Weight			Si	Molar Percentage
		Mg	Sr	Na	So_4	(Quartz)	($MgCO_3$)
I. Species	SE: ±0.05	0.02	0.01	0.04		0.2
Leuconia nivea		2.75	0.22	0.55	0.91	tr	11.2
Clathrina coriacea		3.15	0.02	0.49	0.97	tr	12.9
Leucosolenia complicata		2.00	0.20	0.59	0.99	tr	8.2
Sycon ciliatum[b]		1.30	0.22	0.54	0.88	1.0	5.4
Sycon ciliatum[c]		1.25	0.25	0.56	1.11	1.0	5.2
Grantia compressa		1.90	0.20	0.66	0.95	tr	7.8
Amphiute paulini		2.10	0.22	0.55	1.00	tr	8.6
Leuconia pulima		2.40	0.22	0.59	0.82	tr	9.8
II. Spicule Types							
Leuconia nivea							
Micromonaxons		2.50	—	—	—	2.5	10.4
Small tri-/tetracts		2.60	—	—	—	1.0	10.6
Large triacts		2.65	0.21	0.58	—	tr	10.8
Giant triacts		2.80	0.21	0.53	0.90	tr	11.4

[a]Data taken from Jones and Jenkins (1970); standard errors (SE) are given below the elements.

[b,c]Sponges collected from two different localities.

Table 4-3 Chemical Constituents of the Spicules of *Leuconia nivea*[a]

	Spectrographic Analysis	Wet Chemical Analysis
Major constituents	Ca, Mg	—
Minor constituents	Na, Sr	SO_4^{2-}
Trace constituents	Al, Si (c. 100 ppm) Ba, Mn (c. 10 ppm) Li (c. 5 ppm)	
Not detectable	Ag, Co, Ga, Ni, Sc, V, Bi, Cu, La, Rb, Ti, Zn, Cd, Fe, Mo, Sb, Tl, Zr	Fe, K, Cl, PO_4^{3-}

[a]Data taken from Jones and Jenkins (1970).

gravity of spicules varies significantly from pure calcite, and this may be due to the presence of magnesium as well as other impurities including traces of organic matter derived from the spicule sheaths (Jones and Jenkins, 1970). The lower specific gravity (2.52–2.64) is certainly due to some extent to the presence of water in the spicules, which may occur in submicroscopic vesicles as well as water of hydration (Jones and Jenkins, 1970).

Little is known of the chemistry of the organic component(s) associated with calcareous spicules. Jones (1967, 1970) disputes the presence of an organic axial filament and considers the surrounding organic sheath as the only morphologically discrete organic component. On the other hand, as discussed previously, Travis (1970) has reported small (150 Å) and large (0.2 to 0.3 μm) fibrils in spicules following bulk analyses of cleaned spicules; these fibrils have a 625 Å repeating banding pattern and are considered by Travis as collagen. However, no convincing micrographs of banded fibrils occurring *within* the spicules themselves have appeared to date. The hydroxyproline content of the organic fraction of spicules is low, indicating that, of the total matrix, collagen is only a minor constituent (Travis, 1970). Amino acid analyses of the organic fraction are presented in Table 4-4. As discussed below, there appears to be no direct involvement of collagen fibrils in the early deposition of calcite; thus, there is no resolution of the question of whether collagen becomes incorporated *into* spicules, although this is very unlikely. It is clear, however, that fibrils *do* become associated with the sheath on its *outer* surface (Ledger and Jones, 1977).

Calcareous spicules generally occupy a definite position in the sponge tissue. For example, in *Leucosolenia complicata,* the triactines have their basal ray oriented parallel to the long axis of the oscular tube and the paired rays are parallel to the short axis (width) (Jones, 1954a). Tetrac-

Table 4-4 Composition of the Matrix Derived from Decalcified Spicules of *Scypha*[a]

Amino acids[b]			
Cystine (half)	17	Valine	45
3-Hydroxyproline	—	Methionine	4
4-Hydroxyproline	—	Isoleucine	27
Aspartic Acid	112	Leucine	44
Threonine	53	Tyrosine	10
Serine	86	Phenylalanine	16
Glutamic Acid	98	Hydroxylysine	6.6
Proline	71	Lysine	42
Glycine	221	Histidine	18
Alanine	86	Arginine	38
Hexosamines[c]	Moderate		

[a]Data taken from Travis *et al.* (1967).
[b]Amino acids expressed as number of molecules per 1,000 amino acid molecules.
[c]Hexosamines expressed as relative height of peaks compared to total micromoles of amino acids in the sample.

tines have approximately the same orientation with the gastral ray pushing in the mesohyl and lying at about right angles to the long axis of the oscular tube. Monactines protrude from the exopinacoderm at various angles. In the pharetronid, *Plectroninia vasseuri,* a number of layers of tetractines surround oscules with very precise orientation, forming an "oscular armature" (Vacelet, 1967a) (Fig. 4-3). Triactines, also with a regular arrangement, lie lateral to the oscular armature. A similar perioscular arrangement of tetractines occurs in *Monoplectroninia hispida* (Pouliquen and Vacelet, 1970). Monactines also lie at the surface and give to it a spiny texture. Numerous additional examples of spicule localization and arrangement could be cited, and these are to be found in the taxonomic literature. As a generalization, it can be stated that spicule types in many calcareous sponges have precise localizations, but numerous examples can be found of types with more than a single localization and some types may be imprecisely localized. Calcareous spicules only occur in members of the class Calcarea and as far as is known all are calcitic, although detailed chemical analyses have not been carried out on all groups.

Calcareous Scales

In a number of pharetronid sponges, individual calcareous scales make up part of the skeleton (Vacelet, 1970a, 1977a). The morphology of these scales (Fig. 4-3B) differs from calcareous spicules, but in one case, that of *Murrayona phanolepis,* a developmental series of scales strongly suggests that they are modified triactines in which the space between the rays has

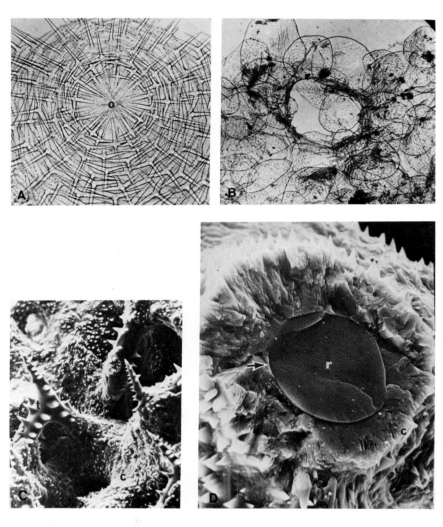

Figure 4-3 Pharetronid skeletons. **A**. Oscular armour of *Plectroninia vasseuri*. The perioscular calcitic spicules include inner tetractines and surrounding triactines; note their highly uniform arrangement. *o*, area of oscular opening (light micrograph) (×110) (Vacelet, 1967a). **B**. Calcitic scales of *Murrayona phanolepis*. Note roughening of one of the scale surfaces (light micrograph) (×60) (Vacelet, 1977a). **C**. The cemented skeleton of *Minchinella lamellosa* showing the spiny tetractines (*t*) embedded in a calcareous cement (*c*) (SEM) (×160) (Vacelet, 1981). **D**. Fractured ray (*r*) of a cemented tetractine of *Minchinella lamellosa*. The surrounding, spiny calcareous cement (*c*) is clearly separate from and laid down at the surface (*arrow*) of the spicule (SEM) (×1,035) (Vacelet, 1981). (All courtesy Dr. J. Vacelet.)

become calcified. It would be extremely interesting to have additional data on the orientation of the optic axis of these scales at various stages in their development since such data would help to evaluate the possibility that they are derived from a pattern like that found in calcareous spicules, which is assumed to be the case by Jones (1979b). Scales are also calcitic and tend to have specific localization in the sponge; in *Murrayona phanolepis* they form overlapping layers in the surface where oscules are present (see Fig. 1-5C,D) (Vacelet, 1977a). In *Paramurrayona,* structures resembling scales are present and are considered by Jones (1979b) as "plaques" since their crystalline orientation is irregular and they are seemingly polycrystalline, whereas the scales of *Murrayona* and of *Lepidoleucon* are apparently monocrystalline and thus like calcitic spicules.

Cemented Calcareous Spicules

Few sponges elaborate skeletons containing calcareous spicules which become cemented together to produce a massive portion of the skeleton. The types of spicules involved in such skeletons are triactines and tetractines usually with a spiny surface and frequently of unusual and/or irregular geometry (see Fig. 1-1). The spicules themselves are calcitic, but it is not known for sure what kind of material cements them together or how such cementing occurs. Earlier observations suggest the cement is calcitic, but it may also include an organic component (Jones, 1979b). Species of calcareous sponges producing such skeletons have been described in the subclass Pharetronida, notably in the family Minchinelidae, and include the genera *Plectroninia* and *Monoplectroninia* (Pouliquen and Vacelet, 1970; Vacelet, 1967a). Cemented triactines and tetractines frequently occur as a basal layer in the sponge and available data suggest that they occur *within* the mesohyl of the sponge and thus constitute an endoskeleton. The orientation of cemented spicules is highly predictable and consists of tetractines that are cemented together by their basal rays with the apical rays protruding upward and free of cement. A smaller-size category of tetractines may also be included and on occassion tuning fork spicules and thin monaxons are also incorporated in the cemented skeleton. Pouliquen and Vacelet (1970) have found that not all of the spicules in the basal skeleton are equally or similarly cemented and in some cases, as with the smaller tetractines of *Plectroninia hindei,* the spicules may simply be physically associated (articulating) without cementing (Fig. 4-4). On the other hand, in *Minchinella* there are substantial quantities of cementing material present in which the spicules are embedded (Vacelet, 1981) (Figs. 4-3C,D).

Aspicular Calcareous Deposits

Within the past fifteen years, a number of new living sponges have been discovered which elaborate relatively massive, aspicular, calcareous skeletons. Such skeletons have been known in a number of fossil groups,

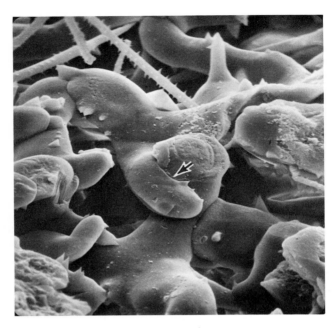

Figure 4-4   The cemented skeleton of the pharetronid *Plectroninia hindei*. Cementing only occurs at the junction of spicule surfaces (*arrow*) and no obvious extra spicular cementing material is seen. Compare with Fig. 4-3D (SEM) (×1,700) (Pouliquen and Vacelet, 1970). (Courtesy Dr. J. Vacelet.)

some of which, based upon these recent finds, can now be identified as sponges. Aspicular calcareous skeletons are secreted by sponges in the class Sclerospongiae and in the subclasses Pharetronida and Sphinctozoidia. In the former subclass, in both *Petrobiona massiliana* and *Murrayona phanolepis,* the "principal skeleton" (see Fig. 1-5) is constituted of microscopic spherulitic units of calcite (Vacelet, 1967a, 1977a) in which needle-like crystals radiate out from centers, although some fossil pharetronids from the upper Triassic may have deposited aragonite rather than calcite in their principal skeletons (Veizer and Wendt, 1976). There is no indication of an organic component in these skeletons. In both of the above species, the living sponge tissue occupies the upper surface of the principal skeleton with the choanosome occurring in the spaces within the solid calcite. In *Petrobiona,* trabecular cords of cells reach down into the skeleton. There is no suggestion that the principal skeleton lies within the organism; available observations suggest that it is extraorganismal and thus an exoskeleton.

A living member of the fossil group Sphinctozoidia, *Neocoelia crypta,* lays down a massive aragonitic skeleton which forms chambers in tiers (see Fig. 1-6B); each tier apparently representing a period of new growth

(Vacelet, 1977b, 1979b). There is an organic matrix present in the skeleton and abundant collagen fibrils are associated with the aragonite (Vacelet, 1979b). There are no visible microscopic units in the aragonite such as spherulites suggesting that the aragonite deposition pattern differs significantly from that of the sclerosponges. At the surface of the aragonite, numerous, relatively uniform pores are present in the skeleton serving as passageways for incurrent canals. Centrally there is a channel leading to a single oscule which may be a secondary oscule (see Chap. 6).

Among the Sclerospongiae, aspicular, calcareous skeletons are always formed and these are either calcitic as in *Acanthochaetetes wellsi* (see Fig. 1-7) (Hartman and Goreau, 1975) and *Tabulospongia japonica* (Mori, 1977) or aragonitic as in *Ceratoporella nicholsoni* (see later, Fig. 4-19) (Hartman and Goreau, 1972), *Stromatospongia vermicola,* and other members of the order Ceratoporellida (Hartman and Goreau, 1970, 1972; Hartman, 1969) and in *Calcifibrospongia actinostromarioides* (Hartman, 1979) and other stromatoporoids. Among some ceratoporellids and in *Acanthochaetetes* an outer, calcareous covering layer, the epitheca, is present in young sponges and basally in older ones (Hartman and Goreau, 1972). In the sclerosponges in general, the aragonite (or calcite) is macroscopically arranged in the form of calicles or crevices at the surface. These occur in a number of patterns but in all cases the living sponge tissue occupies them as well as covers their upper surfaces. In the ceratoporellids, below the level of the calicles is a solid aragonitic skeleton containing entrapped siliceous spicules and proteinaceous fibers. In *Merlia,* however, siliceous spicules occur only within the living sponge tissue and the calicles are walled off horizontally at intervals and those below the surface layer do not become filled in with aragonite, resulting in a skeleton which is not completely solid. In other species, the aragonite, which fills in the calicles basally, is in the form of needles which radiate from centers (sclerodermites) thus giving the skeleton a microscopic subunit structure of radiating centers (spherulites or sclerodermites) (Hartman and Goreau, 1972). In the tabulospongid, *Acanthochaetetes wellsi,* the calicles, which are interconnected by pores, continue down in the basal calcitic skeleton but are interrupted by horizontal walls at intervals and the siliceous spicules are only present within the living tissue at and near the surface of the sponge, a morphological pattern similar to that in *Merlia.* Also in *Acanthochaetetes,* a fibrous matrix is present in the calicle wall following decalcification. The calcite is in the form of stacked lamellae, which themselves consist of irregularly arranged, needle-shaped units of calcite (Hartman and Goreau, 1975). In the recently described sclerosponge, *Calcifibrospongia actinostromarioides,* the aragonite is impregnated with an organic framework which, when the aragonite is removed, has the same shape as the aragonite (Hartman, 1979). The aragonite in this relict stromatoporoid thus impregnates a reticulate meshwork of organic material and siliceous spicules. Among the sclerosponges there is no indication that the aspicular calcite or aragonite is contained within the mesohyl but rather that the sponge covers the calcareous skeleton at its surface.

With the recent description of numerous living species that form massive, aspicular, calcareous skeletons has come an elaborate terminology and classification schemes to describe the microstructure of the calcareous material. Jones (1979b) recognizes four basic patterns of microstructure of the calcareous deposits: (1) pencillate or water jet (as in *Merlia*), (2) spherulitic (the most common), (3) orthogonal (referring to the cement in *Minchinella*), and (4) laminar (as in *Acanthochaetetes*). In *Neocoelia* no pattern is recognizable. An upsurge in the microscopic description of calcareous skeletons has occurred and efforts are being directed toward developing a uniform terminology for both living and fossil forms (Wendt, 1979; Cuif *et al.,* 1979). Despite this and Jone's elegantly clear categorization, there are immense problems remaining, which can best be appreciated by reference to a recent volume dealing with fossil sponges (Hartman *et al.,* 1980).

The Secretion of Calcareous Spicules

In his thoroughgoing review of sponge spicules, Minchin (1909) reiterates the then more prevalant view that calcareous spicules are formed intracellularly in distinction to nineteenth-century (and some twentieth-century) views of an extracellular origin of these calcitic concretions. The question of intra- versus extracellular origin has now been finally, and fully resolved by the electron microscopic studies of Ledger (1975, 1976) and Ledger and Jones (1977). These workers have clearly shown the intercellular nature of calcite deposition and their observations have further made clear the necessity for ultrastructural analyses in order to resolve this question. These investigations also establish that the sclerocytes are cellular, not syncytial as previously stated in the early literature. The following morphological description of calcareous spicule secretion, with the exception of the newer observations of Jones (1967), Ledger (1975, 1976), and Ledger and Jones (1977) is based upon light microscopic studies and upon reviews by Minchin (1909), Jones (1970), and more briefly by Ledger and Jones (1977).

The secretion of monaxons is initiated by a scleroblast (a cell predestined to become a sclerocyte) derived from the exopinacoderm (or, more rarely, from the endopinacoderm). This cell divides to form what was referred to as a "binucleate" sclerocyte. Based upon recent ultrastructural data, which establish that these two nuclei occur in separate cells, it is unlikely that what was described as binucleate cells actually are so. Within the elongate sclerocytes a rod appears and the (inner) cell closer to the choanocyte layer, referred to as the "founder cell," moves closer to the choanocytes, while the "thickener cell" remains close to the pinacoderm. The founder cell is thought to be responsible for pushing the spicule outward during calcite deposition so that the spicule protrudes beyond the sponge surface. As this protrusion occurs, the thickener cell is viewed as thickening the spicule. The very large (giant) monactinal spicules of some calcareous sponges have variously been reported to have one, two, or more sclerocytes associated with them; however, detailed studies of the deposition of such giant spicules have not been reported. Growth of the calcitic spicule rays occurs at rates of 1.0 to 5.0 μm/h (Ledger, 1976; Jones, 1964b).

Triactine spicules are secreted in a fashion comparable to that of monactinals with two sclerocytes involved in the secretion of *each* ray. Initially there is a trio of cells purported to undergo mitosis to produce three binucleate cells. This sextet of nuclei has also been described as a syncytium, but based upon the recent data these views are no longer tenable. The actual division of the cells has never been documented but obviously must occur (see Jones, 1970). The six nuclei may lie in interdigitating planes such that a rosette is formed (Jones, 1970). The initial calcite is deposited within the center of the sextet of cells (Figs. 4-5A,B) and then one (the thickener) of each pair of cells moves outward, depositing a ray as it progresses (Fig. 4-5C, 4-6). Jones (1979a) has indirectly established in *Sycon* that the pool of sclerocytes for both monaxon and triradiate spicules is the same. Thus, if the number of rays being secreted at given times is plotted, a straight line results. In newly metamorphosed larvae of *Sycon ciliatum* monaxons are secreted first and when triradiates appear the rate of monaxon production is greatly decreased by a number equal to the total number of rays of triradiates which are then appearing.

In tetractines, the same sequence has been reported but a seventh sclerocyte joins the sextet after a spicule primordium is laid down and this cell initiates the fourth (apical) ray. This seventh cell has been reported to be derived from a porocyte or endopinacocyte and it may remain undivided or divide once or twice to produce two or four sclerocytes. The division products have also been reported to be syncytial, but again, this conclusion is now no longer tenable. The fate of sclerocytes, once a spicule has matured, is not clear although there are early reports that these cells move back into the mesohyl (see Minchin, 1909).

The junctions of the closely applied sclerocytes which are cooperatively involved in calcite deposition are septate (see Fig. 4-7A) (Ledger, 1975). These septa even occur between different regions of the same plasmalemma when a sclerocyte spirals or curves back on itself. Each septum has a wider central region attaching to two (or sometimes three) plasmalemmae by a narrower neck. The junctions in which septa occur contain membranes that are 15–20 nm apart; the central thick region of the septum may be a repeating unit in the septal system. These septate junctions likely form an impenetrable barrier around the intercellular

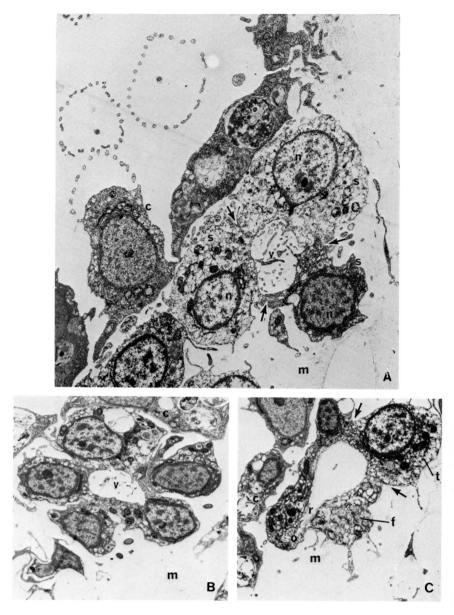

Figure 4-5 The secretion of the calcitic spicules in *Sycon ciliatum* demonstrating the *inter*cellular localization of spicule deposition (TEMs, decalcified). **A.** Three of six sclerocytes (*s*) during early triactine deposition. The calcite is being deposited within an intercellular cavity (*v*) partitioned off by the cells whose junctions (*arrows*) are septate. *n*, nucleus; *c*, choanocytes; *m*, mesohyl (×3,780) (Ledger, 1976). **B.** A sextet of sclerocytes initiating calcite deposition of a triactine. *v*, intercellular cavity in which calcite is deposited. *m*, mesohyl; *c*, choanocyte (×3,690) (Ledger, 1976). **C.** Early secretion of one ray (*r*) of a triactine showing founder (*f*) and thickener (*t*) cells and their junctions (*arrows*). *o*, converging spaces; *m*, mesohyl; *c*, choanocyte (×2,970) (Ledger, 1976). (All courtesy Dr. P. W. Ledger.)

space in which calcite is crystallized and importantly could also serve as a means of coupling the activities of the sclerocytes (Ledger, 1975).

The elegant electron microscopic studies of young stages in spicule secretion have yielded new and exciting information on calcite deposition (Ledger, 1976; Ledger and Jones, 1977). Sclerocytes of monaxons, triactines, and tetractines in *Sycon ciliatum* were shown in all cases to be unicellular and joined by septate junctions. The calcite was demonstrated to be crystallized extracellularly within a thin organic sheath in an intercellular space that is effectively cut off from the mesohyl in early stages of deposition. This space is bounded by the sclerocytes and their septate junctions. The tips of spicule rays occur in association with "dense cups," which consist of the blind ends of large pockets formed by the founder sclerocyte in the case of triactines and tetractines. In the case of monaxons, dense cups are present at both ends of the spicule in both founder and thickener cells (Fig. 4-6). This clearly suggests that the older view that only the founder cell is responsible for growth in length is erroneous and that the protrusion of the monaxon from the wall of the sponge is not solely due to its activity (Ledger and Jones, 1977). Convincingly, Ledger (1976) has demonstrated the incorporation of ^{45}Ca into the calcite which is laid down by the thickener as well as the founder cells secreting monactines. Just proximal to the spicule tips are "converging spaces" (Fig. 4-6) formed by a complex inpocketing of the sclerocyte plasmalemma, undoubtedly representing sites of high secretory activity.

The structure of sclerocytes is similar to that of the pinacocytes (Ledger, 1976) from which they are derived. There appears to be only a single morphological type of sclerocyte, regardless of the spicule type being secreted, which can be considered a megasclerocyte. These cells contain nucleolate nuclei, mitochondria, a few phagosomes, well-developed Golgi bodies, cytoplasmic filaments (Figs. 4-7C,D), sparse rough endoplasmic reticulum, and smooth-surfaced vesicles. The latter are often abundant in sclerocytes (Fig. 4-7B) and some of them are part of a cytoplasmic "tubule" system. Electron microscopic cytochemical localization of calcium (potassium antimonate method) has shown that pinacocytes, choanocytes, and sclerocytes all contain calcium sites in the nucleus, nucleolus, along the cytoplasmic face of the plasmalemma, and on the outer surface of smooth membraned vesicles (Ledger, 1976). In sclerocytes these sites are prominent on, and sometimes in, the latter vesicles particularly in the region of the spicule tips. Calcium also occurs in an orderly array in cisternae of the Golgi and on the cytoplasmic surface of the converging spaces and tubes. These results suggest that sclerocytes have amplified calcium transport and binding systems which are also present in other cell types and have not developed unique structural systems (Ledger, 1976). The absence of demonstrable Ca *in* the converging spaces is unexpected and may be artifactual since no Ca is found localized within spicule rays using this technique either.

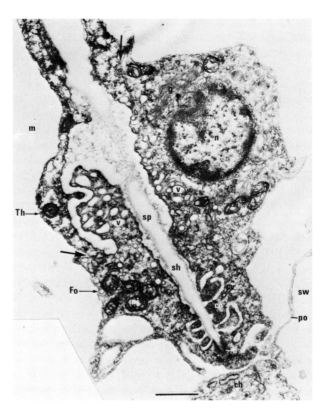

Figure 4-6 The growing tip of a monactine calcitic spicule of *Sycon ciliatum*, decalcified. Junctions (*arrows*) of founder (*Fo*) and thickener (*Th*) cells are indicated. The spicule sheath (*sh*) is visible as a thin surrounding "membrane." *ch*, choanocyte; *co*, converging spaces; *cv*, coated vesicle; *d*, dense cup; *g*, Golgi; *m*, mesohyl; *mi*, mitochondrion; *n*, nucleus; *po*, porocyte; *sp*, space resulting from decalcification; *sw*, sea water; *v*, smooth membrane vesicle (TEM). Scale bar: 1.0 μm (×11,000) (Ledger, 1976). (Courtesy Dr. P. W. Ledger.)

The organic sheath which always surrounds the crystallizing calcite is viewed as providing a space conducive to such crystallization and is not considered to be involved in determining the mineral morph (calcite) formed or the specific orientation of the crystals (Ledger and Jones, 1977). No ordered, organic matrix is present within the spicule nor are collagen fibrils. Although somewhat presumptuous, one is tempted to suggest that the spicule sheath may contain, either temporally or regionally, charge distributions and possibly dissociable ions which could directly influence the crystallization form and pattern. Ledger and Jones (1977) suggest the possible involvement of a bioelectric field and there is no reason why the sheath could not be involved in such a field. Among the

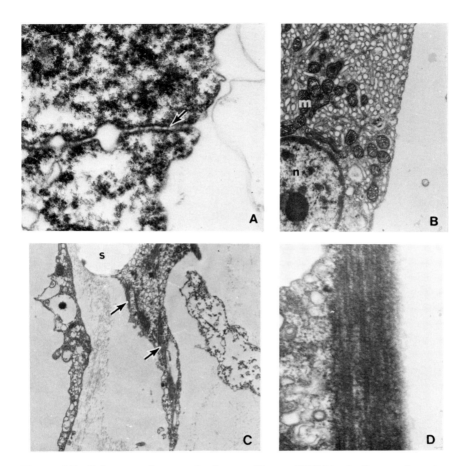

Figure 4-7   Sclerocyte features in *Sycon ciliatum* (TEMs). **A**. Septate junction (*arrow*) between sclerocytes (×49,500) (Ledger, 1976). **B**. Vesiculated sclerocyte cytoplasm. *m*, mitochondria; *n*, nucleolate nucleus (×7,560) (Ledger, 1976). **C**. Bundles of filaments (*arrows*) in sclerocyte cytoplasm. *s*, space previously occupied by calcite (×6,300) (Ledger, 1976). **D**. Detail of filament bundle in sclerocyte cytoplasm (×37,800) (Ledger, 1976). (All courtesy Dr. P. W. Ledger.)

many, critical, outstanding problems is the question of how the optic axis of spicules is determined in relation to the various morphologies of spicules and, further, what causes this axis as well as the morphology to be different in different parts of the tissue. These and other morphogenetic questions are dealt with below.

Ledger (1976) has found that there is no basis for the claim that calcitic spicules contain an internal axial filament. Following decalcification, the collapse of the spicule sheath produces a thin "filament" which is an artifact (Fig. 4-8). The use of uranyl acetate for spicule decalcification

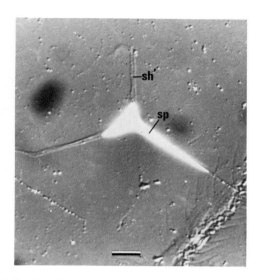

Figure 4-8 Partially decalcified triactine (*sp*) of *Sycon ciliatum*. The spicule sheath (*sh*) has collapsed producing the appearance of an "axial filament" (Nomarski interference micrograph). Scale bar: 10.0 μm (×700) (Ledger, 1976). (Courtesy Dr. P. W. Ledger.)

results in a thicker sheath which can be collapsed by further treatment with HCl. The fact that the "filament" is hollow belies its origin from the sheath which has collapsed.

Factors Affecting Calcareous Spicule Secretion

Employing newly attached and actively metamorphosing larvae of *Sycon ciliatum*, Jones (1971) has studied the effects of varying calcium and carbonate (in the form of bicarbonate, HCO_3) concentrations on spicule secretion. Artificial seawater containing from 0.00 to 10.0 mM Ca and 0.00 to 2.5 mM HCO_3 were used as incubation media for larvae. In order for spicule secretion to occur (at 14°C) both the calcium and the bicarbonate must be greater than about 1.0 mM. In media containing less than these concentrations, spicules previously formed in control media underwent corrosion (dissolution). The rate of corrosion was unaffected by whether the sponge was living, occurring at the same or a higher rate in spicules still within the sponge tissue, but fixed in alcohol. In all experimental media except one, transfer of the young sponges back to normal seawater resulted in a restoration of spiculogenesis within 48 h. Only when no calcium was originally present was there no recovery. Corroded spicules were never remoulded or repaired after such transfers to normal seawater. It was further found that the formation of a functional canal system (with choanocytes) is not a prerequisite in order for spiculogenesis to be initiated during normal metamorphosis as well as in sponges recovering from calcium or bicarbonate deficiency. These results are of much interest, as discussed below, relative to views of the determinants of spicule morphology.

In more recent studies, also of newly metamorphosed larvae of *Sycon,* Ledger (1976) and Jones (1979a) have established that in artificial or modified seawater, as the calcium concentration is increased from the range of 1.0–3.5 mM up to 20 mM that (1) more spicules are formed, (2) their growth rates are increased, and (3) their final lengths are greater. Unexpectedly, at 40 mM Ca fewer spicules are formed and many of them have aberrant morphology (Ledger, 1976). This result is reminiscent of the effect of abnormally high concentrations of silicic acid on the secretion of siliceous spicules (see later) and there may be an unsuspected similarity in the two mineralization systems relative to these conditions. An inhibitor of carbonic anhydrase, Diamox (acetazolamide), mimics the lowering of calcium concentration when present in the range of 10^{-3} to 10^{-7} M. Transfer of sponges from Diamox or low calcium to normal seawater results in rapid recovery of close to normal spicule formation. A still unexplained effect of Diamox is the usual absence of one ray in triactine spicules.

In pieces of the stretched wall of *Leucosolenia complicata,* growth rates of the basal (unpaired) ray of triactines was higher than that for the paired rays initially, but the rates became similar at 1.29–2.5 μm/h (Jones, 1959). The growth rate is dependent to some extent upon the length of the ray; shorter rays (less than 5.0 μm) grow more slowly in length than longer ones. Growth rates of spicule rays in whole (unstretched) oscular tubes were also found to be within this range, the stretching seemingly having little effect. Growth rates of monactinal spicules (1.53–1.59 μm/h) also were similar.

Studies of spiculogenesis in calcareous sponges is severely limited due to the difficulty of maintaining the animals under controlled conditions and investigations of the effects of temperature and other factors have not been reported although using the techniques developed by Jones some basic experiments dealing with such factors are now possible.

Morphogenetic and Developmental Aspects of Calcareous Spicule Secretion

There are two important features of calcareous spicules that make them both useful and interesting models for studying questions of morphogenesis: first, each spicule type has a precise geometry including its optic axis and second, spicules in many calcareous sponges have relatively precise and predictable spatial orientation within the tissue. Jones (see his 1970 review for references) has carried out extensive and detailed studies of spicule geometry and orientation. Indeed, two major processes can be recognized: (1) the determination of specific spicule morphology and (2) the determination of the orientation of spicules relative to the morphology

of the whole sponge. The first of them (spicule morphology) can occur in
the absence of the second (orientation) (Jones, 1971).

In his investigations, Jones (1954a,b) has found (Fig. 4-9) that the optic
angle (the angle of inclination of the optic axis relative to the basal ray of
triactines and tetractines) is greatest (30–33°) at the oscular rim and decreases, fairly abruptly, to about 21–23° at some 200–400 μm below the
oscular rim in *Leucosolenia complicata*. Since the basal rays are parallel
to the wall of the oscular tube, the angle between the optic axis and the
wall of the tube (=angle of inclination) also decreases in the same manner.
In tetractines particularly, but also in triactines, the planar angle (the

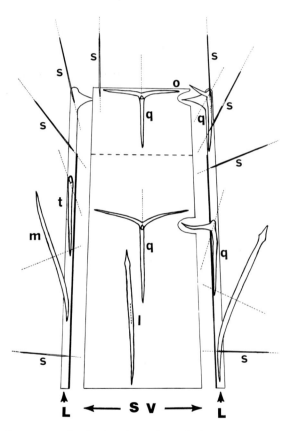

Figure 4-9 Summary of spicule orientation relative to the oscular tube of *Leucosolenia complicata*. The optic axes of each spicule are indicated by a broken line.
m, curved monaxon without lance head; *l*, lance-headed monaxon; *q*, tetractine
(=quadriradiate); *s*, slender monaxon; *t*, triactine (=triradiate); *L*, longitudinal
sectional view; *SV*, surface view. Dashed horizontal line represents the limit of
choanocytes above which endopinacocytes line the cavity. The oscular (*o*) edge
occurs distal to them (approx. ×200) (Jones, 1954a). (Courtesy Dr. W. C. Jones.)

unpaired angle between the oscular rays) is also greatest near the oscule, but there is no correlation in *individual* spicules between the planar and the optic angles. The length of the basal rays also varies with distance from the oscule, their length being greater beginning about 400 μm below the oscule and continuing to the base of the tube (Fig. 4-10) (Jones, 1954b). This is true only for the "outer" triactines and tetractines which are mature spicules. The "inner" ones (closer to the choanocytes) present a wide range of basal ray lengths since they are in various stages of maturation. The curvature of lance-headed monaxons is independent of distance from the oscule (Jones, 1954a). The grastral ray of tetractines, which protrudes into the atrium, in and near the oscule (where there are no choanocytes) curves upward in the direction of the water current and has no region which is perpendicular to the optic axis, whereas gastral rays below the oscule have (1) a short region perpendicular to the optic axis, followed by (2) a short region perpendicular to the choanoderm, followed by (3) a curvature in the direction of the oscule.

On purely crystallographic grounds, oscular rays should always have a planar angle of 120°; since this is not the case, and since the crystallo-

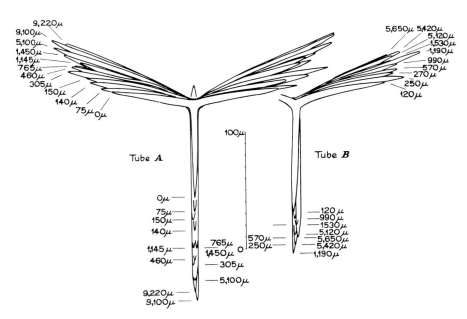

Figure 4-10   Representations in two different individuals (Tubes A and B) of tri- and tetractines showing the dependence of oscular ray curvature and basal ray length on the distance of the spicules from the oscule. In each drawing, the ray curvatures are shown and the distance of each spicule from the oscule is indicated in micrometers. Similarly the basal ray lengths and the distances from the oscule are also shown. The data establish a strict correlation of oscular ray curvature with distance from the oscule (×320) (Jones, 1954a). (Courtesy Dr. W. C. Jones.)

graphic orientation remains uniform throughout the whole spicule, one is led to seek factors that could cause smaller planar angles basally in the sponge. Jones (1955a) has suggested that the ground substance of the sponge is spirally arranged and that there is tighter packing at the oscule with a gradation toward less packing as one moves basally. This static arrangement could account for the varying planar angles if the ground substance is, indeed, involved in directing the morphogenesis of the oscular rays. Such a difference in packing of the ground substance could also be a factor in determining the length of the basal rays which would meet less resistance basally in the sponge tissue.

Uniplanar curvature of oscular rays and of curved monaxons may be related to a displacement of the founder cell by the choanoderm which is viewed as deflecting the ray and shifting the founder cell to one side of the ray (Jones, 1955a). This results in a preferential deposition of calcite on one side and thus the curvature of the resulting ray. This view is further supported by the finding that crystallization occurs preferentially on the transverse surfaces (those at right angles) of the rays under experimental conditions (Fig. 4-11).

The orientation of spicules—basal rays pointing basally, oscular rays lying transversely—was hypothesized to be due to shear in the ground substance which causes a specific orientation of the founder and thickener cells (Jones, 1965). However, available data are now inconsistent with this view (Jones, 1970) although shear could still play some role in spicule orientation. The direction of the water current produced by the sponge in the oscular tube amazingly effects the orientation of newly forming spicules. If an oscular tube is mounted on a water jet with the original basal end farthest from the jet, new spicules at the end of the tube have a reversed orientation with the basal rays pointing toward the original oscular rim (Jones, 1958). Also, within diverticula (outpocketings) of the wall of the oscular tube the basal rays are directed outward away from the sponge despite the resulting reversal in orientation of some of them. The mechanism of orientation is thus highly labile.

The major problem of spicule orientation and morphology still remains: How do the founder cells become specifically oriented so that, as they secrete calcite, variations in their orientation occur producing differences in optic and planar angles and uniplanar curvatures? The data strongly indicate that mechanical forces lie at the basis of these phenomena (Jones, 1970). However, it is not known whether the founder cell for the basal rays is *induced* to become a basal founder or whether the sclerocyte is somehow *predetermined* as such. The capacity to at all secrete specific spicule types resides in the ability of sclerocytes (three individual cells) to initially become associated with one another in a particular configuration and it is this intrinsic property that is not understood. It is clear that sclerocytes are able to become associated and carry out spicule secretion in the absence of the formation of choanocytes and the adult morphologi-

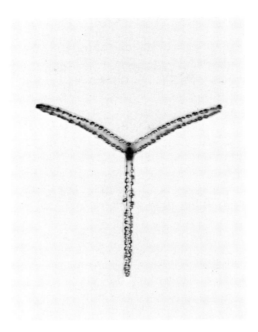

Figure 4-11 Experimentally induced crystallization of calcium carbonate crystals on the surface of a tetractine of *Leucosolenia complicata*. All of the deposited crystals have the same crystallographic orientation as the calcite in the spicule itself. The crystals on the paired rays are bilateral while those on the basal ray are in four rows. The relationship of the orientation of the experimentally deposited crystals to the spicule rays is indicative of the orientation of the spicular crystallographic axis relative to the spicule's geometry (light micrograph) ($\times 250$) (Jones, 1955a). (Courtesy Dr. W. C. Jones.)

cal pattern (Jones, 1971) and thus it is clear that the mechanical properties of the ground substance as they occur in the adult are not mandatory for the appearance of spicules.

Once associated, mechanical forces are theoretically able to influence the relative position of the sclerocytes as they progressively deposit calcite. Since it is now known that crystallization is an intercellular phenomenon it is easier to envisage outside forces as having an effect upon the extracellular cavity into which calcium is secreted. Jones (1954a) originally postulated the presence of organic "rodlets" within the sclerocytes which were supposedly precisely oriented and structurally fixed and acted as a predetermined core around which calcite is deposited. It is now known that no such core exists (Ledger and Jones, 1977); however, it is known that the sclerocytes are anchored by septa and this system of firmly attached cell membranes could result in the formation of a geometrically, predetermined, intercellular space which functionally acts as a "rodlet" in which calcite accumulates within an organic sheath. The septal system would then act by forming a rigid, negative mould of the young spicule. The contours of such a mould could be affected by outside mechanical forces as they impinge upon the sclerocytes in different parts of the sponge. The basis for the establishment of a crystallographic orientation that is uniform throughout a spicule is unknown but must involve the interactions of calcium and carbonate ions with substances contained in the "liquor" of the intercellular cavity (Ledger and Jones, 1977). The dense cups in the sclerocytes at the spicule tips may be sites which influence crystal orientation and they also could, as the sclerocytes move outward, act as dynamic secreting centers for crystallization. In conjunction with the converging spaces and septate junctions these components possibly *functionally* fulfill the abandoned view of an organic rodlet in sclerocytes.

The rate of appearance of new spicules was found to be correlated with the growth in length of the oscular tube (Jones, 1965). New spicules however, appeared randomly within growing areas both in terms of time and spacial distribution. Thus, the differentiation of scleroblasts may also be random and possibly is related to the availability of progenitor cells rather than to any predictable pattern of sclerocyte initiation. If this is the case, the site and timing of sclerocyte initiation are directly dependent upon the activities of the pinacocytes, from which they are derived. In young sponges, a direct relationship between porocyte distribution (which is supposedly spiral) and spicule distribution has been reported (see Jones, 1955a). Although porocyte and spicule arrangements during later growth in older regions of the sponge do not appear related, the situation is quite complex to follow because pores can undergo closure and opening and new pores can form (Jones, 1964a). Thus, it is still possible that there is a continuing relationship between porocyte and spicule distribution that may be more than just a spatial association; the two may be fundamentally related in terms of the origin of sclerocytes.

The mitosis of sclerocytes has never been documented so that it is still possible that the trio of cells initiating sextet formation is derived from two cells only one of which divides. Division of the trio could then result in six cells. This is more than simply a question of the sequence of divisions. If one of two cells divides to form the trio then the descendants of the dividing cell may contain less cytoplasm than the third cell and if this were so, the sextet would contain four smaller cells which form the oscular rays and two larger cells which form the basal ray. The longer length of the basal ray could thus be a result of cell size (=capacity for calcification). Only future investigations will shed light on these and other possible events involved in determining spicule morphology and orientation. As in siliceous sponges, calcareous species (*Leucosolenia*) have been shown to lose spicules to the environment during early growth (Jones, 1964b). Such loss, although possibly accidental, may be involved in the regulation of the skeleton in these young animals.

The Secretion of Other Calcareous Structures

The bases of secretion of calcareous scales, the cementing of calcareous spicules, and the formation of massive, aspicular, calcareous skeletons are scarcely known. Calcareous scales secreted by *Murrayona phanolepis* appear to take their origin as triactines (Vacelet, 1977a). If these structures actually are modified, three-rayed spicules one would expect to find them initiated by sextets of slcerocytes; however, the process whereby the spaces between the rays become filled in with calcite is likely quite different from their initiation. Also, Vacelet (1977a) figures scales as having two different types of surfaces, one side is smooth and the other is roughened by small, somewhat uniformly shaped "lumps" (see Fig. 4-3B) suggesting some basic difference in the calcification process on each side.

The cementing of calcareous spicules is also poorly understood. In some cases it may be due to an actual fusion of parts of spicules, in others to the "gluing together" of spicules, and in still others only to a close physical association (articulation) of spicule parts. Hypochlorite is ineffective in dissolving or loosening the cementing in one case (Vacelet, 1967a). If spicules are actually fused together this could imply a confluence of the intercellular cavities of separate sets of sclerocytes. Alternatively, and more likely, a secondary gluing of regions of spicules could occur through the intervention of cells not included in the sextets. In the case of spicules which become articulated without cementing or fusion, the thickener sclerocytes of the two spicules would have to be involved in a special morphogenetic pattern resulting in such articulation. Despite a scanning electron microscope study, it is still not clear what "cementing" means in all cases (Pouliquen and Vacelet, 1970). However, based upon more recent observations (Vacelet, 1981), it is now clear that at least two different types of spicule cementing occur in pharetronids: in one, surfaces of neighboring spicules are "glued" together as just discussed (see Fig. 4-4); in the second, substantial secondary calcareous deposits enrobe calcitic spicules (see Figs. 4-3C,D). These secondary deposits may become relatively massive and thus reminiscent of sclerosponge and other pharetronid skeletons.

Such aspicular calcareous skeletons are likewise poorly understood in terms of the cellular processes and cell types involved in their elaboration. In the case of sclerosponge aragonite, the ends of siliceous spicules could act as inducers for the initiation of centers of calcification (Hartman, 1969; Hartman and Goreau, 1970). However, the spicule ends are themselves encased in an organic matrix (possibly collagenous) and it may be that the organic matrix acts as the inducer. In any event, a direct relationship between silicification and/or matrix elaboration on the one hand and calcification on the other is clearly suggested. But, not all aragonite-producing sponges have siliceous spicules embedded in the aragonite, as is the case in *Merlia*. The cells which are responsible for the elaboration of aragonite may be a special type, since in *Hispidoptera miniana* relatively large (10 to 20 μm) cells are clustered at the base of the sponge tissue which is in contact with the aragonite (Hartman, 1969). These cells have very long processes, suggesting their possible involvement in calcification. The morphology of the aragonite (with pits, crevices, protruding spicules) at the surface of the sponge seems to be determined by an interaction between the calcification process and the contours of the sponge tissue. In *Ceratoporella nicholsoni,* new pits arise by the subdivision of old ones (Hartman and Goreau, 1972) and since each pit is precisely related to the incurrent pores of the sponge (Hartman, 1969), there must be a tightly coupled morphogenetic pattern between calcification and tissue growth and differentiation which results in the "calicle-incurrent pore relationship." In some sclerosponges with aragonitic skeletons (*Ceratoporella, Stromatospongia*) the aragonite below the surficial exhalant canals is "eroded" such that the pattern of exhalant canals is etched into the aragonite surface. In two other genera (*Goreauiella, Hispidoptera*) such etching is not present but the uppermost surface of the aragonite is irregular and discontinuous so that etching may occur but may not be easily discernible. Etching is an interesting phenomenon which could suggest that the concentration of calcium in the exhalant water is such that an appropriate concentration gradient cannot be maintained on the undersurface of the canals; alternatively, following calcification the absence of a maintainable gradient could result in local decalcification (etching). The origin of the epitheca in sclerosponges is unknown and its differing structure (Hartman, 1969) indicates some modulation of the calcification process.

The aspicular, aragonitic skeleton of a living sphinctozoid (*Neocoelia*) lacks the sclerodermite microstructure in other aragonitic skeletons indicating a significant difference in the pattern of crystallization. The absence of entrapped siliceous spicules in this sponge does not appear to be the cause for the lack of sclerodermites since in *Merlia* sclerodermites are present but entrapped spicules are not (Hartman and Goreau, 1970). The very regular, box-like, tiered pattern of the aragonite in *Neocoelia* and the centrally placed, common exhalant passageway must require precise and repetitive developmental processes linking calcification to the growth of the tissue. The tiers of chambers are supported by pillars and basally the spaces between the pillars are filled in with secondary deposits of aragonite. Consequently, as in many sclerosponges, a second set of calcification processes ensues after the initial box-like arrangement is laid down (Vacelet, 1979b).

The calcitic, aspicular deposits of some pharetronids may be due to less highly organized processes since, as in *Petrobiona,* the calcite does not have a highly ordered morphological pattern. In *Murrayona phanolepis,* on the other hand, the aspicular skeleton forms openings which house oscules only on one side of the sponge (see Fig. 1-5A), the remainder of the surface contains ostia (=incurrent surface). In *Petrobiona* there are very characteristic cords of cells radiating out of the tissue at the lowest levels; these cords are surrounded by calcite. Despite the demonstrated presence of large amounts of reserve substances in these cells and the conclusion that they therefore act as nutritive cells (Vacelet, 1964), there should be further consideration of the possibility that these trabecular cords are involved in calcification. The recently described sclerosponge, *Acanthochaetetes wellsi,* deposits massive amounts of aspicular calcite in a relatively well defined pattern reminiscent of other sclerosponges (Hartman and Goreau, 1975). In this sponge there is also a direct relationship between ostia and the calcites, there being one ostium per calicle, a pattern much like that in *Ceratoporella.* The calcite crystals in *Acanthochaetetes* occur in layers (lamellae) of needles and thus they are arranged in a pattern which differs from that in the calcitic skeletons of the pharetronids in which spheruliths (sclerodermites) are present. Similar developmental patterns to those discussed above must take place in this species.

Vacelet (1980) has described a new species of *Merlia, Merlia deficiens,* in which an aspicular, calcareous skeleton is not produced. Based upon this finding and other considerations Vacelet (1979b) considers that the formation of aspicular calcareous skeletons is a labile process and that many living demosponges without such skeletons are actually descendants of animals which originally formed them. He has consequently made the suggestion to place all the sclerosponges and sphinctozoids in the class Demospongise as orders (Table 1-6) (Vacelet, 1981).

Siliceous Deposits: Morphology, Chemistry, Distribution

Siliceous Spicules of Demosponges

Two size categories of spicules can be distinguished: longer megascleres and smaller microscleres. This size distinction, however, strictly applies only to spicules within the same species, since megascleres in some species can be relatively short in relation to them in other species. Despite this, in a majority of cases microscleres can be easily distinguished interspecifically both on the basis of their size and their morphology, and megascleres can be distinguished, although less easily, on the basis of their morphology. The latter all possess at least one morphological axis of symmetry and some have two, three, four, or more, notably among the tetractinomorph demosponges. Microscleres may have only a single axis of symmetry (such as raphides) but in the majority of them the symmetry is highly complex and does not lend itself to categorization based upon the number of axes present (but, see Chap. 1). Consequently, a highly diverse terminology has arisen for microscleres. Furthermore, some microscleres are ornamented in a fashion not following any symmetry. Megascleres that are ornamented generally possess short spines on their surface which are usually irregularly distributed. The full range of diversity of geometric shapes of siliceous spicules can be fully appreciated by reference to a recent review by Hartman (1981) in which scanning electron micrographs of almost every spicule type are presented. Since the silica in siliceous spicules is not crystalline, an analysis of their morphology cannot include considerations of the axes of crystalline structure as with calcitic spicules.

Siliceous spicules contain a thin, central core, the axial filament (Garrone et al., 1981; Garrone, 1969a; Simpson and Vaccaro, 1974; Schwab and Shore, 1971b) which, due to its different refractive index, is visible under certain circumstances in the light microscope. Axial filaments have been reported in both megascleres and microscleres (Fig. 4-12). Their presence in microscleres has been reported in the freshwater sponges *Heteromeyenia* sp. (Drum, 1968) and *Ephydatia mulleri* (Garrone et al., 1981) and in a marine demosponge, *Neofibularia irata* (Garrone et al., 1981; Wilkinson and Garrone, 1980a). In terms of the extensive diversity of microsclere structure and the limited number of observations, it is not known whether all microsclere types, and variants of them, contain axial filaments but this is likely. On the contrary, in megascleres from a fairly large sampling of different demosponge groups, filaments are routinely present (Reiswig, 1971c). These structures are usually quite thin having diameters at or below the limits of resolution of the light microscope. In fully developed, mature megascleres the central axis of the spicule may contain an axial canal (Fig. 4-12C) rather than an organic structure (Reiswig, 1971c; Garrone et al., 1981). Such canals occur as a result of the breakdown of a previously present axial filament and are frequently seen at the tips of spicules suggesting that they may be a result of the dissolution of the silica as well as of the axial filament (Garrone et al., 1981).

In the case of birotulate microscleres of *Heteromeyenia* sp., the filament subdivides at its ends (Fig. 4-12A) and thin branches are found in a one to one ratio within each spinous process of the spicule. In the spiny megascleres of *Ephydatia,* each short spine along its length contains a short branch of the centrally located axial filament (Pottu-Boumendil, 1975; Garrone et al., 1981). Etching (HF treatment) of ground sections of sterrasters reveals a radial pattern of canals originating from a center (Fig. 4-13A) (Rutzler and Macintyre, 1978). Each canal leads to a separate spine of the microsclere. The canals, doubtless, are cavities previously occupied by the axial filament. Reiswig (1971c) has suggested that the number of axes (rays) present in siliceous megascleres is related to the cross sectional shape (triangular) of the axial filament although additional hard data have yet to be collected to further validate this view. Much work remains to be undertaken in order to support the views that (1) all types of siliceous spicules contain a central, organic axial filament and (2) the branching of this filament lies at the basis of the establishment of the axes and surface features of these spicules. One case of a surface feature (swellings) has been reported in which there is no special branching of the

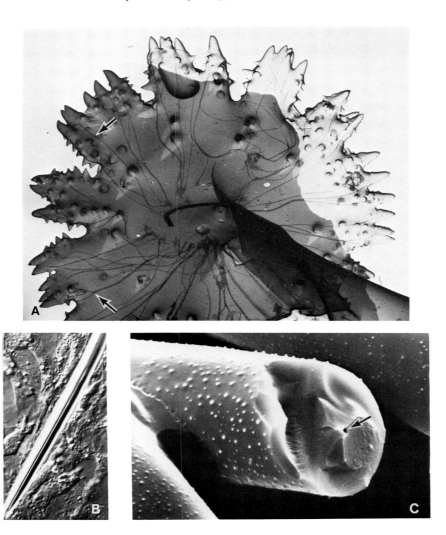

Figure 14-12   Axial filaments and axial canals in siliceous spicules. **A**. Carbon replica of one end of a birotule (see Fig. 8-7B) microsclere showing the branching of the axial filament (*arrows*) into each spine (TEM) (×3,645) (Drum, 1968). **B**. A megasclere (oxea) in *Ephydatia fluviatilis* showing the prominent central axial filament (Nomarski interference micrograph) (×360) (Garrone *et al.*, 1981). **C**. A fractured oxea of *Ephydatia fluviatilis* showing the axial canal (*arrow*) in which the axial filament was previously located (SEM) (×3,600) (Garrone *et al.*, 1981). (**A**, courtesy Dr. R. W. Drum; **B**, **C**, courtesy Dr. R. Garrone.)

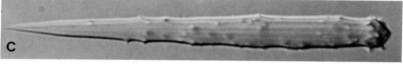

Figure 4-13 Axial structure of an aster and heterogeneity of the silica in siliceous spicules. **A**. Etched, ground section of a sterraster of *Geodia neptuni* showing the radial pattern of the axial canals (*arrows*). This represents convincing data that the axial filament of these microscleres originates from a center (SEM) (×1,350) (Rutzler and Macintyre, 1978). **B**. Cross section of a spicule from *Haliclona rosea* showing prominent, concentric discontinuities in the silica (TEM) (×85,500) (Garrone, 1969a). **C**. Longitudinal striping in a megasclere (acanthostyle) of *Microciona prolifera*. Such stripes are apparently equivalent to concentric rings sometimes seen in cross section in spicules (Nomarski interference micrograph) (×1,260) (Simpson, 1978). (**A**, courtesy Dr. K. Rutzler; **B**, courtesy Dr. R. Garrone.)

axial filament (Simpson, 1981). Bertoldi de Pomar (De Pomar, 1973) also reports a number of instances in which spines do not contain a branch of the filament.

In cross section, megascleres of some demosponges display concentric rings (Fig. 4-13B) which were considered to be due to either differences in the structure of the silica or to the presence of organic material (Butschli, 1901). Schwab and Shore (1971a) have recently shown in at least one case that concentric rings are due to higher levels of hydration than the surrounding silica. When heated to between 300 and 600°C the rings disappear and, using mass spectrometric analyses, water vapor is evolved over this temperature range. They have suggested that this difference in hydration occurs during pauses in the deposition of the silica. Recent scanning electron micrographs of a microsclere (aster) have also demonstrated the presence of comparable concentric rings (Rutzler and Macintyre, 1978). This should not, however, be taken to mean that all concentric structures are due to hydration—some indeed may turn out to be organic in nature.

The silicon which is present in siliceous spicules is in the form of amorphous (non crystalline), hydrated silica, a form of silicon known as opal (Schwab and Shore, 1971b; Vinogradov, 1953) or opaline silica (Kamatani, 1971) in which there is 6–13% water, yielding an approximate formula of $(SiO_2)_{2-5} \cdot H_2O$ (Schwab and Shore, 1971b). This formulation is in good agreement with the reported measurements in the earlier literature (Vinogradov, 1953). In *mature* spicules, the silica immediately surrounding the axial filament is more susceptible to etching with hydrofluoric acid (HF) than the more external silica (Schwab and Shore, 1971b; Vosmaer and Wijsman, 1905) suggesting higher levels of hydration (Vinogradov, 1953). But, in ultrathin secretions of *very young* spicules, etching may occur first at the periphery of the spicule (Simpson and Vaccaro, 1974). In these young spicules, the peripheral area may be comparable to the surface immediately surrounding the filament in *older* spicules.

A recent, thorough, analysis of the chemical composition of siliceous spicules following cleaning in boiling nitric acid has been carried out by Schwab and Shore (1971b) (Table 4-5). The data establish that there is an organic component present within the spicule which is freed by, but is resistant to, HF. Numerous other cations occur in trace amounts. The HF-resistant, organic component, the axial filament, has been further studied and its amino acid composition analyzed (Table 4-6). In the residue remaining following spicule treatment with 12 N HF, about 2% was determined as protein. Low-level incorporation of tritiated leucine into the axial filament fraction has also been demonstrated (Shore, 1972). Dissolution of the axial filament in the presence of citrate (in HF) suggests that a divalent cation is intimately involved in its stability. HF treatment alone does not dissolve the filament although it does make it more flexible. This and the following cited observation establish that silicon is tightly bound or associated with the filament. Garrone (1969a) has clearly shown that protein is contained within the axial filament and is necessary for its integrity. Using both transmission electron microscopy and X-ray diffraction analyses he demonstrated that the filament is susceptible to pepsin digestion, but only following removal of the silica with HF (Fig. 4-14). Based upon the data of both Shore (1972) and Garrone (1969a) the proteinaceous component of the axial filament is clearly *not* collagen. Although Travis *et al.* (1967) have reported the presence of collagen fibrils as well as hydroxyproline and hydroxylysine in spicule residues of the hexactinellid, *Euplectella,* the methods employed for preparing spicules for chemical analyses were not sufficient to remove *surrounding* collagen

Table 4-5   Chemical Constituents in Siliceous Spicules of *Acarnus erithacus*[a]

Constituents	Percentage Weight of Cleaned Spicules[b]	Percentage Weight of Residue[c]
Si, H$_2$O	95.7	—
Residue	4.3	100.0
Si	—	17.5
Na	0.65	13.7
Al	0.154	3.07
K	0.124	2.57
Ca	0.014	0.29
Fe	0.007	0.14
N	0.073–0.57	1.46–11.5
H	0.022–0.08	0.43–1.6
C	0.016–0.042	0.32–0.83
B	—	0.6–6.0
Ba	—	0.03–0.3
Mg, Ni, Ti, Sr (each)	—	0.02–0.2
Pb	—	0.01–0.1
Sr	—	0.006–0.06

[a]Data taken from Schwab and Shore (1971b).
[b]Spicules cleaned in nitric acid.
[c]Residue prepared following desilicification in hydrofluoric acid.

Table 4-6   Amino Acid Composition of Axial Filaments of *Acarnus erithacus*[a]

Amino acids[b]			
Aspartic acid/asparagine	14.0	Proline	5.0
Glycine	11.0	Phenylalanine	5.0
Valine	10.0	Lysine	3.7
Glutamic acid/glutamine	9.0	Methionine	2.9
Alanine	6.8	Histidine	2.7
Serine	6.3	Arginine	2.8
Leucine	6.3	Tyrosine	1.4
Isoleucine	5.9	Tryptophan	Not analyzed
Threonine	5.5		

[a]Data taken from Shore (1972).
[b]Expressed as moles of the protein.

and thus, it is not clear what part of these analyses is due to the axial filament. Drum (1968) has suggested that axial filaments may also contain carbohydrate, but more recent data are not available on this point. Mature and maturing siliceous spicules become, in many cases, embedded within a collagenous matrix; the precise chemical association, if any, between

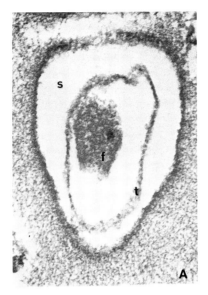
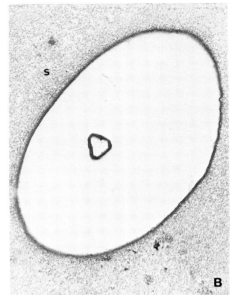

Figure 4-14   Visualization of the chemical nature of siliceous spicules (TEMs).
A. Cross section of a spicule from *Haliclona* sp. following silica dissolution by HF treatment. *s*, space previously occupied by silica; *f*, axial filament; *t*, a third, nonsiliceous component which as shown in B, is not the same as the axial filament (×32,400) (Garrone *et al.*, 1981). **B**. A similar spicule cross section treated with HF and then with pepsin. Both the silica and axial filament have been digested but the third component is still present. *s*, spongin microfibrils (×20,700) (Garrone *et al.*, 1981). (Both courtesy Dr. R. Garrone.)

the collagen and the silica is not known but there may be a narrow band of structured material separating them (Garrone, 1969a). Young intracellular spicules are surrounded by a membrane, the silicalemma (see following sections). There have been no studies of the chemical composition of this membrane, which presents a real challenge in terms of developing techniques for its isolation and purification.

The patterns of tissue localization of spicule types are almost as diverse as the number of spicule types which are formed (Lévi, 1973). In most species, two major localizations can be distinguished: (1) megascleres can be present in the "principal skeleton," which consists of spicule tracts and/or a basal layer of spicules, and (2) megascleres can occur singly or in groups outside of the principal skeleton. The principal spicules which occur in tracts or basal layers are often embedded or held together by spongin. Among tetractinomorph demosponges the principal skeleton frequently consists of megascleres which form a distinct, radial, principal skeleton but these tracts of spicules are not held together with spongin.

Megascleres lying outside the principal skeleton occur interstitially in the mesohyl and may occur at or near surfaces. The latter spicules are not encased in spongin fibers as is also the case with microscleres, which never constitute or contribute to the principal skeleton but which may be concentrated in areas of the mesohyl. Spicules which have specific localization in the principal skeleton (megascleres) or in dermal layers (microscleres and megascleres) must at some time be involved in specific morphogenetic processes.

In many siliceous sponges, megascleres come to protrude from the surface of the animal, possibly forming a protective armour which may prevent the settling of detritus, larvae, and epiphytic organisms. In the few cases in which observations are available, the protruding portion of these spicules is reported to be covered by exopinacocytes (Weissenfels, 1978; Garrone, person. comm.). It is not clear whether all spicules protruding from the surface remain covered by exopinacocytes. For example, among tetractinomorphs spicules may protrude for long distances from the base of the animal and apparently function in anchoring it in bottom sediments. Although conclusions regarding the question of whether these spicules are covered by pinacocytes can be found in the literature (see Jones, 1979b) it is really not clear what the arrangement is. Additional studies are clearly in order.

Megascleres of the principal skeleton in at least one case are reported to be isolated from the mesohyl by a layer of cells thus placing the spicules technically outside the animal (Figs. 4-15, 4-16) (Weissenfels, 1978). It is not known whether all such principal spicules in all species come to have this orientation but it is possible that megascleres which are *not* part of the principal skeleton remain within the mesohyl in an intraorganismal position; microscleres apparently are always intraorganismal with the exception of gemmoscleres (see Chap. 8).

Siliceous spicules are also actively secreted by some demosponge larvae during their maturation and consequently they contain these structures when they are liberated from the maternal tissue and become free swimming. As a generalization, parenchymellae larvae (see Chap. 7) of demosponges contain some or all of the spicule types of the fully developed animal, as in *Halichondria* (Fell and Jacob, 1979), *Spongilla* (Brien and Meewis, 1938; Meewis, 1939a), *Microciona* (Simpson, 1968b), *Mycale* (Lévi, 1964; Borojevic, 1966), *Haliclona* (Fell, 1969) and a number of additional species (Lévi, 1956; Bergquist and Sinclair, 1968). In coeloblastulae larvae no spicules occur even in the mature structure, as in *Polymastia* (Borojevic, 1967). When spicules are present in larvae their localization is usually central, lacking the normal pattern in fully developed sponges. Most gemmules (Chap. 8) possess a single category of microscleres embedded in the surrounding collagenous coat (Penney and Racek, 1968). These are the only known instances when microscleres come to be enrobed in spongin. Among hexactinellids (see following sec-

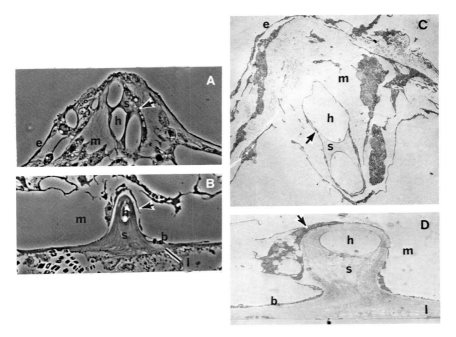

Figure 4-15 Relationship of the spicular and collagenous skeleton of *Ephydatia fluviatilis* to the mesohyl. Tissue desilicified with HF. **A, B**. Cross sections through the surface (A.) and basal (B.) regions of the animal. The spicules were located in the holes (*h*) and are surrounded by spongin (*s*) at the surface of which is a continuous, extremely thin layer (*arrows*) of cells (?=terminal spongocytes). *m*, mesohyl; *e*, exopinacoderm; *b*, basopinacoderm; *l*, basal layer of spongin (Phase contrast micrographs, semithin sections) (A: ×575; B: ×515) (Weissenfels, 1978). **C**. Section comparable to that seen in A. Symbols as in A. and B. (TEM) (×2,250) (Weissenfels, 1978). **D**. Section comparable to that seen in B. Symbols as in A. and B. (TEM) (×2,430) (Weissenfels, 1978). (All courtesy Prof. N. Weissenfels.)

tion), as in *Farrea sollasii*, spicules are also present in the larva (Okada, 1928) but data on this group are very sparse.

Siliceous Scales

These siliceous deposits have been reported in free-floating structures which, based upon a recent study, can now definitely be said to be buds derived from sponges (Chap. 8). In this ultrastructural study (Garrone, 1974) it was shown that ovoid, siliceous scales occur below the surface exopinacoderm and some of them appear still within their sclerocytes (see Fig. 8-5). The scales display the characteristic fracture pattern of demosponge spicules following sectioning. The buds (erroneously referred to

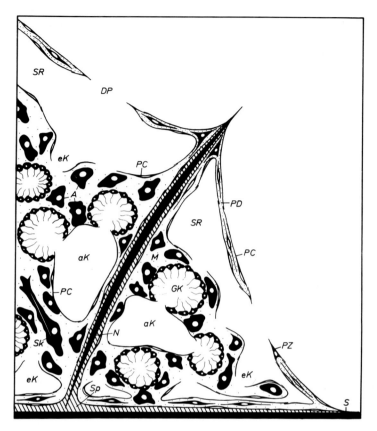

Figure 4-16 Schematic representation of the relationship of the skeleton in *Ephy-datia fluviatilis* to the mesohyl. Also depicted is the relationship of the canals (for this, see Chap. 6). *PC*, pinacocyte; *PZ*, porocyte; *DP*, ostium; *SR*, subdermal cavity; *PD*, dermal membrane; *eK*, incurrent canal; *GK*, choanocyte chamber; *M*, mesohyl; *aK*, excurrent canal; *A*, mesohyl cells (archeocytes); *Sk*, young sclero-cyte; *N*, spicule; *Sp*, spongin; *S*, substratum (×495) (Weissenfels, 1978). (Cour-tesy Prof. N. Weissenfels.)

as ''gemmules'') are likely asexual products of a clionid sponge (probably *Alectona*). Siliceous scales are only known in these unusual, planktonic bodies although Jones (1979b) refers to some types of highly modified *microscleres* as ''scales.''

Siliceous Spicules of Hexactinellids

Hexactinellid siliceous spicules require special comment since many of them have been described as possessing a very complex internal structure [see Minchin (1909) for a review of this early literature] although thinner megascleres have a structure similar to demosponge megascleres with a central axial filament. Hexactinellid microscleres are considered to possess filaments also although they may be difficult to visualize using light microscopy as with demosponge microscleres. The axial filament of thinner hexactinellid megascleres is uniform in width, may extend beyond the spicule tips, and can be seen in all of the separate rays of a spicule. Reiswig (1971c) has reported that hexactinellid axial filaments are square in cross section, differing from those in demosponges which *in the light microscope* appear triangular. In the larger spicules, the axial filament may have small, irregular swellings. In these larger megascleres (and some of them are so large that they can be studied macroscopically) the silica occurs in two general forms—a homogeneous central "axis cylinder" surrounds the axial filament and a number of stratified layers surround the axis cylinder. The two repeating layers constituting the latter stratifications are called spiculin–lamellae and siphons. The siliceous siphons were reported to be rich in organic matter and the spiculin–lamellae were described as lacking silicon and containing only organic matter; the outermost layer is spiculin–lamella. Around the latter Schulze (1904) describes a spicule "sheath" which is fibrous. These early views of the presence of organic material in concentric layers has been disputed by both Schulze (1925) and Schmidt (1926), who concluded that the layering is due to differences in hydration of the silica which is laid down at different times, a conclusion similar to that of Schwab and Shore (1971a). However, as emphasized by Garrone *et al.* (1981) these data do not eliminate the possible presence of organic material either in the layers or otherwise situated. Jones (1979b) considers that the membranous material isolated from hexactinellid spicules by Butschli (1901) occurs within the silica but not in the concentric rings. Travis *et al.* (1967) have examined the spicules of *Euplectella* but unfortunately these were simply washed in water before desilicification permitting considerable potential contamination from the dried specimen studied. These results thus urgently require confirmation and extension through the use of additional preparative techniques. Collagen fibrils were present in the organic residue and following treatment with EDTA, X-ray diffraction data indicated the possible presence of cellulose. Further biochemical analyses are mandatory before it is concluded that cellulose is present as part of the residue of hexactinellid spicules and is not simply a contaminant.

Cemented Siliceous Spicules

Siliceous spicules which become "cemented" together to form a relatively solid latticework of silica are secreted by some demosponges, the lithistids, and by some hexactinellids. In both instances, there are related species possessing the same general types of spicules but in which no cementing takes place (Lévi, 1973; Tuzet, 1973b). Among the lithistids, a specific spicule type, the desma, becomes interlocked with other desmas and their surfaces are then apparently firmly "cemented" (Fig. 4-17) (Hoshino, 1976, 1977; Vacelet and Vasseur, 1971). Hartman (1981) has shown that the surfaces of the desmas which are opposed are tightly

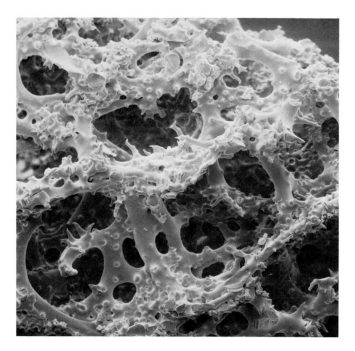

Figure 4-17   The amazingly complex, massive siliceous skeleton of the lithistid, *Scleritoderma* sp., in which individual desmas become articulated to form the final glass network (see Fig. 4-31B) (SEM) (×170) (Hartman, 1981). (Courtesy Prof. W. D. Hartman.)

interlocked (articulated). Although the "cement" has generally been implied to be siliceous there have been no chemical studies of its nature. It would be most illuminating to have X-ray analyses of the regions of articulation of these spicules. Among the hexasterophoran hexactinellids, large hexactines become cemented into a very rigid skeletal framework. In them, the cementing appears much more complete creating a continuum of silica in the latticework (Fig. 4-18). Data on axial filaments of cemented spicules are lacking.

Entrapped Siliceous Spicules

These spicules are treated in this short section separately from other noncemented siliceous spicules because of their unique association with aragonite. No detailed chemical analyses of them have appeared. They are initially secreted within the living sponge tissue, but later as the sponge grows in height, some of them become incorporated into the newly deposited aragonite (Fig. 4-19) (Hartman and Goreau, 1970). Typically the heads (rounded ends) of entrapped spicules are encased in an organic matrix of unknown chemistry and the spicule end is then entrapped in the aragonite. The presence of fibrils in this matrix (Hartman,

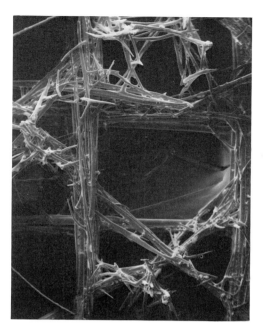

Figure 4-18   The partially fused siliceous skeleton of the hexactinellid *Euplectella speciosa*. These lysacchine skeletons while possessing extensive spicule cementing lack the high degree of regularity of some other glass sponge skeletons (see Fig. 4-31A) (SEM) (×20) (Hartman, 1981). (Courtesy Prof. W. D. Hartman.)

1969) suggests it may be partially collagenous. In older (lower) regions, whole spicules are entrapped whereas in younger regions only the spicule heads are. The heads appear to act as centers for calcifications since the centers of the sclerodermites coincide with the spicule heads. Some degree of etching (erosion) of the silica of entrapped spicules is evident and occurs most frequently on the spicule heads (Hartman, 1969). The organic component surrounding the spicule heads is seen, in decalcified material, to extend outward as thin sheets forming a matrix for the aragonite. Entrapped spicules occur in a number of genera of sclerosponges (*Ceratoporella, Stromatospongia, Hispidoptera, Goreauiella, Calcifibrospongia*).

The Secretion of Siliceous Spicules

Demosponges

Numerous reports of the *intra*cellular origin of many types of siliceous spicules appeared in the nineteenth century and few claims for an *inter*cellular origin of them were made, such that Minchin (1909) stated: ". . . we may well disregard them, and consider it an established truth, that all true spicules or spicular elements in this group (Demospongiae) arise within

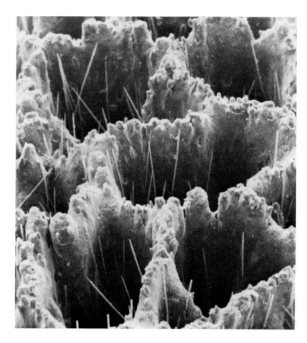

Figure 4-19   The cleaned surface of the sclerosponge, *Ceratoporella nicholsoni*, showing the aragonitic skeleton in which siliceous spicules (protruding needle-like structures) are partially enrobed. Note the considerable regularity of the angle of the spicules relative to the aragonite in which they are partially embedded (SEM) (×75) (Hartman and Goreau, 1972). (Courtesy Prof. W. D. Hartman.)

cells.'' The early literature, in the majority of cases, still represents the most recent studies; some of them require reevaluation employing more sensitive, higher resolution techniques. According to these data, all siliceous spicules begin either as intracellular rods or granules to which are then added new parts through the apposition of additional silica. Namely, a morphogenesis occurs; spicules do not initially appear in their final form. As new parts grow out from the spicule its size increases by apposition, not internal growth, of the silica. Separate parts of spicules do not form and then become fused together except possibly in the case of the desmas of lithistid sponges which, when mature, appear to be secondary spicule types in which silica is added to an original spicule by additional cells. The disagreement as to whether a siliceous granule or an organic thread is the first observable stage of spiculogenesis is considered by Minchin (1909) as due to the lack of distinction by some workers between the organic and mineral components of spicules. Recent data establish that an organic filament precedes or appears simultaneously with the initiation of silicification (see below).

Most earlier observations establish that demosponge spicules are initiated by single cells. When additional cells become associated with growing spicules they migrate and join the sclerocyte–spicule complex (Weissenfels and Landschoff, 1977). In some cases, notably in microscleres, only a single sclerocyte is ever involved in the secretion of the spicule. It will become clear that the seemingly contradictory evidence that some spicules are secreted by single sclerocytes and others by a number of them is undoubtedly due to the failure of recognizing that both processes can occur but in different spicule types. There are similarly conflicting views as to the final fate of sclerocytes—whether they degenerate or move away from the spicule. The former appeared to Minchin (1909) as a more likely sequence in most cases but unfortunately more recent studies shed little light on the question.

Such studies, employing light and electron microscopy, of demosponge siliceous spicule secretion (Lévi, 1963b; Garrone, 1969a; Garrone and Pottu, 1973; Simpson and Vaccaro, 1974; Pottu-Boumendil, 1975; Weissenfels and Landschoff, 1977; Garrone et al., 1981) further support the view that these spicules are secreted intracellularly. Nevertheless, in this context the following data must also be considered: (1) earlier views of the *intra*cellular origin of calcareous spicules, (2) the now-established *inter*cellular origin of calcareous spicules, (3) the limited number of ultrastructural observations of siliceous spicule secretion, (4) the absence of attempts to reconstruct the total relationship of newly secreted spicules to their sclerocytes, (5) the similarity of the plasmalemma and silicalemma as unit-type membranes, and (6) the observed extrusion of spicules from their sclerocytes. These require that some caution be exercised in accepting the conclusion that siliceous spicules are, in the strict sense, intracellular products. For example, the present data do not eliminate the possibility that the silicalemma (see following discussion) is an inpocketing of the plasmalemma and that therefore the axial filament and silica actually occur in an elongate, extracellular pocket. Cross sections of spicules clearly establish that if such an inpocketing of the plasmalemma does occur, the neck region must be localized in only a small area of the plasmalemma. Such an arrangement would be extremely difficult to detect ultrastructurally because of the very few ultrathin sections which could establish the continuity between the two membrane systems. Although seemingly unlikely, the possibility of such an arrangement cannot presently be dismissed.

These investigations also establish that an organic, axial filament is elaborated first and that silica is then deposited around it, inside of a membrane, the silicalemma. The initial length of filaments lies in the range of 40–70 μm for megascleres of freshwater species (Schröeder, 1936; Weissenfels and Landschoff, 1977). Although the number of such studies are small, including observations of the secretion of megascleres in *Haliclona elegans, Ephydatia fluviatilis, E. mulleri,* and *Spongilla lacustris,* it

Table 4-7   Recently Reported Features of Demosponge Siliceous Spicules and Their Secretion

Spicule Type	Species	Initial Secretion in Single Cell	Axial Filaments Present	Axial Filaments Hexagonal	Axial Filaments Crystalline[a]	Special Features	Method[b]	References
Megascleres								
Smooth oxea	*Spongilla lacustris*	Yes	Yes	Yes	No	Swelling without special branching of filament	TEM	Simpson and Vaccaro (1974)
Spiny oxea	*Ephydatia mulleri*	Yes	Yes	Yes	Yes	Spines, each with branch of filament	TEM	Pottu-Boumendil (1975)
Smooth style	*Acarnus erithacus*	?	Yes	?	?	None reported	TEM (carbon replicas)	Schwab and Shore (1971b)
Smooth oxea	*Haliclona elegans*	Yes	Yes	Yes	Yes	Three planes of oriented "tubes" in filament	TEM	Garrone (1969a)
Spiny oxea	*Ephydatia fluviatilis*	Yes	Yes	Yes	?	None reported	TEM (HF removal of silica)	Weissenfels and Landschoff (1977)
Strongyles	*Neofibularia*	Yes	Yes	Yes	Yes	None reported	TEM	Wilkinson and Garrone (1980a)
Microscleres								
Sigmas	*Neofibularia*	Yes	Yes	Yes	Yes	Spicule curves in sclerocyte	TEM	Garrone *et al.* (1981), Wilkinson and Garrone (1980a)
Raphide	*Neofibularia*	Yes	Yes	Yes	Yes	None reported	TEM	Wilkinson and Garrone (1980a)

Spicule type	Species					Notes	Method[b]	References
Microxeas	Neofibularia	Not known	Yes	Yes	Yes	Groups of mature spicules may occur in single cell	TEM	Garrone et al. (1981), Wilkinson and Garrone (1980a)
Spiny birotule	Ephydatia mulleri	Yes	Yes	?	Yes	Filament branches into spines	LM, TEM	Leveaux (1939), Rasmont (1956), Garrone et al. (1981),
Spiny microrhab	Cliona lampa	Yes	?	?	?	Few organelles in cytoplasm; nuclear bulge	TEM	Rutzler and Rieger (1973)
Spiny birotule	Heteromeyenia sp.	?	Yes	?	?	Filament branches into spines	TEM (carbon relicas)	Drum (1968)
Strongylaster	Tethya lyncurium	Yes	?	?	?	None reported	TEM	Connes (1968)
Spheraster	Tethya lyncurium	Yes	?	?	?	Nucleolus present	TEM	Connes (1968)
Unknown[c]	Mycale contarenii	Yes	Yes	?	?	Vacuoles present at end of filament	TEM	Lévi (1963b)
Chelas	Microciona prolifera	Yes	?	?	?	None reported	LM	Simpson (1978, 1968a)
Toxas	Thalysias juniperina	Yes	?	?	?	Cell size large	LM	Simpson (1968a)
Toxas	Microciona prolifera	No	?	?	?	Secretion appears extracellular	LM	Simpson (1978)

[a]Oriented structure.

[b]TEM: transmission electron microscopy; LM: light microscopy.

[c]Lévi does not suggest what spicule type is involved but the sizes of the cell, filament, and nucleus suggest that it is a microsclere.

can be assumed that axial filaments are also found in general as organic precursors in megasclere secretion in other demosponges. The data also support the conclusion that microscleres begin as axial filaments (Table 4-7).

Little attention has been given to the question of whether more than one cell type acts as the origin for all sclerocytes. Evans (1899) seems to be one of the few early workers who emphasized differences between microsclerocytes and megasclerocytes (see also Garrone *et al.*, 1981). In all instances in which megasclere secretion has been recently studied, megasclerocytes develop from cells which are morphologically indistinguishable from archeocytes. On the other hand, sclerocytes which have been described secreting microscleres differ significantly and consistently from megasclerocytes (Fig. 4-20) in one or more of the following features: (1) smaller cell size, (2) smaller nuclear size, (3) absence of a nucleolus, (4) few or no phagosomes. Furthermore, it appears that each individual microsclere is secreted by a single cell as is true of megascleres when they initially appear although an apparent exception has been recently reported: bundles of microxeas in *Neofibularia irata* can be found within a "vacuole" of a single cell. These microscleres may have first been secreted singly, one per cell, and then enclosed collectively in the cell or, multiple spicules may be secreted by one cell (Fig. 4-21) (Wilkinson and Garrone, 1980a). Interestingly, both the single cell secretion of a related microsclere type and the presence of many of them in a single cell were originally reported in the early literature (Minchin, 1909). In *Tedania ignis* occasionally two microscleres are found within the same microsclerocyte (Simpson, 1968a). It appears that certain microscleres will turn out to be interesting exceptions to the rule that initially, single spicules appear within single sclerocytes.

Although megasclere secretion has long been reported to involve more than one cell, with the secondary cell(s) joining a single megasclerocyte–spicule complex, recent investigations suggest, in at least some instances, that these additional cells are not sclerocytes. In *Haliclona elegans* and *Ephydatia mulleri,* spongocytes become closely associated with maturing spicules (Garrone and Pottu, 1973) and in *Ephydatia fluviatilis,* spicule transporting cells have been reported closely associated with spicules also (Weissenfels, 1978; Schröeder, 1936). These cells could easily be considered as secondary megasclerocytes, which they are not. But, in some demosponges (tetractinomorphs) and in hexactinellids, megascleres are relatively immense structures and it is difficult to envisage a single cell as capable of forming the entire length of the spicule. Regardless of their function, secondary cells which join the sclerocyte–spicule complex are characteristic of megasclere formation and not of microsclere formation and likely are involved only in megasclere maturation.

The simplest interpretation of the origin of megasclerocytes is that they are derived directly from archeocytes (Pottu-Boumendil, 1975). Such an

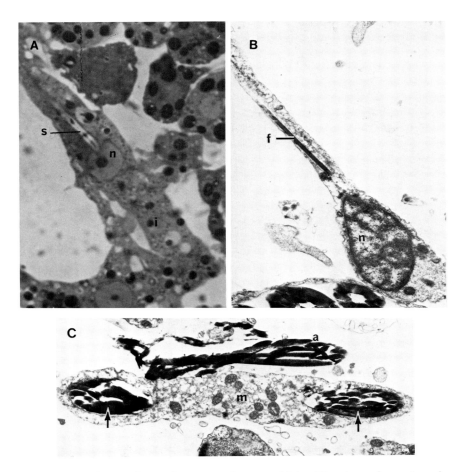

Figure 4-20 Comparison of a megasclerocyte (A.) with microsclerocytes. **A.** Young megasclerocyte of *Spongilla lacustris* showing the nucleolate nucleus (*n*) and a short portion of the secreted spicule (*s*). Cytoplasmic inclusions (*i*) are phagosomes (light micrograph, semithin section) (×1,800) (Unpubl. micrograph, author.) **B**. A very young microsclerocyte of *Neofibularia irata* that is secreting a raphid. The axial filament (*f*) is not yet surrounded by silica. Note the small, anucleolate nucleus (*n*) (TEM) (×9,000) (Wilkinson and Garrone, 1980a). **C.** A microsclerocyte (*m*) secreting a sigma (see Fig. 1-12B). Only the ends of the spicule (*arrows*) are cut giving the false impression of the secretion of two spicules in a single cell. The highly fractured shaft of a sigma is also seen above (*a*) (TEM) (×7,200) (Wilkinson and Garrone, 1980a). (**B**, **C**, courtesy Dr. R. Garrone.)

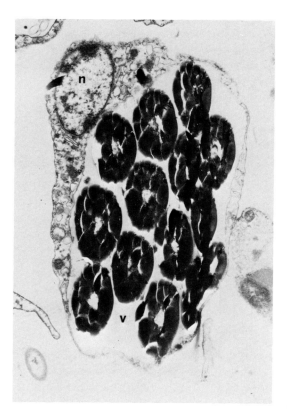

Figure 4-21 A microscleroctye of *Neofibularia irata* that contains numerous cross-sectioned microxeas in a single large vacuole (*v*). It is not known if a single cell also secretes all the spicules. *n*, nucleus (TEM) (×10,000) (Wilkinson and Garrone, 1980a). (Courtesy Dr. R. Garrone.)

archeocyte origin may be highly predetermined (genetic). When thesocytes in germinating gemmules are inhibited by puromycin from dividing and breaking down their reserves (platelets) they nevertheless differentiate into megasclerocytes (see Fig. 8-30); there thus appears to be no necessity for a physiological sequence of events (Rozenfeld, 1980). There are continuing suggestions (Minchin, 1909; Simpson, 1968a) that some microsclerocytes may be derived from or may be modified pinacocytes. Such a possibility is of much interest based upon the known origin of sclerocytes from pinacocytes in calcareous sponges. However, serious consideration must also be given to the possibility that one or more special cell types (Chap. 3) may give rise to them. This is clearly indicated in the case of toxa secretion in *Microciona* (Simpson, 1968a).

The axial filament of demosponge megasclerocytes has been shown to be hexagonal in cross section (Table 4-7) (Garrone *et al.*, 1981), although light microscopic observations indicate a triangular shape (Reiswig, 1971c). The latter observation led to the suggestion that the triangular shape lies at the basis of the morphology of four-rayed spicules. While of much potential importance, the problem of triangular versus hexagonal shape must be resolved relative to views that the cross sectional morphology of the filament predetermines the principal axes of spicule types (Garrone *et al.*, 1981). In a number of spicule types, including some microscleres, the filaments contain oriented tubular or fibrillar ultrastructure (Fig. 4-22) (Garrone *et al.*, 1981). A partial resolution of the triangular versus hexagonal shape of megasclere filaments lies in the observation that in *Haliclona elegans* the oriented tubules in the filament lie in three separate planes. These three planes could come to predominate in the filament shape in *mature* spicules. The shape of microsclere filaments also is hexagonal (Wilkinson and Garrone, 1980a) and although oriented structure appears in the filament it is not known whether the tubules lie in three planes.

In all cases in which young, newly forming spicules have been examined by transmission electron microscopy, the freshly polymerized silica

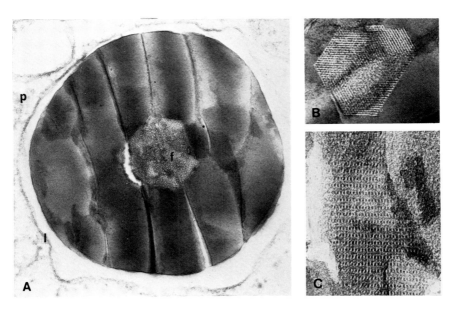

Figure 4-22 Axial filament of *Haliclona* sp. (TEMs). **A**. Cross section of a whole intracellular spicule showing the hexagonal shape of the filament (*f*). Note fracturing of the silica and the presence of the surrounding silicalemma (*l*). *p*, cytoplasm of megasclerocyte (×64,350) (Garrone, 1969a). **B**. Cross section of filament showing highly ordered structure (×144,000) (Garrone *et al.*, 1981). **C**. Longitudinal section of the filament further establishing a highly ordered array of the structure (×180,000) (Garrone *et al.*, 1981). (Courtesy Dr. R. Garrone.)

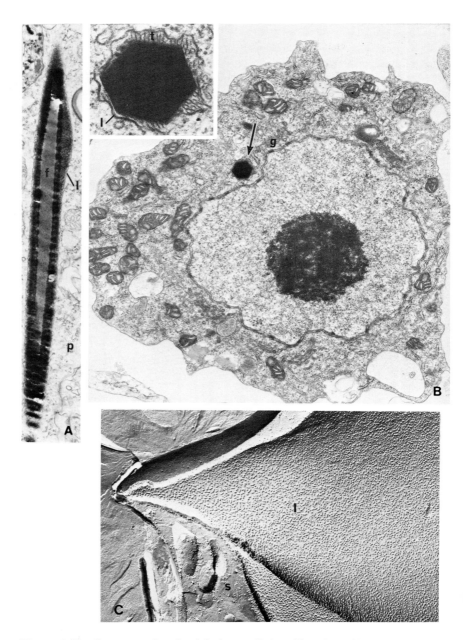

Figure 4-23 Structures involved in intracellular silica deposition. **A**. A young spicule of *Spongilla lacustris* (longitudinal section) showing the axial filament (*f*), newly deposited silica (*s*), and surrounding silicalemma (*l*). *p*, cytoplasm of the megasclerocyte (TEM) (×9,000) (Simpson and Vaccaro, 1974). **B**. The earliest-known stage in megasclere secretion (*Ephydatia mulleri*). The megasclerocyte possesses a prominent nucleolus, numerous mitochondria and an axial filament

is deposited around the organic axial filament which is in turn surrounded by a unit type membrane, the silicalemma (Figs. 4-23, 4-24) (see for example, Garrone, 1969a; Simpson and Vaccaro, 1974). As previously discussed, the silicalemma appears to form an elongate vacuole in the cytoplasm with no direct connections to the Golgi complex, endoplasmic reticulum, or other membrane system. The P face of this specialized and unique membrane has recently been shown by freeze fracture techniques to contain a high density of particles (Fig. 4-23C) (Garrone *et al.*, 1980) which distinguishes it from the plasmalemma (Lethias *et al.*, 1983). In older spicules, the silicalemma is not present and the deposited silica comes into contact with the ground substance, spongin, or other cells. This membrane apparently covers the total surface of the developing spicule and its contours follow that of the silica. In a very early stage of megasclere secretion in *Ephydatia mulleri,* prior to any silicification, tubular elements occur between the silicalemma and axial filament as well as apparent fusion of smooth-membraned vesicles with the silicalemma (Fig. 4-23B) (Pottu-Boumendil, 1975). The significance of the former is not clear but may signal the involvement of these tubules in silicification as indicated in other silicification systems (Volcani, 1981). Numerous cytoplasmic microtubules are characteristic of sclerocytes.

Based upon presently available information the events in silica deposition can be broadly outlined. The initial stage of spicule formation involves the synthesis and assembly of the axial filament and silicalemma neither of which are known to form in the absence of the other. Soluble forms of silicic acid are then transported within the silicalemma and initial polymerization occurs immediately surrounding the axial filament. Further silicification then occurs just inside of the silicalemma and peripheral to the initially polymerized silica. Thus, the outermost silica is granular and the innermost is fully polymerized and fractures during sectioning (Fig. 4-24A,D). The silicalemma can be viewed as possessing the capacity to act as a silicic acid pump. The presence of swellings (Brønsted, 1931) in young spicules may be due to differences in silicic acid transport in different regions of the silicalemma. Such swellings also raise the possibility of spreading of the transported silicic acid and polymers (Simpson, 1981;

(*arrow*) that has appeared in the region of the Golgi (*g*) (TEM) (×12,150). **Inset:** Axial filament enlarged to show its hexagonal shape, localization within the silicalemma (*l*), and the presence of tubular elements (*t*) which connect the two (TEM) (×60,300) (Pottu-Boumendil, 1975). C. Freeze fracture of a spicule spine (pointed structure) of *Ephydatia mulleri* showing the surface (PF) of the silicalemma (*l*) which is studded with numerous particles. *s*, sclerocyte cytoplasm (SEM) (×54,000) (Garrone *et al.*, 1980). (**B**, courtesy Dr. J. Pottu-Boumendil; **C**, courtesy Dr. R. Garrone.)

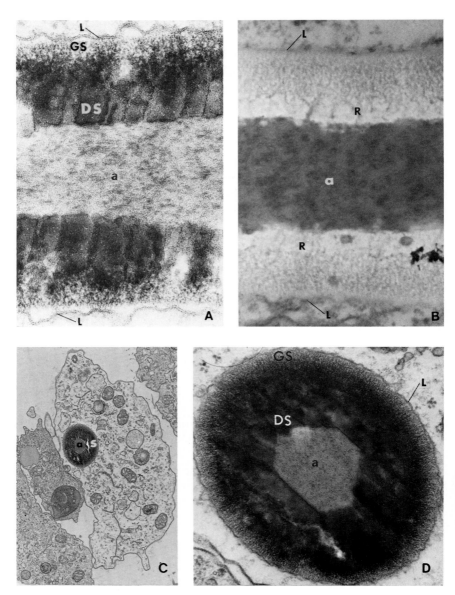

Figure 4-24 Early silica deposition in megascleres of *Spongilla lacustris*. In all cases the structures are intracellular (TEMs). **A**. Longitudinal section of a small part of a spicule showing the axial filament (*a*), silicalemma (*L*), internal denser silica (*DS*), peripheral granular silica (*GS*) (×78,300) (Simpson and Vaccaro, 1974). **B**. The same spicule as in A. following HF treatment. The silica has been removed leaving faint residue lines (*R*). *a*, axial filament; *L*, silicalemma (×90,000) (Simpson and Vaccaro, 1974). **C**. Cross section of a spicule within its megasclerocyte. *a*, axial filament; *s*, silica (×6,750) (Simpson and Vaccaro, 1974). **D**. Higher magnification of a cross section showing the hexagonal shape of the filament (*a*), dense (*DS*) and granular (*GS*) silica, and silicalemma (*L*). Note in this species with these very young spicules that the filament does not contain ordered structure (see Fig. 4-22 and text) (×38,250) (Simpson and Vaccaro, 1974).

Davie *et al.*, 1983). The movement of silicic acid from the medium is a highly complex process regardless of whether the forming spicule is intra- or extracellular. The boundaries and compartments to be traversed include (1) either outer exopinacocyte or choanocyte plasmalemma, exopinacocyte or choanocyte cytoplasm, inner exopinacocyte or choanocyte plasmalemma or leakage or transport at the junctions of opposing plasmalemmae of exopinacocytes or choanocytes; (2) the mesohyl, including either intracellular transport and/or facilitated ground substance transport; (3) the sclerocyte plasmalemma and cytoplasm; (4) the silicalemma. The latter, (3) and (4), would be replaced by direct transport to the axial filament (or spicule) if the system is extracellular (Simpson, 1981). The transport of silicic acid must be highly efficient since newly developing sponges initiate silicification almost immediately after attachment (Pé, 1973; Weissenfels and Landschoff, 1977). Schröeder (1936) has recorded the presence of vacuoles in living megasclerocytes of freshwater sponges and has suggested that they are involved in transporting silicic acid to the developing spicule, the silicic acid within the vacuoles supposedly becomes progressively gelated so that when the vacuole is applied to the spicule the silica is already in a state of polymerization. Jorgensen (1944) disputes Schröeder's interpretations. No electron microscopic data support a vacuolar transport system although vesicles have on occasion been seen associated with the axial filament or silicalemma (Lévi, 1963b; Pottu-Boumendil, 1975). Similarly, no convincing evidence of the transport of silicic acid *to* the sclerocyte by other cells is available and there is a real possibility that such transport is at least partially intercellular, through the ground substance (Elvin, 1971). The question of vacuolar transport of silicic acid is an important one relative to views of the mechanism of silicification, and it will be difficult to secure relevant data.

It is possible that trace amounts of organic material become entrapped within the polymerizing silica since a "texture" is apparent in newly deposited silica (Garrone *et al.,* 1981). It would be most interesting to know if connections exist between the silicalemma and the axial filament or if the filament itself has fine strands of material extending from its surface. In desilicified, newly secreted spicules, "residue lines" are seen in the region previously occupied by silica (Fig. 4-25) (Simpson and Vaccaro, 1974) and in desilicified, pepsin-treated preparations in which both silica and axial filament have been removed, a circle of material remains that is pepsin resistant and that originally surrounded the filament (see Fig, 4-14B) (Garrone, 1969a). The characteristic, rather uniformly shaped and sized "units" of silica (Fjerdingstad, 1970) that are seen following sectioning are probably sectioning artifacts (Garrone, 1969a; Simpson and Vaccaro, 1974) but the possible inclusion of organic material at regular intervals within the silica may influence this regularity (Garrone *et al.,* 1981).

Rates of increase in spicule length fall within the range of 1–10 μm/h

Figure 4-25 Cross section of an intracellular megasclere from *Ephydatia mulleri* treated with HF. A thin band of peripheral silica (*r*) remains. A distinct residue at the edges (*e*) of the fractured silica is also present. *p*, cytoplasm; *l*, silicalemma; *f*, axial filament (TEM) (×30,000) (Garrone *et al.*, 1981). (Courtesy Dr. R. Garrone.)

which thus represents the rate of growth of the axial filament which has a static, uniform diameter (Elvin, 1971; Weissenfels and Landschoff, 1977). Rates of increase in width have been dealt with by considering a 1.0 μm^3 portion of a spicule; using this basis, both Elvin (1971) and Jorgensen (1947) have found similar deposition rates in the range of 1.5×10^{-18} to 2×10^{-17} mole Si deposited/μm^2/min. Additional, more precise studies are required in order to further extend their findings.

All spicules grow in at least two dimensions after their initial appearance—in length and in width (Elvin, 1971). Both of these growth components must include the growth of the silicalemma, which has to expand around the spicule as it increases in width and around the axial filament as the latter grows in length. Growth in width may include only the growth of the silicalemma while growth in length must involve both components; the growth of each spicule ray, when more than one is present, must also include these two processes. Axial filaments have very uniform widths and there is no suggestion that they continue to grow in width as the spicule does. There must be a highly specialized set of processes resulting in the synthesis and assembly (=transport to the ends of the filament) of precursors for the growth in length of the filament. Silicalemma synthesis could include fusion with vesicles as observed in a single case (Pottu-Boumendil, 1975). Based upon studies of the morphology of the axial filament, its branching into a new plane results in a reshaping of the overlying silicalemma and thus of the newly deposited silica. Such branches can be short and result in the formation of spines (Pottu-Boumendil, 1975; Garrone *et al.*, 1981) or long and result in the formation of new "rays" (Drum, 1968). There is some suggestion that some microscleres are secreted in a close to all or none fashion (Simpson, 1978); in them, silicification must occur very rapidly.

Megasclerocytes contain numerous mitochondria, which Pottu-Boumendil (1975) suggests is a specific attribute of their differentiation as distinct from archeocytes. Microtubules and glycogen are sometimes present in the cytoplasm in the vicinity of the spicule. Only sparse amounts of rough endoplasmic reticulum occur but ribosomes are numerous. Smooth vesicles also appear to play some role in silicification based on their relative abundance. Well-developed Golgi bodies are present and could possibly be involved in silicalemma and filament elaboration. Megasclerocytes always possess a well-developed nucleolus and some phagosomes and residual bodies are seen in the cytoplasm.

In distinction, most microsclerocytes lack nucleoli and are small in cell and nuclear size relative to megasclerocytes. Little is known of organelle arrangement or special features (Chap. 3). The secretion of toxas in microcionid species appears on a light microscope level to be uniquely extracellular, the newly secreted spicule being associated with membranous, coiled material (Simpson, 1968a, 1978). Future ultrastructural studies of their secretion should yield interesting information. Toxas in other related species are secreted intracellularly by single cells which, relative to other microsclerocytes, are large in size (Simpson, 1968a). This dichotomy in toxa secretion is the first instance of two obviously different *cellular* mechanisms which are involved in the secretion of the same morphological spicule type (Fig. 4-26).

Early observations (Butschli, 1901) as well as recent ones (Weissenfels, 1978) establish that spicules can be moved form one position to another within the mesohyl during or following their secretion. In a species of *Ephydatia,* microscleres, still situated in their microsclerocytes, are moved into the epithelium surrounding newly forming gemmules (Evans, 1901). More recent observations confirm this in a number of additional freshwater species (Rasmont, 1956; Rasmont and De Vos, 1974). In *Ephydatia fluviatilis,* newly secreted megascleres are first extruded from the megasclerocyte and then are moved by another cell (identified as a collencyte) into their final position (Weissenfels, 1978). Two additional processes can thus be recognized toward the end of spicule secretion; relocation of the spicules and their extrusion from the slcerocytes. Whether one or both of these processes take place with all spicules is not known, but

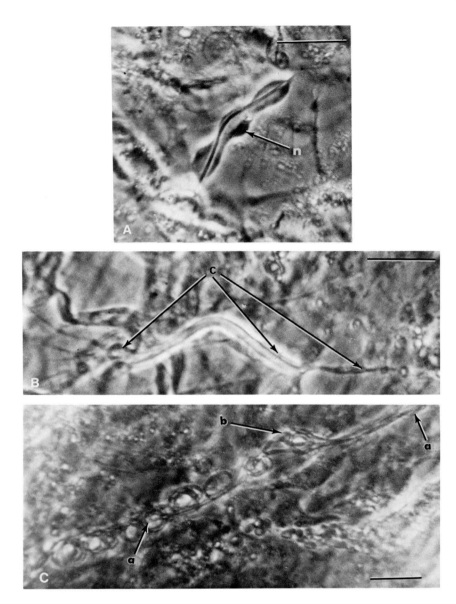

Figure 4-26 Two divergent modes of toxa (=microscleres) secretion (phase-contrast micrographs, living material). **A**. Toxa secretion within a microsclerocyte possessing a small anucleolate nucleus (*n*) in *Thalysias juniperina*. Note the contours of the cell follow that of the bow-shaped spicule. Scale bar: 11.0 μm (×1,620) (Simpson, 1968a). **B**. Newly secreted toxa in *Microciona prolifera* in which a thin, membranous, coiled material (*c*) is associated with the spicule which appears completely extracellular. Scale bar: 11.0 μm (×1,620) (Simpson, 1968a). **C**. Toxa secretion in *Microciona spinosa* in which the coiled material is more prominent. *a*, ends of the spicule; *b*, crest of spicule. Scale bar: 10.0 μm (×1,350) (Simpson, 1968a).

they should be looked for. Megascleres in many demosponges become associated with spongin (Chap. 5), and by the time this occurs, there is no longer a sclerocyte investing the spicule (Garrone and Pottu, 1973). Following extrusion in *Ephydatia,* megascleres become surrounded by cells that also contact the pinacoderms and the spicule thus is situated in a compartment that does not communicate with the mesohyl (Weissenfels, 1978); these spicules thus technically come to lie outside the animal (see Figs. 4-15, 4-16). Collagen is secreted on the spicule surface and is continuous with the layer of basal collagen secreted by basopinacocytes. No such arrangement has been reported for microscleres which occur exclusively in the mesohyl matrix. A number of studies establish that young, miniature demosponges eject some of their spicules. This occurs either by extrusion into the excurrent flow of water leaving the oscule (Mawet and Rasmont, 1971) or by the abandonment of spicules on the substratum when the growing edge of the sponge recedes (Pé, 1973; Simpson, 1968a). Some microscleres (asters) undergo significant maturation of their siliceous geometry (Fig. 4-27). Such final processes in silicification are unexplored.

Hexactinellids

Very little can be definitely stated concerning the secretion of siliceous spicules among the hexactinellids. No recent studies have appeared and the available information deals only with spicules in mature sponges (Minchin, 1909). Furthermore, as emphasized in another context the condition of the sponge tissue analyzed in these turn-or-the-century studies is suspect. These observations must therefore be carefully considered with this in mind. According to Ijima (1901) and others, microscleres appear within a multinucleate mass. The larger, single, nonfused spicules (megascleres) according to Schulze (1904) are also secreted within a multinucleate, discontinuous epithelium and an axial filament is formed by a group of cells lying within the tissue. The newly developing spicule is then pushed outward beyond the sponge surface, in much the same way as was erroneously ascribed to the mechanism in calcareous species whereby monaxons come to be protruded from the sponge surface (Ledger and Jones, 1977). It must be emphasized that these views are basically speculative; if the mechanisms suggested actually occur, they represent a drastic departure from what is known about silicification in demosponges. Pavans de Ceccatty (person. comm.) has recently observed that sclerocytes in *Rhabdocalyptus* are multinucleate and are probably bordered by a thin layer of fibrils. Based upon the highly complex, stratified structure, supposed high organic content, and the presence of a central, homogeneous axial cylinder in megascleres, it is likely that the secretion of the axis cylinder follows a comparable pattern to that in demosponges and that the stratified layers of silica and organic material are added as secondary processes. The secondary nature of the addition of stratified layers in

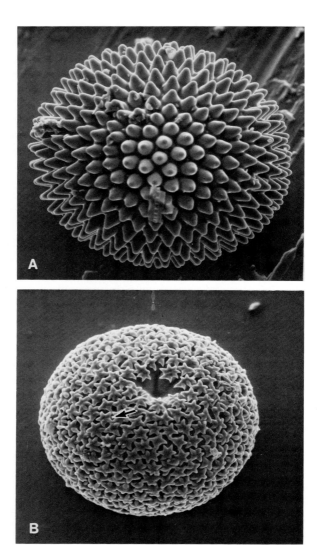

Figure 4-27 Two developmental stages of sterrasters in *Geodia gibberosa* (SEMs). **A**. Intermediate stage in which each of the spine tips has become rounded. In the earliest stages the tips are extremely tapered to a sharp point (×1,200) (Hartman, 1981). **B**. Final stage of maturation in which each spine tip has formed a flat, five-pointed structure (*arrow*). The concavity in the almost solid siliceous ball is where the microsclerocyte nucleus was located (×1,000) (Hartman, 1981). (Both courtesy Prof. W. D. Hartman.)

single spicules is a view compatible with the probable secondary nature of processes involved in the cementing of spicules. Thus, the cementing of siliceous spicules can be considered as an extension in time and space of secondary processes also involved in forming stratified layers in individual megascleres. Future investigations of spicule secretion in the hexactinellids continue to present a real challenge.

Factors Affecting Siliceous Spicule Secretion

The concentration of dissolved silicic acid effects spicule secretion under field conditions as demonstrated in a classic ecological study of the distribution of freshwater sponges in relation to water chemistry. In that study, Jewell (1935) found that the formation of normal spicules generally requires a silicic acid concentration of 0.005 mM or greater. Only in one instance were normal spicules present when only traces of silicic acid were recorded. Silicic acid concentration can fluctuate and spicule size, both length and width, has been found to be correlated with such seasonal fluctuation in the marine demosponge *Hymeniacidon perleve* (Stone, 1970c). Seasonal fluctuation in size, particularly width, have been recorded for freshwater sponges in which higher temperatures were correlated with thinner spicules and the presence of swellings on megascleres (Schröeder, 1936). In *Haliclona oculata,* spicule size is large in sponges inhabiting more northerly, colder regions (Hartman, 1958a).

Experimental studies have shed some light on the specific effects of silicic acid concentration and temperature upon spicule morphology and dimensions. One of the earliest of these were studies by Jorgensen (1944, 1947). Using newly hatched sponges derived from gemmules of *Spongilla lacustris* and synthetic media, Jorgensen found that microsclere secretion was affected differently than megasclere secretion. At relatively high silicic acid concentration (1.28 mM) the number of megascleres secreted was fewer than at 0.02–0.16 mM, whereas the number of microscleres was unaffected. In both spicule types, increasing silicic acid (from 0.02 to 0.1 mM) substantially increases spicule width but has no or little effect upon microsclere length. Megasclere length, on the other hand, increases over the range of 0.02–0.06 mM. Thus, microsclerocytes physiologically respond differently than megasclerocytes, which correlates with the known differences between the two types of sclerocytes. At 1.28 mM silicic acid, many more microscleres have central swellings which Jorgensen suggests are abnormal, but which, based upon other information (Simpson *et al.,* 1979) are normal features of many spicules during their secretion; their increase in number suggests an amplification of a normal process. Differences in spicule dimensions occur only over certain ranges of silicic acid concentration and the range chosen for experimental work is thus critical.

Pé (1973) has carried out the most thorough study to date and has quantified the effects of silicic acid concentration on spicule secretion in

Ephydatia fluviatilis, employing hatched gemmules. Unfortunately, this freshwater species forms only a single type of megasclere and the data do not yield further insight into the interesting differences between mega-sclerocytes and microsclerocytes initially reported by Jorgensen. Table 4-8 reviews the data of Pé and as can be seen, increasing silicic acid concentration results in longer and wider megaslceres. Not shown in the table is the finding that when young sponges were fed (heat-killed bacteria), at the end of sixteen days they produced about two and one half times more spicules than unfed controls. The fed sponges also lose many fewer spicules from the tissue due to the pulling back of the edge of the sponge. Pé also confirmed that high silicic acid (0.25 mM) results in a reduction of the number of megascleres formed suggesting an involvement of silicic acid availability in the differentiation of megasclerocytes from archeocytes. Further, at very high silicic acid concentration (1.0 mM) many spicules contain large bulbous expansions reminiscent of the swellings in microscleres reported by Jorgensen (1947) at comparable concentrations. A possible explanation of this has been suggested (Simpson, 1981) and will be discussed later. Higher silicic acid concentration (0.25 versus 0.025 mM) exerts its effect on spicule number only during a 48 h period (fourth and fifth days of growth) which apparently is a critical stage in megasclerocyte differentiation. At 0.0033 mM Si no visible spicules appear. At ~0.5 μM silicic acid, sclerocytes still differentiate and form flexible axial filaments that do not become silicified; the sclerocytes eventually become degenerative (Yourassowsky and Rasmont, 1983). Silicification thus does not appear to be an essential process in order for the filament to form (see also Simpson and Vaccaro, 1974).

Elvin (1971) has carried out direct observations of the growth rates of megascleres of a closely related species, *Ephydatia mulleri,* and has found that the rate of increase in spicule length decreases in longer spicules and with increased silicic acid concentration. The explanation for the latter is not clear but may have something to do with saturating sites at the ends of the axial filament. Rates of length increase are higher at higher temperatures. Rates of increase in spicule width are greater at 16° than at 10°C at all silicic acid concentrations, but at 25°C the rate of width increase is greater only at 0.178 mM Si not at 0.136 and 0.89 mM Si. The data suggest a highly complex interaction between metabolic processes, transport, entrapment, polymerization, and silicic acid availability.

Employing explant outgrowth of the marine sponge, *Microciona prolifera,* temperature was shown to directly effect final megasclere width (Table 4-9) (Simpson, 1978); lower temperature stimulated the formation of wider spicules suggesting a more efficient entrapment of silicic acid, namely, less escape of soluble forms of silicon from the polymerization system. The effect of temperature on megasclere and microsclere length had little correlation with the temperatures employed except in the case of one type of microsclere, toxas, which were longer at higher temperatures.

Table 4-8 Effects of Silicic Acid Concentration on Megasclere Secretion in *Ephydatia fluviatilis*[a]

Silicic Acid Concentration (mM)	Spicule Length (μm)	Spicule Width (μm)	SiO$_2$/Spicule (ng)	SiO$_2$/Sponge (μg)	Number of Spicules Per Sponge
0.025	159 ± 13	2.95 ± 0.05	2.37	0.69	292
0.250	173 ± 29	6.0 ± 0.1	6.00	1.26	212
1.0	173 ± 18	6.4 ± 0.1	—	—	—

[a]Data taken from Pé (1973). Mean values have been calculated and are presented.

Table 4-9 Temperature Effects on Spicule Secretion in *Microciona prolifera*[a]

Spicule Type and Dimension	Means ± SEM (in μm)			P (at 95% Confidence Level)			
	15°C	20°C	25°C	15°C vs 20°C	20°C vs 25°C	15°C vs 25°C	
Megascleres							
Thick styles							
Length	220.1 ± 5.4	190.6 ± 5.1	211.5 ± 5.3	s.	s.	n.s.	
Width	9.4 ± 0.14	9.0 ± 0.12	8.4 ± 0.14	s.	s.	s.	
Acanthostyles							
Length	82.4 ± 1.1	83.9 ± 1.1	84.3 ± 0.9	n.s.	n.s.	n.s.	
Width	6.8 ± 0.1	6.5 ± 0.1	5.5 ± 0.1	n.s.	s.	s.	
Microscleres (Lengths only)							
Chelas	17.6 ± 0.06	17.6 ± 0.16	16.9 ± 0.14	n.s.	s.	n.s.	
Toxas	13.9 ± 0.56	15.9 ± 0.66	17.2 ± 0.69	s.	n.s.	s.	

[a]Data taken from Simpson (1978); n.s., not significant; s., significant.

As demonstrated in other silicification systems (Azam and Volcani, 1981), notably in diatoms, the element germanium (Ge) acts as a strong inhibitor of silicification in sponges (Elvin, 1972; Simpson *et al.*, 1979). At equimolar concentration, germanium completely inhibits silica deposition. At lower ratios (Ge/Si 0.1, for example) spicules are secreted and display a number of interesting features, some of which are comparable to low and high silicon concentration effects. In *Spongilla lacustris,* at a Ge/Si of 0.14, shorter, narrower, and fewer spicules (both mega- and microscleres) are formed. The reduction in the number of microscleres is four times greater than that in megascleres resulting in proportionately fewer microscleres. These effects are completely comparable to those of low silicic acid concentration, including the reduction in percentage of microscleres (Jorgensen, 1944), and indicate that germanium lowers the effective silicic acid concentration, possibly through competition. In addition, permissive concentrations of Ge, down to relatively low Ge/Si ratios of 0.005, result in the formation of bulbs on megascleres (Fig. 4-28) (Elvin, 1972) and of either bulbs or irregular thickenings on microscleres (Simpson *et al.*, 1979). At Ge/Si of 14.0, ultrastructural studies of nonsilicified spicules demonstrates "excess" silicalemma synthesis concomitant with large expansions of this membrane (Simpson and Vaccaro, 1974). The axial filament is assembled despite the absence of silicification thus establishing that silicification is not a requirement for its synthesis (Fig. 4-28A). These short "spicules" with expanded silicalemmae suggest that germanium inhibits the growth in length of the axial filament but not the assembly of new silicalemma (Simpson, 1981). The employment of an isotope of germanium, [68]Ge, has recently demonstrated that Ge is incorporated into the silica and thus may produce abnormal morphology of the spicules because of this (Davie *et al.*, 1983).

Morphogenetic and Developmental Aspects of Siliceous Spicule Secretion

As with calcareous spicules, two general morphogenetic processes are recognizable: the determination of spicule morphology and the orientation of spicules in relation to the overall morphology of the animal or to "local" morphology. There are many examples of specific spicule morphology and of relatively precise localization, although in the case of localization there are varying degrees of regularity. A specific spicule type may occur only encased in spongin but may have various orientation relative to the whole animal, suggesting that the overall morphological pattern of the animal is not a directing influence for spicule placement but that spongin secretion is. It appears rare that specific spicule types have precise orientation relative to the axes of the whole animal as occurs with calcareous spicules. On the other hand, there have been no precise quantitative, detailed studies of such orientation which are required in order to establish if, indeed, it exists. It seems probable in species with radially

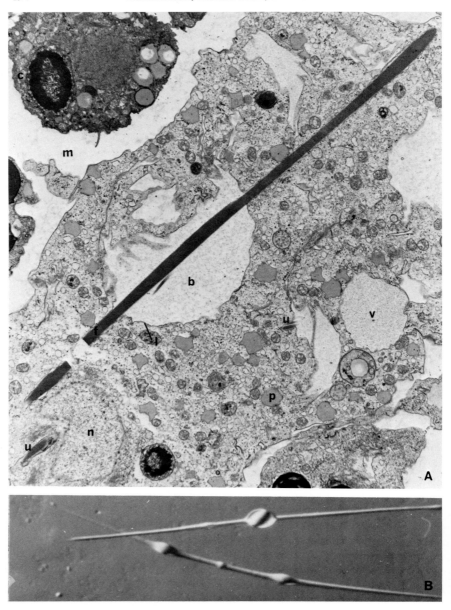

Figure 4-28 Effects of germanium (Ge) on silicification in *Spongilla lacustris*. **A.**
A megasclerocyte that has developed an axial filament (*f*) without silicification.
The silicalemma (*l*) has formed a large bulbous structure (*b*). Abnormal, supernu-
merary filaments (*u*) also are present as well as abnormal, large vacuoles (*v*). *n*,
nucleus; *p*, lipid; *c*, choanocyte; *m*, mesohyl (TEM) (×6,300) (Simpson and Vaccaro, 1974). **B.** Megascleres formed in a medium containing a Ge/Si molar ratio of
0.1. Note the large, abnormal bulbs and compare with A. (×135) (Simpson, 1981).

arranged spicules that some degree of uniformity in spicule orientation does occur. This is also very likely in the hexactinellids (Tuzet, 1973b). Siliceous spicules are not crystalline so the question of an orientation of a crystallographic axis need not be raised. In the case of the entrapped spicules of sclerosponges, these may very well have specific orientation relative to the crystalline axes of the aragonite in which they are embedded as well as specific orientation relative to the major axes of the whole animal (see Fig. 4-19).

It is very clear that specific spicule morphology can develop in the absence of an adult morphological pattern (as with calcitic spicules), since in hatching gemmules and metamorphosing larvae, spicules are secreted in the absence of any functional canal system or mature morphological pattern. This point is important to keep in mind in considering morphogenetic questions of silica deposition. The determination of such specific morphology has been related to the shape of the axial filament by Reiswig (1971c) in megascleres of demosponges and hexactinellids and since the morphology of megascleres in sclerosponges is similar to that in demosponges this view is probably also applicable to them. The square cross-sectional shape of hexactinellid axial filaments is viewed as giving rise to three separate axes and thus to the hexactine configuration, and the supposed triangular filament of demosponges could likewise give rise to the four axes of tetraxons in some demosponges (tetractinomorphs). Monactinal spicules could arise due to the absence (inhibition) of branching of the filament. There are a number of problems with this model including whether the shape of the axial canal can be considered the same as that of the axial filament and the observed hexagonal, rather than triagonal, shape of demosponge spicules examined ultrastructurally. Despite these problems, this formulation provides a useful basis for future investigations. If correct, then all major axes of siliceous spicules would be determined by the intrinsic geometry of the axial filament. There is no way of applying this view to microscleres, however. Also, swellings on megascleres are not interpretable on this basis, since in some cases no special feature of the axial filament is associated with them (Simpson, 1981). Consequently, the silicalemma must also be considered as a determinant for certain spicule features. This membrane appears to be the silicic acid transporting system and thus the growth in length of the axial filament (or its branches) must be precisely coupled with growth and activity of the silicalemma. Such a conclusion is supported by results obtained with germanium which appears to uncouple these two components by inhibiting the growth (in length) of the filament but not that of the silicalemma (Fig. 4-29). The large bulbs formed in germanium appear to be a result of excess silicalemma synthesis and assembly. However, it is still not clear why there is a localization of the excess silicalemma and thus of silica along the filament. Possible explanations are that regions of the silicalemma are continuous with the plasmalemma, or more likely that regions of the silicalemma have

NORMAL, COUPLED GROWTH

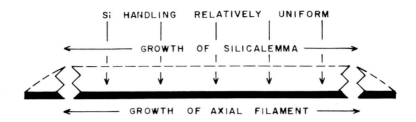

GERMANIUM UNCOUPLING OF GROWTH

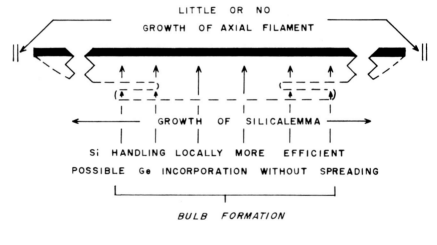

Figure 4-29 Suggested model of the mode of germanium induced changes in spicule morphology. Under control conditions, the growth of the silicalemma and axial filament are coupled producing a uniform spicule morphology. Germanium is hypothesized to uncouple the two components, inhibiting filament growth in length but permitting silicalemma growth resulting in a piling up of the latter in localized regions where bulbs form. It is still not clear why the silicalemma piles up at *specific points*, but this suggests a discontinuous growth mechanism of the silicalemma along the length of the developing spicule (Simpson, 1981).

higher growth or transport rates. The presence of swellings in control spicules may also be a result of unevenness in activity. Thus, some features in the silica of spicules may be related solely to the silicalemma and its activity (Simpson, 1981). A great deal of difficult ultrastructural work remains to be undertaken.

Assuming that the information for the geometry of the filament is contained within the sclerocyte, the question arises as to how certain sclerocytes are triggered to begin spicule secretion in a specific region of the tissue. Of all the developmental questions that can be raised, this is probably the most difficult to address and the absence of relevant data attests to this. During development there are two broad possibilities: sclerocytes could be distributed evenly throughout the tissue and then could secrete spicules whenever they have differentiated, or specific initiation sites could be present with which sclerocytes interact resulting in spicule secretion. The latter seems more probable in view of the regularity of distance between newly secreted spicules reported in developing reaggregation masses of *Ophlitaspongia seriata* (Lévi, 1960). Garrone (1978) has suggested a possible role for proteoglycans in the immobilization of cells during development and such could play an important role in these processes. Following the initial formation of the skeleton, it is much simpler to envisage it as acting as an inducer for further patterned spicule secretion. In demosponges in which spicules eventually become encased in spongin, it has been established that spiculogenesis of megascleres occurs first, followed by the association of spongocytes with the spicule (Lévi, 1960; Garrone and Pottu, 1973; Simpson, 1963; Weissenfels, 1978) and then by the secretion of spongin which comes to surround the megasclere and join it to other megascleres in a spongin network (Fig. 4-30). The initial megasclere–spongin complex could act as an induction site for continued megasclere and collagen secretion and thus the further production of the primary skeleton could become a closed, self-initiating system. The silica in spicules is considered to act as a chemotactic site for the attraction of spongocytes which come to aggregate around them (Garrone, 1978). It is of significance that spongocytes do not aggregate around microscleres (and thus the absence of their encasement in spongin). Possibly, the cell surface components of megasclerocytes or their spicules are different from those of microsclerocytes; certainly the cells differ significantly. The early megascleres secreted have been reported to be actively moved in a position whereby one of their ends becomes embedded in the basal layer of collagen (Weissenfels, 1978); the other end is then covered by one or more exopinacocytes which are pushed outward as they are reflected over the spicule surface. During protrusion, the exopinacocytes are thought to secrete spongin on the spicule surface. The protrusion of exopinacocytes by developing spicules in demosponges is a similar phenomenon to that which occurs in calcareous sponges and neither process is fully understood. The positioning of these megascleres may be further

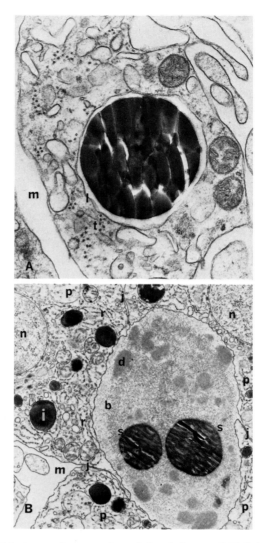

Figure 4-30 Initiation and maturation of the skeleton of *Haliclona* sp. (TEMs).
A. Cross section of intracellular spicule secretion. Note the presence of numerous
microtubules (*t*). *m*, mesohyl; *l*, silicalemma (×20,800) (Garrone, 1969a). **B**. Following extrusion of the spicules from their megasclerocytes, spongocytes (*p*)
surround the freed spicules (*s*) and enrobe them in spongin microfibrils (*b*), some
of which form dense bodies (*d*) in the developing spongin fiber. The spongocytes
characteristically possess well-developed rough endoplasmic reticulum (*r*) and
dense inclusions (*i*). *n*, spongocyte nucleus; *m*, mesohyl; *j*, junctions between
spongocytes (×10,400) (Garrone *et al.*, 1981). (**A**, courtesy Dr. R. Garrone; **B**,
courtesy Dr. J. Pottu-Boumendil.)

influenced by mechanical forces such as tension (Borojevic, 1971) and contraction of the sponge tissue (Pavans de Ceccatty, 1974a,b).

There are many remaining problems to be addressed concerning the maturation of the primary skeleton. In some species it is very regular and the factors responsible for this are not clear. Furthermore, the preceding discussion is based upon very meager data and therefore should be taken only as a vague outline of some of the events. The interaction of spicules with spongocytes most certainly cannot be at the basis of the morphogenesis of spongin networks in horny sponges because the latter do not secrete spicules. If silicon is still involved, it must be bound to ground substance elements as has been reported in the connective tissue of vertebrates (Schwarz, 1973).

With the exception of gemmoscleres, the secretion of microscleres presents a somewhat different situation since they are not associated with spongin or spongocytes. The means of control for the placement of them is unknown, but some form of regulation must occur in some species. For example, in a number of tetractinellid demosponges, there are layers of asters which specially contribute to the cortex (Chap. 3). In gemmule formation, microscleres are actively moved, by their microsclerocytes and "helper" cells (Chap. 8), into a specific position in the developing collagenous coat (Evans, 1901; Rasmont, 1956). The latter is an intriguing event since spongocytes are known to be attracted to megascleres and/or their megasclerocytes (Garrone, 1978) while in the case of gemmoscleres, microsclerocytes appear to react chemotactically toward spongocytes and/or the spongin. Some microscleres, while tending to occur in association with the pinacoderms are also apparently randomly distributed in the mesohyl. There has been no detailed, quantitative mapping of microsclere distribution in any sponge and until this information is available it is really too soon to decide whether specific localizations occur with some types. The absence of them in spongin suggests a complex situation in which the secretion of spongin may be causally related to the secretion of megascleres, but not to microscleres and in which the continued secretion of megascleres, but not microscleres (except in the case of gemmules), may be related to prior spongin secretion. The appearance of spongin is thus not a necessary event in order for microscleres to form. For example, in undifferentiated areas of outgrowth in *Microciona prolifera,* microscleres appear before any local formation of spongin occurs (Simpson, 1963).

The Secretion of Other Siliceous Structures

Although there have been no studies of the initial secretion of entrapped siliceous megascleres, it can be assumed, based upon their morphology, that they are formed in the same manner as demosponge megascleres; namely, initial secretion by a single megasclerocyte in the mesohyl. The erosion of their surface, predominantly the surface entrapped in aragonite, suggests a unique interaction between silicification, matrix elaboration, and calcification. It is not known if the localization of these megascleres in the sponge tissue is regular, but this is possible based upon their arrangement after entrapment. The angle of the entrapped spicules relative to the aragonitic skeleton also seems very regular and the rounded ends of styles appear always to be the first part of the spicule to be entrapped. This same spicule end is first encased in an organic, fibrillar matrix, either prior to or following the extrusion of the spicule from its megasclerocyte. Now, there is good documentation that during growth and development the edges of encrusting sponges are periodically pulled centrally, leaving some abandoned spicules on the surrounding substratum (Pé, 1973). In sclerosponges, a similar pulling "up" of the tissue in contact with the old aragonite could similarly result in such spicule abandonment. In this case, the released spicules would have to have precise orientation when released and would than become entrapped in the newly deposited aragonite. If such a phenomenon occurs, there must be a coordinated sequence of events resulting in partial release, followed by calcification, followed by additional release and continuing calcification. During pulling back, the tissue would have to be in contact with the old aragonite long enough to carry out further calcification.

Nothing can be said concerning the secretion of siliceous scales except that they appear to be secreted within sclerocytes of unknown structure (Garrone, 1974). It is not established whether axial filaments are present but if they are, their geometry is a matter of some interest due to the unique morphology of the scale.

Schmidt (1879), Sollas (1888), and others concluded that the cemented desmas of lithistids arise initially as single spicules within single sclerocytes and that the cementing of them occurs through the intervention of additional, secondary sclerocytes. There are no recent data on such skeletons other than scanning electron micrographs (Vacelet and Vasseur, 1971; Hartman, 1981) which verify that the articulations include separate spicules (Fig. 4-31B). Specific portions (the rhabdomes) of the articulated desmas of *Racodiscula incrustans* are directed toward the surface of the animal (Vacelet and Vasseur, 1971) indicating specific orientation of the individual spicules during their morphogenesis. Among hexactinellids, cemented skeletons in the Lychniscophora have been described as originating from the secondary deposition of silica on the rays of hexactines. The original hexactine then comes to form a lantern-like structure in the interstices of the cemented principal skeleton (Fig. 4-31A). The formation of these lanterns entails (1) the initial secretion of the hexactine, (2) the secondary deposition of silica on the hexactine rays, (3) the cementing together of their rays with the rest of the siliceous latticework. The secretion of the principal latticework of glass skeletons defies even conceptualization and pioneering work is required in order to gain insight into the mode of development of cemented skeletons in both lithistids and hexactinellids.

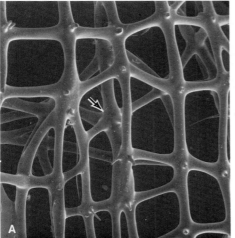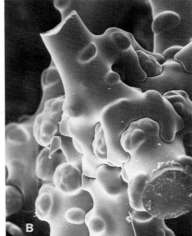

Figure 4-31 Fused and articulated siliceous skeletons (SEMs). **A.** The fused, dictyonine skeleton of the hexactinellid, *Farrea facunda*. The interstices (*arrow*) of the latticework are hexactines each of which has become fused to single rays of six others although the pattern of fusing may not always be absolute (×40) (Hartman, 1981). **B.** Cemented (articulated) skeleton of the lithistid, *Racodiscula* sp. The extremities of the individual desmas grow together in a very precise manner to form articulations. It is not clear whether cementing material is present at the junctions (×400) (Hartman, 1981). (Both courtesy Prof. W. D. Hartman.)

Iron Containing Deposits

The presence of significant amounts of iron (Fe) in some sponges has been known for many years [see Vinogradov (1953) for an excellent review of the early literature] and granules of iron oxide were conjectured to be foreign to the sponge (see Towe and Rutzler, 1968). A recent restudy by the latter authors of iron containing granules embedded within the spongin fibers of *Ircinia* and *Spongia* has appeared. X-ray and electron diffraction analyses demonstrated that the iron is in the form of lepidocrocite. The small crystals of lepidocrocite appear very pure, are embedded in the collagenous matrix of the spongin, and at least some of them are "membrane" bound (Fig. 4-32). Based upon these observations, Towe and Rutzler (1968) conclude that the granules are the result of biological activity and represent true biomineralization in species that do not secrete calcareous or siliceous secretory products. Garrone *et al.* (1973) have also identified lepidocrocite crystals but within the special collagenous filaments of *Ircinia* (Chap. 5) as well as in the spongin fibers, and Garrone (1978) has observed them in an organic spiculoid of *Igernella*. They are also present in *Aplysina* (*Verongia*) (Vacelet, 1971a) and in *Hippospongia* fibers (Junqua *et al.*, 1974).

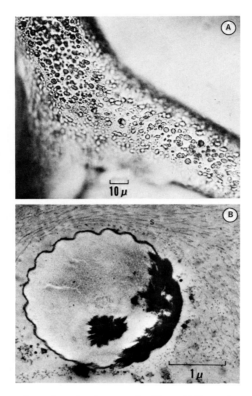

Figure 4-32 Iron deposits. **A**. A spongin fiber of *Spongia graminea* containing numerous iron containing granules of lepidocrocite (light micrograph) ($\times500$) (Towe and Rutzler, 1968). **B**. A "membrane-bound" granule that is partially mineralized. *S*, spongin (TEM) ($\times15,000$) (Towe and Rutzler, 1968). (Copyright 1968 by the American Association for the Advancement of Science.) (Both courtesy Dr. K. M. Towe.)

Excavation of Calcareous Substrata

General Features of Burrowing and the Species Involved

The etching and excavation of calcareous substrata (Fig. 4-33) by marine demosponges have usually been considered restricted to the orders Hadromerida and Haplosclerida with species in the families Clionidae, Spirastrellidae, and Adociidae displaying this capacity to "bore into" or burrow such substrata (Rutzler, 1971, 1974). Recently, however, species in the order Poecilosclerida (possibly of the genera *Acarnus* and *Acanthacarnus*) have also been found to possess this ability (Pomponi, 1976) (Table 4-10). The substratum which is burrowed by them consists of calcium carbonate but there appears to be no specificity for the type of

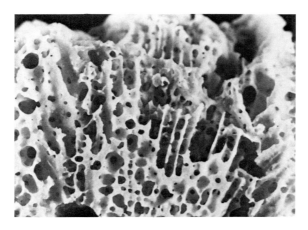

Figure 4-33   A portion of an aragonitic coral skeleton into which *Cliona lampa* has burrowed. Note the extensive removal of calcium carbonate and the tunnels (holes) seen in cross-sectional view (light micrograph) (×3.0) (Rutzler, 1974). (Courtesy Dr. K. Rutzler.)

crystalline morph present; the rates of removal of substratum by *Cliona lampa* are the same regardless of whether calcite, magnesium calcite, aragonite, or mixed calcite and aragonite compose the substratum (Neumann, 1966) (Table 4-11). When burrowing sponges attack living coral, they show a marked tendency to grow on and into the basal parts (oldest) where there is no living coral tissue and they do not directly affect the living polyps (Goreau and Hartman, 1963). The regularity of the substratum surface directly effects the efficiency of burrowing, since in areas where the sponge does not make contact with the substratum there is no burrowing (Neumann, 1966), establishing the essentiality of direct cellular contact for the process to take place. The degree of burrowing depends upon the species and the length of time that the tissue has been in contact

Table 4-10   Burrowing Species[a]

Species	References
Class: Demospongiae	
Subclass: Tetractinomorpha	
Order: Hadromerida	
Family: Spirastrellidae	
Spheciospongia othella	Rutzler (1974), Pomponi (1977)
Anthosigmella varians	Pomponi (1977), Vicente (1978), Pang (1973)

Continued

Table 4-10 Burrowing Species[a] (*Continued*)

Species	References
Order: Hadromerida *cont.*	
Family: Clionidae	
Cliona with numerous species:	
celata, lobata, vastifica, truitti	Hartman (1958a), Pomponi (1976, 1977), Warburton (1958a,b), Guida (1976), Cobb (1969, 1975)
caribbaea, lampa, flavifodina, paucispina, dioryssa, varmifera, amplicavata	Hechtel (1965), Pang (1973), Pomponi (1976), Rutzler (1974, 1975), Rutzler and Rieger (1973), Neumann (1966)
euryphylla	Bergquist (1968)
rovignensis, albicans, schmidti, hancocki, viridis	Hartman (1957), Pomponi (1977), Pang (1973), Hechtel (1965)
delitrix	Pomponi (1977), Pang (1973)
peponaca, langae, aprica, laticavicola, janitrix, rhodensis	Pang (1973)
Thoosa mollis	Rutzler and Bromley (1981), Hartman (1957)
Order: Uncertain	
Family: Uncertain	
Alectona jamaicensis	Pang (1973)
Subclass: Ceractinomorpha	
Order: Haplosclerida	
Family: Adociidae	
Siphonodictyon	
mucosa	Bergquist (1965), Rutzler (1971)
brevitubulatum	Pang (1973)
cachacrouense, siphonum, coralliphagum	Rutzler (1971)
Order: Poecilosclerida	
Family: Clathriidae	
? *Acarnus* or *Acanthacarnus* sp.	Pomponi (1976)

[a]Only the more recent papers dealing with burrowing sponges are included. For a review of some of the earlier literature, see Hartman (1958a).

Table 4-11 Rates of Burrowing of *Cliona lampa* into Various Substrata[a]

Experimental Conditions	Substratum Material	Texture	Mineralogy	Initial Substratum Weight (g)	Total Weight Loss (g)	Area (cm²)	Weight Loss (g) m⁻²/100 Days⁻¹
Laboratory aquaria[b]	Algal ball	Porous	Mg–calcite	10.48	0.11	10.67	223
	Coral	Porous	Aragonite	6.80	0.04	5.92	145
	Calcarenite	Porous	Calcite–aragonite	7.09	0.04	6.72	128
Laboratory aquaria[b]	Coral	Dense	Aragonite	3.48	0.04	4.23	206
	Stalactite	Dense	Calcite	8.60	0.05	5.56	193
	Algal ball	Porous	Mg–calcite	10.77	0.09	10.72	180
Laboratory aquaria[b]	Coral	Dense	Aragonite	7.71	0.13	5.65	498
	Shell	Dense	Aragonite	3.59	0.06	3.10	421
	Stalactite	Dense	Calcite	6.25	0.08	5.11	340
Natural habitat[c]	Shell	Dense	Aragonite	6.30	0.77	7.66	3,000
	Shell	Dense	Aragonite	7.80	0.27	7.34	1,100
	Algal ball	Porous	Mg–calcite	12.59	0.28	10.34	810
Natural habitat[d]	Limestone	Dense	Calcite	17.00	3.68	5.65	6,513
	Marble	Dense	Calcite	8.05	2.18	4.21	5,178
	Shell	Dense	Aragonite	6.81	2.32	5.64	4,113

[a]Data taken from Neumann (1966).
[b]Sponges maintained for 46 days.
[c]Sponges grown for 33 days.
[d]Sponges grown for 100 days.

with the substratum; under field conditions this is directly related to the age of the sponge. As a result of burrowing the surface of the substratum becomes pitted by adjoining, more or less regularly shaped, depressions that remain when ''chips'' of the substratum have been burrowed out (Fig. 4-34). All surfaces eroded by sponges display this surface characteristic. The sponge may eventually burrow deep into the substratum pro-

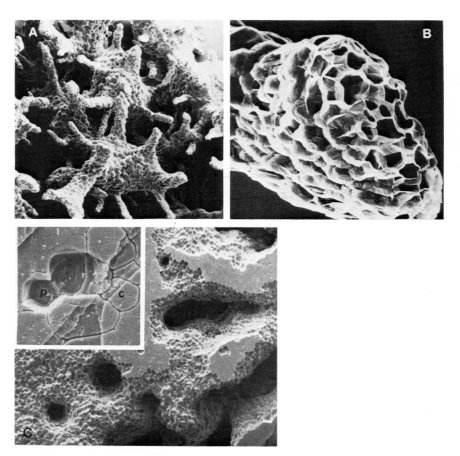

Figure 4-34 The formation of tunnels, pits, and chips by *Cliona lampa* (SEMs). **A**. Epoxy cast of tunnels showing the pitted surface (negative image) of the walls (×36) (Rutzler and Rieger, 1973). **B**. Epoxy cast of the blind end of a tunnel showing (in negative image) the polygonal crevices identical to surface etching patterns (×27) (Rutzler and Rieger, 1973). **C**. Surface view of etching of a crystal of Iceland spar. Large tunnels have also been produced in the substratum (×45). **Inset:** Initial etching pattern on the surface of Iceland spar showing pits (*p*) and chips (*c*) the latter of which are not yet removed from the substratum (×450) (Rutzler and Rieger, 1973). (All courtesy Dr. K. Rutzler.)

ducing tunnels or galleries, the walls of which look just like the originally eroded surface (Fig. 4-34B). The process of burrowing has two basic components: the dissolution of calcium carbonate and the physical removal of small chips of the substratum. According to Rutzler and Rieger (1973) only 2–3% of the total calcium carbonate removed is due to dissolution, the remaining 97–98% is in the form of chips, which eventually are thrown off by the sponge. Since the process of etching encompasses the movement of cell processes into the etched substratum it also has a mechanical component.

Cellular Basis of Etching

A number of recent electron microscopic studies of the process of burrowing have appeared and a general outline of this highly complex process can be presented based upon the pioneering studies of Warburton (1958a), Cobb (1969, 1975), Pomponi (1976, 1977, 1979a,b), and Rutzler and Rieger (1973), the latter being the most comprehensive investigation. Pomponi (1980) has recently reviewed the question of the cell mechanisms involved in burrowing. The etching cells initially possess archeocyte features (Rutzler and Rieger, 1973) but during etching they lose their nucleoli, a condition further recorded in a number of additional species by Pomponi (1977, 1979a,b). The cell size is variable but lies within the range of $25–30 \times 3–15 \ \mu$m. Each cell in contact with the calcareous substratum etches a polygonally shaped crevice into it; the crevice so produced by *Cliona lampa,* for example, is 150 to 250 nm in width but can be up to 300–800 nm where it is closest to the point of origin, namely, the first etched surface. The initial etchings are about $39 \times 37 \ \mu$m in maximum diameters and are some $12–17 \ \mu$m deep. The crevices are filled with extremely thin filopodia of the etching cells which measure about 200 nm in diameter. These filopodia then change direction and come to undercut the substratum resulting in the freeing of a calcareous chip from the surface. Filopodia from neighboring cells may also be found within a crevice. An immense number of filopodia are involved in etching, thus creating a huge surface area of cell membrane in contact with the surface. When the chip is freed these filopodia make up a surrounding "filopodial basket"; on the surfaces of the filopodia is a flocculent material. The chips have very uniform dimensions both within and between species (Table 4-12) and, when freshly produced, such chips can be identified in marine sediments (Rutzler, 1975) since they have very characteristic surfaces. Scanning electron micrographs of them and of the sides of the microscopic depressions left at the substratum surface display a terracing pattern (Pomponi, 1976; Cobb, 1975) or a lamellate one, suggesting that etching by each cell may occur in waves of activity. Etching cells, one per chip, gradually undergo disintegration during, as well as following, the etching process. A flocculent secretory product is formed within the etching cells and its appearance marks the beginning of cell degeneration. Once the chip is

Table 4-12 Range of Diameters of Chips and Pits Produced by Burrowing Sponges[a]

Pits[b]	Chips[b]	Species	Substratum	Reference
45–70			*Crossostrea* shell	Hartman (1958a)
	30–50		*Crossostrea* shell	Warburton (1958a)
25–82			*Mercenaria* shell	Hartman (1958a)
	20–60		*Venus* shell	Warburton (1958a)
65–85		*Cliona celata*	Calcarenite	Rutzler and Rieger (1973)
35–45	25–45		Calcite crystal	Warburton (1958a)
	85(X̄)		Calcite crystal	Cobb (1969)
	15–30		Conchiolin	Warburton (1958b)
	19–26		Conchiolin	Cobb (1969)
50–75	31–71	*Cliona lampa*	*Chama* shell	
18–45			Calcarenite	
18–64	28–30		Calcite crystal	
	22–40		Conchiolin	
24–62		*Clinoa* sp.	Calcarenite	Rutzler and Rieger (1973)
45–65		Pliocene clionid	Coral	
49–94		*Cliona hancocki*	Calcarenite	
20–35		*Anthosigmella varians*	Calcarenite	
45–60		*Spheciospongia othella*	Calcarenite	
30–50		*Siphonodictyon coralliphagum*	Coral	

[a] Data taken from Rutzler and Rieger (1973).
[b] In micrometers.

totally etched it is moved into an excurrent canal. Through direct observation, chips have been seen to be pushed out of the tissue in the excurrent stream of water emitted from oscules. The initial movement of the chip apparently involves the invasion into the crevice of new etching cells which help to dislodge it (Rutzler and Rieger, 1973). When bivalve shells (such as *Mytilus*) serve as a substratum for *Cliona celata,* the etching cells also etch the periostracum (Nassonov, 1924; Warburton, 1958b; Cobb, 1975) demonstrating that the process is able to dislocate, denature, or destroy organic matrix as well as remove calcium carbonate. Some destruction of the hinge ligament of oysters has also been reported (Warburton, 1958b).

After burrowing has proceeded for some time, holes (tunnels) are produced in the substratum (if the sponge produces this more advanced form of burrowing) and the choanosome somes to occupy them except at their blind ends where etching is actively proceeding; such etching proceeds on the walls of the tunnels in the same fashion as at the surface. The tunnels at the surface of the substratum house tissue that functions either as excurrent or incurrent passageways (Fig. 4-35) or papillae (Goreau and Hartman, 1963) (see Chap. 6). In some species of *Siphonodictyon* the structures are relatively large and extend above the surface of the substratum to form "cones" (Rutzler, 1971). Burrowing may not proceed this far and the surface of the substratum alternatively can remain overlain by tissue and the depressions (or chambers) contain extensions of the surface

Figure 4-35 *Cliona lampa* burrowed into the coral, *Favia fragum.* The coral surface is covered by a thin layer of sponge tissue without evident etching. The sponge has burrowed two large tunnels into the coral, which apparently houses the canal system (light micrograph) (×2.2) (Rutzler and Rieger, 1973). (Courtesy Dr. K. Rutzler.)

tissue. The distribution of tunnels suggests that there are specific areas of the basal layer of the tissue that become more active than neighboring areas. In some species, such as *Cliona celata,* this can result in relatively uniformly distributed holes in the substratum (Hartman, 1958a). The substratum surface between these holes is surficially etched and may contain depressions or chambers establishing that the tissue overlaid it at some time. In many species, the tissue at the substratum surface between the incurrent and excurrent papillae is thin or lost and the only visible tissue is the papillae (Hartman, 1958a). In *Cliona dioryssa,* however, some additional tissue surrounding the papillae may be maintained (Rutzler, 1974). When only papillae are visible at the substratum surface, this growth stage is referred to as the alpha stage and is typical of burrowing clionids but occurs also in *Spheciospongia othella* (Rutzler, 1974). In many species, the walls of the tunnels of the alpha stage are further etched and eventually neighboring tunnels interconnect until finally there is no more substratum remaining and the sponge exists as a large, sometimes unattached organism referred to as the gamma stage. The beta stage is that which is intermediate between the alpha and the gamma stages (Hartman, 1958a). Gamma stage explants, when tied to calcareous substrata initiate new etching (Hartman, 1958a) demonstrating that there is no loss of etching capacity with either age or size. However, alpha-stage explants etch replicate substrata at much higher rates (Hartman, 1958a) possibly indicating that the stock of etching cells is somewhat depleted in the gamma-stage tissue (Table 4-13).

Mechanisms of Burrowing

The physical events in etching are now well established in terms of the activities of individual etching cells. It is clear that earlier views of mechanical abrasion of the substratum as a sole means of etching must be abandoned [see Goreau and Hartman (1963) for a review of this literature]. The very thin filopodia (Fig. 4-36), while possibly exerting a positive pressure against the substratum, must be involved in chemical or biochemical dissolution to produce the resulting crevice. Warburton (1958a) was unable to demonstrate the presence of an acid secretion, however. It is still not established whether such an acid secretion is involved nor has it been shown whether the etching process is totally intra- or extracellular. The presence of a flocculent material both intracellularly and on the surfaces of the filopodia suggests that an organic product is involved, and there is evidence to suggest that this substance is secreted from the filopodia during etching. If its action is based upon direct chemical interaction with the calcium carbonate, secretion would have to take place first. Rutzler and Rieger (1973) initially suggested the involvement of carbonic anhydrase in etching and this has now been clearly established. Hatch (1980) has biochemically demonstrated the presence of carbonic anhydrase in *Cliona lampa* and has found higher

Table 4-13 Comparison of Burrowing of Alpha- and Gamma-Stage
Transplants of *Cliona celata*[a]

Age of Shell (years)	Side of Shell on which Sponge was Attached	Penetration of Shell[b]			
		By Alpha Transplant (days)		By Gamma Transplant (days)	
		at 66	at 115	at 66	at 115
2	Lower	12	20	NR[c]	NR
2	Upper	1	3	NR	NR
3	Lower	9	12	NR	NR
3	Upper	13	24	0	3
4	Lower	7	22	0	6
5	Lower	18	18	0	0
5	Upper	NR[c]	NR	0	4
6	Upper	0	3	0	6

[a]Data taken from Hartman (1958a).
[b]Number of holes burrowed through to the opposite side of the shell.
[c]Not recorded.

enzyme activity in actively burrowing sponges (alpha stage) as compared
to nonburrowing ones (gamma stage). The enzyme activity is associated
with a particulate cell fraction and sonication or solubilization with isobu-
tanol places it into solution. Acetazolamide, a specific inhibitor of carbonic anhydrase, inhibits etching but does not affect respiration, water

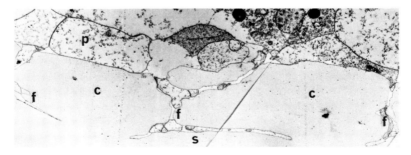

Figure 4-36 Etching cells (in cross section) of *Cliona lampa* in the process of
undercutting chips (*c*) in the substratum (*s*). The etching cell filopods (*f*) in two
adjacent cells have burrowed into the substratum which is here decalcified and
replaced with epoxy embedding medium. The chips are clearly outlined by the
filopodia. Note the degenerate appearance of the etching cell cytoplasm (*p*)
(TEM) (×2,500) (Rutzler and Rieger, 1973). (Courtesy Dr. K. Rutzler.)

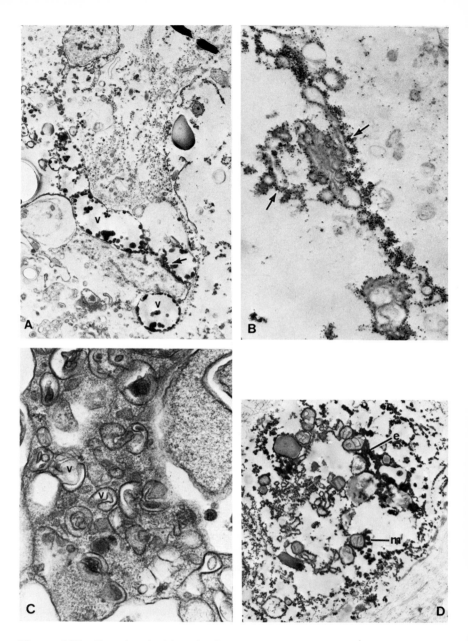

Figure 4-37 Cytochemical localization of enzymes in etching cells of clionids (TEMs). **A.** Localization of acid phosphatase activity (*arrow*) on the inner surfaces of the membranes of clear vesicles (*v*) in *Cliona langae*. Unstained (×7,470) (Pomponi, 1979a). **B.** Acid phosphatase activity (*Cliona delitrix*) can also be shown to be localized on the outer surfaces of cell processes (*arrows*) that are in contact with the substratum. Unstained (×26,280) (Pomponi, 1979c). **C.** Near the cell–substratum junction (*Cliona caribbaea*) etching cells can contain an array of

Table 4-14 Burrowing Rate and Inhibition of Carbonic Anhydrase in *Cliona lampa*[a]

Experimental Conditions	Milligrams CaCO$_3$ Removed/Day/Sponge (Two Experiments)	
Circulating fresh sea water (25 liters/min)	49.4 ± 6.5	39.9 ± 7.1
Recirculating (83%) sea water (Total rate 25 liters/min)	43.2 ± 9.4	39.1 ± 4.9
With 10^{-5} M sodium acetazolamide	3.3 ± 0.78	0.27 ± 0.89
With 10^{-6} M sodium acetazolamide	13.4 ± 1.1	13.8 ± 1.7

[a]Taken from Hatch (1980).

pumping, or cause contraction of the papillae (Table 4-14). Pomponi (1979b) has cytochemically localized this enzyme on the outer surfaces of the etching cell filopodia and between cell processes. Further cytochemical investigation has established the presence of acid phosphatase in etching cell endoplasmic reticulum, Golgi, lysosomes, phagosomes, vesicles, and tubular structures as well as on the surfaces of cell processes (Fig. 4-37) (Pomponi, 1979b,c). Such a widespread distribution also suggests the ability of these cells to digest organic matrices during burrowing, an observation previously discussed. Burrowing can thus be viewed as being both chemical and mechanical (Pomponi, 1980). Chemically, carbonic anhydrase is viewed as shifting the pH sufficiently to solubilize the substratum; acid phosphatase and other degradative enzymes are released and solubilize organic components while the movement of filopodia mechanically remove the chip at the end of the chemical phase (Pomponi, 1980). The flocculent material on the cell surfaces may consist partly of these two enzymes, but it is also possible that this material (or some other substance) acts intracellularly through chelating calcium ions. Many proteins as well as sponge proteoglycan (Chap. 9) are known to bind calcium and such substances could act by causing a calcium flux from substratum to cytoplasm. Indeed, excessive accumulation of calcium ions within the etching cells could be a reason for cell disintegration, including the release of flocculent material. Two of the difficulties encountered in studying such aspects of etching are the slowness of the process and the inaccessibility of the etching cells.

complex vesicles (*v*) some of which may eventually become exocytized in the region of etching (×36,270) (Pomponi, 1979a). (**A–C** Copyright Cambridge University Press.) **D**. Localization of carbonic anhydrase activity (*Cliona delitrix*) on membrane surfaces (*m*) and in extracellular spaces (*e*) of the etching cell surface (×11,250) (Pomponi, 1979b). (All courtesy Dr. S. A. Pomponi.)

The mechanism of movement of freed chips into the excurrent canals is not known but it is indicated that the etching cells may not be involved since they disintegrate. Other cells likely wedge themselves under the chip and help to dislodge it, initially, but the mechanism of its movement into the canal system can only be conjectured at present. As suggested regarding the entrapment of siliceous spicules in sclerosponges, the overlying tissue in burrowing sponges may contract thus moving the chips along with it. When relaxed, the chip could be left behind at some distance from the etched surface but still within the tissue. More than one chip, indeed many, in an entire area of the tissue could be simultaneously moved in this fashion. A number of rounds of such contractions can be envisaged with the chips finally reaching an excurrent canal. Such contractions (see Chap. 6) could also be instrumental in "squeezing" the chips between the endopinacocytes and into the excurrent stream of water. Regardless of the mechanism of chip movement, the process is a unique one, since in most biological systems foreign particles are either phagocytized or are walled off by connective tissue; both of these processes occur in sponges (Chaps. 6, 9).

The etching cells in these sponges are apparently special basopinacocytes and they are unique in that they do not secrete a basal layer of spongin. This fact may be of much importance for views of the chemical nature of the etching process. For example, it may be that these modified basopinacocytes have a highly altered collagen metabolism, which is expressed through the production (and secretion) of calcium chelators. Abundant collagen fibrils are produced intercellularly so there is no loss of this capacity in all cells (Rutzler and Rieger, 1973). If etching cells are considered modified basopinacocytes, their origin can be assumed to be the same as normal basopinacocytes, namely, from archeocytes or, when present, collencytes (Chap. 9). There are no definitive data on this question, and techniques will have to be developed for labeling and following cells. The typical archeocyte features of etching cells argues for an archeocyte origin as is the case with basopinacocytes in species lacking collencytes.

Morphogenetic Aspects of Burrowing

The growth and burrowing of these sponges entails a highly complex set of events in which a small, young, encrusting sponge begins etching the superficial substratum below it leading to the final development of an organism occupying a number of tunnels and interconnecting tunnels within the substratum with only a limited amount of tissue, the papillae, exposed to the sea water. We know most about the early phases of the process leading to surficial etching. In contrast, there is little information dealing with the overall events leading to the establishment of alpha and gamma stages. It is clear that a number of important, major morphogenetic events occur. In alpha-stage development, it is not certain whether the young sponge initially covers the total surface which then later contains only separate papillae. This seems likely since etching has been reported between papillae in some species (Rutzler, 1974). Alternatively, tunnels within the substratum could form branches that come back to the original surface and break through to form new papillae. Such U-shaped tunnels have actually been reported in *Cliona lampa* (Rutzler and Rieger, 1973). In the latter, no etching would be found between papillae since no tissue had been there. Both of these processes may be involved in the establishment of the alpha stage, but there may also be species differences in this regard. A further process must also be involved and that is the determination of whether a papilla will be incurrent or excurrent and no data or views are available on the subject. Possibly the constitution of the original overlying tissue is the determinant. Where tunnels form, the etching cells must have been more active or there must have been a better supply of them, again implying a degree of predetermination. The formation of the gamma stage ultimately involves the breaking through of all tunnels at the surface. Parts of the basopinacoderm (etching surface) might then be converted to exopinacoderm, a process unknown in other sponges. Very precise studies of the pattern of growth leading to alpha and gamma stages are needed in order to elucidate these intriguing events. Such investigations will require long-term observations of the same animals and will not be easily accomplished.

CHAPTER FIVE

Collagen Fibrils, Spongin, Matrix Substances

Collagen fibrillogenesis is a universal process in sponges and in some species represents *the* secretory process while in others it is overshadowed by mineralization. In some ceractinomorph demosponges, colossal quantities of collagen are elaborated and requirements for precursors are undoubtedly very high. Although a major process, fibrillogenesis is a relatively slow one that presents challenging problems experimentally as does the resistance of sponge collagens to enzymatic degradation. Sponges also elaborate glycoproteins, and proteoglycans, and evidence is accumulating that some of these are associated with cell surfaces and collagen fibrils in addition to their presumed role in forming the intercellular ground substance. Some aspects of these substances as well as sponge lectins are dealt with further in Chapter Nine. Collagen has been best studied and an outstanding monograph on sponge collagens has recently appeared (Garrone, 1978). There is a wealth of information in this volume, including some original data not reported elsewhere, and reference to it is mandatory for those requiring complete details.

Collagen: Morphology, Chemistry, Distribution

Collagen Fibrils

Intercellular fibrils, which require electron microscopy to elucidate their structure, are present in sponges in two forms as categorized by Garrone (1978): smooth fibrils and rough fibrils. These two forms tend to be taxonomically distinct—smooth fibrils occurring in tetractinomorph demosponges and rough fibrils in ceractinomorphs. Also, in general, fibrils tend to be more densely packed in the former group than in the latter. However, since information is fairly limited, these two distinctions should be accepted with some caution (as, see below). Fibrils may be more concentrated in certain areas of the tissue such as in the ectosome or in tracts as in *Chondrosia* (Garrone, 1971), *Polymastia* (Boury-Esnault, 1974), and *Suberites* (Connes *et al.*, 1972). In species such as *Ephydatia mulleri* that have no ectosomal region but that have a dermal membrane, fibrils are more dense within the membrane and adjoining dermal areas than elsewhere (Pottu-Boumendil, 1975). The invasion of sponge tissue by commensal organisms can also lead to a walling off of the commensal by the sponge including the laying down of dense fibrous deposits (Connes *et al.*, 1971b) (Chap. 9).

Smooth fibrils, *in situ* (as distinguished from those isolated and purified from the tissue), are characterized by having a smooth surface, by usually appearing hollow, and by having a diameter of approximately 20 nm as in the demosponges *Chondrosia* (Garrone *et al.*, 1975), *Cyamon* (Smith and Lauritis, 1969). *Cliona* (Rutzler and Rieger, 1973), a clionid bud (Garrone, 1974), *Suberites* (Connes *et al.*, 1972), *Tethya* (Connes, 1967, 1968; Pavans de Ceccaty and Thiney, 1963, 1964), in freshwater species (Feige, 1969; Pottu-Boumendil, 1975), in the calcareous sponges *Leucandra* and *Sycon* (Ledger, 1974) and *Leucosolenia* (Jones, 1967) (Fig. 5-1). The freshwater species are an exception to the rule that smooth fibrils occur in tetractinomorph demosponges. In *Chondrosia*, the fibrils have a banding periodicity of approximately 22 nm. In general, such cross banding of fibrils is indistinct *in situ* but much better developed in isolated fibrils (see below). The fibrils in *Oscarella*, which like *Chondrosia* has no other skeleton, may actually be intermediate between smooth and rough fibrils in their morphology (Garrone, 1978).

Rough fibrils (Fig. 5-1C), *in situ*, possess thickenings, spaced at 22–25 nm, and are also about 20 nm in diameter; they occur widely in the ceractinomorph demosponges particularly as known in dictyoceratids (horny sponges) (Garrone, 1978). These fibrils generally do not appear tubular and do not occur in tight bundles as far as is known. In *Hippospongia communis* and *Ircinia variabilis* rough fibrils have a 20-25 nm banding pattern (Junqua *et al.*, 1974).

When fibrils are isolated from the sponge, their banding pattern can be studied more easily and in general they possess a 62 to 65 nm periodicity and in some cases have interband periods at 20 nm (as in *Microciona prolifera*) (Gross *et al.*, 1956), but other patterns may also be present and fibril diameters can also vary. For example, in *Leucandra* and *Sycon*, two types of fibrils are present: (1) small with 8 to 15 nm diameters and 25 to 30 nm periods and (2) giant fibrils with 30 to 150 nm diameters and 62 nm periods. Further, in juvenile individuals of *Sycon* there are 20 nm diameter fibrils with 50 nm periodicity (Ledger, 1974). The latter apparently consist of aligned groups of smaller fibrils with 5 nm diameters (Ledger, 1974). In *Scypha*, 15 nm fibrils with a periodicity of 62 nm occur as well as much larger fibrils with 200 to 400 nm diameters and 62 to 66 nm periods (Travis *et al.*, 1967; Travis, 1970). In the hexactinellid, *Euplectella*, 80 to 100 nm diameter fibrils are present with a very faint period of 54 nm (Travis *et al.*, 1967). In *Chondrosia* a 66 nm period is present within which are two light bands and one dark band each of 22 nm width (Garrone *et al.*, 1975). In the hexactinellid *Rhabdocalyptus dawsoni*, fibrils occur,

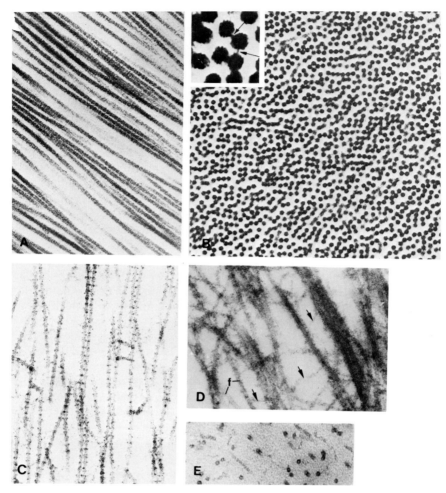

Figure 5-1   Collagen fibrils (TEMs). **A**. Intercellular, smooth, mesohyl fibrils of
Chondrosia reniformis showing a faint banding pattern (×90,000) (Garrone *et al.,*
1975). **B**. Cross section of *Chondrosia reniformis* fibrils. The inset demonstrates
cross links (*arrows*) between the fibrils (×67,500; **Inset:** ×252,000) (Garrone *et al.,*
1975). **C**. Rough collagen fibrils of *Euspongia officinalis*. Note distinct banding
pattern and roughened surface of each fibril (×49,500) (Garrone, 1978). **D**. Cross
links (*arrows*) between collagen fibrils (*f*) of *Sycon ciliatum* (×54,000) (Ledger,
1976). **E**. Cross section of fibrils in *Microciona prolifera* showing their hollow
nature (×74,700) (Bagby, unpubl.). (**A–C**, courtesy Dr. R. Garrone; **D**, courtesy
Dr. P. W. Ledger; **E**. courtesy Dr. R. M. Bagby.)

uniquely, in thin elongate tracts within the trabeculum (Fig. 2-15E) and especially in the dermal membrane (Fig. 2-15A); they have diameters of 15 nm and a period of 20 nm (Mackie and Singula, 1983).

Based upon staining patterns, there is reasonably good evidence that glycoproteins occur in association with fibrils. In *Chondrosia reniformis* and *Hippospongia communis,* phosphotungstic acid and ruthenium red staining indicate the presence of such associated proteins (Thiney and Garrone, 1970). Concanavalin-A binding to *Ephydatia mulleri* fibrils also demonstrates the presence of associated sugars (Pottu-Boumendil, 1975). In some cases, specific patterns emerge with ruthenium red staining (Garrone et al., 1975; Thiney and Garrone, 1970), and in *Ircinia* rough fibrils, filaments can be seen interconnecting the fibrils (Pavans de Ceccatty, 1973). Similar filaments connect the fibrils in *Chondrosia reniformis* which are surrounded by a layer of ruthenium red staining material (Garrone et al., 1975). Ruthenium red staining also results in a highlighted banding pattern in *Haliclona* and *Euspongia* fibrils (Garrone, 1978), suggesting that the roughness of these fibrils is due to glycoprotein association.

The chemistry of collagen fibrils has been studied in detail in three demosponges: *Ircinia variabilis* (Junqua et al., 1974), *Chondrosia reniformis* (Garrone et al., 1975), and *Spongia graminea* (Piez and Gross, 1959) (Table 5-1). No detailed analyses are available for demosponge species that also secrete siliceous spicules or for calcareous or hexactinellid sponges. Although Travis et al. (1967) have analyzed the amino acid composition of fibrils in a calcareous sponge, *Scypha,* these preparations were obviously not pure since no hydroxyproline content was detected and the glycine content was low (22.1%) in comparison to other collagens. Similarly, in the hexactinellid, *Euplectella,* the glycine content was even lower (13.2%) although 1.1% hydroxyproline was detected (Travis et al., 1967).

The data in Table 5-1 clearly establish that fibrils are collagen and that a very high percentage of glycosylated hydroxylysine is present; further, aspartic and glutamic acid contents are high. Infrared absorption spectra of sponge fibrils yield the same results as vertebrate collagens (Garrone et al., 1975; Garrone, 1978). Sponge fibrils are extremely resistant to chemical dissolution and are *not* solubilized by the following enzymes: collagenases, pronase, papain, elastase, chymotrypsin, pepsin, lysozyme (Gross et al., 1956; Garrone el at., 1975). Fibrils are associated with carbohydrate-rich substances containing glucosamine, uronic acids, mannose, fucose, and arabinose in *Spongia graminea* (Gross et al., 1956) and *Hippospongia gossyrina* (Katzman et al., 1970). In the latter species, glycosaminoglycans were found associated with the fibrils, and the unusual pentose, arabinose, was present in the polysaccharide (Katzman et al., 1970). Recently, Wilkinson et al. (1979) have discovered, in six demo-

Table 5-1   Composition of Fibrils[a]

| | Species | | |
Amino Acids	*Chondrosia reniformis*[b]	*Ircinia variabilis*[c]	*Spongia graminea*[d]
Glycine	306	316	315
Aspartic acid	104	89	92
Hydroxyproline	98	103	108
Glutamic acid	90	104	95
Alanine	62	64	78
Proline	63	64	78
Arginine	46	45	47
Threonine	43	44	43
Serine	45	43	38
Leucine	36	34	28
Valine	29	40	29
Isoleucine	25	27	—
Hyroxylysine	16	13	12
Phenylalanine	18	10	9.3
Lysine	7	9	9
Half-cystine	—	7	—
Tyrosine	6	4	4.7
Histidine	4	2	3.9
Methionine	2	Trace	4.7
Percentage lysine hydroxylated	70	59	57
Percentage hydroxylysine glycosylated	70	70	—

[a]Quantity of amino acids expressed as residue per 1,000 residues.
[b]Data taken from Garrone *et al.* (1975).
[c]Data taken from Junqua *et al.* (1974).
[d]Data taken from Piez and Gross (1959).

sponges, symbiotic bacteria capable of modifying the morphology of fibrils, thus suggesting that they are able to partially digest them.

Intercellular sponge collagen fibrils, which are defined on the basis of their diameter (20 nm) and on their position in the tissue—intercellular but not the major fibril component of the much larger spongin fibers— have been observed in all species studied ultrastructurally. They occur in all demosponges examined, but data for sclerosponges, calcareous sponges, and hexactinellids are fragmentary. In the latter, fibrils have a unique location in cytoplasmic pockets (Mackie and Singula 1983). It is clear that fibrils are present in calcareous sponges (Travis, 1970; Jones, 1967; Ledger, 1974) but not whether they are completely comparable to demosponge fibrils. There are no ultrastructural observations for sclerosponges, and data for hexactinellids are not detailed. Fibrils, 19 nm in diameter with a 22 nm banding pattern, are clearly present and very numerous in the free-floating buds of a clionid species (Garrone, 1974), and dense tracts of fibrils occur in the buds of *Tethya* (Connes, 1967, 1968). Banded fibrils are also present in the larvae of *Oscarella* (Lévi and Porte, 1962) and *Mycale* (Lévi, 1964). In developing larvae of *Eunapius fragilis,* connective tissue elements develop, which also probably contain fibrils (Harrison and Cowden, 1975b). Fibrils occur around, and are possibly secreted by, developing oocytes in *Aplysina* (*Verongia*) (Gallissian and Vacelet, 1976) and are secreted around spermatogenic masses in *Aplysilla rosea* (Garrone, 1978). Fibrils of 20 nm have also been reported to occur in small numbers within the large spongin fibers (Gross *et al.*, 1956), which will now be discussed.

Spongin Fibers

Spongin fibers, in distinction to fibrils, are large structures which have been described for many decades employing only light microscopy. Two gross morphological types of fibers occur in the Demospongiae: those that contain siliceous spicules (megascleres) embedded within them and those that are not spiculiferous but may contain entrapped foreign particles. The latter occur in the horny sponges in which two patterns can be distinguished—reticulate (forming a network) fibers of the dictyoceratids and single (sometimes fused) branching fibers in the dendroceratids. In addition to spongin fibers, other structures that can be considered as spongin include the acellular coat of gemmules, the "filaments" in the genus *Ircinia*, and the enigmatic spiculoids of some dendroceratids. All of these spongins are made up of small microfibrils, about 10 nm in diameter (see, for example, Garrone and Pottu, 1973; Garrone *et al.*, 1975; Junqua *et al.*, 1974; Gross *et al.*, 1956; De Vos and Rozenfeld, 1974; Vacelet, 1971a; Garrone, 1978). In gemmule coats, however, the diameter of the fibrils is larger and mixed types may occur (see below).

In spiculated fibers (Fig. 5-2), the banding pattern is vague except when the microfibrils are in register and then a periodicity of about 60 nm can be detected. There have been relatively few studies, of any kind, of spiculated fibers and most of these are of haplosclerid species: *Haliclona rosea* (Garrone, 1969a), *Haliclona elegans* and *Ephydatia mulleri* (Garrone and Pottu, 1973), and of an axinellid, *Axinella verrucosa* (Garrone, 1978) and a poecilosclerid, *Microciona prolifera* (Gross *et al.*, 1956). The microfibrils in the fibers may be randomly oriented but tend to form layers and there may be dense bodies (Fig. 5-2B) enclosed within the fibers (Garrone, 1969a; Garrone and Pottu, 1973). At specific points the basal (anchoring) layer of spongin is continuous with the spiculated fibers, and both basal and fiber spongin can be considered to lie outside the organism (see Figs. 4-15, 4-16) (Weissenfels, 1978). Brønsted and Carlsen (1951) first described the *fibrillar* nature of the basal anchoring material in

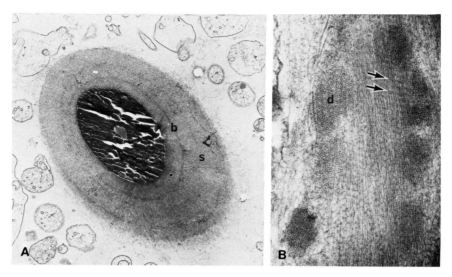

Figure 5-2   Spiculated spongin (TEMs). **A**. Spongin (*s*) enrobing a siliceous spicule of *Haliclona rosea*. Note concentric bands (*b*) in the fiber (×6,660) (Garrone, 1969a). **B**. Structured bodies (*d*) in a spongin fiber of *Haliclona elegans*. Note banding (*arrows*) (×22,950) (Garrone and Pottu, 1973). (Both, courtesy Dr. R. Garrone.)

Spongilla, a freshwater haplosclerid. In other haplosclerids this basal layer is constituted primarily of spongin microfibrils but also contains collagen fibrils as clearly documented by Mazzorana (1982). In *Mycale contarenii* (a poecilosclerid) Borojevic and Lévi (1967) earlier found a mixture of microfibrils and larger fibrils in this layer.

In the nonspiculated fibers of horny sponges, Garrone (1978) has designated two types: heterogeneous, with a denser, surrounding, cortical layer and a more granular-appearing medulla, and homogeneous fibers in which there is no medullary portion. In *Spongia graminea,* homogeneous fibers occur containing microfibrils of less than 10 nm in diameter with a 65 nm periodicity. In *Cacospongia scalaris, Hippospongia communis* (Fig. 5-3), and *Ircinia variabilis,* the microfibrils are about 8 nm in diameter with a 55 nm period (Junqua *et al.,* 1974). The fibers of these species, although not heterogeneous, are layered and in *Ircinia* fibers there is a dense cortex at the periphery. In *Aplysina* (*Verongia*) the fibers are clearly heterogeneous and contain a lacunose medulla and a very thick (up to 25 μm) cortex consisting of layers of microfibrils 4 to 6 nm in diameter (Fig. 5-4). Information on the structure of spongin fibers among dendroceratids consists of only preliminary observations reported by Garrone (1978). The fibers in *Aplysilla rosea* appear homogeneous with concentric layers between which may be foreign particles; in *Darwinella*

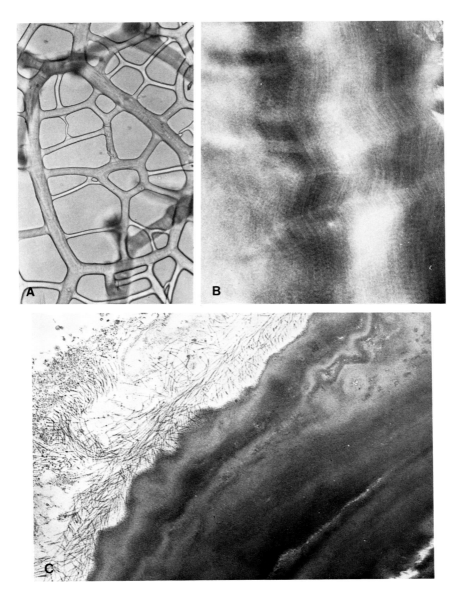

Figure 5-3   Homogeneous, nonspiculated spongin. **A**. Spongin fibers of *Hippospongia communis*. Note primary (larger) and secondary (smaller) fibers (light micrograph) (×180) (Garrone, 1978). **B**. Longitudinal section of *H. communis* fiber showing 550 Å periodicity (TEM) (approx. ×32,400) (Junqua *et al.*, 1974). **C**. Cross section of part of a fiber of *Cacospongia scalaris*. Concentric bands are present in the fiber; mesohyl collagen fibrils are present at the fiber surface (TEM) (×36,000) (Junqua *et al.*, 1974). (All, courtesy Dr. R. Garrone.)

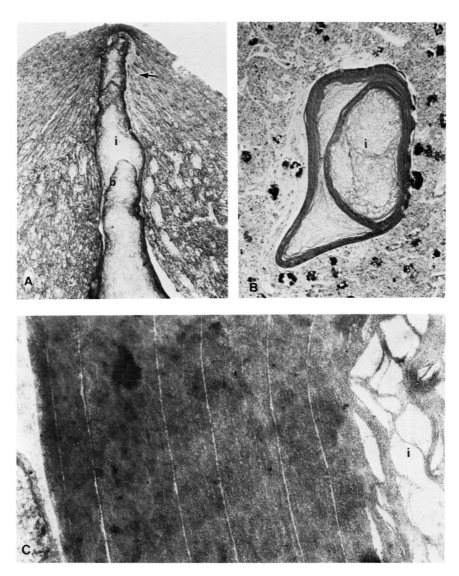

Figure 5-4 Heterogeneous, nonspiculated spongin fibers of *Aplysina (Verongia)*
cavernicola. **A**. Longitudinal section of a fiber running to the surface of the
animal. The spongocytes (*arrow*) "flow" down the fiber laying down microfibrils.
Note less dense inner core (*i*) of the fiber and the internal denser bands (*b*) (light
micrograph) (×180) (Vacelet, 1971a). **B**. Cross section of a fiber showing the
alveolar inner core (*i*) and bands of dense microfibrils at the surface and internally
(light micrograph)(×925) (Vacelet, 1971a). **C.** Cross section through the surface of
a fiber showing the concentric "gaps" and part of the inner core (*i*) (TEM)
(×13,500) (Vacelet, 1971a). (All, courtesy Dr. J. Vacelet.)

australiensis, heterogeneous fibers are found in which cell remains may be trapped. Additional studies of these fibers are required in order to elucidate further their structure and will doubtless appear in due course.

In the genus *Ircinia,* unusual, elongate, spongin fibers, referred to as "filaments", are secreted and range in size up to 8 mm in length and to 13 μm in diameter; at their ends are terminal bulbs (Fig. 5-5). Filaments have been investigated by Marks *et al.* (1949), Lévi (1965), Garrone *et al.* (1975), and Junqua *et al.* (1974). They are covered by a dense cortical layer (30 nm thick) and contain, internally, oriented microfibrils, 5 to 7 nm in diameter, which may be hollow. In larger filaments the microfibrils are wound around a central, more dense, thread-like core while in smaller ones the microfibrils are linearly arranged. The cuticle contains characteristic grooves and the microfibrils in the terminal bulbs are disorganized rather than aligned. The banding pattern is indistinct but when treated with cupraammonium hydroxide a 60 nm periodicity is revealed.

The second unusual type of spongin fiber are the spiculoids of some dendroceratids, so called because these fibers may occur in the shape of triaxons or polyaxons (Garrone, 1978). Their structure appears remarkably close to that of *Ircinia* filaments with a dense surface layer, concentric layer of microfibrils below this, and a less dense core or axis.

The chemistry of spongin fibers has been thoroughly elucidated primarily in the dictyoceratid horny sponges. No data are available for spiculoids and only incomplete data for spiculated fibers. In the latter, X-ray diffraction and infrared absorption spectra yield profiles substantially identical with other collagens; such data have been reported by Garrone (1969a) in *Haliclona rosea.* In the fibers of horny sponges, good data are available on the amino acid composition and on carbohydrate content (Table 5-2); these establish the collagenous nature of the spongin fibers and of *Ircinia* filaments. High sugar content is typical of spongin fibers as is the case with intercellular fibrils (see previous section). In their study of spongin fibers of three marine sponges, Junqua *et al.* (1974) found small amounts of galactosyl-hydroxylysine and much more substantial amounts of glucosylgalactosyl-hydroxylysine, an unusual disaccharide moiety to be found in collagen. In *Spongia graminea,* glucose, galactose, xylose, mannose, and arabinose were found as part of the spongin fibers. Cupraammonium hydroxide has little effect on fibers but causes *Ircinia* filaments to undergo a characteristic twisting, indicating a difference in the physical basis of microfibrillar interactions in them as compared to spongin fibers (Garrone *et al.,* 1975). Spongin is also very resistant to enzymatic hydrolysis and relatively harsh methods are required in order to solubilize it, namely, treatment with strong alkali (Junqua *et al.,* 1974). Ethanolic alkali is much faster acting then aqueous solutions, suggesting a role of hydrophobic interactions in maintaining their integrity (Junqua *et al.,* 1974).

Spongin fibers occur in many demosponge species but are char-

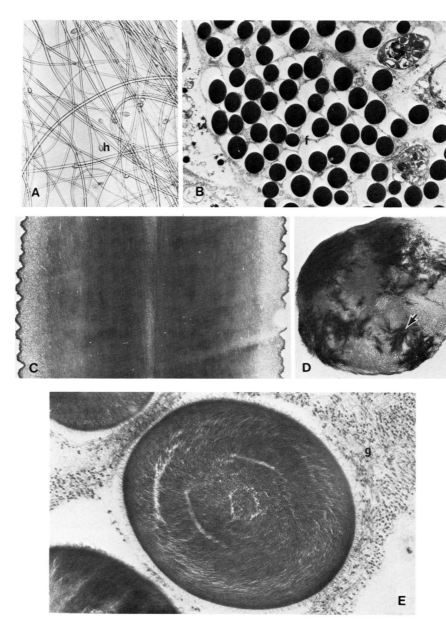

Figure 5-5 Spongin filaments of *Ircinia*. **A**. Filaments of *Ircinia oros* showing the swollen heads (*h*) at the ends of each filament (light micrograph) (×160) (Garrone *et al.*, 1973). **B**. Cross section of a group of filaments in the mesohyl of *Ircinia muscarum* where they are surrounded by collagen fibrils (*f*) (TEM) (×4,500) (Garrone *et al.*, 1973). **C**. Longitudinal section through a filament of *Ircinia*

acteristic of the ceractinomorphs, with the notable exception of the genus *Halisarca,* which lacks a skeleton. Fibers are not known in the Calcarea or the Hexactinellida, but in sclerosponges substantial deposits of an organic substance around spicules, or parts of them, and within the aspicular aragonitic skeleton may well turn out to consist of spongin fibers. Megascleres in some demosponge larva are grouped together nearer one end of the larva and may be partially embedded in fibers since material around them stains with connective tissue reagents in *Microciona prolifera* (unpubl. results). Future investigations can be expected in the near future dealing with both these points.

Gemmule Coats

The spongin present in gemmule coats can occur in the form of one, two, or three layers which are discernible by light microscopy (Simpson and Fell, 1974). The two layered coats may be incomplete three-layered ones and are much less frequently encountered (Penney and Racek, 1968). Triple-layered coats usually contain siliceous spicules embedded within the middle layer (Fig. 5-6) and in gemmules of marine species the single-layered coats may likewise include spicules (Simpson and Fell, 1974). The internal surface of the gemmule coats of *Spongilla lacustris* (Fig. 5-7) and *Ephydatia fluviatilis* is lined by a thin, dense band of noncollagenous material (De Vos, 1977; Langenbruch, 1981; Simpson *et al.,* 1973); this appears not to be the case in marine gemmule coats (Carrière *et al.,* 1974). In *S. lacustris* gemmule coats, the fibrillar elements have a 10 to 13 nm periodicity (Simpson *et al.,* 1973), which is close to that in the coats of the gemmules of the marine sponge *Suberities domuncula,* where hollow fibrils have a diameter of 15 to 25 nm and microfibirls, 5 to 7 nm. The single-layered coats in *Suberites* contain clearly demarcated bands (see Fig. 8-10) (Carrière *et al.,* 1974). In *Ephydatia fluviatilis* coats in the inner and middle layers there are giant fibrils (Fig. 5-6C) that are 65 to 70 nm in diameter and have a 20 nm periodicity subdivided by an electron-lucent band (De Vos, 1972). The outer layer of these coats is much less organized than the inner layer in which there are alternating bands of fibrils and of denser material in four bands. The middle layer is highly alveolar with many spherically shaped, membrane-bound holes (see Fig. 8-9) (De Vos, 1972; De Vos and Rozenfeld, 1974). The fibrils in the inner layer have the same diameter and periodicity as the giant fibrils. The diameter ·of these fibrils and some in *Suberites* can be taken to indicate basic differ-

---

variabilis showing the dense surface layer (TEM) (approx. ×45,000) (Junqua *et al.,* 1974). **D.** Cross section of a filament of *Ircinia variabilis* in which dark crystals of lepidocrocite are embedded (*arrow*) (TEM) (approx. × 22,500) (Junqua *et al.,* 1974). **E.** Cross section of *Ircinia spinosula* filaments showing the whorl-like arrangement of the microfibrils. *g,* mesohyl collagen fibrils (TEM) (×27,000) (Garrone *et al.,* 1973). (All, courtesy Dr. R. Garrone.)

Table 5-2 Composition of Spongin[a]

Amino Acids	Fibers[b]			Filaments[b]	Gemmule Coat	
	Ircinia variabilis	*Hippospongia communis*	*Cacospongia scalaris*	*Ircinia variabilis*	*Ephydatia fluviatilis*[c]	*Suberites domuncula*[d]
Glycine	323	319	260	328	201	280
Aspartic acid	110	94	110	82	120	107
Hydroxyproline	92	97	72	100	82	0
Glutamic acid	83	79	69	80	77	41
Alanine	83	84	69	101	38	42
Proline	67	67	87	74	99	73
Arginine	42	45	50	42	43	81
Threonine	24	26	20	27	38	27
Serine	19	25	21	20	48	109
Leucine	23	27	33	22	42	24
Valine	24	30	31	28	43	33

Isoleucine	19	21	23	20	17	33
Hydroxylysine	25	29	32	30	—	0
Phenylalanine	10	10	18	9	15	18
Lysine	25	34	56	20	34	59
Half-cystine	16	7	37	6	24	Trace
Tyrosine	9	2	4	3	37	22
Histidine	4	4	4	5	24	25
Methionine	2	Trace	4	3	5	Trace
Percentage lysine hydroxylated	50	48	39	62	—	—
Percentage hydroxyllysine glycosylated	—	46	53	48	—	—

[a] Quantity of amino acids expressed as residues per 1,000 residues.
[b] Data taken from Junqua et al. (1974).
[c] Data taken from De Vos (1974) as quoted in Garrone (1978).
[d] Data taken from Connes and Artiges (1980).

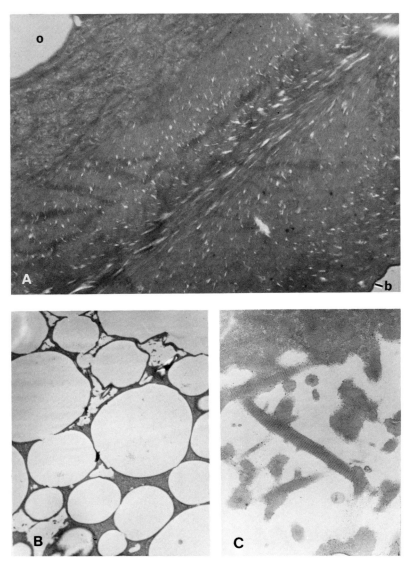

Figure 5-6 The triple-layered collagenous gemmule coat of *Ephydatia fluviatilis* (external layer not pictured) (see Fig. 8-9) (TEMs). **A**. The internal layer of the coat is bounded on its inner surface by a dense, non collagenous band (*b*). The remainder of the inner layer is textured and has parallel, band-like regions. *o*, alveolus in the adjoining middle coat layer (×10,000) (De Vos and Rozenfeld, 1974). **B**. The middle (alveolar) layer of the coat with large empty spaces bounded by a network of collagen and membrane fragments (latter not visible) (×7,500) (De Vos and Rozenfeld, 1974). **C**. Giant collagen fibrils in the alveolar layer. Note complex banding pattern (×30,000) (De Vos, 1972). (All courtesy Dr. L. De Vos.)

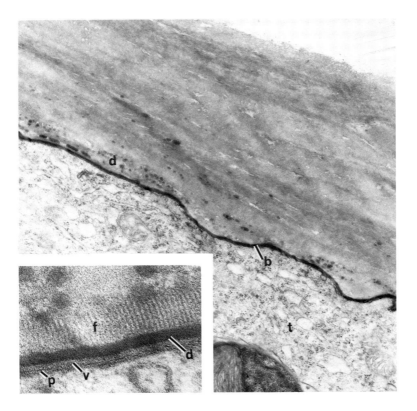

Figure 5-7 The single-layered coat of *Spongilla lacustris* (TEM). An inner dense band (*b*) of noncollagenous material is present as well as spherical dense deposits (*d*) in the coat. *t*, thesocyte cytoplasm (×19,600). **Inset:** Junction of the coat with a thesocyte. *P*, thesocyte plasmalemma; *v*, gemmule cavity; *d*, dense band; *f*, collagen banding in the coat (×113,000) (Simpson *et al.*, 1973).

ences between the collagen in spongin fibers and that in gemmule coats. However, further studies of fibril structure are called for before this conclusion is firmly accepted, particularly because during the secretion of the gemmule coat in *Ephydatia*, 5 nm microfibrils are initially present (De Vos, 1977) and become associated to form the larger 65 nm fibrils. On this basis, the spongin in the gemmule coat can be viewed as being fundamentally microfibrillar and thus similar to spongin fibers. A thin, raised, spherical area of the gemmule coat, the micropyle, is formed by the joining of the internal and external layers, there being no middle layer present. This small area is quite thin (1.0 μm) and serves as an exit for the internal cells during hatching (De Vos and Rozenfeld, 1974). In *Suberites* gemmule coats, where there is only a single layer present, the micropyle is a thin, raised portion of this layer (Carrière *et al.*, 1974). The chemical analyses of Huc and De Vos (1972) and De Vos (1974) establish the collagenous nature of gemmule coats (Table 5-2). Although the amino acid analyses are similar to those of spongin fibers, the glycine content is significantly lower, and the histidine, lysine, tyrosine, and alanine contents are notably higher suggesting the possible presence of other proteins (Garrone, 1978). Glucosamine was also found in relatively high amounts. The seeming absence of hydroxyproline and hydroxylysine in *S. domuncula* gemmule coats is a drastic departure from other sponge and nonsponge collagens (Connes and Artiges, 1980). The internal dense band present at the inner surface of some gemmule coats does not appear to be collagen (Simpson *et al.*, 1973). Gemmule coats occur wherever gemmules are produced and are an important attribute of such structures for recognizing them as gemmules. These structures are formed by many freshwater and a few marine species (see Chap. 8 for a detailed discussion of gemmule structure, distribution, formation, and physiology including gemmule coats).

Collagen Synthesis and Secretion

Biochemical Aspects of Collagen Synthesis

The extreme insolubility and resistance to solubilization of sponge collagens make incorporation studies difficult. Because of this, available data are based upon electron microscope autoradiographic techniques utilizing pulse–chase protocols. Even using this technique, difficulties are encountered because of the very slow incorporation rates of amino acids into the collagens, suggesting a very slow metabolism. The results discussed below are due to the efforts of Professor Max Pavans de Ceccatty and Dr. Robert Garrone, whose laboratory has been instrumental in working out methods for investigating the biosynthesis of sponge collagens. The most successful experiments have dealt with the secretion of collagen fibrils by a specific type of cell, the lophocyte, which is morphologically distinct and which carries with it a long trailing tuft of fibrils that it secretes (see below). Thus, employing the marine sponge, *Chondrosia reniformis,* which possess a large population of lophocytes and no other collagens other than fibrils, Garrone (1978) has shown, through pulse-labeling experiments, using tritiated proline and electron microscope autoradiography, that this amino acid is incorporated first into the rough endoplasmic reticulum and to a lesser degree in the cytosol (Fig. 5-8B) followed by its appearance in the Golgi bodies. The label is then lost from the rough endoplasmic reticulum and cytosol and appears within dense cytoplasmic inclusions. Following this, the posterior (=tuft-secreting end of the cell) microtubular elements gain label and then, finally, label appears in the trailing fibrils. The pharmacologic agents, colchicine and cytochalasin B, have pronounced effects upon collagen fibril biosynthesis (Garrone, 1978;

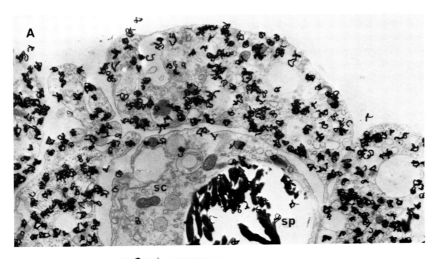

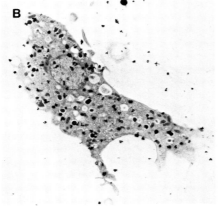

Figure 5-8 Tritiated proline incorporation by spongocytes and lophocytes in *Ephydatia mulleri* (TEMs). **A**. Autoradiograph showing heavy labeling over the spongocytes encircling a sclerocyte (*sc*) in which a siliceous spicule (*sp*) is being secreted (×6,615) (Garrone and Pottu, 1973). **B**. Autoradiograph of a lophocyte demonstrating incorporation (×3,870) (Pottu-Boumendil, unpubl.). (**A**, courtesy Dr. R. Garrone; **B**, courtesy Dr. J. Pottu-Boumendil.)

Pottu-Boumendil, 1975). With either or both of these drugs, labeling accumulates within the large, fibrillar-containing inclusions of lophocytes and no label appears in the fibrils, suggesting a direct involvement of microtubules and microfilaments in biosynthesis and/or secretion. These drugs also affect cell motility in general and their effects, or part of them, on collagen biosynthesis may also be related to their effects on cell movement and cell shape. Pavans de Ceccatty and Thiney (1964) have suggested the direct involvement of the plasmalemma of lophocytes in the final assembly of the fibrils. The long fibrillar tuft of lophocytes is, under normal conditions, not released as a whole by the cell so that the fibrils must be deposited in small numbers continuously or periodically. Cycloheximide, employed as a control for pulse–chase experiments, effectively inhibits proline incorporation into lophocytes and fibrils, although the symbiotic bacteria present in *Chondrosia* continue to incorporate proline in its presence. Hydroxyurea appears to enhance fibrillogenesis and thus may prove to be an important agent for future investigations (Garrone and Rozenfeld, 1981).

Pulse–chase experiments have been performed to elucidate spongin fiber biosynthesis in *Haliclona elegans* and *Ephydatia mulleri*, which involves spongocytes as the collagen-secreting cell type (Fig. 5-8A). Label is found first in the groups of spongocytes surrounding spicules and after 48 h it appears within the newly deposited spongin (Garrone and Pottu, 1973). A great deal of additional work dealing with biosynthesis and assembly pathways (Fig. 5-9) of sponge collagen deposition remains outstanding and additional new methods will have to be developed in order to

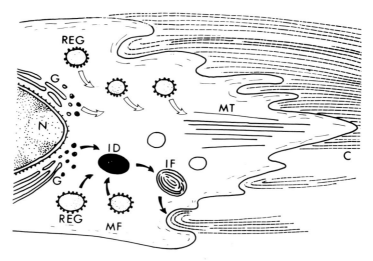

Figure 5-9 Two pathways for collagen fibrilogenesis in lophocytes. Above, synthesis of precursors occurs in the rough endoplasmic reticular cisternae (*REG*). Such precursors are then supposedly transported through the intervention of microtubules (*MT*) to the cell surface where assembly occurs and produces a collagen tuft (*C*). This pathway appears to be fairly rapid accounting for the buildup of fibrils in the tuft. Below, biosynthesis of precursors results in the formation of dense inclusions (*ID*) in which fibrillogenesis occurs producing fibrillar inclusions (*IF*) which are then released at the cell surface probably involving microfilaments (*MF*). The latter pathway appears to be slow. In both cases, products from the Golgi (*G*) probably interact with steps in the processes. *N*, nucleus (Garrone, 1978). (Courtesy Dr. R. Garrone.)

carry out meaningful experiments. Of particular interest would be experiments dealing with the incorporation of carbohydrates into the collagens as well as into associated glycoproteins. In *Haliclona elegans,* the newly secreted fibrils in the dermal membrane initially have little associated substance on their surface; later, these same fibrils stain well with ruthenium red, indicating the presence of glycoproteins (Garrone, 1978). In *Hippospongia* and *Cacospongia,* fibrils are "coated" by material (Thiney, 1972) and in *Ircinia,* serotonin stimulates the elaboration of such substances which become associated with the collagen fibrils (Pavans de Ceccatty, 1973; Garrone, 1978).

There are some indirect data suggesting that collagen fibrils may normally be phagocytized as in *Tethya* (Connes, 1968). In explants of *Chondrosia,* fibrils become disorganized and some appear within vacuoles of archeocytes (Garrone, 1975). Further, the maintenance of explants of pieces of this sponge on corneal collagen results in the release of acicular fibrils from the cornea indicating a collagenolytic activity of the symbiotic bacteria (Garrone, 1975). In addition, sponge collagen fibrils are broken and then appear within phagosomes of the sponge cells. In the hatching of gemmules, the thin collagen layer in the micropyle disappears probably not by mechanical means, since the surfaces are completely smooth, but by a chemical mechanism (Rozenfeld, 1971; Garrone, 1978) that might well involve a sponge collagenase. The existence of such an enzyme would be of much interest since known collagenases have little effect upon sponge collagens (Junqua *et al.,* 1974; Garrone *et al.,* 1975).

Cellular Aspects of Collagen Secretion

The types of cells implicated in the synthesis and secretion of collagen are numerous. For three of them—lophocytes, spongocytes, and basopinacocytes—there is very solid evidence that the cells themselves are involved in such activity. In the case of the first two, authoradiographic data establish the secretory events. It is very likely that the other cell types, archeocytes, collencytes, exo- and endopinacocytes, and gray cells, are likewise involved, but the present data do not categorically eliminate the possibility that these cells are *associated with* fibrils actually secreted by a different cell type. Choanocytes, have never been implicated in collagen secretion, and there are no indications that they possess this capacity. Some special cell types (Chap. 4), globoferous cells, rhabdiferous cells, microgranular cells, and others are also clearly not implicated in collagen biosynthesis while others—sacculiferous and spumeuse cells—definitely are implicated. Additional studies on these cells would be most useful.

Lophocytes.   It is now established that lophocytes synthesize and secrete intercellular, collagen fibrils. Their morphology, which is directly related to their collagenic activity, is unique (Fig. 5-10) (Pavans de Ceccatty and Thiney, 1964; Pavans de Ceccatty and Garrone, 1971; Tuzet and

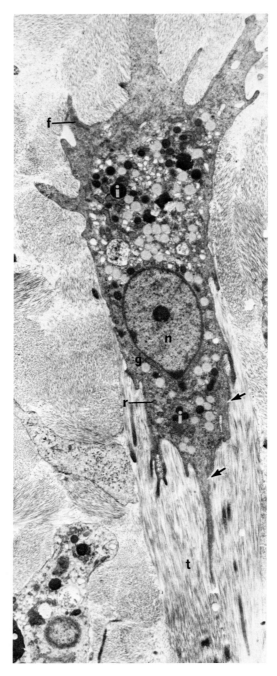

Figure 5-10 A lophocyte of *Chondrosia reniformis* (TEM). The cell is polarized relative to collagen fibrillogenesis with fibril assembly and release occurring at the posterior end of the cell and forming a conspicuous tuft of fibrils (*t*). The posterior filopods (*arrow*) contain microtubules and there are characteristic dense inclusions (*i*) and rough endoplasmic reticulum (*r*) throughout the cytoplasm. *n*, nucleus; *g*, Golgi; *f*, microfilaments (×7,500) (Garrone, 1971). (Copyright Archives de l'Académie des Sciences de Paris.) (Courtesy Dr. R. Garrone.)

Paris, 1966; Garrone, 1971; Pavans de Ceccatty, 1957; Garrone, 1978). Lophocytes have been described in a number of demosponges and in a calcareous sponge (Table 5-3). Their ultrastructure involves an array of usual organelles: nucleolated nucleus, Golgi bodies, free cytoplasmic ribosomes, moderate numbers of mitochondria, occasional lipid inclusions, smooth-membraned vesicles, and small amounts of cytoplasmic glycogen. They are unusual in relation to other sponge cell types by their possession of highly developed rough endoplasmic reticulum, which forms numerous ribosome-studded sacs in the cytoplasm. Further, these cells possess large (1.0 μm), membrane-bound inclusions containing either very dense homogeneous material or numerous, sometimes aligned, fibrillar elements. Lophocytes are polarized in their structure; their anterior end, which leads during movement, is made up of a few lobose pseudopods while the posterior end has attached to it a long, trailing tuft of fibrils. Those fibrils closest to the cell membrane appear "cemented" to it. The nucleus is located about midway between the poles, and posterior to it are prominent 25 nm microtubules. Microfilaments occur below the plasmalemma including the posterior portions. The posterior surface of the plasmalemma possesses characteristic microvilli-like structures. The origin of lophocytes is not clear, although Connes *et al.* (1972) have suggested that they may arise from archeocytes or from gray cells in

Table 5–3 Reports of Lophocytes

Species	References
Class Calcarea	
Sycon raphanus	Tuzet and Connes (1964)
Class Demospongiae	
Subclass Tetractinomorpha	
Chondrosia reniformis	Pavens de Ceccatty (1957), Pavans de Ceccatty and Garrone (1971), Garrone (1971), Garrone *et al.* (1975), Garrone and Pottu-Boumendil (1976)
Pachymatisma johnstoni	Tuzet and Pavans de Ceccatty (1953)
Suberites domuncula	Paris (1961), Tuzet and Paris (1966)
Suberites massa	Connes *et al.* (1972)
Tethya lyncurium	Tuzet and Paris (1957), Pavans de Ceccatty and Thiney (1963, 1964), Connes (1968)
Subclass Ceractinomorpha	
Ephydatia fluviatilis	Ankel and Wintermann-Kilian (1952), De Vos (1977)
Ephydatia mulleri	Pottu-Boumendil (1975)
Spongilla lacustris	Harrison and Davis (1982)
Tedania ignis	Simpson (1968a)

Suberites, and Pavans de Ceccatty and Garrone (1971) indicate a possible endopinacocyte origin for them. Mitoses have not been reported in lophocytes; however, if the trailing tuft were shed during cell division, it would require a very detailed analysis to identify the diving cell as a lophocyte. A number of authors have reported the degeneration of lophocytes as in *Suberites* (Connes *et al.,* 1972), *Tethya* (Pavans de Ceccatty and Thiney, 1964), and *Chondrosia* (Pavans de Ceccatty and Garrone, 1971). Although four ceractinomorph species have been reported to possess lophocytes, these cells appear much more characteristic and numerous in tetractinomorphs and thus could be the basis for the secretion of smooth (rather than rough) fibrils.

Spongocytes.   Spongocytes (Fig. 5-11) can only be identified as such with certainty when they are seen involved in the act of secreting spongin. Their ultrastructure is very close to, if not overlapping with, that of archeocytes (Chap.3), except their rough endoplasmic reticulum is more extensive (Garrone and Pottu, 1973). In some cases *(Haliclona elegans)* spongocytes contain membrane-bound, dense inclusions, similar to those in lophocytes and these become less dense prior to discharge from the cell surface; however, in *Ephydatia mulleri* few such inclusions are present (Garrone and Pottu, 1973). On a light microscopic level, spongocytes have been described in *Ophlitaspongia seriata* (Lévi, 1960) and in *Microciona prolifera* (Simpson, 1963); in the latter, intense staining of cytoplasmic RNA occurs. Spongocytes that secrete the spongin of spiculated fibers form an epithelium around the depositing spongin and the cell junctions are frequently interdigitated—a situation reminiscent of sclerocytes secreting calcareous spicules (Ledger and Jones, 1977) and of the spongocyte epithelium surrounding developing gemmules (see below and Chap. 8). In horny sponges, spongocytes [in *Aplysina (Verongia)*] begin secretion at the fiber tip and then flatten out and move down the fiber (see Fig. 5-4A). Each wave forms a new layer of the dense, surrounding cortical layer of the fiber, which thus becomes a layered structure (Vacelet, 1971a). Vacelet has suggested that precursors to collagen form in the endoplasmic reticulum and are then transported to the secretory cell surface, are released, and then the final assembly occurs extracellularly. The lacunae in the medulla of *Aplysina (Verongia),* heterogeneous fibers seem to result from a periodic pulling back of the spongocytes, which leaves spheroidal spaces that eventually make up the central portion of the fiber. According to this view, homogeneous fibers would be formed by spongocytes that display restricted cell motility and thus the microfibrils are uniformly deposited.

The spongocytes that secrete the coat of gemmules are unusual in that they take on a columnar shape and form a classical columnar epithelium (see Fig. 3-2B) around the central mass of cells (see, for example, Leveaux, 1939; Rasmont, 1956; De Vos, 1977). These cells are tightly joined

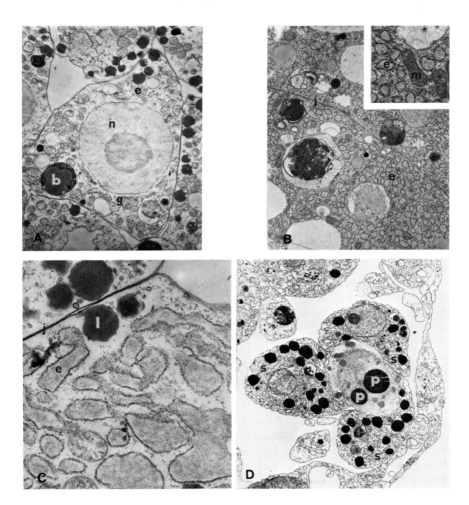

Figure 5-11 Spongocytes of the gemmular epithelium of *Ephydatia fluviatilis* (A.–C.) and of *Haliclona elegans* (D.) (TEMs). **A.** Cross section through the gemmular epithelium at the level of the nucleus (*n*). A platelet-like body (*b*) is present. *e*, endoplasmic reticulum; *g*, Golgi (×4,500) (De Vos, 1971). **B.** Portion of a spongocyte showing highly developed rough endoplasmic reticulum (*e*). *j*, cell junction (×6,750) (De Vos, 1977). **Inset**: Rough endoplasmic reticulum (*e*); *m*, mitochondrion (×13,500) (De Vos, unpubl.). **C.** Spongocyte showing rough endoplasmic reticulum (*e*), lipid (*l*), and cell junction (*j*) (×54,000) (De Vos, 1977). **D.** Spongocytes (*s*) secreting spongin around spicules (*p*) (×3,330) (Garrone and Pottu, 1973). (**A–C**, courtesy Dr. L. De Vos; **D**, courtesy Dr. R. Garrone.)

together with interdigitating processes of the cell surface and by occasional septate junctions (De Vos, 1977). They are also unusual in that without undergoing major shape changes, the same cells secrete both homegeneous layers of spongin (internal and external layers) as well as a highly alveolar middle layer, which can be considered similar to the medulla of heterogeneous fibers. This lacunose, middle layer forms as a result of the release of the remains of whole inclusions, the fibrillar contents of which have been released (Fig. 5-12). The membrane surrounding these inclusions is maintained after it is secreted from the cell and comes to surround relatively large spaces within the middle layer of the coat in *Ephydatia fluviatilis* (De Vos, 1977) (Chap. 8).

Basopinacocytes.   The basal layer of spongin that acts as an anchoring device for sponges is undoubtedly secreted by basopinacocytes (Fig. 5-13A) (Borojevic and Lévi, 1967; Weissenfels, 1978; Garrone and Pottu, 1973; Mazzorana, 1982). These cells are similar to spongocytes and lophocytes in their endoplasmic reticular development and presence of dense inclusions during the period when they are active in depositing spongin, namely, early in development (Garrone, 1978; Garrone and Rozenfeld, 1981).

Collencytes.   In addition to lophocytes, spongocytes, and basopinacocytes there is evidence that collencytes are also involved in collagen fibril deposition (see Fig. 3-3A). In them (Chap. 3), fibrils have been reported to be intimately associated with the plasmalemma in *Suberites massa*

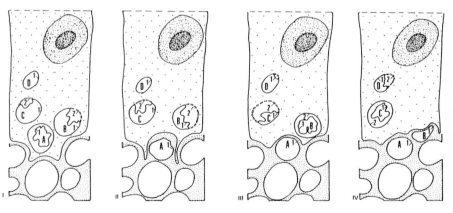

Figure 5-12   Supposed sequence of the secretion of the alveoli in the middle layer of gemmule coats. Vacuoles (*A* to *D*) undergo an evolution as indicated by vacuole *B*. The membrane collapses inward and a new membrane forms around the old one. The inner membrane of the double-membraned vacuole is then exocytized and forms a "hole" around which collagen is secreted (De Vos, 1977). (Courtesy Dr. L. De Vos.)

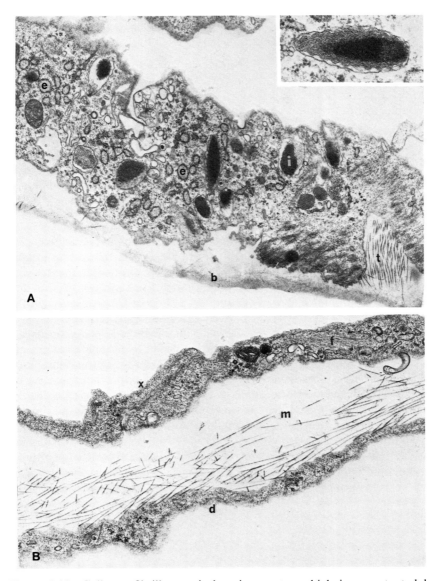

Figure 5-13 Collagen fibrillogenesis by pinacocytes which is accentuated by hydroxyurea treatment in *Ephydatia fluviatilis* (TEMs). **A**. Fibrillogenesis by a basopinacocyte. The basal layer of collagen (*b*) is secreted below the cell on the substratum. A small tuft (*t*) of fibrils is being released from the cell. Dense inclusions (*i*) and rough endoplasmic reticulum (*e*) occur in the cytoplasm as is typical of collagen-secreting cells (×14,450). **Inset:** A dense inclusion containing parallel wavy fibrils (×34,000) (Garrone and Rozenfeld, 1981). **B**. Collagen fibrillogenesis by pinacocytes of the dermal membrane. The thin mesohyl (*m*) between the exopinacocyte (*x*) and the endopinacocyte (*d*) contains fibrils secreted by the cells. In this micrograph the endopinacocyte appears more closely associated with them (see text). *f,* microfilaments (×17,000) (Garrone and Rozenfeld, 1981). (Both, courtesy Dr. R. Garrone.)

(Connes *et al.*, 1972), *Haliclona rosea* and *elegans* (Garrone, 1969a, 1978), *Mycale contarenii* (Lévi, 1964) and *Cliona lampa* (Rutzler and Rieger, 1973). In *Haliclona* collencytes, the proposed sequence of events during collagen fibril deposition involves synthesis in the cytoplasm, probably within the cisternae of the endoplasmic reticulum, formation of vacuoles which contain fibrillar material, and then release of the vacuolar contents. Since it is known that collencytes in the mature larvae of *Mycale contarenii* form pinacocytes (including basopinacocytes) (Borojevic and Lévi, 1967), it is not surprising to find data suggesting that collagen fibrils can be deposited by similar cells in the mesohyl. The problem with the conclusion that collencytes display fibrillogenic activity is that these cells are very difficult to define clearly as a specific cell type (Chap. 3).

Exopinacocytes. There is also good, although indirect, evidence that exopinacocytes deposit collagen fibrils (Fig. 5-13B). In *Oscarella,* many fibrils are present intercellulary and there are very few archeocytes and spherulous cells in the mesohyl (Lévi and Porte, 1962). A similar situation applies to *Sycon* and *Leucandra* (Ledger, 1974). In *Haliclona,* when the dermal membrane first appears in early development there are very few cells within the mesohyl of the dermal membrane, but many fibrils are present suggesting that exopinacocytes and possibly endopinacocytes are the origin of these fibrils (Garrone and Pottu, 1973; Pottu-Boumendil, 1975). Exopinacocytes have also been demonstrated to incorporate [³H] proline, and the glycoprotein coat of fibrils that occur very close to the exopinacocyte plasmalemma can be seen in some cases to be continuous with a similar coat on the cell surface (Pottu-Boumendil, 1975). During early development in *Ephydatia fluviatilis,* Weissenfels (1978) has reported that exo- and basopinacocytes may migrate from their epithelia and become applied to the surface of newly secreted megascleres where they secrete spongin (Chap. 4).

Archeocytes. The question of whether archeocytes elaborate collagen fibrils is difficult to resolve. These cells are highly mobile and are routinely associated with fibrils. When fibrils are seen in moderate numbers, closely associated with the plasmalemma, it is not clear whether the cell should be viewed as a highly active archeocyte involved in collegen fibrillogenesis or whether it should be considered as a lophocyte. As pointed out by Garrone (1978), an important difference between lophocytes and archeocytes is the macrophagic activity of the latter. However, there have been no detailed, simultaneous studies of fibrillogenesis and phagocytosis in archeocytes or lophocytes; only the static morphological evidence suggests this difference. In *Microciona prolifera,* there are no collencytes or lophocytes present (Simpson, 1963) but there are many intercellular fibrils (Bagby, 1966; Gross *et al.*, 1956), and although gray cells (see below) are also present in this sponge, it is possible that the fibrils are secreted by archeocytes, which is reported to be the case during regeneration following cell dissociation in the closely related species *Ophlitaspongia seriata* (Borojevic and Lévi, 1965). The level of fibrillogenesis per cell is high, possibly suggesting that these cells should be considered as lophocytes; however, lophocytes have also not been described in this species (Simpson, 1968b; Borojevic and Lévi, 1965). These and additional data have actually led Feige (1969) and Efremova (1967) to question the validity of referring to lophocytes as a separate cell category. Although the evidence for a separate cell type is impressive (Garrone, 1978), the question of whether the designation, archeocyte, includes or excludes lophocytes still requires further evaluation. Thus, the question of whether archeocytes secrete fibrils still requires specific experimental demonstration; as an interim view it may be best to view these cells as probably capable of fibrillogenesis.

Special Cells. In a number of tetractinomorph demosponges, certain special cells (Chap. 3) are perhaps involved in collagen fibril deposition. In *Cyamon neon,* the sacculiferous cells contain unique, partially fibrillar inclusions and ultrastructural observations are very suggestive of a role in fibril secretion (Smith and Lauritis, 1969). In the free-floating, asexual buds of a clinoid sponge (Fig. 5-14) and in *Suberites massa* there are reports that gray cells are involved in fibrillogenesis (Garrone, 1974; Connes *et al.,* 1972). In the latter, this has been interpreted to mean that gray cells develop into lophocytes (Connes *et al.,* 1972). There seem to be no reports in ceractinomorph species of special cell types that are involved in fibril elaboration, and it may be that this distinction is of much importance in the context of our understanding of the evolution of this group. Although Donadey and Vacelet (1977) have described the occurrence of spumeuse cells in a ceractinomorph, *Pleraplysilla,* the fibrillar material released by them appears to be primarily polysaccharide. In *Tethya lyncurium* (also a tetractinomorph) spherulous cells can release the contents of their large inclusions into the mesohyl (Connes, 1968), but there is no real suggestion that this is fibrillogenesis despite the fact that the released material may be associated with fibrils (Garrone, 1978). In *Hippospongia* and *Cacospongia,* pinacocytes, myocytes, archeocytes, and collencytes may all be involved in the elaboration of materials which become associated with collagen fibrils (Thiney, 1972).

Other. The mechanism of secretion of filaments in *Ircinia* is unknown as are the cells involved. Garrone *et al.* (1973) have suggested that fibrillar inclusions are released from cells and in the presence of specific cell debris (such as vesicles) this material undergoes a very rapid self-assembly process extracellularly. The smallest filaments are completely comparable to the larger ones indicating that no morphogenetic progression or maturation occurs (Garrone, 1978). The secretion of spiculoids is unknown.

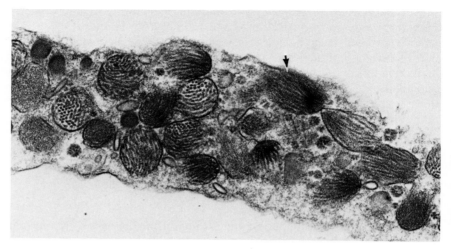

Figure 5-14 Exceptional fibrillogenesis within inclusions of a pseudopod of a gray cell in a clionid bud (?*Alectona*) (TEM). Bundles of fibrils are cut in various planes and some are joined to the plasmalemma (*arrow*) possibly in preparation for release (×28,800) (Garrone, 1974). (Courtesy Dr. R. Garrone.)

Other Organic Products

Biochemical Studies

Relatively meager biochemical data are available on noncollagenous matrix and cell surface materials, although sponges are known to contain plentiful glycoproteins, some of which have been reported to be species specific based upon immunological criteria (MacLennan, 1969, 1970, 1974; Junqua et al., 1975a,b; Junqua and Garrone, 1982). In three species of demosponges, *Suberites massa, Ircinia variabilis,* and *Spongia officinalis,* glycoproteins have been extracted and characterized biochemically (Junqua et al., 1975a,b) (Table 5-4). The amino acid composition in all cases is strikingly similar while the carbohydrate content is not. Depending upon the extraction procedure (10 mM EDTA or hot TCA–urea) the glycoproteins appear species specific. When extracted by the EDTA method, antisera prepared against *Suberites* glycoproteins do not react with *Spongia* glycoproteins but do react with the homologous antigen (Junqua et al., 1975b). In all three species, regardless of the extraction procedure, two or three absorption maxima of the extracts are seen around 230 nm and three around 280 nm. The two types of growth forms of *Suberites*—massive or digitate—are, in this respect, comparable biochemically (Table 5-4) and immunologically. There is no cross-reactivity of antisera of these glycoproteins with crude, soluble collagen extracts from cornea and skin, and their amino acid composition is very different from that of *Ircinia* intercellular, collagen fibrils (see Table 5-1) (Junqua *et al.*, 1975a). The localizations of these glycoproteins within the sponge tissue are not precisely known, but glycoproteins and polysaccharides in a number of other sponges have been shown to be associated with cell surfaces (MacLennan, 1969). In *Spongia graminea,* the amorphous substance in extracts is probably at least partially glycoprotein, but was found to be highly variable in composition (Gross *et al.*, 1956). In *Spongia officinalis,* five matrix protein fractions have been analyzed (Junqua *et al.*, 1979). Based upon similarities there are, however, only three categories of substances—two glycoproteins and one sulfated glycosaminoglycan complex (Table 5-5). The glycoproteins were shown, using fluorescent-coupled lectins and antibodies, to be localized in the matrix of the mesohyl particularly associated with cell membranes, especially around choanocyte chambers (Junqua and Garrone, 1982). The glycosaminoglycan is drastically different from vertebrate types and is insensitive to chondroitinase and hyaluronidases. The glycoproteins may be involved in cell–cell contacts during reaggregation. Glycosaminoglycans from the intercellular matrix have also been isolated from *Hippospongia gossypina* (Katzman *et al.*, 1970). An exceedingly high-molecular-weight proteoglycan can be prepared from *Microciona prolifera* and *parthena* through incubation of dissociated cells in calcium–magnesium-free sea water (Cauldwell *et al.*, 1973; Henkart *et al.*, 1973; Burger *et al.*, 1975). This molecule, also known as aggregation factor, is involved *in vitro* in cell–cell contacts and is discussed further in Chapter Nine. Its localization in the sponge tissue has not been determined and although it can be assumed to be associated with cell surfaces there is no reason to think that this is an exclusive localization (Chap. 9). Katzman *et al.* (1970) have also identified the presence of D-arabinose in glycosaminoglycans of *Hippospongia.* This sugar is rarely found in animals and is not a component of sponge nucleic acids as once thought. Glycoproteins are widespread among demosponges, but based upon the detailed biochemical data of Junqua *et al.* (1975a,b, 1979), the chromatographic identification of hyaluronic acid, dermatan sulfate, and other vertebrate glycoproteins in sponges (Evans and Bergquist, 1977) is open to question. Junqua *et al.* (1979) find no suggestion of a repeating disaccharide in the saccharide of *Spongia officinalis.*

Cytochemical and Morphological Studies

Ruthenium red and phosphotungstic acid staining patterns indicate that glycoproteins are associated with collagen fibrils. Further studies of this kind employing these and other staining methods and electron microscopy also indicate the presence of glycoproteins and mucopolysaccharides at the cell surface (Garrone *et al.*, 1971; Garrone, 1978). Such staining of choanocytes intensifies the cell surface material which, however, is easily discernible even without it (Chap. 2). In choanocytes, fine fibrillar material is associated with the microvilli of the collar, the flagellum, and the

Table 5-4 Composition of Glycoproteins[a]

| | Spongia[b] | | | Ircinia[c] | Suberites[c] | | | | | |
	Peak I	Peak II	Peak III	Unfractionated	Unfractionated	Peak I	Peak II	Peak III	Massive Form Peak I[b]	Digitate Form Peak I[b]
Aspartic acid	109	98	119	114	108	102	105	64	111	108
Threonine	67	60	67	51	49	53	55	33	66	60
Serine	56	47	50	46	38	38	38	38	57	62
Glutamic acid	97	101	114	102	98	106	110	110	101	100
Proline	49	52	49	48	46	45	50	45	48	56
Glycine	93	90	114	98	89	91	92	91	90	86
Alanine	87	87	83	81	92	97	96	120	78	75
Valine	76	76	69	82	87	94	100	92	69	73
Half-cystine	13	9	9	12	21	19	17	3	12	13
Methionine	26	27	25	20	25	17	18	22	23	25
Isoleucine	66	54	56	57	63	68	65	71	60	65

Leucine	88	83	67	87	80	81	77	103	76	91
Tyrosine	29	32	25	40	39	21	10	13	38	35
Phenylalanine	45	46	37	55	54	53	52	53	47	47
Lysine	37	48	48	46	43	49	54	79	57	52
Histidine	14	20	21	12	17	17	18	26	22	10
Arginine	48	60	47	49	51	49	43	50	45	42
Hexoses (% protein)	—	—	—	6.2%	8.4%	6%	—	—	—	—
Hexosamines (% protein)	—	—	—	2.2%	1.7%	—	—	—	—	—
Ratios of monosaccharides with galactose taken as unity										
Galactose	—	—	—	1.0	1.0	1.0	—	—	—	—
Glucose	—	—	—	0.46	0.93	0.93	—	—	—	—
Mannose	—	—	—	0.78	0.24	0.44	—	—	—	—
Fucose	—	—	—	0.8	1.2	±	—	—	—	—
Arabinose	—	—	—	0.1	None	None	—	—	—	—

[a] Data taken from Junqua et al. (1975a,b). Amino acids expressed as residues per 1,000 residues.
[b] EDTA extraction.
[c] Hot TCA–urea extraction.

Table 5-5   Glycoproteins of *Spongia officinalis*[a]

Carboxylic Amino Acids[b]	Fractions				
	A-I (235)	A-II (211)	B (209)	C-I (182)	C-II (181)
Glycine[b]	88	87	83	79	78
Alanine[b]	88	80	78	89	84
Isoleucine + leucine[b]	130	143	147	157	155
Lysine[b]	38	47	48	57	60
Neutral sugars[c]	20.4	2.4	3.1	6.0	5.5
Hexosamine[c]	6.8	2.6	2.6	1.4	2.0
Uronic Acids[c]	1.5	0.3	0.3	0.4	0.3
Sulfate[c]	2.7	0.0	0.0		
N-Acetyl-glucosamine[c]	4.2				
N-Acetyl-galactosamine[c]	1.5				
Glucose[c]	0.0				
Galactose[C]	2.9				
Mannose[c]	1.0				
Fucose[c]	5.1				
Arabinose[c]	3.7				
Glucuronic acid[c]	1.0				
Percentage of total protein	37	57		6	
Molecular weight		16,000/32,000		21,000	

[a]Data taken from Junqua *et al.* (1979). Blank spaces for undetermined data.
[b]Per 1,000 residues.
[c]As percentage of protein present.

bases of the microvilli (see Fig. 2-9) (see, for example, Brill, 1973; Feige, 1969; Pottu-Boumendil, 1975; Rasmont, 1956). The chemistry of this material is unknown but can be assumed to be partially glycoprotein in nature.

Special cells in a number of species have been shown to release their contents into the mesohyl. In *Microciona prolifera* and *spinosa*, in *Ophlitaspongia seriata*, and in *Cyamon neon*, rhabdiferous cells undergo an evolution, ending with the complete release of cytochemically defined glycosaminoglycans (Simpson, 1963; Borojevic and Lévi, 1964b; Simpson, 1968b; Smith and Lauritis, 1969). The sacculiferous cells in *Cyamon* release microfibrillar material intercellularly from their large, unusual inclusions; the fibrils measure 2.0 to 4.0 nm in diameter and thus, if they are collagenous, do not fit within the category of spongin microfibrils (Smith and Lauritis, 1969); they also have no discernible banding pattern. Microtubules are found within these inclusions and some are continuous with the membrane surrounding the inclusion. Spherulous cells in *Tethya* (Connes, 1968), *Hippospongia* (Thiney, 1972), *Pleraplysilla* (Donadey and Vacelet, 1977), and *Chondrosia* and *Chondrilla* (Garrone, 1978) clearly have a secretory function and are known either to release the contents of their inclusions or the whole cell undergoes disintegration. The inclusion contents in some of these cells have tentatively been labeled as glycoprotein (Thiney and Garrone, 1970) and in others as glycosaminoglycan (acid mucopolysaccharide) (Donadey and Vacelet, 1977). Spherulous cells in *Axinella polyploides* also release their contents, which contain an interesting lectin of unknown physiological significance (Bretting and Konigsmann, 1979; Bretting, 1979). Exopinacoctyes in *Microciona prolifera* possess a glycocalyx on their outer surface that is both granular and fibrillar (Bagby, 1970); a similar coat has been reported in other species (Fig. 5-15) (Feige, 1969; Boury-Esnault, 1973; Ledger, 1976) (Chap. 2). Although no chemical studies are available, it seems worthy of consideration that this cell surface material is probably different from that which faces the ground substance of the sponge.

In two species of *Aplysina* (*Verongia*), there is a thin (1.0 μm) cuticle below which is the mesohyl (Vacelet, 1971b); Garrone (1978) has found a similar structure in *Ircinia* and *Cacospongia* (see further, Chap. 2). The chemical nature of these unusual surfaces is unknown. It is probably the case that an exopinacocyte layer was originally present and after formation of the cuticle the cells either migrated away from the surface or underwent degeneration. Possibly these cuticles are a sign of aging, since in *Microciona prolifera* the external coat on exopinacocytes is not present during the spring (Bagby, 1970) when the new dermal membrane is forming and the sponge is undergoing renewed growth and development (Simpson, 1968b). There is no suggestion that contact of the mesohyl with sea water induces the formation of cuticles (Garrone, 1978). The surface of cuticles in the above horny sponges is, on occasion, somewhat reminiscent of the dense, internal band of material in gemmule coats (Chap. 8).

A further unusual type of structure, which is technically not extracellular, are the "segmented fibers" in *Haliclona elegans* (Fig. 5-16) (Tuzet, 1932; Herlant-Meewis, 1948a; Lévi, 1967). Garrone (1978) has recently restudied these "fibers" and has found that they are definitely not collagenous. The fibers consist of a chain of cells, end to end, in each of which is a dense, longitudinal, microfibrillar axis. In each of these cells, the dense strip is perfectly aligned with the strips in the adjoining cells so that a "fiber" appears to be present which is segmented, the segmentation being due to spaces between the aligned cells; the cell junctions are very resistant to separation. In the cytoplasm of the cells are inclusions containing both dense material and microtubular structures. Both the contents of the inclusions and the "fiber" are sensitive to pronase, the former more so than the latter. The function of "segmented fibers" is not clear and they have only been reported in a single species.

In *Microciona spinosa*, long, thin tracts of rhabdiferous cells, spicules (toxas), and an apparently extracellular, coiled, membranous material

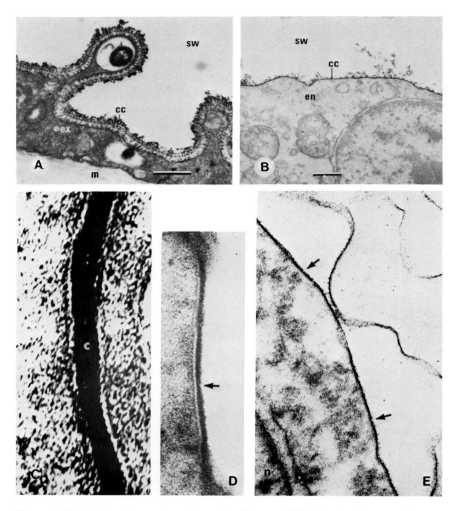

Figure 5-15   Ruthenium red staining of cell coats (TEMs). **A**. The complex cell coat (*cc*) on the surface of an exopinacocyte (*ex*) of the calcareous species, *Sycon ciliatum. sw,* sea water; *m,* mesohyl. Scale bar: 0.5 μm (×19,800) (Ledger, 1976). **B**. A simple coat (*cc*) on the surface of an endopinacocyte (*en*) of *Sycon ciliatum. sw,* sea water. Scale bar: 0.5 μm (×14,400) (Ledger, 1976). **C**. A cell coat (*c*) joining the cell membranes of two mesohyl cells of *Haliclona elegans* (×378,000) (Garrone *et al.,* 1971). **D**. A simple thin coat (*arrow*) on a mesohyl cell of *Haliclona elegans* (×82,800) (Garrone *et al.,* 1971). **E**. Staining pattern of the cell coat (*arrows*) in other mesohyl cells of *Haliclona elegans. n,* nucleus (×72,000) (Garrone *et al.,* 1971). (**A, B,** courtesy Dr. P. W. Ledger; **C–E,** courtesy Dr. R. Garrone.)

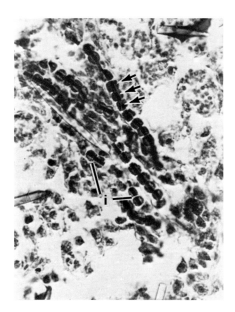

Figure 5-16 Segmented fibers of *Haliclona elegans*. These unusual structures consist of a series of aligned cells (*arrows*). In each cell a dense band is produced which is aligned with the dense bands of the other cells in the fiber. At *i*, somewhat isolated cells and their dense bands are visible (light micrograph) (×400) (Liaci *et al.*, 1973). (Courtesy Dr. L. Scalera-Liaci.)

occur in new growth areas (Simpson, 1968a). The rhabdiferous cells contain and release polysaccharide and the coiled material is intensely PAS positive and may represent a hitherto undescribed matrix element. In the larvae of *Mycale*, short, thin, slightly curved strands of material, referred to as "connective tissue straps," are abundant and may also represent an unusual form of collagen secretion (Reiswig, 1971c), although ultrastructural studies are essential to support this view.

Fibronectin

Robert *et al.* (1981) have demonstrated the presence of fibronectin in *Ephydatia mulleri* using highly specific antibodies and indirect immunofluorescence (Fig. 5-17). This was found localized in the membranes of pinacocytes, choanocytes, and within mesohyl cells (probably archeocytes), and in lesser amounts in the intercellular matrix. Of much potential importance was the finding that antifibronectin antiserum appeared able to inhibit cell reaggregation, suggesting a possible role for fibronectin in cell–cell adhesion.

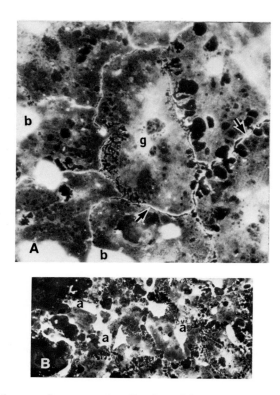

Figure 5-17   Immunofluorescent localization of fibronectin in *Ephydatia mulleri*.
A. Immunofluorescence at the edges (*arrows*) and in the region of the Golgi (*g*) in
a basopinacocyte. Other bright areas (*b*) of fluorescence also are present (UV light
micrograph) (×1,000) (Robert *et al.*, 1981). **B**. Whole cell fluorescence of archeocytes (*a*) which is obviously different from that in basopinacocytes (UV light
micrograph) (×200) (Robert *et al.*, 1981). (Both, courtesy Dr. R. Garrone.)

Morphogenetic and Developmental Aspects of Organic Matrix Substances

Studies of the role of matrix macromolecules and cell surface components
in development now make up a veritable discipline in their own right. The
purpose of this section is to explore a number of potentially important
attributes of these kinds of molecules as they relate to sponge structure
and development. Matrix and cell surface substances which have been
investigated in cell reaggregation studies are treated separately in Chapter
Nine. The role of these substances within the sponge tissue has not been
determined.

Sponge collagens stand out as exceptionally inert components of the matrix, possibly undergoing little or no biodegradation. Therefore, the location and arrangement of fibrils and spongin fibers probably have a profound effect upon a number of processes and morphogenetic patterns. Such a general feature as the overall shape of sponges, however, does not seem to be influenced by these arrangements—for example, an encrusting morphology may occur without fibers (*Halisarca*) or with fibers that are either spiculated (many demosponges) or nonspiculated (*Aplysilla*); upright, branching species may contain spiculated (many haplosclerid species and others) or nonspiculated [as in *Aplysina* (*Verongia*)] fibers. On the other hand, the presence or absence of spongin fibers, their density, and arrangement probably effect growth rates since when very dense, rates of cell migration will be retarded. This has been confirmed for three demosponges; annual volume increases (a measure of growth) for *Mycale* sp., which contains a low density of collagen, is on the order of 60% while in *Tethya crypta* and *Aplysina* (*Verongia*) *gigantea,* sponges possessing dense collagenous matrices, increases are on the order of only 5% annually (Reiswig, 1973). The arrangement or rearrangement of components of the canal system (Chap. 6) will also be strongly affected by fibril and fiber arrangement. The presence of the canal system does not appear related to the presence of spongin, since all species lacking fibers also have canal systems. However, in calcareous species, fibers are absent and the canal system tends to be simplified suggesting that its complexity in fiber-bearing species may be related to the complexity of fiber arrangement. Homoscleromorphs and hexactinellids also lack spongin fibers and tend toward more simplified canal systems. Metamorphosing larvae initially form a simple canal system without first developing spongin fibers, and the formation of fibers later is accompanied by a remodeling of the more simplified initial system (Brien, 1973).

Collagen has been considered essential for the anchorage of sponges to their substrata (Garrone, 1978), but this is not universally the case. Among tetractinomorphs and hexactinellids, extremely long spicules may function as an anchor in soft bottoms of the ocean, and in burrowing sponges no basal layer of spongin forms and basopinacocytes become "anchored" to the calcareous substratum by the pattern of their etching activities (Chap. 4).

Both collagens and other matrix substances are doubtless involved in determining to a large extent the elasticity of sponge tissue; there being no confirmed reports of the presence of elastic fibers. In *Haliclona elegans,* the segmented fibers are very resistant to stretch and may thus oppose deformations of the surrounding tissue (Garrone, 1978). The elasticity of the tissue will, in turn, directly affect the overall patterns of contractions which occur in some sponges and have now been fully documented (De Vos and Van de Vyver, 1981; Pavans de Ceccatty, 1974a, 1979; Pottu-Boumendil and Pavans de Ceccatty, 1976). One type of tissue contraction involves the periodic pulling back of the thin, undifferentiated edge of young, encrusting sponges (Pé, 1973; Simpson, 1963) where no spongin fibers are present and where probably minimal numbers of collagen fibrils occur; the latter condition can be presumed to permit a higher degree of contractility (lowered resistance) than in fully structured tissue.

The level and distribution of tension within the tissue may also be affected by the density of fibrils and presence or absence of fibers, since if these resist deformation the lines of tension will be diverted around them producing nonlinear patterns which may be of significance for maintenance (or rearrangements) of cells and epithelia (Borojevic, 1971).

Matrix and cell surface substances and fibrils may also be critical in inducing, through cell–cell or cell–matrix interactions, cytodifferentiation; cell aggregation *in vivo,* as during gemmule formation (Chap. 8) and wound healing; and the secretion of additional matrix materials such as spicules or massive calcareous deposits (Chap. 4). Glycoproteins and collagen fibrils may also be instrumental in establishing bioelectric fields, which have been indicated as possibly important factors in determining cell activities and in remodeling morphogenetic patterns, such as in bone.

The major cell types responsible for collagen biosynthesis—spongocytes, lophocytes, pinacocytes—are all generally considered to be derived from archeocytes which themselves may be involved in fibrillogenesis. Some workers (Feige, 1969; Effremova, 1967) suggest that possibly all of these cell types are different expressions of archeocytes and they thus may not represent separate categories of cells. Data supporting or refuting this view are insufficient at the present time (see Chap. 9), and only further studies establishing the final fate (if there is one) of these cells and their potential for reversion to an archeocyte morphology will help to resolve this question. Only a few special cells are indicated as having the potential for fibrillogenesis and others are known to secrete matrix materials (Chap. 2). We can thus view special cells in the context of matrix elaboration as constituting two categories: (1) those involved in matrix elaboration and (2) those not so involved. Some of the latter may be transitory stages on the differentiative pathway to the former and others may be involved in apparently unrelated functions, such as microsclere secretion. Cell types involved in matrix and fibril biosynthesis and secretion have not been clearly demonstrated to undergo mitosis, and studies are required on this point. Differentiated exopinacocytes do not appear to divide (Simpson, 1963; Bagby, 1972) and special cells also have not been recorded to be mitotically active (Simpson, 1963). It may turn out that none of the matrix elaborating cell types divide, and archeocytes could then be characterized as a separate cell category on the basis of their mitotic ability.

CHAPTER SIX

Canal System Structure, Development and Activities

It is surprising that so few detailed studies of the components of the canal system have been accomplished. Numerous descriptions of certain aspects appear in many systematic and other monographs (Vacelet, 1964; Connes, 1968; Thiney, 1972; Pottu-Boumendil, 1975; Diaz, 1979a; Hartman, 1958a; Sollas, 1888; and others) but few of these data are comprehensive. The general absence of thoroughgoing, quantitative data is emphasized by the fact that there has not been a full, three-dimensional reconstruction of the canal system in any sponge. Until such reconstructions have been accomplished we will not have available all of the essential, quantitative and configurational information that is required for detailed biophysical analyses of water flow and other physiological parameters. The dynamics of water flow is somewhat better documented than morphology but only in a few species. The morphogenesis of the canal system is *the* major process during growth and development and there are only incomplete data on this highly complex phenomenon.

The primary physiological functions of this system are food procurement and processing, elimination, gas exchange, and possibly gamete release; the latter two functions are very poorly known. Another possible function not seriously considered is the involvement of the canal system in osmotic and ionic regulation including intertidal species which, when they are exposed to air, trap environmental fluid in the canal system. The canal system of burrowing sponges uniquely functions as a passageway for the movement of calcareous chips from the substratum to the environment (Chap. 4).

An excellent review of some aspects of the canal system emphasizing earlier observations is to be found in Jones (1962), and Lawn (1982) has recently reviewed questions relative to conduction systems.

Ostia

Among the descriptions of ostia, there are some that are of particular note because they review the earlier literature: Brien (1943, 1973), Jones (1964a, 1966).

Structure in Calcarea

It has long been reported that ostia in common calcareous sponges are formed by single cells, called porocytes (Jones, 1964a, 1966), which are part of the exopinacoderm (Fig. 6-1). These cells form a short pore canal leading either (1) to the choanoderm in asconoid and some syconoid species, such as *Leucosolenia*, or (2) to incurrent canal spaces in other syconoid and leuconoid species. The pore canal has two openings, one dermal (external) and one gastral (internal) (Jones, 1964a). Occasionally there are two gastral openings, a condition possibly due to the secondary inward folding of the lower edges of the porocyte. In the region of the dermal opening the porocyte plasmalemma contacts exopinacocytes (Jones, 1966). Below these contacts the porocyte borders the mesohyl in which long, thin, pseudopodial extensions of the cell are sometimes found in contact with the ground substance or with "amebocytes." Basally the porocyte surface contacts endopinacocytes except in the case of asconoid and some syconoid species in which choanocytes are contacted. In the

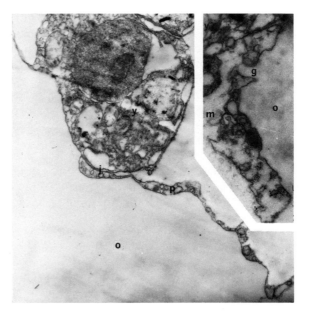

Figure 6-1 Porocytes of *Leucosolenia complicata* (TEMs). These early transmission electron micrographs are the only specific ultrastructural data on porocytes in the phylum. A longitudinal section through part of an ostium showing the pore canal (*o*) which is limited by the porocyte (*p*). The porocyte is seen forming a junction (*j*) with a choanocyte (*y*) (×10,125). **Inset:** A portion of a porocyte lining the pore canal (*o*). The porocyte makes contact with the mesohyl (*m*) and a choanocyte (*y*). *g,* gap in the pore wall (×15,450) (Jones, 1966). (Courtesy Dr. W. C. Jones.)

latter, there is usually considerable overlap rather than simple apposition of the porocyte with both exopinacocytes and choanocytes. No cell membrane specializations are reported. Although there are few other ultrastructural studies of porocytes in other groups (Boury-Esnault, 1972, 1974) the above description of the contacts made by them probably can be considered to be of general occurrence. There is little ultrastructural specialization of porocytes and these cells are morphologically similar to exopinacocytes (Jones, 1966).

In terms of contractility (Jones, 1961a) porocytes are unreactive to light and temperature in *Leucosolenia,* but simultaneous closure of pore canals in many ostia has been recorded (Jones, 1964a) suggesting the presence of some type of conduction system. Contact of the porocytes with calcitic spicules appears to act as a stimulus for constriction of the pore canal. Pores have also been seen to coalesce (Jones, 1964a) but the details and significance of this process are unknown. The original hypothesis that there is a continuous porocyte epithelium that underlies the choanocytes (Jones, 1961a) was later found to be unacceptable (Jones, 1966).

Pore Canal: Intracellular or Extracellular? The pore canal has most often been referred to as intracellular. In the only ultrastructural study of porocytes, Jones (1966) has referred to it as such. It cannot be emphasized too strongly that there are no compelling data to support this contention. As a matter of fact, the electron micrographs presented by Jones (1966) clearly show the presence of a plasmalemma-like membrane lining the pore canal. It is difficult to conceive that the pore canal runs directly *through* the porocyte. This type of cytomorphology is exceedingly rare and thus there are no appropriate models or data to support such a morphology in porocytes. An alternative interpretation is that the pore canal arises as a result of the porocyte forming a "sleeve" in the center of which is the canal. The apposition of the free edges of the cell membrane is clearly possible on an ultrastructural level as was originally surmised by Annandale (1907). In fact, Jones (1966) has found gaps in the pore wall which support this view. On a light microscope level, it is not surprising that such edges would not be visible since areas of contact between pinacocyte cell membranes in sponge cells are notoriously difficult to resolve with light microscopy. Additional ultrastructural investigation of porocytes are very much in order given the classical interpretation of the intracellular location of ostia and the very limited nature of the available data.

Structure in Demospongiae

Although there have only been cursory ultrastructural examinations of ostia in this group (Weissenfels, 1980; De Vos, 1979; Boury-Esnault, 1972, 1974), other available data indicate that single porocytes also form them in at least some species (Weissenfels, 1980; Reiswig, 1975a; Harrison, 1972b; Brien, 1932; Wilson, 1910; Fauré-Frémiet, 1932a). Since

Wilson concluded that the pinacoderms are syncytial, his descriptions of ostia are couched in these terms. Although Jones (1962) states that Wilson's description of them conforms to those of Brien (1943), Kilian (1952), and Wintermann-Kilian *et al.* (1969) (see following), it can, however, also be interpreted as conforming to those of Jones (1964a, 1966) and Weissenfels (1980), since in *Reniera* the pore membrane was described as always being associated with a single nucleus (Wilson, 1910). In *Corvomeyenia carolinensis,* Harrison (1972b) considers the pore canal as intracellular and formed by a single porocyte. Weissenfels (1980) has recently investigated ostia in newly developing individuals of *Ephydatia fluviatilis* and also finds them to be single cells which make contact with both exopinacocytes and endopinacocytes, thus straddling the dermal membrane (Fig. 6-2). The dilation of the pore canal within 10 min could be stimulated by a temperature reduction possibly suggesting a "relaxation" of cytoplasmic contractile elements although myofilaments have not been described in them. Weissenfels (personal communication) considers the pore canal to be intracellular.

On the other hand, De Vos (personal communication) suggests that the formation of ostia may occur by means of the separation of neighboring exopinacocytes so that the pore actually occurs *between* cells (Fig. 6-2D). In some demosponges, ostia may be formed by the latter method and thus are bordered by two or more exopinacocytes (Simpson, 1968a; Boury-Esnault, 1972). Indeed, if this is the case then ostial porocytes *per se* do not exist in these animals.

In summary, although convincing data are available establishing that ostia are formed by single porocytes in demosponges, these data are restricted to quite young animals and it is not clear whether in fully developed ones they are similarly constructed. This will be a very difficult point to establish, since it requires ultrastructural observations of sections that are parallel to the exopinacoderm and pass through the dermal membrane in areas where ostia are present. Such sections will also help to clarify the question of whether pore canals are indeed "intracellular."

Structure in Hexactinellida

Ostia in hexactinellids are intrasyncytial occurring in the thin, syncytial "dermal membrane" (Mackie and Singula, 1983). In distinction to other sponges, they also appear to lack contractility (Mackie *et al.,* 1983) and thus apparently do not function in the control of water pumping.

Development

Porocytes have been viewed as secondarily differentiated exopinacocytes (Weissenfels, 1980; Harrison, 1972b), but there is little definitive information on the subject and it has also been claimed that collencytes may form them in freshwater sponges (Brien, 1943) and "amebocytes" (Prenant, 1925) or endopinacocytes (Jones, 1966) in calcareous species. Brien (1943,

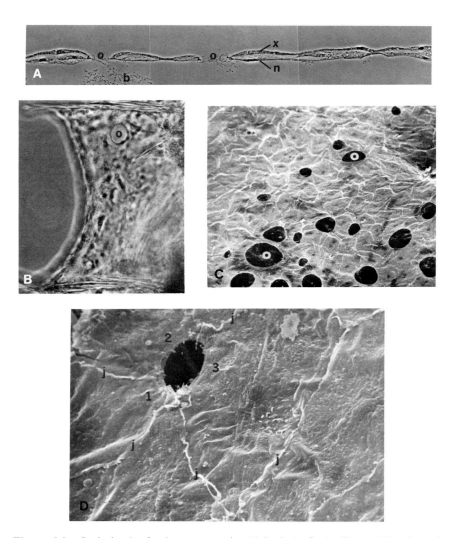

Figure 6-2 Ostia in the freshwater species *Ephydatia fluviatilis*. **A.** The dermal membrane showing two ostia (*o*) which are formed by porocytes that are considered to bridge the region between exopinacoderm (*x*) and prosendopinacoderm (*n*). *b,* bacteria (phase-contrast micrograph, semithin section) (×450) (Weissenfels, 1980). **B.** Exopinacoderm showing a porocyte surrounding an ostium (*o*) (phase-contrast micrograph, living) (×180) (Weissenfels, 1980). **C.** Exopinacoderm showing numerous ostia (*o*) as well as the outlines of the exopinacocytes (SEM) (×235) (De Vos, 1979). **D.** An ostium that clearly appears to be formed by a number of cells. *j,* junctions between exopinacocytes. The opening seems to have three separate cells (*1, 2, 3*) forming it, thus presenting a possible second means by which these openings are structured (SEM) (×1,240) (De Vos, unpubl.). (**A, B,** courtesy Prof. N. Weissenfels; **C, D,** courtesy Dr. L. De Vos.)

1973) has reported the following sequence in the formation of ostia in young, freshwater sponges: an exopinacocyte forms an intracellular pore canal, and the cell then contracts and sinks below the level of the exopinacoderm. The spherical space that remains is then surrounded by collencytes, which come to border the definitive, intercellular ostium. This description encompasses almost all of the varying points of view expressed by other workers relative to the origin and structure of porocytes, but it has not been corroborated and is at variance with the more recent data of Weissenfels (1980). Kilian (1952) and Wintermann-Kilian *et al.* (1969) also describe ostia as consisting of an intercellular space in the exopinacoderm and an underlying porocyte with an intracellular pore canal. It must be stated that the origin of porocytes still remains in doubt, and only future investigations will further resolve differences in the literature. Porocytes clearly become an integral part of the exopinacoderm and available observations give no indication that they multiply by mitoses (Jones, 1964a). The appearance of new ostia in a relatively short time, up to 10 h in stretched pieces of the wall of *Leucosolenia variabilis* (Jones, 1961a) and within 10 min in *Ephydatia fluviatilis* (Weissenfels, 1980), is indicative of nonmitotic morphogenesis. In *Leucosolenia* new ostia arise just below the oscule in the region where new choanocytes are also forming (Jones, 1964a).

The size of ostia is variable, since contraction or dilation of the porocyte will directly effect its diameter (Table 6-1).

Incurrent Canals

Many variations in the overall structure of incurrent canals are known (Brien, 1973; Tuzet, 1973a,b) despite the general absence of detailed morphological investigations. These canals are lined by prosendopinacocytes and can be relatively simple structures leading directly to groups of choanocytes as occurs both in some syconoids and in a few leuconoids. However, in most leuconoid species, two or more subdivisions of them can be distinguished (Fig. 6-3). In the latter, ostia open either directly or via short, thin canals (referred to as "canicules") into a larger space, the vestibule. Incurrent canals proper then lead from the vestibule to the choanocyte chambers (Weissenfels, 1982). A number of arrangements occur, the most complex of which results in what has been referred to as an inhalant "organ" (Boury-Esnault, 1972).

Inhalant "Organs"

Excellent historical reviews of the distribution and histology of inhalant organs will be found in Sollas (1909), Minchin (1900), and Brien (1973). They have recently been studied in *Hamigera, Anchinoe, Hymedesmia, Hemimycale,* and *Crella* by Boury-Esnault (1972), and their structure is

Table 6-1 Diameters of Ostial Openings

Class and Species	Size[a]	References
Calcarea		
Neocoelia crypta	50.0[b]	Vacelet (1979b)
Leucosolenia variabilis	10.0	Jones (1961a)
Demospongiae		
Tetractinomorpha		
Polymastia mamilaris	10.0–40.0	Boury-Esnault (1974)
Other species[c]	20.0–50.0	Brien (1973)
Ceractinomorpha		
Spongilla lacustris	Up to 63–84	Kilian (1952), Van Tright (1919)
Corvomeyenia carolinensis	15.0–25.0	Harrison (1972b)
Ephydatia fluviatilis	15.0–50.0[b]	Brien (1943), De Vos (1979), Weissenfels (1980)
Haliclona permolis	20.6[d]	Reiswig (1975a)
Halichondria panicea	17.9[d]	Reiswig (1975a)
Hamigera hamigera	1.0– 3.0	Boury-Esnault (1972)
Microciona prolifera	13.4[d]	Reiswig (1975a)
	10.0–42.0	Simpson (1968a)
Microciona spinosa	1.0–48.0	Simpson (1968a)
Thalysias juniperina	6.0–19.0	Simpson (1968a)
Thalysias schoenus	8.0–18.0	Simpson (1968a)
Tedania ignis	3.5–14.0	Simpson (1968a)
Hexactinellida		
Hexasterophora		
Rhabdocalyptus dawsoni	11.0[d]	Mackie and Singula (1983)

[a]Ranges or estimations or means of diameters in micrometers.
[b]Some sizes estimated from figures.
[c]Separate species not listed by author.
[d]Mean diameter.

remarkably complex (Fig. 6-4). Ostia are grouped together to form a sieve; short, endopinacocyte-lined canicules lead from the ostia into an endopinacocyte-lined vestibule, which in turn gives off a number (1 to 3) of incurrent canals that course inward into the choanosome; the ostia are present at the surface of the sieve plate which, together with the vestibule, constitutes a "crib." In *Hamigera hamigera* the cribs are 1.6 to 2.0 mm in diameter and there are about twelve cribs/cm² surface area; each vestibule has a volume of approximately 10 μl; in other species, dimensions vary. The sieve plate, which is about 50 μm thick, is a complex superficial area of the mesohyl perforated by ostia and canicules. The exopinacocytes are of the T form (Chap. 2), underlain by unoriented collagen fibrils. The middle region of the plate contains dense accumula-

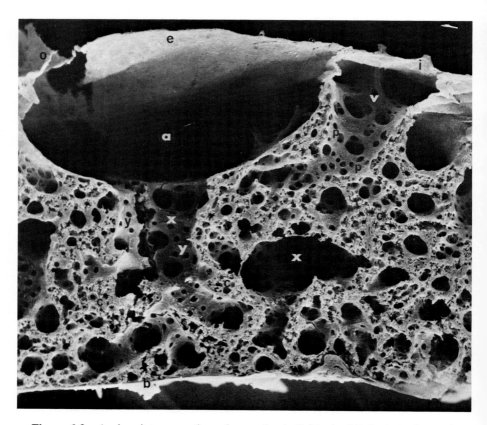

Figure 6-3 A view into a portion of an entire individual of *Ephydatia fluviatilis* which, using a newly developed technique, was sectioned prior to visualization (SEM). The preparation shows most major aspects of the canal system. *i,* incurrent dermal membrane overlying a subdermal cavity (vestibule) (*v*); *p*, pores in the vestibule wall; *c,* choanocyte chambers; *x*, excurrent canals; *y,* apopyles; *e,* excurrent dermal membrane overlying an atrial cavity (*a*); *o,* wall of the oscule; *b,* basopinacoderm and basal spongin layer (×110) (Weissenfels, 1982). (Courtesy Prof. N. Weissenfels.)

tions of collagen fibrils parallel to the exopinacoderm and similarly oriented myocytes. The inner area, which makes up about two thirds of the plate, contains archeocytes, spherulous cells, collencytes, and numerous vacuolar cells. Underlying the endopinacocytes that line the vestibule is a continuous layer of myocytes joining those in the sieve plate and acting as a sphincter. Similar inhalant organs are fairly common among tetractinomorph demosponges as originally described by Sollas (1888) and recently reviewed by Brien (1973). In some of them (*Erylus*) only a single pore leads into the vestibule; in the mesohyl surrounding the vestibule there

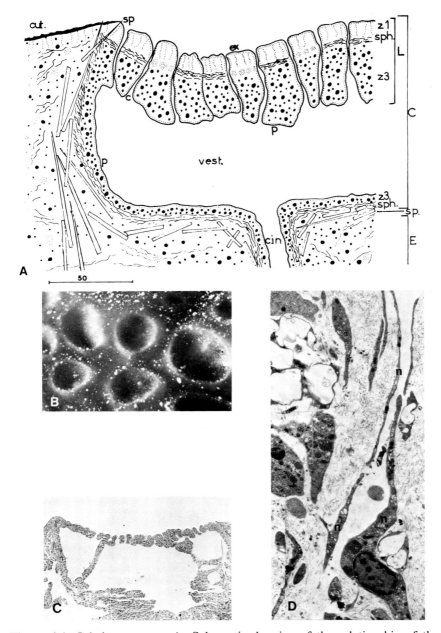

Figure 6-4 Inhalant organs. **A**. Schematic drawing of the relationship of the components: *C*, crib; *c*, canicule; *c. in.*, incurrent canal; *cut.*, cuticle; *E*, ectosome; *ex*, exopinacoderm; *L*, sieve plate; *p*, prosendopinacoderm; *sp.*, spicule; *sph.*, sphincter; *vest.*, vestibule; *Z 1*, superficial zone; *Z 3*, internal zone (Boury-Esnault, 1972). **B**. Surface view of *Hamigera hamigera* showing the cribs (light micrograph) (×7.2) (Boury-Esnault, 1972). **C**. Crib of *Hemimycale columella* (light micrograph) (×18) (Boury-Esnault, 1972). **D**. A canicule of *Hamigera hamigera* showing the endopinacocytes (*n*) forming the passageway. Note the lining of the canicule is multicellular (TEM) (×3,960) (Boury-Esnault, 1972). (All courtesy Dr. N. Boury-Esnault.)

are supporting spicule tracts. In those species with a cuticle, none is present on the surface of the sieve plate. These unusual "organs" predominate in demosponges with cortical specialization, thus isolating the ostia in spherical patches. Among the sclerosponges, in *Ceratoporella nicholsoni* and *Acanthochaetetes wellsi,* the tissue within each calicle (that is, a depression surrounded by aspicular aragonite) has only one (or two) ostium that conducts water into the incurrent canals. The ostium of each calicle is thus topologically similar to all of the ostia of a single crib.

A special and unusual arrangement of the incurrent system occurs in *Disyringa* and *Tribrachium* (Fry and Fry, 1979). In the former, ostia, vestibules, and incurrent canals are localized at one end of the tube-like body of the animal. There are four incurrent canals leading to the central choanosome; the ostia thus occur in series. The single excurrent canal and oscule are located at the other end of the tube. This arrangement adapts the animal for living in loose, unconsolidated sediments through which water is drawn into the incurrent system. The oscule protrudes above the sediments. In *Tribrachium,* the choanosome is basal, the incurrent and excurrent systems are localized on the tube, but the incurrent stream of water courses basally before entering the excurrent system and water is not drawn in through the sediments to which the sponge is attached.

Papillae

A second type of incurrent structure resulting in the localization of incurrent canals is papillae, which are present in some demosponges such as *Cliona* and *Polymastia*. In the latter, a more recent study of them has shown that some papillae possess a terminal oscule and others do not, while both types contain incurrent canals (Fig. 6-5) (Boury-Esnault, 1974). Thus, functionally there are two types; incurrent papillae and mixed papillae; both structures stand 0.1 to 7.0 cm in height above the sponge surface and are 1.0 to 5.0 mm in thickness. Ostia on the papillae are in groups of six to eight and lead by canicules into a vestibule with 20 to 40 ostia per vestibule, reminiscent of cribs. For incurrent papillae, vestibules each open by a single, central pore into a central incurrent canal, 0.5 to 1.5 mm in diameter, which runs the length of the papilla. In mixed papillae, the incurrent system is similar, except that in the center of the papilla is a single excurrent canal leading to a terminal oscule and the displaced incurrent canals are superficial and are multiple. There is much less mesohyl organization around vestibules of *Polymastia* than around cribs of *Hamigera;* in the former the papillary mesohyl is similar to that in other areas of the animal.

Other Patterns

In leuconoid species without cribs or papillae, the incurrent canal system is similar, but diffuse, with ostia scattered over much of the surface (Reiswig, 1975a). However, in some species there are large areas of the

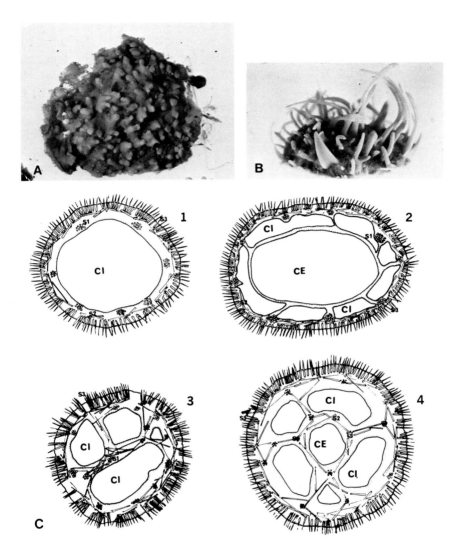

Figure 6-5 Papillae. **A**. Surface view of *Tedania suctoria* (light micrograph) (×1.4) (Simpson, 1968a). **B**. Side view of papillae of *Polymastia mamillaris* (light micrograph) (×0.9) (Boury-Esnault, 1974). **C**. Internal structure of incurrent papillae in *Polymastia mamillaris* (*1*) and *Polymastia robusta* (*3*) and of mixed incurrent and excurrent papillae in *Polymastia mamillaris* (*2*) and *Polymastia robusta* (*4*) (cross sections). *CE*, excurrent canal; *CI*, incurrent canal; *S1*, principal spicules; *S2*, tangential spicules; *S3*, ectosomal spicules (Boury-Esnault, 1974). (**B**, **C**, courtesy Dr. N. Boury-Esnault.)

surface that contain all of the ostia in distinction to other areas that have none but contain oscules, as in *Murrayona* (see Fig. 1-5A) (Vacelet, 1977a). In newly formed freshwater sponges the ostia are also localized only in one area of the exopinacoderm (Van de Vyver, personal communication). The vestibules in these sponges are meandering, endopinacocyte-lined cavities giving rise to incurrent canals (see Fig. 6-3). The vestibular cavities have frequently been referred to as "subdermal spaces" and the very thin, overlying tissue as the "dermal membrane," a term still useful in identifying this structure (Pottu-Boumendil, 1975). The dermal membrane can be compared to the sieve plate in crib-bearing species; both structures consist of a layer of mesohyl (very thin in the case of the dermal membrane) sandwiched between exopinacocytes and endopinacocytes; choanocyte chambers are not present in dermal membranes but myocytes usually are (Bagby, 1966). A similar dermal membrane overlies superficial *excurrent* canals when they are present and should be referred to as the excurrent dermal membrane to distinguish it from the incurrent dermal membrane (see Fig. 6-3). The structure of the connections between ostia and vestibules in these sponges has not been studied ultrastructurally but may be similar to canicules in crib-bearing species or, as recently described by Weissenfels (1980), ostia may lead directly to the vestibule without the intervention of discrete, transmembrane canicules. In mature individuals of *Suberites massa,* for example, available data are not completely sufficient to decide whether the former or the latter condition prevails (Connes *et al.,* 1972; Diaz, 1979a). This is generally also the case in most species and is due in part to the difficulty of obtaining appropriate sections for ultrastructural analysis. Although not fully substantiated, it has been conjectured that the vestibular cavities in these animals are interconnected (Hartman and Reiswig, 1973) such that water entering an ostium may be distributed to vestibular cavities which are at some distance from the pore. Sizes of incurrent canal components are given in Table 6-2.

Cellular Features

The structure of the endopinacocytes that line the incurrent canals have been discussed in Chapter Two. A few unusual, but important different cellular features are reviewed here.

The endopinacoderm lining the vestibule and incurrent canals (=prosendopinacoderm) in freshwater sponges contains numerous porocytes whose pore canal leads directly to the mesohyl (Weissenfels, 1975; De Vos, 1979). These porocytes thus expose the mesohyl directly to the environment, a finding of much significance in considering feeding and gas exchange (Fig. 6-6). It is, however, to be emphasized that such openings have not yet been described in mature sponges. Also, Weissenfels (1980) has reported that at the point at which incurrent canals end, close to the choanocyte chambers, they open directly into the mesohyl via a terminal

Table 6-2 Canal System Components in Four Demosponges[a]

Component	Halichondria panicea	Haliclona permolis	Microciona prolifera	Ephydatia fluviatilis[b]
Ostia	6.5–17.9–32	4.5–20.6–44	4–13.4–28	15–50
Incurrent apertures[c]	50–200	50–340	30–300	
Pinacocytic prosopyles	5	5	5	
Choanocytic prosopyles	1–4	1–5	4–6	5
Choanocyte chambers	18–25–35	22–30–37	20–31–39	40–60
Apopyles	7–13–17	14	9	25–30
Excurrent apertures	140–150	100–650	30–500	
Atrium[d]	2,100	2,300		
Oscules	1,200	2,100	400–520–700	80
Dermal membrane (thickness)	2–3	4–5	1–3	1–2
Subdermal space (vestibule depth)	70–200	60–170	20–60	
Choanocytes/chamber	40–80–120	95	57	43–60[e]
Chambers/mm³	18,000	12,000	10,000	7,600

[a]Data taken from Reiswig (1975a) and Kilian (1952); range and means (italics) in micrometers.
[b]See also Pourbaix (1933).
[c]Openings from the vestibule into individual incurrent canals.
[d]Space into which excurrent canals open.
[e]Estimation based upon chamber and choanocyte volumes.

porocyte (see Pinacocytic Prosopyles). Collencyte pseudopods and some-times whole cells have been observed within incurrent canal spaces (Wintermann, 1951; Kilian, 1952) apparently gaining access to them in areas where the prosendopinacoderm is incomplete or through the poro-cytes now known to be present.

Among some homoscleromorphs, *Plakina* and *Oscarella* (Donadey, 1979; Lévi and Porte, 1962) but not *Octavella* (Tuzet and Paris, 1963a), the endopinacocytes are uniflagellated, but without collars. It is not yet completely clear if both prosendopinacocytes as well as apendopinaco-cytes are so flagellated. Further observations are required in order to specifically determine if flagella are present on prosendopinacocytes. Flagellated endopinacocytes (possibly some prosendopinacocytes) have also been described in *Hippospongia communis* (Thiney, 1972) and *Tethya lyncurium* (Pavans de Ceccatty, 1966). Their significance is un-clear but suggests in some species an unexpected degree of plasticity in the expression of morphological differences between cell types (see Chap. 9). In hexactinellid species, the lining (trabeculum) of the incurrent canals is syncytial (Reiswig, 1979; Mackie and Singula, 1983) and is continuous with the dermal membrane. Neither vestibules nor canicules have been described.

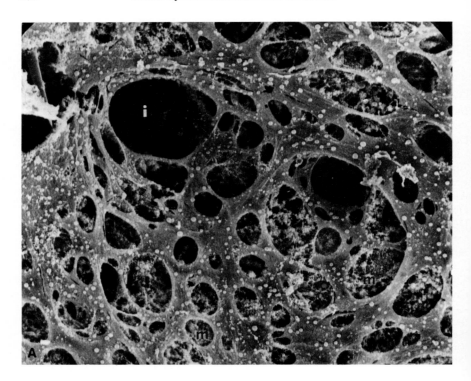

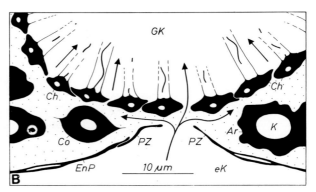

Figure 6-6 Features of the incurrent canal system. **A**. The vestibule of *Ephydatia fluviatilis* showing incurrent canals (*i*) and pores that open into the mesohyl (*m*) (SEM) (×475) (De Vos, 1979). **B**. A representation of the relationships of the incurrent canals (*eK*) to the choanocyte chambers (*GK*) showing a porocyte (*PZ*) forming the end of the canal (pinacocytic prosopyle) that opens directly to the mesohyl (*horizontal arrows*). *Ar*, archeocyte; *Co*, collencyte; *Ch*, choanocytes; *K*, nucleus; *EnP*, endopinacocyte (×1,900) (Weissenfels, 1980). (**A**, courtesy Dr. L. De Vos; **B**, courtesy Prof. N. Weissenfels.)

Development

The formation of the incurrent system has been described particularly in earlier works (see for example, Wilson, 1894; Brien, 1932, 1936; Galtsoff, 1925a,b; Fauré-Frémiet, 1932a; Wintermann, 1951; Mergner, 1970). It is clear from these studies of newly developing leuconoid sponges that the incurrent canal spaces arise from lacunae developing within the mesohyl. In *Ficulina ficus* (Fauré-Frémiet, 1932a) and freshwater species (Brien, 1936; Wintermann, 1951) small lacunae fuse with one another below the exopinacoderm to produce larger spaces which later function as the vestibule. These lacunae come to be partially lined by prosendopinacocytes, but many of the cells act as porocytes keeping the mesohyl in communication with the canal spaces. Wintermann (1951) views the incurrent canal system as not having a fixed mode of formation and as a rather plastic, irregular system. Studies prior to (Fauré-Frémiet, 1932a) and following (Hartman and Reiswig, 1973) hers amply support this perspective. The origin of prosendopinacocytes is not altogether clear, but they may be derived from collencytes or archeocytes as appears to be the case with exopinacocytes (Bagby, 1972) and basopinacocytes (Brønsted, 1953; Borojevic, 1966). Ankel (1949) has suggested, on the other hand, a separate origin for exopinacocytes and endopinacocytes. It is completely clear that the formation of the prosendopinacoderms does not involve mitotic activity of the first formed cells. Relative to the appearance of ostia, it is not established if there is a specific sequence in the formation of incurrent canal spaces, although the exopinacoderm is always in place before the development of either (Wintermann, 1951).

The Terms Prosopyles and Apopyles

The passageways leading from the incurrent canals directly into the choanocyte chambers and those leading from the chambers directly to the excurrent canals have been referred to, respectively, as prosopyles and apopyles. More often than not, both of them have been described as *single* passageways (see for example, Sollas, 1909; Brien, 1932; Hyman, 1940; Kilian, 1964; Simpson, 1968a; De Vos, 1979). Each passageway is compound, however, consisting of two sets of openings, one in the endopinacoderm and the other in the choanocyte chamber (Fig. 6-7). Appropriate terms are thus required to refer to the cells that form these openings.

The term prosopyle(s) as used here refers to the *whole passageway* leading from incurrent canals into choanocyte chambers and the term apopyle(s) refers to the *whole passageway* leading from choanocyte chambers into excurrent canals. The cells in the incurrent canal that form the opening which conducts water toward the choanocyte chambers, are referred to here as pinacocytic prosopyles. The cells in the choanocyte

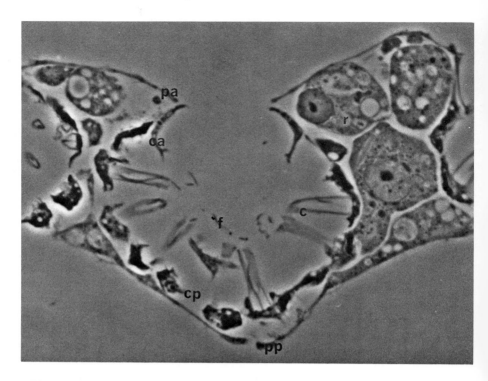

Figure 6-7   A choanocyte chamber of *Ephydatia fluviatilis* showing all structures involved in forming the prosopyle and apopyle. *pp,* porocyte in the prosendopinacoderm which forms the pinacocytic prosopyle; *cp,* space between choanocytes which form the choanocytic prosopyle; *ca,* special cone cells (modified choanocytes) which form the choanocytic apopyle; *pa,* porocyte in the apendopinacoderm which forms the pinacocytic apopyle. Large archeocytes (*r*) are seen in the surrounding mesohyl and choanocyte collars (*c*) and flagella (*f*) are seen in section (phase-contrast micrograph, semithin section) (×1,830) (Weissenfels, 1981). (Courtesy Prof. N. Weissenfels.)

chamber that form the opening through which water flows into the chamber lumen are referred to here as the choanocytic prosopyles. The cells in the choanocyte chamber forming the opening which conducts water toward the excurrent canals are referred to here as the choanocytic apopyles. The cells in the excurrent canal that form the opening which conducts water into the excurrent canal are referred to here as the pinacocytic apopyles. These four new terms are needed in order to identify specifically the cells involved in forming the prosopyles and apopyles. In the literature, one should critically evaluate the use of the terms apopyles and prosopyles to determine the manner in which they are used. The incurrent canals leading directly to the pinacocytic prosopyles and the excurrent canals beginning with the pinacocytic apopyle may be discrete, thin channels that branch off of larger canals. These small connecting passageways, when present, are referred to, respectively, as prosodal and aphodal canals (Hyman, 1940). Both of these terms can be retained without confusion relative to the new descriptive terms introduced here.

Aphodal, Diplodal, Asconoid, and Syconoid Arrangements

In the earlier literature particularly (see Hyman, 1940), some demosponges have been described as possessing both prosodal and aphodal canals; such an arrangement is referred to as "diplodal." In others, no prosodal canals are observed and the connection to the chambers is considered to be directly via a pinacocytic prosopyle. In the latter case when an aphodal canal leads away from the pinacocytic apopyle the arrangement is referred to as "aphodal." These two types of structural arrangements, diplodal and aphodal, can be considered to differ due to the construction of the distal portion of the incurrent canal, which ends in the pinacocytic prosopyle, rather than to the presence or absence of this opening. By definition, a pinacocytic prosopyle must be present in all leuconoid (and some syconoid) animals.

Asconoid species such as *Leucosolenia* represent a special case in which the porocyte that forms an ostium also forms the pinacocytic prosopyle (Jones, 1966), there being no endopinacoderm present at all in this location. In syconoid species, the incurrent canal system has not been studied in detail ultrastructurally; however, on a light microscope level, both discrete tubular (see Hyman, 1940) and lacunar (Borojevic, 1968) connections of the incurrent canal with the choanocyte chambers have been reported in some, whereas in others (*Sycon*) the incurrent system is identical to that in asconoid species—ostium only (Ledger, 1976). The condition in hexactinellids is not clear.

Pinacocytic Prosopyles

These are the openings in the incurrent canals that connect the latter to the choanocyte chambers. Until recently, based upon light microscopy, they were considered to form regions of contact between prosendopinacocytes and choanocytes. The contact areas have been described as relatively discrete, short tubes or as diffuse lacunae with both types sometimes occurring in the same animal (*Haliclona permolis*) (Reiswig, 1975a). Given the inherent limitations of the light microscope, such observations must be viewed with some caution particularly in view of the following, recent ultrastructural observations of pinacocytic prosopyles. In young individuals of *Ephydatia fluviatilis*, Weissenfels (1980) has found that these openings in the incurrent canals consist of porocytes; the terminal end of each incurrent canal possesses a single porocyte whose pore canal then opens, surprisingly, directly into the mesohyl but close to the choanocytes (see Fig. 6-6B). These observations drastically alter present as well as classical views of the functional structure of the incurrent canal system. Many years ago, Brien (1932) described the pinacocytic prosopyles of *Spongilla lacustris* and *Ephydatia fluviatilis* as being porocytes which, however, he viewed as making contact with choanocytes. The recent observations now raise the question of whether the incurrent canal system is open or closed in older organisms and other species. The porocytes constituting the pinacocytic prosopyle do not appear to differ in structure from the porocytes in the prosendopinacoderm of the vestibule or from those that form ostia. Interestingly, Brien (1932) also pointed out the similarity in structure between them and ostial porocytes. On theoretical grounds, any porocyte in the vestibule might have the potential of developing into a pinacocytic prosopyle during growth and development of the canal system. Such a transformation in their structural association may lie at the basis for the addition of new choanocyte chambers to a preexisting incurrent canal system. Future studies dealing with the morphogenesis of the canal system are needed in order to investigate such a possibility.

Choanocytic Prosopyles

Spaces between choanocytes have been observed and described in many species (Van Tright, 1919; Brien, 1932; Wintermann, 1951; Kilian, 1952; Vacelet, 1964; Simpson, 1968a; Reiswig, 1975a; Weissenfels, 1976, 1980). There is no known structural specialization of the choanocytes that form the choanocytic prosopyles, and one or more openings may occur in each chamber. In *Ephydatia fluviatilis,* the choanocytes can put out thin filopods which partially form the choanocytic prosopylar opening (Weissenfels, 1982) (see Fig. 2-7). In the hexactinellid sponges, *Aphrocallistes vasta* and *Chonelasma calyx,* choanocytic prosopyles are also spaces which, however, occur between the collar units and are apparently formed as intracellular "holes" in the trabecular syncytium (Fig. 6-8) (Reiswig, 1979). In demosponges and calcareous sponges, choanocytic prosopyles are not necessarily fixed, structural elements and can appear or disappear as has been directly observed in freshwater species (Wintermann, 1951). In the calcareous sponge, *Leucosolenia variabilis,* the choanocytes are mobile (Jones, 1964a) and choanocytic prosopyles may be transient elements in them also. Diaz (1979a) has carried out a thorough ultrastructural investigation of *Suberites massa* and finds that there are no prosopyles present and that a single apopyle serves as both an entranceway and an exit for water circulation. Fauré-Frémiet (1931) and others

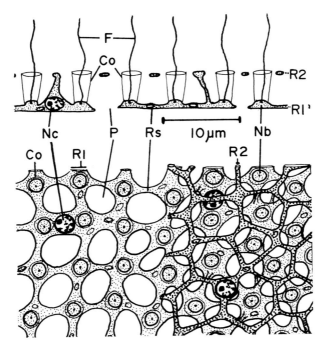

Figure 6-8 Reconstruction of the choanosyncytium in the hexactinellid *Aphrocallistes vastus*. **Above**, a vertical section of the syncytium is shown and **below** a facial view from the exterior of the chamber. On the left side of the facial view the secondary reticulum is omitted. *Co*, collars; *F*, flagella; *Nb*, nodal body; *Nc*, choanosyncytium nuclei; *P*, prosopyle; *Rs*, connecting strands of the main reticulum; *R1*, main reticulum of the chamber wall; *R2*, secondary reticulum of the chamber wall (Reiswig, 1979). (Courtesy Dr. H. M. Reiswig.)

before him also experienced difficulty in finding prosopyles in some animals. According to the recent findings of Diaz, the latter sponges (including *Ficulina*) may also possess choanocyte chambers with only a single passageway (Fig. 6-9).

Choanocyte Chambers

Spherical or subspherical groups of choanocytes are present in most species (see Figs. 2-7, 6-7). In asconoid species and newly metamorphosed syconoid ones (olythus stage), the choanocytes form an epithelial lining that faces the atrium, sometimes referred to as the *spongocoel* (see Fig. 1-3C). Choanocytes are anchored basally on the mesohyl and make contact with neighboring choanocytes. But, in *Callyspongia diffusa*, many choanocytes in each chamber "hang" freely in the incurrent canal spaces.

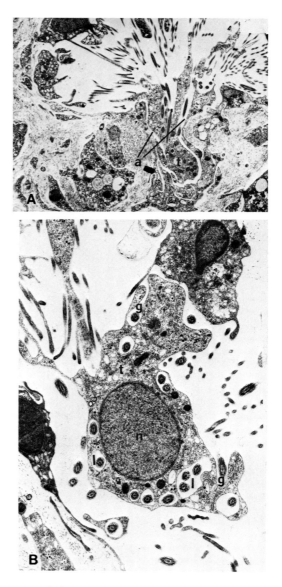

Figure 6-9 Features of choanocyte chambers in *Suberites massa* (TEMs). **A.** A section through a chamber showing the only single opening, the apopyle (*a*), in which is situated the cellule centrale (*t*) (×3,180) (Diaz, 1979a). **B.** A cellule centrale (*t*) in which cell processes form troughs (*g*) that encircle some flagella and what appear to be intracellular channels (*l*) encircling other flagella. *n,* nucleus of cellule centrale (×7,880) (Diaz, 1979a). (Both courtesy Dr. J-P. Diaz.)

Thin pseudopodia from cell to cell appear to hold the cells together (Johnston and Hildemann, 1982). A similar condition also occurs in a species of *Reniera* (Langenbruch, 1983). In some syconoid and in leuconoid forms, some choanocytes contact pinacocytic prosopyles and pinacocytic apopyles and in other syconoids and in asconoids some choanocytes border the porocytes that form ostia (Jones, 1964a, 1966; Ledger, 1976). While the cells are mobile they are also probably under tension (Jones, 1961a). The following factors are known to influence their movements and repositioning: contraction or dilation of the tissue in general (Jones, 1964a; De Vos and Van de Vyver, 1981), mitosis (Jones, 1964a; Kilian and Wintermann-Kilian, 1979), and growth processes (Chap. 9). During growth and development, whole choanocyte chambers have been observed to shift their position in the mesohyl (Kilian and Wintermann-Kilian, 1979). Some choanocytes are involved in forming the choanocytic prosopyles and choanocytic apopyles, and the latter may be structurally modified as cone cells (see following section).

In a recent study of hexactinellid sponges, Reiswig (1979) has presented evidence supporting earlier claims of the presence of a syncytium—the choanosyncytium—which forms flagellated chambers (see Fig. 6–8). This syncytium is very thin but possesses small swellings, called nodal bodies, each one of which gives rise to a collar and flagellum (called a *collar unit* or *body*). The ratio of collar units to nuclei in a single chamber is about 10 : 1. At the level of the distal rim of the collars is a second syncytial network in which there are regularly spaced pores through which the collars and flagella project, one flagellum per pore (see Fig. 6-8). However, a more recent study (Mackie and Singula, 1983) employing more satisfactory preparative techniques for higher resolution transmission electron microscopy has shown that "discrete" cells, choanoblasts, form the collar bodies with many such bodies formed by a single cell (see Fig. 2-15D). Both choanoblasts and collar bodies are connected to the trabeculum by plugged junctions so that the question of whether there is a choanosyncytium *per se* is difficult to address and depends upon the definition employed.

Among calcareous sponges (but not in the sphinctozoid, *Neocoelia*), choanocytes are larger than in demosponges, both nuclear and cell sizes are close to those in pinacocytes (Vacelet, 1964; Tuzet, 1973a; Ledger, 1976). In others (except homoscleromorphs) they are relatively small. The size of choanocyte chambers is highly variable but most lie within the range of 25 to 50 μm in diameter and contain 30 to 150 cells (Reisweig, 1975a; Vacelet, 1964; Diaz, 1979a; Hartman, 1958b; Simpson, 1968a; Lévi, 1956; Connes, 1968) (Table 6-2). However, in dendroceratid and homoscleromorph demosponges and syconoids, choanocyte chambers and the number of cells per chamber are much larger as in *Sycon* (Duboscq and Tuzet, 1939), *Halisarca* (Lévi, 1956), *Aplysilla* (De Laubenfels, 1948), and others (Tuzet, 1973a; Brien, 1973; Boury-Esnault *et al.*, in press).

Structural Heterogeneity of Chambers

Until relatively recently, choanocyte chambers were considered to be formed only of choanocytes. Recent investigations as well as those of Duboscq and Tuzet (1939) have established that in addition to collar cells the following types of cells may also be a part of chambers: cellules centrales (central cells), which do not possess flagella or collars (Connes *et al.*, 1971a, 1972; Reiswig and Brown, 1977; Diaz, 1979a; Pavans de Ceccatty, 1955; Vacelet, 1964; Duboscq and Tuzet, 1939); cells with dense inclusions, which eventually lose both collars and flagella (Donadey, 1978, 1979); and developing gametes, which have no collars but may possess flagella (Diaz *et al.*, 1975; Diaz, 1979a; Tuzet and Pavans de Ceccatty, 1958; Tuzet *et al.*, 1970a,b). Each of these will be discussed in order.

Reiswig and Brown (1977) have reviewed the earlier literature describing the presence of nonflagellated central cells in choanocyte chambers and have categorized six types based upon position in the chamber and the arrangement (or absence) of their pseudopodia. Those types (D and E) with pseudopods are closely associated with choanocyte flagella while two other types (A and B) appear to be part of the lining of the chamber. Connes *et al.* (1971a, 1972) and Diaz (1979a) have investigated the ultrastructure of central cells in *Suberites massa* and have found that these cells make contact with the apopyle and form one or more "intracellular" canals through which the choanocyte flagella project (see Fig. 6-9). The possibility that these canals are actually extracellular, that is, formed by the cell wrapping around itself to form a sleeve, or forming blind ended pockets, should be considered, particularly since some micrographs actually appear to demonstrate this (Diaz, 1979a) although others do not (Fig. 6-10). These authors suggest that central cells are able to regulate the flow of water through chambers by partially or totally blocking the apopyle, a view also espoused by Duboscq and Tuzet (1939) and Pavans de Ceccatty (1955). In a number of demosponges in which large central cells contact the flagella of 5 to 7% of the choanocytes, Reiswig and Brown (1977) suggest that they are also involved in causing the cessation of flagellar activity, thus permitting prosopyles and incurrent canals to be cleansed rather than regulating water flow. This is most clear in *Mycale,* a species with central cells but with no predictable pattern of water pumping (Reiswig, 1971a). In other species [*Tethya crypta, Aplysina (Verongia)* sp., *Merlia normandi*] with small central cells which make only superficial contact with choanocyte flagella, these workers suggest that central cells function in the elimination of particulate wastes through migration to and then subsequently away from the excurrent canals, via choanocyte chambers. These views still require further substantiation.

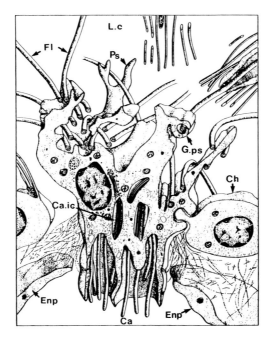

Figure 6-10   Reconstruction of a cellule centrale of *Suberites massa. Ca.,* canal; *Ca. ic,* intracellular channel; *Ch,* choanocyte; *Enp,* endopinacocyte; *Fl,* flagella; *G. ps,* troughs formed by cell prolongations; *L. c,* lumen of choanocyte chamber; *Ps,* cell prolongation (Diaz, 1979a). (Courtesy Dr. J-P. Diaz.)

In two recent reports, Donadey (1978, 1979) has presented reasonably convincing ultrastructural evidence of the transformation of choanocytes into cells that contain numerous dense inclusions but lack flagella and collars (see Fig. 3-8). These cells in *Plakina trilopha* are apparently released into the chamber lumen and may have as their primary function the elimination of particulate wastes (in the inclusions) into the excurrent canals (Donadey, 1978).

In a few demosponges, choanocytes have been reported to transform into spermatogonia (Tuzet *et al.,* 1970a,b; Tuzet and Pavans de Ceccatty, 1958; Diaz, 1979a) and also into oogonia (Diaz *et al.,* 1975; Diaz, 1979a). In the former case, either some or all choanocytes of a chamber are transformed into sperm, thus eliminating the chamber. In the latter transformation, single choanocytes appear to form oogonia, which later move into the mesohyl (see Chap. 7, however).

These data plus some discussed in the next section establish a new view of choanocyte chambers emphasizing their heterogeneity. It should be kept in mind, though, that all species do not possess central cells and thus choanocyte chambers in some may indeed be homogeneously constructed.

Other unusual structural aspects of choanocyte chambers include a report of the intertwining of flagella of adjacent choanocytes (Kilian and Wintermann-Kilian, 1979), which may alter water pumping, slowing or arresting it. Further, in a very early observation, Sollas (1888) described a thin "membrane" that connects the distal ends of the collars of choanocytes in the same chamber. This "membrane of Sollas" is now considered as an artifact (Vacelet, 1964; Rasmont, 1959).

Development

Choanocytes are known to multiply by mitosis (Shore, 1971; Jones, 1964a; Efremova and Efremov, 1979; Kilian and Wintermann-Kilian, 1979). Using Colcemid and tritiated thymidine, the length of the cell cycle of collar cells in *Hymeniacidon sinapium* has been estimated at 20 h (Shore, 1971). Theoretical consideration of thymidine uptake leads to the conclusion that the G_1 phase of these cells is long and the DNA synthesis, postsynthetic period, and mitosis periods are short. Such an interpretation is compatible with the low DNA content of sponge nuclei (Sinsheimer, 1957). Efremova and Efremov (1979) have similarly used tritiated thymidine to investigate the cell cycle of choanocytes in newly metamorphosed larvae of *Baikalospongia bacillifera*. They also find the synthesis period to be short, 1.6 to 3.7 h, but the total cell cycle is somewhat shorter, 13 to 15 h. In these young sponges, the whole choanocyte population (100%) is dividing in distinction to other cell types in which only 18 to 37% are. The fate of new choanocytes formed by these mitoses is not always clear. In *Leucosolenia,* they extend the choanocyte lining just below the oscular rim in what appears to be growth of the tube (see Chap. 9). In demosponges, however, new collar cells if continuously added to chambers would result in very large structures, which is not the case in many species. Thus, there must either be some attrition of choanocytes due to death and/or some of these cells must leave a chamber and/or mitoses must cease in chambers once they have reached a certain size. There are no data that bear on this very important problem. The dynamics of cell replacement, cell emigration, and cell death in choanocyte chambers is of much significance relative to the origin of spermatogonia from collar cells. A change in such dynamics may act as a trigger for gametogenesis.

During the initial differentiation of choanocytes, their ultrastructure may differ somewhat as has been shown by Watanabe (1978b) in *Tetilla serica*. During larval metamorphosis in this species, the flagellum of a new choanocyte is surrounded by a tubular collar that is not constituted of separate microvilli (Fig. 6-11). Numerous Golgi-derived vesicles appear in the cytoplasm in the tube, at first basally. These vesicles fuse with the inner surface of the "collar" plasmalemma at very regular intervals pro-

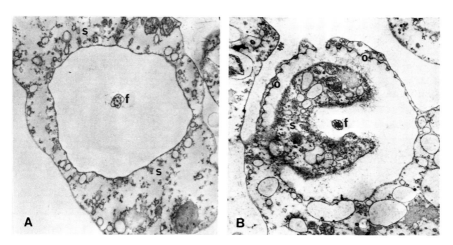

Figure 6-11 Development of choanocytes in *Tetilla serica* (TEMs). **A**. In newly forming cells a structure (*s*) similar to the periflagellar sleeve of *Suberites massa* (see Fig. 2-10) develops around the flagellum (*f*) (×14,400) (Watanabe, 1978b). **B**. In later development the sleeve (*s*) is less developed but present eccentrically and to its exterior a very thin cylinder comes to surround the flagellum. The cylinder membrane becomes scalloped (*o*) and through vesicular fusion with the plasmalemma, individual collar microvilli are formed. *f,* flagellum (×13,500) (Watanabe, 1978b). (Both courtesy Dr. Y. Watanabe.)

ducing a scalloped appearance. As the collar extends upward, thin columns of cytoplasm become separate, thus forming a microvillar structure. The microvilli remain connected extracellularly by strands of mucoid material which, when they are dense and thick, give the collar the appearance of being nonmicrovillar. According to Watanbe (1978b), the presence of this mucoid material depends upon the fixative employed —it is evident in osmium tetroxide-fixed cells but not in glutaraldehyde-fixed ones. The microvilli are regularly arranged when fixed in the former but not in the latter. Such material which connects the microvilli and also connects the flagellum to the microvilli has been described by other workers (Brill, 1973; Fjerdingstad, 1961; Garrone, 1978) (Chap. 2).

While the origin of new choanocytes within a preexisting chamber occurs due to mitotic activity, the origin of choanocytes in newly forming ones during development, growth, and regeneration is not clear except in the case of gemmule hatching (Chap. 8) where archeocytes form them. During larval metamorphosis (Chap. 7) and other forms of development (Chap. 9) the question of their origin is, in some cases, still unsettled. In these other systems, two sources of cells for newly forming chambers have been suggested: from preexisting choanocytes (Wintermann, 1951) or larval flagellated cells (Borojevic, 1966), and from archeocytes (Diaz,

1979a). Newly formed chambers may consist of as few as four cells (Simpson, 1968a), but even in very young ones that are not open to the excurrent canal system the flagella become active (Fauré-Frémiet, 1932a; Wintermann, 1951; Simpson, 1963; Weissenfels, 1981). Fauré-Frémiet (1932a), in a now classical study of *Ficulina ficus,* further observed that such flagellar activity results in the movement of fluid, indirectly suggesting that such fluid movement may induce the morphogenesis of the excurrent canals. In a further study (Fauré-Frémiet, 1932b) it was shown that X-irradiation destroys choanocytes selectively and then results in the disorganization of the canal system, primarily the excurrent canals, but that lacunae still remain. Such a result is consistent with the notion that flagellar activity and fluid movement (? pressure) act as stimuli for modeling the excurrent canals. In a still later study, Wintermann (1951), using freshwater sponges, reported that chambers first develop, are then connected to incurrent canal spaces (lacunae), and finally to excurrent canals further supporting the view that chambers are involved in an induction of excurrent canal formation. However, Weissenfels (1981) has conducted a recent study of the formation of choanocyte chambers (Fig. 6-12) and reports the following sequence in newly hatching gemmules: the division products of archeocytes, choanoblasts, form small groups in which the cells first develop flagella and later collars. These cells then migrate to the excurrent canals, make contact, and form a choanocytic apopyle consisting of cone cells (see following section). The endopinacoderm then forms a pinacocytic apopyle. Connection with the incurrent canals apparently occurs during or just following contact with the excurrent system. This sequence differs from that reported by Wintermann (1951) and suggests that contact of the choanoblasts with the excurrent canals stimulates (? induces) formation of the incurrent canals. Thus the excurrent system appears, according to Weissenfels (1981), to be the first formed and consequently the controlling factor in the further development of the canal system. Such a view is consistent with the emerging concept that incurrent canals are highly plastic structures which not only may be continuously remodeled but also are open to the mesohyl.

Choanocytic Apopyles

These are openings in the choanocyte layer that lead to the excurrent canals and do so by contacting the pinacocytic apopyles which are part of the excurrent canal (Fig. 6-13). They have been described by Van Tright (1919), Brien (1932), Kilian (1952), and others as a single space occurring between choanocytes in each chamber; according to these observations, they are morphologically similar to choanocytic prosopyles but larger in

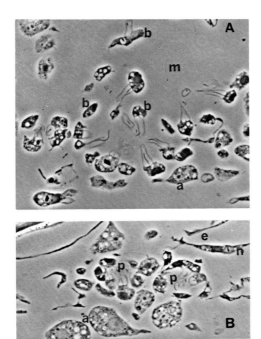

Figure 6-12   Early development of choanocyte chambers in *Ephydatia fluviatilis*.
A. Small choanoblasts (*b*) develop collars and flagella even prior to forming a
chamber. *a*, archeocyte; *m*, mesohyl (phase-contrast micrograph, semithin section) (×890) (Weissenfels, 1981). **B**. Later, after the chamber primordia (*p*) have
formed, the chambers migrate to and attach to the excurrent canal system (*e*). *n*,
apendopinacocyte; *a*, archeocyte (phase-contrast micrograph, semithin section)
(×890) (Weissenfels, 1981). (Both courtesy Prof. N. Weissenfels.)

diameter. Choanocytic apopyles also occur in syconoid species, but their
morphology is not well established.

Recent ultrastructural studies in a freshwater species have revealed
that two or three choanocytes per chamber form a single, tubular opening
(Weissenfels, 1980, 1982); these cells have been called *cone cells* and they
form long, thin, flat, pseudopod-like extensions (see Fig. 6-7) that hang
down into the chamber and form a cone-shaped exit from it. It is not
known how widespread their presence is; the extensions are exceedingly
thin (50 to 800 nm) accounting for the lack of their observation in light
microscopic and even electron microscopic studies. Choanocytic apopyles in glass sponges are apparently the collars that protrude above or to
the level of the secondary syncytium as well as spaces within this syncytium itself (Figs. 2-15E, 6-8) (Reiswig, 1979).

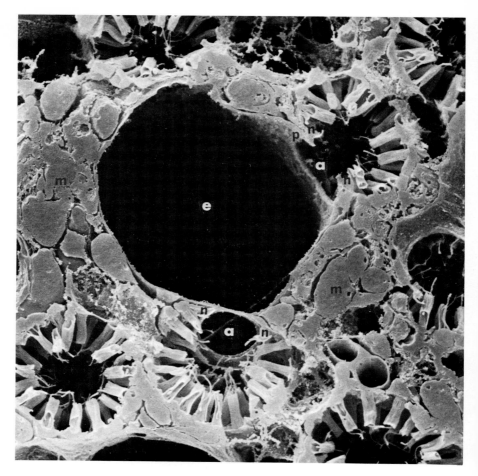

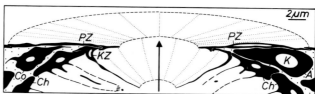

Figure 6-13 Apopyles of *Ephydatia fluviatilis*. **Above**: This micrograph clearly shows two apopyles (*a*) that empty into an excurrent canal (*e*). Each apopyle is formed by a choanocytic apopyle consisting of cone cells (*n*) and a pinacocytic apopyle formed by a porocyte (*p*) in the apendopinacoderm. *m*, mesohyl cells (SEM; material sectioned prior to visualization) (×1,040) (Weissenfels, 1982). **Below**: Drawing of the relationships of cone cells (*Kz*) to the pinacocytic apopyle formed by a porocyte (*PZ*). *CH*, choanocytes; *A*, archeocyte; *Co*, collencyte; *K*, nucleus (×2,500) (Weissenfels, 1980). (Both courtesy Prof. N. Weissenfels.)

Pinacocytic Apopyles

These openings occur in the apendopinacoderm and were early described as comparable to ostia (Brien, 1932; Kilian, 1964). However, it is still not known for sure whether they are formed by a single cell as reported by Weissenfels (1980, 1982) for *Ephydatia fluviatilis* and Simpson (1968a) for a number of poecilosclerid demosponges or whether the opening is formed by two or more cells as reported by Reiswig (1975a) and Connes *et al.* (1971a) (Fig. 6-14). In scanning electron micrographs of *E. fluviatilis* (De Vos, 1979) the pinacocytic apopyle appears structurally similar to an ostium which is known in some species to be formed by a single porocyte (Weissenfels, 1980). Further ultrastructural analyses of their morphology are called for. Regardless of whether they are uni- or multicellular, the cells that form them are part of the apendopinacoderm. According to

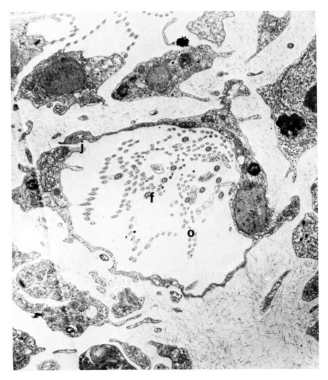

Figure 6-14 Cross section through a pinacocytic apopyle of *Suberites massa*. The wall of the circular opening clearly contains a junctional region (*j*), which could be a result of the cell forming a sleeve as suggested for porocytes in general (see text). Choanocyte flagella (*f*) and collars (*o*) project into the opening (TEM) (×5,450) (Diaz, 1979a). (Courtesy Dr. J-P. Diaz.)

Weissenfels (1980), ostia, pinacocytic prosopyles, and pinacocytic apopyles are comparable and are all formed by single porocytes. In hexactinellids, the structure of pinacocytic apopyles is not known and the term may, indeed, not be applicable. The pinacocytic apopyles in two homoscleromorphs, *Oscarella* and *Corticium,* have been observed with SEM and found to be formed by apendopinacocytes which possess both a flagellum and a collar (Boury-Esnault *et al.,* in press) and are thus similar to the choanocytic apopyles as described in *E. fluviatilis* (Weissenfels, 1980, 1982).

Excurrent Canals

Structure

The canals that conduct water away from the pinacocytic apopyles and eventually to the oscules are lined by apendopinacocytes. In asconoid species, apendopinacocytes occur only at the oscular rim and there are no excurrent canals *per se.* In syconoids, the apendopinacoderm lines a large cavity, the atrium, and technically this can be considered an excurrent canal although it usually is not referred to as such. In leuconoid species these canals are clearly demarcated and, when there are no aphodal canals present, the arrangement is referred to as "eurypylous," a condition common in many animals. Two other arrangements (aphodal and diplodal) have been previously described and there is little recent information on them. The eurypylous condition as well as being typical of many leuconoid animals also is found in newly metamorphosed larvae of them (Brien, 1973) where the initial configuration is referred to as the "rhagon" stage. In distinction to the prosendopinacoderm, there have been no reports of porocytes in the walls of the apendopinacoderm which thus forms a continuous epithelial layer. Homoscleromorph apendopinacocytes are uniflagellated (Boury-Esnault *et al.,* in press).

Smaller excurrent canals join together to produce larger ones (Fig. 6-15) and eventually these lead to an oscule. At the point at which the largest canals merge, a water-filled apendopinacocyte-lined cavity, the atrium, is formed (see Fig. 6-3). The atrium may be small as in *Microciona prolifera* or large as in *Halichondria panicea* where it has a diameter of about 2.0 mm (Reiswig, 1975a) (Table 6-2).

Excurrent canals are more regularly arranged than incurrent ones (Fauré-Frémiet, 1932a) and, at least in freshwater species, differ from them in that collencytes are routinely found within and associated with incurrent canals but not with excurrent ones (Kilian, 1952; Wintermann, 1951). However, in *Suberites massa,* some excurrent canals are surrounded by a number of layers of collencytes (Diaz, 1979a) that may be myocytes; these collencytes are known to be involved in remodeling phenomena (Chap. 9).

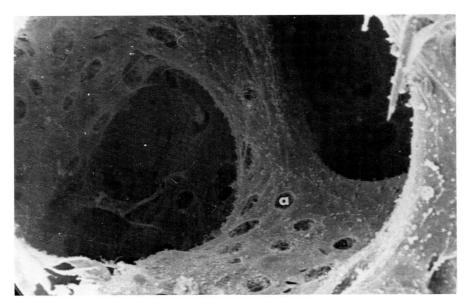

Figure 6-15 Junction and surfaces of large excurrent canals in *Ephydatia fluviatilis*. The pinacocyte apopyles (*a*) are clearly demarcated in the apendopinacoderm (SEM) (×500) (De Vos, 1979). (Courtesy Dr. L. De Vos.)

Development

The initial formation of the excurrent canal system is similar to that for incurrent canals and only fragmentary data are available. Lacunae develop in the mesohyl and these are, according to Brien (1936), Fauré-Frémiet (1932a), and Wintermann (1951) somewhat larger than the lacunae which are the anlage for the incurrent canals. The excurrent lacunae fuse together, giving rise to a star-shaped pattern in the center of which an atrial anlage develops. The apendopinacocytes are derived from mesohyl cells; although no absolutely conclusive data are available, it is likely that they originate from archeocytes or collencytes as with prosendopinacocytes (Borojevic, 1966). No evidence of mitoses of initially differentiated apendopinacocytes has been presented. The newly formed excurrent lacunae and canals are not attached to, or in continuity with, the choanocyte chambers (Wintermann, 1951). Later, after the chambers have become confluent with them, the canals may not yet be open to the environment since the oscule can still be incomplete and closed (Fauré-Frémiet, 1932a; Brien, 1932). In the latter condition, however, fluid is nevertheless circulated in the excurrent system by the choanocytes (Brien, 1932). Such fluid movement may induce the ensuing morphogenesis of the excurrent canals as with the incurrent canals (see previous section) (Fauré-Frémiet, 1932a). Other factors that likely effect their morphogenesis include periodic contractions and relaxations of localized areas (Simpson, 1963) or of the whole animal (Kilian, 1952; Rasmont, 1963; Pottu-Boumendil and Pavans de Ceccatty, 1976; Kilian and Wintermann-Kilian, 1979; De Vos and Van de Vyver, 1981). Such contractions displace choanocyte chambers and excurrent canals and although not substantiated they may, over long periods of time, directly influence the shape, position, and interconnections of the excurrent canals. The individual, independent movement of mesohyl cells and the rhythmic contractions and relaxation of the whole animal may interact in a complex fashion thereby influencing the morphogenesis of the excurrent canals as well as their remodeling (Chap. 9).

Morphological Patterns

Excurrent canals are not equally distributed throughout the tissue and a number of different patterns can be recognized. In some leuconoids, including the well-known marine species, *Microciona prolifera* (Bagby, 1970; Simpson, 1968a; Reiswig, 1975a), in many sclerosponges (Hartman, 1969; Hartman and Goreau, 1970, 1975), and other demosponges such as *Prosuberites* and *Spongilla,* smaller, internal excurrent canals drain upward toward the exopinacoderm where they empty into larger superficial ones that are roofed over by a thin excurrent dermal membrane. These superficial canals form star-burst patterns at the sponge surface called astrorhizae. In most cases, a single oscule is present at the point of merger of these canals but, in *Hispidoptera miniana* and *Stromatospongia vermicola,* oscules also occur along the length of the superficial canals regardless of where they merge (Hartman, 1969). The dermal membrane overlying these superficial excurrent canals should not be confused with that overlying the vestibules of the incurrent canal system (see Fig. 6-3). No detailed comparisons of these two types of dermal membrane have been made. Based upon known behavioral patterns and ultrastructural observations (Bagby, 1966) the excurrent-dermal membrane is characterized by contractility and the presence of myocytes. It is not known if the incurrent-dermal membrane also possesses these features. In both cases, however, spicules are generally absent or reduced in the thin layer of mesohyl that is sandwiched between exopinacoderm and endopinacoderm.

Another general pattern that can be recognized is one in which the excurrent canals drain into an atrium that opens via an oscule that is either flush with the surface (*Ophlitaspongia*) or is elevated and cone shaped (*Haliclona, Halichondria*) (Fig. 6-16). In the first of these there is no excurrent-dermal membrane and in cone-shaped oscules the walls of the atrium, which are topologically comparable to the excurrent-dermal membrane, are thick. The second pattern also occurs in tubular species such as *Aplysina (Verongia),* but here the oscules open into a very spacious secondary atrium leading via a terminal aperture (secondary oscule—see following) to the environment. This last-mentioned arrange-

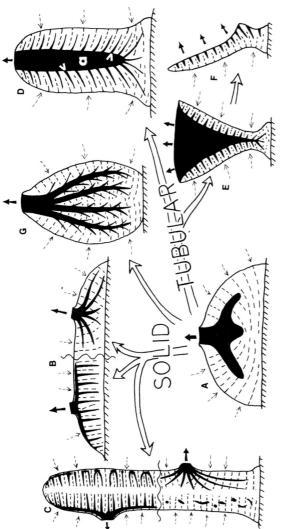

Figure 6-16 Types of excurrent canal systems in demosponges. **A.** Choanocyte chambers open directly into a large atrium (rhagon type). **B.** In encrusting species, excurrent canals drain upward to the atrium and oscule. On the left the largest excurrent canals can be superficial, thus forming surface astrorhiziae. **C.** Similar arrangements to those shown in B., but occurring in upright projections (branches) of the animal. **D.** The complex leuconoid arrangement in which primary oscules (*arrow heads*) open into a secondary atrium (*a*), which opens via a single secondary oscule. **E, F.** Derivations of D., in which the growth pattern results in a funnel shape (E.) or plate morphology (F.) with the concomitant loss of the secondary oscule. **G.** An intermediate type in which it is not clear whether secondary atria and oscule are present. Dashed arrows, incurrent water flow; solid arrows, excurrent water flow (modified from Reiswig, 1975a). (Courtesy Dr. H. M. Reiswig.)

ment presents a number of problems in terminology which will now be addressed. There are three major structures present in these animals but not in others: (1) a water-filled, excurrent cavity fed by oscules; (2) an epithelium lining this cavity; and (3) a large excurrent opening of the cavity. Since the characteristics and/or functions of these structures may vary from others, it is necessary to introduce new terms to refer to them in order to avoid confusion. The following terms are suggested, respectively: (1) secondary atrium, (2) secondary apendopinacoderm, and (3) secondary oscule. In some tetractinomorph species, a similar arrangement has been described although the sponges are not tubular (Brien, 1973). In them, contractile oscules also open into a secondary atrium which opens to the environment via one or more secondary oscules.

An interesting variant of astrorhizal-type excurrent canals occurs in the sclerosponge *Calcifibrospongia actinostromarioides* (Hartman, 1979). Large vertical excurrent canals course upward to the surface. At intervals along their length, four to six excurrent canals merge with it at the same level forming an internal astrorhizal pattern. Since these astrorhizae are surrrounded by aragonite, they are outlined by the calcareous skeleton as is often seen in fossil stromatoporoids (Hartman, 1979). Their presence does not appear to be due to vertical overgrowth of *surface* astrorhizae since none are present at the surface. Each large, vertical excurrent canal ends in an oscule at the surface.

Oscules

Morphological Types

The structure of oscules is variable; in all animals the outer surface is bounded by exopinacocytes and the inner surface by apendopinacocytes. In *Ephydatia fluviatilis,* for example, Ankel (1949) has described such a morphology of oscules and further found a difference between the exopinacocytes and apendopinacocytes. The former have their long axes parallel to the tube wall, the latter have theirs at right angles to it. Differences in silver staining between the two suggest differences in the nature of the cell contacts, although such differences have not been further evaluated. In hexactinellids these epithelia are apparently syncytial (Reiswig, 1979; Mackie and Singula, 1983).

The following specific types of oscules can be recognized: (1) Oscules in some calcareous species are openings leading directly to the environment from the choanoderm (asconoid structure) or from choanocyte chambers (syconoid structure) with no intervening excurrent canals. In asconoids, the inner surface of the oscular rim is lined for a short distance by endopinacocytes, which border the choanocytes at their distal extremity (Jones, 1966; Ledger, 1976); in syconoids, short strips of endopinacocytes also occur between the choanocyte chambers. (2) Oscules in some demosponges are formed through the merging of excurrent canals within the tissue (as in *Ophlitaspongia seriata;* Simpson, 1968a). (3) Oscules in some demosponges and sclerosponges are formed through the merger of superficial, astrorhizal excurrent canals as described above. (4) Some oscules which are basically type 2 have a thin, possibly contractile membrane that forms a rim around the edge of the opening (Simpson, 1966). (5) In some demosponges, relatively large secondary oscules are present as previously described. There is, surprisingly, an urgent need for a thorough, comparative study of the structural relationships within oscules; numerous species have not been investigated and the categorization of oscules presented above is doubtless oversimplified. For example, in *Haliclona permolis* in which a detailed description of the canal system has been reported (Reiswig, 1975a), it is still not clear whether the larger excurrent openings mounted distally on tube-like structures are secondary oscules or are oscules proper. Specifically, in this and other species, it must be determined empirically, not assumed *a priori,* whether oscules are of type 2 or type 5. This is such a fundamental question, it is amazing that heretofore it has not been addressed.

In a penetrating discussion and review of the behavior and organization of oscules, Hartman and Reiswig (1973) have emphasized the possible transitory nature of oscules and their associated excurrent canals. These openings can, in some species, be obliterated and new ones can form. The processes involved in and the determination of these changes are addressed in Chapter 9.

Cellular Features

Oscules are formed through a joining of the exopinacoderm with the apendopinacoderm (Brien, 1932; Ankel, 1949; Kilian, 1952; Wintermann, 1951; Pavans de Ceccatty *et al.,* 1970; Thiney, 1972; Weissenfels, 1975, 1980). In animals with type 3 oscules, the structures are delicate, containing relatively few cells and a low density of extracellular materials (Fig. 6-17) (Pavans de Ceccatty *et al.,* 1970; Bagby, 1966), whereas in other types they are thicker, more substantial structures. In the relatively few instances in which detailed studies have been conducted, both types may possess myocytes within the mesohyl (Parker, 1910; Bagby, 1966; Pavans de Ceccatty, 1966; Pavans de Ceccatty *et al.,* 1970; Vacelet, 1966; Thiney, 1972). However, in the astrorhizial-like oscule present in young freshwater sponges, myocytes have not been reported (Weissenfels, 1980) and in species with type 2 oscules, the absence of contractility also suggests the lack of myocytes. Secondary oscules of *Aplysina* (*Verongia*) are contractile (Reiswig, 1971a) and myocytes are known to be present (Vacelet, 1966; Pavans de Ceccatty *et al.,* 1970) as is the case in oscules of *Tedania ignis* (Bagby, 1966), a species in which, incidentally, it is not clear whether the oscules are of the secondary type. The secondary oscule of *Geodia* is apparently not contractile, but the oscules proper are

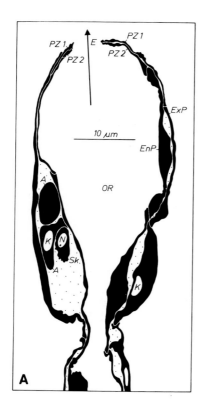

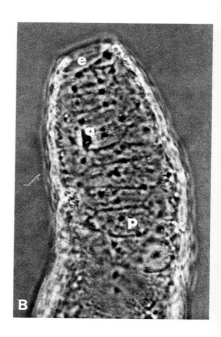

Figure 6-17   The oscule of a young individual of *Ephydatia fluviatilis*. **A**. Drawing of the relationships of the structural components. *PZ1,* porocyte in the exopinacoderm (*Exp*); *PZ2,* porocyte in the apendopinacoderm; *A,* archeocyte; *K,* nucleus; *Sk,* sclerocyte; *N,* spicule; *E,* oscular opening; *OR,* cavity within the oscular tube (×1,600) (Weissenfels, 1980). **B**. A whole oscular tube showing the outlines of some exopinacocytes (*p*), an archeocyte (*a*), and the opening of the oscule (*e*) (phase-contrast micrograph) (×200) (Weissenfels, 1980). (Both courtesy Prof. N. Weissenfels.)

(Brien, 1973). Thus, as is the case with oscules proper, some secondary oscules are contractile and others are not. There have been few detailed, comparative studies of oscules and none in which microscopic anatomy and contractility have been specifically correlated. There is an obvious and pressing need for such investigations.

Within the mesohyl of oscules of *Tedania ignis,* there is a discrete layer of myocytes parallel to the exopinacoderm and constituting a sphincter (Bagby, 1966). Each myocyte is elongate (50 × 2–3 μm), uninucleate, and contains membrane-bound inclusions centrally. Peripherally, microfilaments are present which are 100 to 500 Å in diameter; only a single size class of such microfilaments occurs. A similar sphincter occurs in *Aplysina (Verongia) cavernicola,* but the myocyte microfilaments are 70 to 100 Å in diameter, and centrally in the myocyte cytoplasm there are groups of microtubules lying parallel to the peripheral microfilaments as also occurs in *Hippospongia* (see below) (Vacelet, 1966). In *Microciona prolifera,* myocytes in the excurrent dermal membrane and in oscules do not form a sphincter and are oriented in various planes relative to the exopinacoderm (Bagby, 1966). In both species, myocytes rarely touch one another and there is abundant extracellular space—49% in *Tedania* and 57% in *Microciona.* The microfilaments in the latter are of two diameters—150 to 250 Å and 50 to 70 Å. The thin microfilaments are clustered around the thick ones reminiscent of the arrangement in striated muscle. In *Hippospongia communis* the arrangement of myocytes is similar to that in *Tedania* (Thiney, 1972). These cells have been better characterized and contain in addition to microfilaments of 100 Å diameter, a few phagosomes, lipid inclusions, glycogen, lysosomes, mitochondria, and Golgi bodies; the latter are not well developed in *Tedania* and *Microciona.* Thiney (1972) further describes the presence of microtubules (200 Å diameter), which lie parallel to the microfilaments but more internally in the cell. Also, in *Hippospongia,* a number of types of contacts between myocytes and other cells are routinely present. In distinction, Bagby (1966) has reported the absence of such contacts in *Tedania* and *Microciona* and this may be of much physiological importance, particularly in terms of coordination. Alternatively, the presence or absence of contacts may be a result of the contractile state of the oscule at the time of fixation. Bagby (1966) suggests that collagen fibrils act as a means of mechanical continuity, substituting for cell contacts. Indirect immunofluorescent demonstration of the presence of actin in pinacocytes (Figs. 2-5C,D) and mesohyl cells (Pavans de Ceccatty, 1981) suggests that this contractile protein may also be present in myocytes. The occurrence of two sizes of microfilaments adds credence to the view that an actin–myosin type of system lies at the basis of contractility in sponges.

Employing cytochemical procedures coupled with ultrastructural analyses of reaction sites, Thiney (1972) has found that only myocytes contain the enzyme cholinesterase which is associated with the microfilaments and also, surprisingly, with the nucleus. The microfilament cholinesterase is sensitive to inhibitors (eserine and ambenonium) of the enzyme while the nuclear is not, and the nuclear localization is considered as a nonspecific response to the cytochemical agents and not due to the enzyme. Lentz (1966) has also reported the presence of this enzyme in *Sycon ciliatum;* it similarly is sensitive to inhibitors. In this species, the enzyme is abundant in cells in the oscule which tend to form a circular arrangement. Although Lentz (1966) does not consider these cells as effectors (myocytes), this interpretation obviously requires consideration as suggested by Thiney (1972). Cholinesterase in *Hippospongia* myocytes may be involved, in addition to contractility and communication, in permeability, transport phenomena, and the exchange or release of products (Thiney, 1972). Other features of myocytes in *Hippospongia* strikingly overlap those of other cell types which occur in the oscular mesohyl (Table 6-3).

In a comparative study of the oscules and secondary oscule of four demosponges [*Hippospongia communis, Aplysina (Verongia) cavernicola, Haliclona rosea,* and *Euspongia officinalis*], Pavans de Ceccatty *et al.* (1970) have found that the structures are cytologically similar. The mesohyl contains collagen fibrils, archeocytes and myocytes; some species also possess spherulous cells. The density and arrangement of myocytes differs, there are fewer bundles of them in *Haliclona* than in the remaining three species. In all four, cell contacts are present and some are desmosome-like while others are interdigitate. Pinacocytes, archeocytes, and myocytes may all contain microfilaments and the level of differentiation between them is not especially distinct as also noted by Thiney (1972).

Development

In newly formed sponges emerging from gemmules, Brien (1932) has described the sequence of events which lead to the development of oscules. Initially, a bloated area of the excurrent dermal membrane appears, producing a "hernia." According to Brien (1932) this is due to internal pressure in newly formed excurrent canals, which are already in contact with and are connected to the choanocyte chambers. At the summit of the hernia a pore forms, which according to Brien is identical to an ostium. Later development was not followed. Weissenfels (1980) has recently confirmed that the newly formed oscule in *Ephydatia* opens via an exopinacodermal porocyte which is like the porocytes which form ostia. But, the apendopinacocyte which makes contact with the porocyte is itself a porocyte. The oscular opening is thus constituted of a double porocyte arrangement (Fig. 6-17). Due to the large diameter of oscules and secondary oscules in many other species it is not possible that a similar arrangement is present in them, but the double porocyte arrangement may be a stage in their development also.

Canal System Elements in Reproductive Stages

The presence of choanocyte chambers has been reported in free-swimming larvae of some freshwater species (*Ephydatia fluviatilis*) although infrequently (Meewis, 1939a, 1941; Brien and Meewis, 1938; Harrison and Cowden, 1975b). These chambers are not obviously connected to canals and may form a simple closed system. Their presence suggests the ability of the larva to form choanocytes precociously, even in the absence of

Table 6-3 Characteristics of Cell Types in Oscules of *Hippospongia communis*[a]

Cell Type	Characteristics[b]						
	Nucleoli	Lipid Inclusions	Lysosomes	Phagosomes	Microfilaments	Multivesicular Bodies	Cholinesterase
Exopinacocytes	+	+	+	+	+	+	−
Endopinacocytes	+	+	+	+	+	+	−
Archeocytes	++	+	+	++	−	−	−
Spherulous cells	−	−	+	−	−	−	−
Myocytes	+	+	+	+	++	+	+

[a]Data taken from Thiney (1972).
[b]Lysosomes identified by the presence of acid phosphatase; cholinesterase identified cytochemically through electron microscopy; other components identified morphologically by transmission electron microscopy.

attachment to a substratum. No ultrastructural studies of them have been reported and thus their possession of collars has been surmised, not demonstrated. In the larvae of freshwater sponges there is a large fluid-filled, pinacocyte-lined cavity which Brien and Meewis (1938) consider to be a floatation device, although there is no experimental evidence to support this. This cavity is reminiscent of a canal space and these authors suggest that it acts as an anlage of the canal system with which choanocytes make connections.

A highly unusual condition has been described in the free-floating buds of a Mediterranean clionid, probably of the genus *Alectona*. These buds have been examined by transmission electron microscopy and contain choanocyte chambers in their central portion (Garrone, 1974). The choanocytes frequently are bent in an L shape with the nucleus in one arm and the collar and flagellum in the other (see Fig. 8-6B). Garrone suggests that the chambers possibly open to the environment, but no evidence of this is presented. Although no comment is made in the paper, one of the micrographs raises the interesting question of whether choanocytes possess more than one collar and flagellum. If these choanocytes indeed possess multiple collars and flagella, this would only be the second example of such a modified morphology, the other being the normal structure of chambers in hexactinellid species (Chap. 2).

Water Currents

Origin and Direction

The origin of water currents has now been demonstrated to consist of two components—an active one, which is the movement of the flagella of choanocytes; and a passive one, which is the water current in the environment flowing across the sponge surface.

Active Origin.   The active component, flagellar beating, has been studied particularly well by Van Tright (1919) and Kilian (1952) in *Ephydatia fluviatilis* through direct observations of living sponges. Van Tright presents a very useful review of the older literature dealing with flagellar activity as well as original observations. In this species as well as other freshwater sponges (Wintermann, 1951) and in the calcareous sponge *Leucosolenia variabilis* (Jones, 1964a), it is clear that the motion of the flagella are not synchronized either within or between chambers; some flagella even become motionless for periods of time (Van Tright, 1919; Kilian, 1952; Jones, 1964a; Kilian and Wintermann-Kilian, 1979). The plane in which beating occurs and the rate of beating both vary from cell to cell (Jones, 1964a; Kilian, 1952). The collars may be extended or retracted, in the latter condition flagellar motion is whip-like and in the former it consists of a number of waves within the collar and distal to it

(Kilian, 1952). The latter work formulates the only model of flagellar movement in sponges recently suggested (Fig. 6-18). In *E. fluviatilis* the flagella beat only in one plane at a given time but this plane shifts through approximately 360° during the course of 1 to 2 min. Earlier observations suggesting that flagella move by a spiral motion rather than a uniplanar undulation (Van Tright, 1919) appear to have been in error. However, according to Kilian, the cyclical, spiral displacement of the uniplanar undulation lies at the basis of the movement of water through the chambers and thus, the direction in which the collars and flagella face within the chamber are critical. In *fluviatilis* they all are pointed toward the apopyle so that the movement of water due to each of them is in the same direction (Van Tright, 1919; Kilian, 1952). The cumulative prosopylar cross-sectional area is much less than that of other incurrent spaces and is less than the apopyles and other excurrent spaces (Reiswig, 1975a; Kilian, 1952). Thus, at the prosopyles there is a squirting of water into the chambers where, due to their larger cumulative volume, the pressure is lower. This lower pressure, particularly also at the apopyles, causes a suction effect, draining water from incurrent spaces to excurrent ones (Kilian,

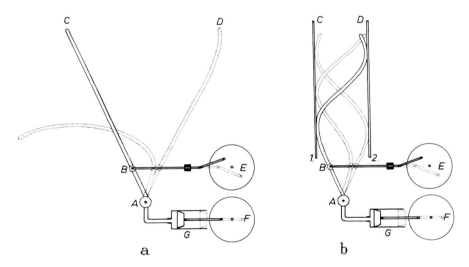

Figure 6-18 Theoretical model of choanocyte flagellar motion. **A.** Vibration of the flagella without side limits, corresponding to the condition when the collar is retracted. *A,* fixed point of the base of the flagellum which is connected to the piston chamber (*G*) which is filled with water. The pressure is controlled via the piston, *F. B,* starting point of the lever arm (corresponding to the point of emergence of the flagellum from the cytoplasm), which is moved to and fro by the eccentric, *E. C, D,* limits of flagellar movement. **B.** Vibration of the flagellum can be limited by the collar walls, *1* and *2,* whereby waves of motion arise through reflection of the flagellum against the walls of the collar (Kilian, 1952). (Courtesy Prof. E. F. Kilian.)

1952). Van Tright (1919) originally concluded that the pressure is lowest at the bases of the flagella and prosopyles and higher at the center of the chamber and that due to its larger diameter water is sucked through the apopyles into the excurrent canals thus further draining water through the prosopyles into the chambers.

Direction. According to Van Tright (1919) and Kilian (1952) water is driven from the base of the flagella toward their tips and then is sucked out of the chamber. When all of the flagella are directed toward, or sometime through, the apopyle, water is moved to the excurrent canals. Although the direction in which the flagella face is critical relative to the direction of water flow (Van Tright, 1919; Kilian, 1952), since they normally face the apopyle it is not their motion that determines the direction of water flow but the size, volume, and pressure relationships of the incurrent canals, prosopyles, collar slits, apopyles, and excurrent canals (Reiswig, 1975a). The ability to produce a current of water (regardless of direction) ultimately is due to the movement of the flagella which cause water to flow along the flagellar axis from base to tip. Thus, the direction of water flow in the canal system is dependent upon the relative resistances of the canal system and also, theoretically, upon external currents (see following section). The former has been directly demonstrated by Jones (1964a) in *Leucosolenia*. When oscular tubes are cut basally, the basal edges stick together and water continues to flow out of the oscule. If the basal end of the tube is opened mechanically, water flows out *both* ends, clearly establishing that the movement of the flagella does not determine the direction of water flow. According to Jones (1964a), in the simple asconoid sponges the movement of choanocyte flagella thrusts the cell body against the tube wall thus expanding the latter. The excess water drawn into the atrium by flagellar activity is pushed out of the oscule by the tension produced in the tube wall. Water moves out of the oscules because the resistance to movement is least in them. As the flagella beat, water is drawn into the incurrent system. Although there are no data in leuconoid or syconoid sponges, it is also possible that the displacement of choanocyte cell bodies during flagellar beating similarly produces tension in the adjacent mesohyl which could similarly aid in "pushing" water out of the chambers. Viewed from the perspective of hydrodynamics, a single choanocyte chamber is strikingly similar to (disregarding size) the whole oscular tube of an asconoid sponge, the apopyle being functionally similar to the oscule and the prosopyle to ostia.

Water currents can sometimes reverse their direction as occurs in young sponges in which the canal system is being remodeled during growth and development (Kilian, 1952). Storr (1976) has observed an interesting case of current reversal. When sediment is placed on the ostial surface of *Spheciospongia vesparium,* forceful backflow occurs dispersing the material; such a reaction is referred to as backwashing and obviously includes a degree of coordination. Long-term reversal of current flow is accompanied by a total remodeling of the canal system during which the original incurrent canals do *not* form excurrent canals or the reverse (Wintermann, 1951). It is also possible that remodeling precedes and thus is a causative agent of current reversal. Such remodeling is not, however, restricted to young animals (Chap. 9). The measured internal resistance of the canal system in specimens of *Haliclona viridis* ranges from 180 to 550 dynes/cm^5/sec. However, this range may be abnormally high due to collection trauma and a resistance of about 100 dynes/cm^5/sec appears as a probable realistic value of undisturbed sponges based upon theoretical considerations (Vogel, 1978).

In *Suberites massa* in which there is only a single opening in each choanocyte chamber a novel method of production of water currents has been suggested by Diaz (1979a). According to his model, a current of water must occur in the single canal feeding each chamber. This current is presumed to occur as a result of contractions and dilations of the canal system and mesohyl and/or as a result of external currents as proposed by Vogel (1974). The flagellar beating in the chambers could then greatly enhance the exchange of water into and out of the canal. A critical question relative to this model is how a single opening can be used as both an entranceway and an exit simultaneously. Since the chambers in *Suberites massa* contain a single central cell located within the apopyle, it seems possible that the morphology of this cell may be involved in forming incurrent and excurrent channels within the chamber although Diaz does not raise this possibility. In any event, appropriate differential resistances must be structured in order for the apopyle to function in this dual manner.

Passive Origin. A completely different mechanism which can result in the movement of water through the canal system of sponges has been suggested by Vogel and Bretz (1972). This mechanism is operative when the current flow of environmental water is more rapid across oscules than across ostia. Given such a differential flow, the pressure across the oscules is lower thus sucking water through the canal system; or, the viscosity is greater resulting in "viscous sucking." The efficacy of such a passive mechanism of water flow through sponges has been experimentally established. In *Halichondria bowerbankii*, significant water flow through the canals occurred after flagellar activity was inhibited (by treatment with fresh water) and this flow was proportional to the environmental current across the sponge (Vogel, 1974). Further experiments were carried out *in habitat* (also using a thermistor flowmeter) on active as well as inactive sponges including species of *Cliona, Haliclona, Ircinia, Aplysina (Verongia), Spheciospongia, Tedania,* and *Leucetta* (Vogel, 1977).

These studies further support an important role for environmental currents in producing the passive movement of water through the canal system. A possibly important component in such water movement appears to be the shape of the oscules as determined from observations on models (Vogel, 1974).

However, such passive water flow through the canal system requires a mechanism for preventing back flow—from oscule to ostia—due to ostia located downstream (Vogel, 1978). Using specially designed models, Vogel (1978) has found that in the absence of valves, higher ambient currents result in progressively more back flow and that the presence of one-way valves in the "canals" of the model only prevents back flow at external currents of 25 cm/sec or higher; below this, one way valves have no effect. If the downstream "ostia" in the model are shielded, no back flow occurs throughout an external current range of 0 to 45 cm/sec. According to Vogel (1978), these results suggest the presence of valves in the incurrent canals possibly associated with the ostia. Using living sponges, he has shown that a specific range of negative pressures (=water forced into the oscule) in the canal system of living sponges results in no back flow of water (Vogel, 1978); when the negative pressure is further increased, back flow through the ostia then does occur. Such evidence is taken to indicate the presence of valves within the living sponge tissue. While of much significance, these experiments raise a number of questions which still remain unanswered. The "valves" in living sponges respond within a second or two, thus they cannot involve contraction of any known canal system structure (see Responses of Effectors to Experimental Stimuli). Further, some species contain ostia only in specific areas of the surface and if there are few, or no, downstream ostia, then there is little need for a functional valve system. Despite this, other species have more uniformly distributed ostia and thus valves may be of significance. In the absence of any known structure that can act as a rapidly responding valve, some consideration should be given to the possibility that the valves demonstrated in living sponges are actually choanocyte collars (or whole cells) that become pushed into the choanocytic prosopyles and obstruct them. Such a response would be rapid, but according to results with models these "valves" would not be located at an appropriate position in the canal system. Alternatively, the models themselves may not be completely comparable to the living sponge. Nevertheless, it is established that ambient currents do increase the flow through the canal system (Vogel, 1978), and if significant numbers of ostia occur downstream some mechanism must oppose back flow. Of historical interest in this regard is the suggestion made by Vosmaer and Pekelharing (1898). These workers conjectured that dependent upon differences in pressure, the choanocyte collars can be either inflated or deflated and thus they may act as valves, reducing flow when inflated and increasing it when deflated.

Transport Rates and Velocity

Frost (1976a) has presented a very useful review of measured transport rates in a variety of sponges (Table 6-4). As discussed by him, a range of pumping rates is recorded and some of the variability is likely due to the diversity of methods employed in the measurements. Reiswig (1974, 1971a) and Vogel (1977) have directly measured pumping rates *in situ* using flow meters, and their data are doubtless closer to actual rates. Significantly their measurements are quite comparable, as pointed out by Vogel (1977). Some of the variability is real and according to Vogel (1977) is due to differences in the external current passing across the sponges. Other sources of variability include effects due to laboratory conditions and indirect, rather than direct, methods of calculating flow rate. Other poorly controlled factors include temperature and the general condition of the animals employed in the measurements.

Table 6-4 Water Transport Rates[a]

Species	Transport Rate (ml/sec/ml sponge)	References
Demospongiae		
Suberites domuncula	0.002	Pütter (1908)
Spinosella sororia	0.007	Pütter (1914)
Suberites massa	0.01[b]	Pütter (1914)
Freshwater sponge	0.4	Schröeder (in Arndt, 1930)
Ephydatia fluviatilis	0.28	Kilian (1952)
	0.15	Willenz and Rasmont (1979)
Halichondria bowerbanki	0.24	Vogel (1974)
Mycale sp.	0.24	
Aplysina (Verongia) gigantea	0.077	Reiswig (1974)
Tethya crypta	0.125	
Haliclona permolis	0.131	Reiswig (1975a)
Spongilla lacustris	0.0118	Brauer (1975)
	0.053–0.063	Frost (1978b)
Haliclona viridis		
Haliclona variabilis		
Ircinia fasciculata	0.1–0.4	Vogel (1977)
Aplysina (Verongia) fistularis		
Others		
Calcarea		
Leucandra aspers	0.84	Bidder (1923)
Grantia compressa	0.003–0.0057[b]	Jorgensen (1949)
Sycon coronatum	0.0054[b]	Jorgensen (1949)

Based upon Frost (1976a).
Calculated from filtering rates of particulates.

Recent, long-term, *in situ* measurements of the velocity of water flow out of oscules has yielded interesting but complex results (Reiswig, 1971a) (Table 6-5). In *Mycale* sp., off the coast of Jamaica, velocities are surprisingly constant during the calm season (April to November) when temperature is also relatively constant (29°C). With decreasing temperature (to 27.8°C) velocities decreased from 7.8 to 6.8 cm/sec. Strom-induced turbidity, resulting in clogging of ostia, reduced velocities (in the population as a whole) by only 18%. In *Aplysina* (*Verongia*) *gigantea,* water pumping was found to be relatively stable but interrupted by short periods of cessation of pumping during which oscules were closed. The current velocity decreased during the winter months coincident with temperature reduction as in *Mycale*. In this same ecosystem, *Tethya crypta* displays a complex cycle of water pumping and cessation in which current velocity increases to a maximum of about 17 cm/sec after sunrise and then decreases to about 12.5 cm/sec a few hours after sunset. This study clearly demonstrates the pitfalls involved in making isolated measurements of velocity and then considering them as "typical" values for comparison with other species and for use in calculating transport rates.

Types of Changes in Water Transport

The repertoire of changes in water pumping appears both limited and straightforward. The following types of changes have been recorded: (1) increase or decrease in current velocity, (2) increase or decrease in volume transported, (3) cessation and initiation of transport, (4) reversal in the direction of transport. The following discussion reviews observations of these changes and their causes. It should be noted that to date there has

Table 6-5   Velocity of Water Currents in Some Demospongiae

Species	Velocity[a] (cm/sec)	References
Suberites domuncula	0.5	Pütter (1908)
Spinosella sororia	0.4	Parker (1914)
Halichondria bowerbanki	2.8–6.8	Vogel (1974)
Mycale sp.	6.1–9.1($\bar{X}$ = 7.3)	
Aplysina (*Verongia*) *gigantea*	2.5–16.8($\bar{X}$ = 11.1)	Reiswig (1974)
Tethya crypta	13.2–18.2($\bar{X}$ = 14.6)	
Haliclona permolis	5.0	Reiswig (1975a)
Aplysina (*Verongia*) *fistularis* Others	7.5–22.0	Vogel (1977)
Ephydatia fluviatilis	8.0	Kilian and Wintermann-Kilian (1979)

[a]Velocity measured at the level of oscules.

not been a comprehensive study correlating changes in the activity of all relevant canal system components with observed changes in water transport. Consequently, conclusions as to the basis of changes remain more or less conjectural depending upon the thoroughness of the investigation. There are immense difficulties in conducting such investigations since methods are not yet available for accurate and quantitative recording of changes in many individual components as well as simultaneous recording of the activity of all of them. Despite these shortcomings, recent investigations have added a new dimension to our understanding of the hydrodynamics of water transport.

Effectors Which Directly Influence Water Currents

There have been numerous reports describing the ability of ostia to close or open; an excellent review of the early literature is presented by Jones (1962). Such observations have been made on a variety of demosponges, both marine (*Hymeniacidon:* Parker, 1910; *Stylotella, Reniera, Lissodendoryx:* Parker, 1910; Wilson, 1910; *Cliona:* Hartman, 1958a) and freshwater (*Ephydatia:* Brien, 1943; Weissenfels, 1980; *Spongilla:* Brien, 1943; *Corvomeyenia:* Harrison, 1972b) and in the calcareous sponge, *Leucosolenia* (Jones, 1957, 1964a). Ostial closing appears to be an attribute of individual porocytes, but the contractile state of the pinacoderms and surrounding mesohyl may also be involved. For example, in crib bearing species (see Ostia), numerous aligned myocytes are associated with ostia and may influence the size of the pore canal. But in hexactinellids, ostia are noncontractile (Mackie *et al.,* 1983).

The contractility of oscules [again, see Jones (1962) for earlier literature] and secondary oscules is also well documented in freshwater demosponges (*Spongilla:* Prosser *et al.,* 1962; *Ephydatia:* McNair, 1923), marine demosponges [*Stylotella:* Parker, 1910; *Tethya:* Pavans de Ceccatty *et al.,* 1960; *Euspongia, Hippospongia:* Pavans de Ceccatty, 1969, 1971; *Damiriana, Zygomycale, Hymeniacidon, Tedania, Ircinia, Dysidea, Xytopseus, Microciona:* Prosser *et al.,* 1962; *Crambe, Hymedesmia:* Prosser, 1967; *Cliona:* Hartman, 1958a; Emson, 1966; *Tethya, Aplysina (Verongia):* Reiswig, 1971a), and calcareous species (Minchin, 1900, p. 29). Although the above list is long and includes many taxa, it cannot be assumed that oscules in all species are contractile. For example, *Mycale* sp. possesses oscules which are clearly not contractile (Reiswig, 1971a). Further, in species possessing secondary oscules, such as larger individuals of *Aplysina (Verongia) gigantea,* the latter can be noncontractile (Reiswig, 1971a). In the "fleshy" species, *Dysidea avara,* and *Chondrosia reniformis,* short-term observations also suggest an absence of oscular contractility (Prosser, 1967) (see further, Oscules). However, caution is suggested relative to the latter study, since if what are being referred to as "oscules" are in reality secondary oscules, then data on oscules *per se* are lacking. Oscluar contraction is presumed due to the contractility of myocytes that form sphincters but contractility of the pinacoderms and mesohyl may also be involved.

In the last thirty years, investigations, particularly on freshwater species, have documented that the pinacoderms lining the incurrent vestibules and the exopinacoderm spontaneously undergo contraction (Ankel, 1949; Wintermann, 1951; Kilian, 1952; Pottu-Boumendil and Pavans de Ceccatty, 1976; Pavans de Ceccatty, 1974a). In freshwater sponges, such contractions can result in a stoppage of water pumping due, at least partially, to the compression of the choanocyte chambers (Kilian, 1952). It appears that Wilson (1910) was the first to observe that endopinacocytes are contractile and are thus able to decrease the diameter of canals. The recent observations of De Vos and Van de Vyver (1981) establish that there also are very significant changes in excurrent canal diameter as well as compression and dilation of choanocyte chambers.

There are no conclusive data on the question of whether pinacocytic prosopyles and pinacocytic apopyles are contractile. According to Weissenfels (1980) these pores are completely comparable to ostia and thus may be contractile. The recently described pores in the prosendopinacoderm (Weissenfels, 1975; De Vos, 1979) have an unknown physiology but may likewise be contractile and are doubtless affected by contractions of the prosendopinacoderm. When they are open they probably cause some degree of turbulence in the flow of water through the vestibules. Thus, myocytes which are the basis for oscular contractility; porocytes which form ostia, pinacocytic apo- and prosopyles; and the pinacoderms which limit the canals are all effectors which can influence water flow through the system.

Choanocytes are also able to affect water transport by the synchronous stoppage of flagellar beating as, for example, in hexactinellid species (Mackie, 1979; Lawn et al., 1981) and in Tethya crypta (Reiswig, 1971a). In hexactinellids, flagellar beating or its absence appears as the sole effector of water currents since myocytes are apparently absent and ostia are noncontractile (Mackie et al., 1983). Choanocytes may affect water transport in ways other than the stoppage of flagellar beating, which can occur sporadically and randomly in the choanocyte population (Wintermann, 1951; Kilian, 1952; Jones, 1964a; Kilian and Wintermann-Killian, 1979). Specifically, the plane of flagellar beat, the position of the collars (retracted or expanded), and the rate of beating may all affect water pumping rates, although appropriate experimental data are not available. Further, the position of the choanocyte cell body may influence water pumping; in freshwater species, for example, choanocytes can alter their position in the chamber and are thus able to close or open the choanocytic prosopyles (Wintermann, 1951). In Leucosolenia variabilis, choanocytes also display limited mobility and can alter their positions (Jones, 1964a), although it is not clear if they ever limit or block the pore canal. Central cells in chambers can also be intimately associated with water flow

(Reiswig and Brown, 1977; Connes *et al.*, 1971a, 1972) (see Choanocyte Chambers), and finally, choanocyte flagella can become tangled, thus slowing their movements (Kilian and Wintermann-Kilian, 1979) and probably the flow of water.

Growth processes also alter water pumping; the canal system can undergo remodeling leading to cessation of water flow in young animals (Ankel, 1949; Kilian, 1952) and probably to alteration of pumping rates in older animals; the precise relationship of growth processes to water transport will be very difficult to work out. Wintermann (1951) indicates that long-term reversal of water flow can result in major remodeling of the canal system including the formation of a new oscule. A relationship of hydrostatic pressure to morphogenesis in sponges as previously noted is an intriguing notion which definitely merits further consideration.

The elasticity of the mesohyl has long been considered by Jones and earlier workers as an important factor in the physiology of calcareous sponges including water pumping (Jones, 1961a,b) and may also be of equal importance in other species. For example, in *Dysidea avara,* the superficial tissue displays both elastic rebound and long-term deformation (Prosser, 1967). Such elasticity may act as an agonistic component to water pumping and thus exert an important influence on velocities, water pressure, and cross-sectional areas of canals and pores.

Many sponges are able to contract their tissue in general, sometimes resulting in a measurable decrease in the overall size of the animal. This has been reported in *Tethya* (Pavans de Ceccatty *et al.*, 1960) and also in *Stylotella* (Parker, 1910). Further, *Cliona* is able to retract its papillae, which normally project beyond the surface into which the sponge has burrowed (Hartman, 1958a; Emson, 1966). In *Ephydatia fluviatilis,* the whole sponge rhythmically contracts and dilates during a period of some 30 min, and excurrent canals and ostia show changes in their diameter (without total closure) correlated with these pulsations; choanocyte chambers are also rhythmically displaced (Kilian and Wintermann-Kilian, 1979) or alternately compressed and dilated (De Vos and Van de Vyver, 1981). Removal of tissue from various demosponges and *Leucosolenia* results in a contraction of the excised tissue (Storr, 1976; Jones, 1957), and the capacity for contraction is doubtless of significance *in vivo* for water transport since the volume of some (possibly all) canal components will be directly affected.

Long-term effects upon water pumping are probably also caused by gametogenesis and viviparity. In species in which choanocytes form spermatozoa (Chap. 7), there will be a reduction in flagellar activity due to choanocyte loss (transformation). In viviparous species, developing larvae likewise lead to the disorganization of canal system components (Chen, 1976; Simpson and Gilbert, 1973; Diaz, 1979a) likely leading to lowered water transport.

Responses of Effectors to Experimental Stimuli

Oscules.   Jones (1962) has reviewed the nineteenth- and early twentieth-century data on the effects of stimuli on oscules. The following factors were reported to stimulate oscular closure: air, absence of currents, low temperature, high temperature, lack of oxygen, mechanical stimuli (rubbing, etc.), turbulence, injury, and electrical stimulation. Further, certain chemical substances were reported to stimulate oscular closure. Unfortunately, one of the earliest such studies (von Lendenfeld, 1889) yielded contradictory and unreliable results (Jones, 1962). A somewhat more recent study, still of much importance, is that of Parker (1910), the results of which are presented in Table 6-6. Of some note is the contradiction that cold causes oscules to close in *Ephydatia* (McNair, 1923) but not in *Stylotella* (Parker, 1910). Similar contradictions dealing with other stimuli, effectors, and species are frequently encountered in the literature, and it is still not clear what their bases are. Thus, it is very difficult to present a list of factors that cause oscules to close in all species investigated. For example, earlier laboratory data suggested that light and darkness are ineffective in producing any changes in oscules (Parker, 1910; McNair, 1923). Yet, in an *in situ* study, a diurnal cycle of oscular closing and opening has been reported and there is good evidence that light controls the cycle since artificial illumination at night is able to alter it (Reiswig, 1971a). On the other hand, periods of oscular closure in *Aplysina (Verongia)* are not correlated with light.

Other recent studies center on the question of the effects of ions and mechanical and electrical stimuli on oscules. In an ecological study, Hartman (1958a) found that lower salinities of 10 to 15‰ cause oscular closure in *Cliona celata*. In a still more recent investigation of marine and freshwater species, it was demonstrated that appropriate mechanical stimuli definitely result in oscular closing; the response has a latent period of 0.1 to 0.4 sec, a contraction phase of 1 to 5 seconds, and a relaxation time of 15 to 60 sec. Several rapid taps result in a greater response than a single one but no spatial summation (addition of responses from taps at two locations) occurred and the responses were local, not conducted (Prosser *et al.*, 1962). Maximum contraction occurred when an air bubble distends the oscular rim. Substitution of K^+ for Na^+ had no effect on the response which, however, was shown to be dependent upon Ca^{2+} (but see below). However, in *Leucosolenia* reduction of the calcium to one half its normal concentration is without effect upon contractility of the excised pieces of the sponge (Jones, 1957), possibly indicating that the calcium level has to be brought lower in order for there to be an observable effect. In *Tedania ignis,* the hydrostatic pressure in the atrium was shown to affect oscular closure; reduction of this pressure resulted in partial closure (Prosser *et al.*, 1962), supporting the view (Kilian, 1952) that water pressure is critical in determining the degree of oscular closure. Jets of freshwater or acid and electrical stimuli had no effect on the oscules

Stimulus	Oscule Response	Ostial Response	Flagellar Activity
Mechanical			
Water currents	Opens, remains open	No reaction	No reaction
Quiet water	Closes, remains closed	No reaction	No reaction
Brushing	No reaction(?)	No reaction	No reaction
Silt	—	No reaction	No reaction
Exposure to air	Closed, remains closed	No reaction	No reaction
Injury	Closes	Closes	No reaction
Thermal (°C)			
9–10	No reaction	No reaction	Slowed
25–28	Normal	Normal	Normal
35	Slight constriction	Remains open; if closed, opens	Normal
40	Slight constriction	?	Ceases
45	Flabby contraction	?	Ceases
Chemical			
0.5% Ether	Closes, remains closed	Closes, remains closed	Ceases
0.5% chloroform	Closes, remains closed	Closes, remains closed	Ceases
75% seawater	Closes slightly, reopens	Remains opens; if closed, opens	No reaction
50% seawater	Contraction, no closure	Remains open(?); if closed, opens	Ceases
25% seawater	Contraction, no closure	—	—
Fresh water	Remains open	?	Ceases
Deoxygenated seawater	Closes	Opens, remains open	High then ceases
Strychnine (6.7×10^{-5})[b]	Closes, remains closed	Closes	High
Cocaine (1×10^{-3})[b]	Closes, remains closed	Closes, remains closed	No reaction
Cocaine (1×10^{-4})[b]	Remains open, closure inhibited	Remains open; if closed, opens	No reaction
Cocaine (2×10^{-5})[b]	Remains open		No reaction
Atropine (1×10^{-3})[b]	Remains open, closure inhibited	Remains open; if closed, opens	No reaction
Atropine (1×10^{-4})[b]	Remains open	—	No reaction

[a]From Parker (1910).
[b]In g/ml.

(Prosser *et al.*, 1962), while stretching the oscule of *Tedania* for short periods (15 sec) resulted in contraction, but longer stretches caused its deformation without subsequent contraction. In a later study (Prosser, 1967), using mechanical stimuli and artificial sea water, oscular contractions have been shown in a number of demosponges to be dependent upon the presence of a monovalent cation in the bathing medium—either sodium, potassium, or lithium is necessary and choline is ineffective; potassium potentiates the response. Similarly, responses to mechanical stimuli were found dependent upon the presence of a divalent cation—either calcium, magnesium, or strontium, or combinations of them at appropriate concentrations.

In distinction to the above results, Pavans de Ceccatty (1971), using the oscules of *Euspongia officinalis* which display short-term, spontaneous, local contraction, has reported a requirement for calcium which cannot be substituted for by magnesium, and one for sodium which cannot be substituted for by potassium. Potassium as the only monovalent cation results in contracture, and magnesium as the only divalent cation results in oscular closure. Further, it was shown that acetylcholine or adrenaline increases the frequency of the spontaneous local contractions. When used in sequence, the whole oscule undergoes closure following administration of the second drug, and short-term local contractions cease. Both substances applied together result in depletion of myocyte cytoplasmic vesicles containing glycoproteins. The basis of spontaneous short-term contractions in this species thus appear substantially different from responses to mechanical stimuliu in other marine demosponges (see also following). This is most unexpected, since it might be assumed that both types of activity are due to similar cells. For the present, these differences can be viewed as a result of different contractile processes in different species. Further studies of spontaneous and mechanically induced contractility in the same species are needed in order to appropriately evaluate the apparent discrepancies.

Emson (1966) has also investigated the reaction of oscules, but in *Cliona celata*. He similarly finds no response to electrical stimuli, but graded responses to mechanical stimuli without temporal summation were recorded. The mechanical stimuli (jets of water) in these experiments were substantially different from those in the previously described experiments (Prosser, 1967; Prosser *et al.*, 1962) in which tapping with a glass needle, wire, or balsa wood stick was the stimulus. The absence of temporal summation may therefore be due to experimental procedure. Also the duration of the stimulus and the interval between stimuli differed considerably in the two studies. Emson (1966) investigated the effects of a number of pharmacological agents (Table 6-7); none had an effect at concentrations below 10^{-4} g/ml, and only did at this relatively high level. Emson (1966) considers that those producing some oscular closure do so because they slow or stop flagellar beating. Lower pH and increased CO_2

both caused oscular closure as well as reduction in the velocity of the excurrent water stream probably due to their effect upon flagellar beating. No evidence of conduction of the responses to other parts of the sponge was evident.

In a somewhat earlier study, the response of oscules of *Tethya lyncurium* was investigated by Pavans de Ceccatty *et al.* (1960). Mechanical stimuli (needles) result in oscular closure; local responses begin within a few seconds and last for about 30 sec. The secondary oscule can also constrict in response to mechanical stimuli, but this is related to a general contraction of the whole sponge. When CO_2 is bubbled in standing water for 4 to 5 min, the oscules close maximally after 15 min. Although the response is not due to the mechanical disturbance of bubbling, as stressed by Emson (1966) it is not possible to separate a carbon dioxide effect from a pH effect. Oscules that are closed due to CO_2 can be stimulated to open by continuous bubbling of O_2 in the medium. If this is then followed by CO_2, they close again. These responses appear due to general contraction of the whole sponge rather than to local oscular contractions. Suspended particulates and mechanical disturbance due to storms have recently been shown to cause oscular and secondary oscular closing in *Tethya crypta,* and it is conjectured that massive sperm release by *Neofibularia* was able to stimulate oscular closing in neighboring individuals of *Aplysina (Verongia)* (Reiswig, 1971a).

Ostia. Investigations reported during the last century established that ostia close when stimulated mechanically (including overfeeding with carmine particles), by sunlight, agitated water, cold temperature, and contact with the air [see Jones (1962) for this earlier literature]; not all ostia in an individual closed simultaneously. A number of more recent studies of ostial response have appeared, and as is the case with oscules, some of the data contradict earlier reports. In a relatively thorough study of *Stylotella,* Parker (1910) devised a technique to distinguish between ostial closure, oscular closure, and changes in flagellar activity. Using the cut end of a finger-like portion of the sponge for observations, the movement of carmine particles into the ostia (on the intact lateral surface) could be distinguished from the movement of particles into the incurrent vestibules at the cut surface. When particles did not enter at the ostial surface but did so at the cut surface, ostia could be said to be closed, since flagellar beating was continuing as shown by the movement of particles into the vestibules. Thus the condition of all three major components could be recorded simultaneously (Table 6-9). In contradiction to earlier results, cold and sunlight had no effect on ostia. However, Weissenfels (1980) has recently reported maximal opening of an ostium at lower temperatures (15°C) in *Ephydatia.* Mechanical deformation (change in shape) and movement of spicules across a pore canal—both relatively natural processes—cause partial closure of ostia in *Leucosolenia,* but light and tem-

Table 6-7 Effects of Drugs on Oscular Papillae of *Cliona celata*[a]

Chemical[b]	Number of Experiments	Percentage Closure of Oscule	Effect upon Response to Mechanical Stimulus	Effect upon Oscular Current
Adrenaline	3	0	None	N.R.
	1	70	N.R.	Slight reduction
Acetylcholine	5	0	None	N.R.
	1	10	None	No effect
Cocaine	3	0	None	N.R.
Hexamethonium	4	0	None	N.R.
	1	75	N.R.	No effect
Glutathione	1	30	N.R.	Slight reduction
	1	30	None	N.R.
	1	0	None	N.R.
Eserine	1	100	N.R.	Current lost
	1	30	None	N.R.
	1	40	None	Current reduced

ATP	1	45	None	Current reduced
Serotonin	3	0	None	N.R.
γ-Amino butyric acid	5	0	N.R.	N.R.
Nicotine	2	100	N.R.	Current lost
	1	50	N.R.	Current reduced
Histamine	1	66	N.R.	N.R.
	1	30	N.R.	Current reduced
Atropine	3	0	None	N.R.
D-Tubo curarine	3	0	None	N.R.
Tryptamine	1	100	N.R.	Current lost
	1	100	N.R.	Current reduced
	1	100	N.R.	N.R.
	1	70	N.R.	N.R.
All of the above drugs at 10^{-5} and 10^{-6} g/ml	133	0	None	N.R.

[a]Data taken from Emson (1966) and presented in a modified form. N.R. = not recorded.
[b]All drugs used at a concentration of 10^{-4} g/ml except as noted.

perature were without apparent effect (Jones, 1964a). The ostium and the pore canal were also found quite resistant to stretch and do not easily deform (Jones, 1961a). In *Cliona celata,* stretch was found to be a stimulus for pore closure (Emson, 1966). In *Leucosolenia* occasionally many pores closed simultaneously in pieces of the oscular tube that were observed microscopically. Hartman (1958a) also observed ostial closure in *Cliona* in sea water with lowered salinity.

Studies of the responses of ostia are much more difficult to conduct than those of oscules, which are nevertheless also technically difficult. Much work remains to be undertaken in order to expand our knowledge of the normal role of ostia in water transport as well as to resolve conflicting results, which may, however, have a species or organization-specific basis.

Choanocytes.   Early observations on the responses of choanocytes were mostly based upon indirect data—the velocity of the water leaving the oscules. As emphasized by Jones (1962), it is difficult to evaluate these data, since changes could have also been due to closure or opening of ostia (for example, McNair, 1923). The pioneering work of Parker (1910) has no such defect. He found in general that choanocyte flagellar activity is unaffected by many stimuli (Table 6-6) with the exception of cold (9–10°C) and lack of oxygen, which slowed or stopped activity. Other relatively drastic stimuli (fresh water, temperatures of 40 and 45°C, ether, chloroform) also resulted in cessation of activity. Emson (1966) more recently investigated the effects of several pharmacological agents (including some investigated by Parker) on flagellar activity in *Grantia* (Table 6-8). He concluded that these agents are inhibitory and since such high concentrations are necessary for any response that the effects were due to toxicity. In *Leucosolenia,* a current of water is ineffective in changing the plane of flagellar beating, but cessation of activity resulted from extended periods of observation microscopically (Jones, 1964a). The initial reduction in water transport during the night and the resumption of higher transport rates during the day in *Tethya* are also likely a result of the cessation and initiation of flagellar activity (Reiswig, 1971a), although no data are available for ostial effects. It has been tentatively suggested that flagellar activity in this species responds to levels of illumination. In two other species, water transport decreases when temperatures are lower (Reiswig, 1971a), but it is not known if this is related to a change in flagellar activity. Such activity can also be passively brought to cessation through the contraction of the sponge tissue in general (Kilian, 1952; De Vos and Van de Vyver, 1981), although the contraction (and effective closing) of canals in *Ephydatia fluviatilis* by cytochalasin B does not immediately effect flagellar beating. In three potentially very important and recent papers, it has been reported that electrical (or mechanical) stimulation of hexactinellid sponges (*Rhabdocalyptus, Staurocalyptus*)

Table 6-8   Effect of Chemicals on Choanocytes and Oscular Currents[a]

Chemical[b]	Effect on Oscular Current of *Cliona*	Effect on Flagellar Activity in *Grantia*
Acetylcholine	Slight reduction	No effect
Histamine	Very marked reduction	Almost stopped at 20 min
Physostigmine	Marked reduction	50% reduction at 20 min
γ-Amino butyric acid	Some reduction	No effect
Nicotine	Very marked reduction	Completely stopped at 20 min
Tryptamine	Very marked reduction	25% reduction at 20 min
Chloroform (0.5%)	—	Completely stopped at 2 min
Ether (0.5%)	—	Completely stopped at 2 min
Cocaine (0.001%)	—	Reduction in vigor of flagellar beating

[a]Data taken from Emson (1966).
[b]Concentration of chemicals 10^{-4} g/ml except as indicated.

results in cessation of water transport, and this response is most likely due to cessation of flagellar activity (Mackie, 1979; Lawn *et al.*, 1981; Mackie *et al.*, 1983). This is the first absolutely clear instance in which it is demonstrated that electrical stimuli can elicit a *propagated* response in a sponge. There was no response of ostia or oscules, and the response was conducted throughout the tissue at a rate of 0.2 cm/sec. The conduction system has an electrical basis and occurs via the syncytial trabeculum and dermal membrane. The response, flagellar arrest, appears to be all or none with a short latency period (Mackie *et al.*, 1983).

Pinacoderm and Tissue Contraction.   In many studies cited above, two additional effector components may be involved: contraction of the pinacoderms and contraction of the tissue (mesohyl) in general. The role of these two components is very difficult to assess, and no single study has been reported in which one or both of them have been analyzed in detail as discrete effectors. Furthermore, it has not been possible to separate clearly their effects from each other. Indeed, when oscular and/or ostial contractions are recorded, these may also involve pinacoderm and/or tissue contractions. Thus, it should be borne in mind that recordings of pore contractions or dilations may be complex phenomena not simply involving the pores themselves. Despite these complications, the contraction of pinacoderms and tissue can at least be discussed in broad terms.

In a number of freshwater species, the contraction of the exopinacoderm, vestibules, and incurrent canals has been reported (Wintermann, 1951; Kilian, 1952; Pavans de Ceccatty, 1974a; Pottu-Boumendil and

Pavans de Ceccatty, 1976) and in some cases toxic substances, light, and increased temperature are able to stimulate this (Wintermann, 1951). In *Spheciospongia vesparium,* when particulates (fine sand and detritus) are taken into the ostia, this leads to the forceful expulsion of the material, probably due to the contraction of the incurrent canal system and surrounding mesohyl (Storr, 1976). In *Tethya lyncurium,* mechanical stimuli result in general tissue contraction ("contraction globale") which can reduce the volume of the animals by one third (Pavans de Ceccatty *et al.,* 1960). Increased CO_2 (or lowered pH) and electrical stimulation similarly result in tissue contraction in general. The result of the latter stimulus is very similar to backwashing in *Spheciospongia.* The slow, tonic contractions of oscules of *Euspongia* and *Hippospongia* involve the underlying mesohyl as well as the pinacoderms and thus appear like tissue contraction except they are localized. The oscular tubes of *Leucosolenia* undergo general contraction following excision, and the choanocytes appear to be involved in this response but the pinacoderm also plays some role (Jones, 1957). In *Ephydatia mulleri,* cytochalasin B causes exopinacoderm contraction and eventually (after 24 h) leads to the disappearance of microfilaments in the cells (Pottu-Boumendil, 1975). In a related species, *E. fluviatilis,* general tissue contraction has also been well established (Ankel, 1965; Rasmont and De Vos, 1974; Kilian and Wintermann-Kilian, 1979). In *Stylotella heliophila* exposure to air results in tissue contraction, but such a general contraction of the body as a whole did not occur as a "directed" response (such as geotropism) (Parker, 1910). Also, in *E. fluviatilis,* oscular tubes undergo significant changes in shape suggesting general tissue contraction as its basis (McNair, 1923), and strong currents of water directed at such tubes result in contraction of the whole tube, not simply the oscule *per se.* Other stimuli (brushing, sharp blow, low temperature) also caused oscular tube contraction. Electrical stimuli were found to cause tissue contraction which was sometimes conducted (0.17 mm/ sec) for short distances. In *Cliona celata,* mechanical stimuli can cause the whole oscular papilla to contract and thus withdraw into the calcareous substratum (Emson, 1966). In the same species, both oscular and ostial papillae as a whole can so contract due to lowered salinity (Hartman, 1958a). In *Aplysina (Verongia) gigantea,* the closure of the oscules is accompanied by contraction of the secondary apendopinacoderm (Reiswig, 1971a) and the contraction of the tissue in general may be involved in this case also.

Spontaneous Changes in Water Currents

A number of recent studies that have been partially reviewed above demonstrate that spontaneous contractions (some cyclic) occur in oscules, the pinacoderms, and the tissue, and that spontaneous (also sometimes cyclic) changes in water transport can also occur. The most thorough of these investigations is that of Reiswig (1971a) in which an array of changes in activity was monitored *in situ*. In *Aplysina (Verongia) gigantea,* short periods (average of 42 min) of cessation of water transport occur. Such cessation is not synchronous between different sponges and occurs irregularly in a given individual with a periodicity of 6.5 to 32.2 h. Cessation of water transport is correlated with the closure of oscules and contraction of the secondary apendopinacoderm. In smaller individuals, in which the secondary oscule is able to completely close the secondary atrium, the onset of cessation is more rapid than that in older ones. No correlation with any environmental factors could be found, and it is considered that this behavioral pattern is endogeneously generated. In *Tethya crypta,* there is a synchronized, diurnal cycle of oscular closure in the population with consequent reduction in water transport at night and oscular opening and increased water transport during the day. The onset of reduction in transport is not completely coincident with oscular closing, and cessation of flagellar activity is likely involved also. A second spontaneous cycle also occurs in *Tethya* in which every 9 to 21 days individuals undergo oscular closure and cessation of water transport for periods of 1 to 5 days. The latter cycles are asynchronous in the population and are independent of environmental factors, except that during the stormy season, storms cause oscular closure and water transport cessation in all individuals thus synchronizing the population. Observations on other species suggest that such spontaneous activity is more common than expected (Table 6-9).

Table 6-9 Spontaneous Changes of Oscules and Water Transport in Some Demosponges[a]

Taxa	Species	Spontaneous Activity
Subclass: Tetractinomorpha		
Order: Hadromerida	*Tethya crypta*	Oscular contractions (diurnal synchronous cycle; 2-week asynchronous cycle)
	Anthosigmella varians	Oscular contractions
Subclass: Ceractinomorpha		
Order: Dictyoceratida	*Aplysina (Verongia) gigantea*	Periodic cessations (asynchronous)
	Aplysina (Verongia) archeri	Periodic cessations
	Ianthella sp.	Oscular contractions
Order: Poecilosclerida	*Mycale* sp.	None
	Agelas sp.	Periodic cessation
	Hemectyon ferox	Oscular contractions

[a]Data from Reiswig (1971a).

Additional examples and forms of spontaneous activity have also been reported as previously discussed. In *Euspongia* and *Hippospongia,* local spontaneous contractions of the oscular rim occur as well as more widespread contractions, some of which appeared propagated (Pavans de Ceccatty, 1969). In *Ephydatia fluviatilis,* periodic, spontaneous tissue contractions occur which reduce the diameter of excurrent canals and thus slow or stop flagellar activity in some chambers as well as causing or stimulating spontaneous, cyclic changes in the diameter of ostia (Kilian and Wintermann-Kilian, 1979; Kilian, 1952). These contractions have also been reported to result in temporary reversal of the water current (Wintermann, 1951). The periodic contraction of the tissue in outgrowths of explants (Simpson, 1963) is probably an analogous phenomenon to that described in young sponges derived from gemmule hatching (Pé, 1973). Pavans de Ceccatty (1974a, 1979) and Pottu-Boumendil and Pavans de Ceccatty (1976), in a time-lapse film, have observed spontaneous, propagated contraction of the pinacoderm.

De Vos and Van de Vyver (1981) have studied such spontaneous changes in the size of the excurrent canals and choanocyte chambers in juvenile individuals of *Ephydatia fluviatilis* maintained under constant culture conditions (Fig. 6-19). When the excurrent canals are fully expanded, the chambers and mesohyl are highly compressed; when the canals are narrowed, the chambers are of normal shape (relaxed) and the mesohyl is not compressed. When the chambers are compressed, flagellar activity ceases as does water pumping (Fig. 6-20). It is not clear how the contraction and relaxation of choanocyte chambers and/or pinacocytes are involved in these conformational changes. Since there apparently are no myocytes in these young sponges, either choanocytes and/or pinacocytes are the effectors. As more investigations are carried out, it is to be expected that spontaneous contractility and spontaneous changes in the activity of canal system components will appear very important controlling elements in water transport and possibly also in morphogenesis.

Environmental Factors Influencing Water Currents

Although an array of experimental stimuli are known to elicit responses of the canal system, there have only been a few studies of the role of naturally occurring environmental conditions in water pumping activities. As already described, the environmental current velocity can be a potent factor for increasing (or decreasing) water transport (Vogel, 1977). Conversely, turbulence caused by storms can cause oscular closure and cessation of pumping (Reiswig, 1971a). However, in the latter study, mechanical stimuli in the form of sand scour were not separable from wave action. In this same study, an interesting case of cessation of water pumping in *Aplysina (Verongia) gigantea* was reported in which sperm release from *Neofibularia* was correlated with the stoppage of water transport in *Aplysina (Verongia).* In *Tethya crypta,* light acts as a stimulus for oscular opening and thus water pumping, and in *Mycale* sp. and

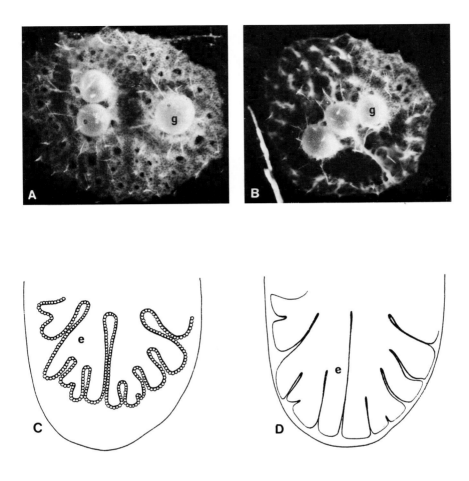

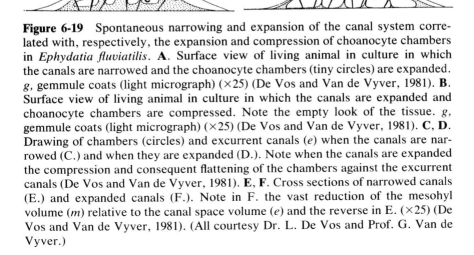

Figure 6-19 Spontaneous narrowing and expansion of the canal system correlated with, respectively, the expansion and compression of choanocyte chambers
in *Ephydatia fluviatilis*. **A**. Surface view of living animal in culture in which
the canals are narrowed and the choanocyte chambers (tiny circles) are expanded.
g, gemmule coats (light micrograph) (×25) (De Vos and Van de Vyver, 1981). **B**.
Surface view of living animal in culture in which the canals are expanded and
choanocyte chambers are compressed. Note the empty look of the tissue. *g*,
gemmule coats (light micrograph) (×25) (De Vos and Van de Vyver, 1981). **C, D**.
Drawing of chambers (circles) and excurrent canals (*e*) when the canals are narrowed (C.) and when they are expanded (D.). Note when the canals are expanded
the compression and consequent flattening of the chambers against the excurrent
canals (De Vos and Van de Vyver, 1981). **E, F**. Cross sections of narrowed canals
(E.) and expanded canals (F.). Note in F. the vast reduction of the mesohyl
volume (*m*) relative to the canal space volume (*e*) and the reverse in E. (×25) (De
Vos and Van de Vyver, 1981). (All courtesy Dr. L. De Vos and Prof. G. Van de
Vyver.)

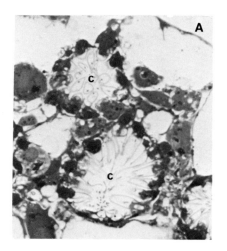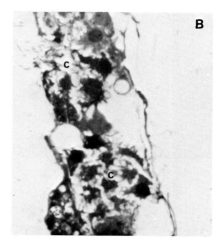

Figure 6-20 Expansion and compression of choanocyte chambers in *Ephydatia fluviatilis* (light micrographs, semithin sections). **A.** Expanded choanocyte chambers (*c*). (×790) (De Vos and Van de Vyver, 1981). **B.** Compressed choanocyte chambers (*c*). Compression is so extensive that choanocytes are barely discernible (×1,080) (De Vos and Van de Vyver, 1981). (Both courtesy Dr. L. De Vos and Prof. G. Van de Vyver.)

Aplysina (Verongia) gigantea, lower water temperatures are correlated with reduced transport. Since in *Mycale* there are no oscular contractions, the activity of choanocyte flagella is probably reduced. However, lower temperatures occur during the stormy season when turbulence and increased suspended particulates also occur. The particulates probably clog the ostia to some extent thus also lowering transport rates (Reiswig, 1971a). In the freshwater species, *Spongilla lacustris,* the clearance rates of radioactively labeled particulates were reduced at lower temperatures (13°C), and this is probably a result of lower flagellar activity (Frost, 1980a). In tropical freshwater sponges, water currents tend to cease at midday, possibly as a result of increased temperature (Annandale, 1907). In marine species, lowered salinity has profound effects upon water pumping resulting in cell death or degeneration (Hartman, 1958a). In those species that are estuarine, although no field data are available, fluctuations in salinity may thus cause significant changes in water transport. Similarly, it is obvious that in littoral sponges that become exposed to air either seasonally or daily, water pumping ceases, but, it is not known if the water trapped in the canal system is refluxed and if so whether flagellar activity is normal.

Intrinsic Control of Water Currents

The observations of Parker (1910), Kilian (1952), Wintermann (1951), Jones (1964a), and others suggest that the control of water transport is due to the contractile states of ostia and oscules, not to the regulation of flagellar beating. More recent investigations challenge this view of water transport control. In particular, the experiments of Mackie (1979), Lawn *et al.* (1981) and Mackie *et al.* (1983) establish that flagellar activity can be synchronously stopped implying, therefore, a mechanism of flagellar control which theoretically could be the primary one. This is also supported by the data on *Tethya crypta* (Reiswig, 1971a). In this species and *Tedania ignis* (Prosser *et al.*, 1962), the data suggest that the degree of openness of oscules is directly affected by the pressure of the excurrent stream of water and thus partially by the activity of flagella. Oscular diameter, according to the early views of Bidder (1923), is adjusted in order to maintain a constant *velocity* of water expulsion, and the results just cited tend to support this view. Thus, at this time, it is not completely clear if the control of water transport is basically flagellar or contractile, and it seems more and more likely that it has at its basis both components. Analyses of control of water transport will require simultaneous recordings of activities of all components in order to finally resolve this question.

A little studied aspect of water transport is the effect of size on transport rates. Frost (1980a) has found that very small sponges of *Spongilla lacustris* (=0.5 g dry weight) transport water at higher rates. Similar results are reported for marine species (Reiswig, 1974). Above a small size, however, no significant differences were apparent. However, the size of the smaller individuals in each species is not necessarily the same or even overlapping. Surprisingly, the obvious organizational differences between some sponges (tubular versus solid) have been found to have little effect upon parameters such as choanocyte chamber density and cross-sectional area of canals (Reiswig, 1975a), and based upon these data, fundamental differences in hydrodynamically important components may only occur when comparing asconoid to syconoid and leuconoid levels of development. Even in the latter case, it is not clear whether significant differences exist (see Reiswig, 1975a).

Coordination by Neuroid Cells

Coordinated closure of oscules, stoppage of water currents, and global contraction of pinacoderms and tissue all suggest the presence of an underlying system for the generation and conduction of signals throughout large areas. In fact, a conduction system has now been documented in a hexactinellid (Lawn *et al.*, 1981; Mackie *et al.*, 1983). Although it was not possible to record propagated action potentials or electrical activity, the spread of the response (0.2 cm/sec) is considered electrical, namely, too fast for chemial diffusion; on the other hand it is also substantially slower than that for typical neurons. The response appears to involve the simultaneous stoppage of flagellar activity. Although attempts to experimentally demonstrate similar propagated behavior in demosponges have thus far failed (Prosser *et al.*, 1962), it is clear that such propagated, spontaneous behavior does indeed occur in some species (Pavans de Caccatty,

1979). Furthermore, highly coordinated flagellar activity is known to occur in free-swimming larvae, and the release of sexual products in some
species can be a highly coordinated event both within a population and
within a single individual (Warburton, 1966; Bergquist *et al.*, 1970;
Reiswig, 1976). It is clear that the concept of neuroid cells and their
involvement as fixed tissue coordination pathways as put forth by Pavans
de Ceccatty (1966, 1974a,b) are completely applicable to the behavioral
patterns now documented in some species. The major challenge which
now presents itself is to document the chemical bases of such coordination and to determine the specific nature of the cells taking part in these
functions (Chap. 3). Pavans de Ceccatty (1974a) has formulated a morphological and physiological framework in which both of these can now
be investigated, and the pressing requirement is the development of appropriate techniques.

Neuroid cells in *Tethya* have been characterized ultrastructurally and
they display specific types of cell contacts and contain small dense cytoplasmic vesicles in the contact areas (Pavans de Ceccatty, 1966). They
further contain bundles of small (60 Å diameter) microfilaments resembling neurofilaments and more randomly arranged groups of thicker filaments (80–130 Å diameter) as well as microtubules. In these and other
respects, neuroid cells are strikingly similar to myocytes (see Oscules),
and indeed the same cells may function as both contractile and coordination elements (Pavans de Ceccatty, 1974a). According to the latter view,
the term neuroid cell refers to a functional state and not to a specific cell
type (see also Chap. 3). The network patterns of these cells in the mesohyl
are precisely what one would expect to find as the basis of coordination in
an animal that lacks typical neurons but is capable of spontaneous, propagated behavior (Fig. 6-21). The pinacoderms are also considered as neuroid tissue and their continuity (and syncytial nature in hexactinellids) may
be a key aspect of some types of coordination. One of the most difficult
problems to solve will be the determination of the role of the neuroid
function of the pinacoderms versus neuroid function of mesohyl cells in
specific behaviors.

Feeding

A primary function of water transport through the canal system is the
provision of a source of nutrients. When in particulate form, the dynamics
of their entrapment and ingestion have been investigated both *in habitat*
and experimentally in terms of their retention or clearance rate from the
ambient water. Further processing involves transport, digestion, and
elimination, and a number of important studies of the latter have been
published recently.

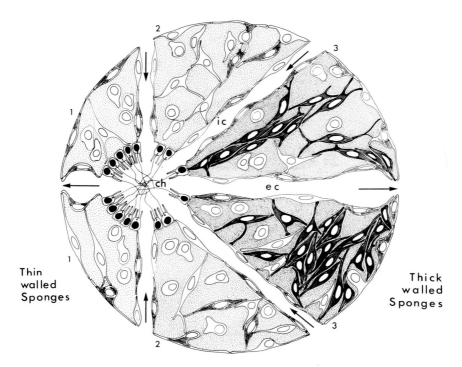

Figure 6-21 Diagramatic representation of neuroid tissue and hypothesized conduction pathways in sponges. *ch,* choanocyte chamber; *ic,* incurrent canal; *ec,* excurrent canal; *arrows,* water flow. Three types of sponges are depicted: thin-walled with weakly developed mesohyl (*1*), those with moderately developed mesohyl (*2*), and those with thick walls and highly developed mesohyl cells (*3*). Conduction and communication pathways consist of: exchanges via diffusion within the extracellular, mesohyl compartment; transitory cellular contacts via cell mobility; and permanent or semipermanent fixed pathways via bundles and networks of contractile cells (*black*). The pinacoderms can function in communication of all types. Note that neuroid cells are defined functionally and include other morphological cell types (see text) (Pavans de Ceccatty, 1974a). (Courtesy Prof. M. Pavans de Ceccatty.)

Retention of Particulates

There have been relatively few investigations involving direct measurements of the retention (or removal) of particulates from the water pumped through the canal system. The fraction of particulates that is so removed can be determined by measuring the concentration of particulates in the water entering the ostia (=ambient) and their concentration in the excurrent stream leaving the oscules. Thus, the retention (retention rate) or removal (removal rate) can be determined quite simply by the following formula (Reiswig, 1971a):

$$\frac{\text{ambient} - \text{excurrent}}{\text{ambient}} = \text{retention rate}$$

Such a rate can also be expressed as a percentage: retention rate $\times$ 100 = percentage retention. The retention rate is also sometimes called the efficiency (Frost, 1976a, 1980a) or the removal efficiency (Reiswig, 1975a), both of which can likewise be expressed as percentages. In distinction to the retention rate of particulates, the clearance or filtration rate is an indirect measure of the removal of particulates and is determined by measuring the rate of decrease in concentration of particulates in a known, static volume of ambient water due to retention by the sponge. The clearance rate is expressed as milliliters per second per milliliter of sponge, or milliliters per second per unit of sponge (usually wet weight or dry weight) and assumes that 100% of the particulates passing through the canal system are retained by the sponge. The clearance rate is thus a theoretical value which is very useful for the comparison of feeding activities. In sponges possessing small oscules, it is technically not feasible to sample the excurrent stream of water, and thus determination of the clearance rate is the only means of assessing feeding (Frost, 1978a,b). If the retention and clearance rates are both known, the water transport can be calculated by clearance rate $\times$ 1/retention rate = water transport rate. The water transport rate is the actual volume of water transported per unit time and can also be determined directly by measuring the velocity of the excurrent stream and the area of the oscular opening (Reiswig, 1971a, 1974). This can only be accomplished in sponges with appropriately large oscules or secondary oscules.

Reiswig (1971a, 1975b) has carried out thorough studies of retention rates in a number of demosponges. Depending upon the type of particulate, such rates range from about 0.30 to 0.95 (Table 6-10). Retention rates for bacteria are extremely high (0.96) as are those for unarmored unicells (0.87). Armored cells are removed much less efficiently (0.50), particularly those with smaller size (0.20–0.45). Retention rates of bacteria were found to be similar over a concentration range of 3.9×10^4 to 1.1×10^5 cells/ml. Wilkinson (1978a) has also found a high retention rate (efficiency) for bacteria. Interspecific variation in rate was related to ostial size, length of the canal system, and size of the choanocyte chambers. Small ostia and chambers and long canals result, according to this study, in higher retention rates. A very significant reduction in retention occurred *in habitat* during the winter months due to storms, clogging of the canal system, and partial degeneration of tissue (Reiswig, 1975b). In *Haliclona permolis* and *Suberites ficus,* bacterial retention was found to be somewhat lower (0.70). Of much significance is the discovery that a fraction of microscopically unresolvable particles is also retained by the

Table 6-10 Efficiency of Retention of Naturally Occurring
Particulates by Demosponges[a]

	Percentage Retention[b]		
	Mycale sp.	*Aplysina (Verongia) gigantea*	*Tethya crypta*
Bacteria			
By number	96.9 (95.0–98.4)	94.8 (91.3–97.5)	96.5 (94.7–98.0)
By volume	97.6 (95.6–98.9)	95.1 (90.2–98.4)	96.2 (94.0–98.0)
Unarmored cells[c]			
By number	80.4 (73.9–86.2)	82.5 (76.8–87.6)	94.4 (91.0–97.0)
By volume	88.2 (83.2–92.3)	88.4 (83.9–92.2)	91.7 (82.4–97.7)
Armored cells[d]			
By number	41.2 (30.3–52.5)	38.7 (19.3–60.2)	66.0 (53.4–77.5)
By volume	64.5 (44.9–81.8)	77.0 (61.7–89.4)	80.1 (64.5–92.0)

[a]Data taken from Reiswig (1971b).
[b]95% confidence interval of the mean.
[c]Size range: 5.0–50.0 μm.
[d]Size range: Two small classes: 2.0×2.0 and 3.0×4.0 μm; Remainder: 5.0–100 μm.

sponge although at relatively low rates (0.35) (Reiswig, 1971b). This fraction, which is apparently colloidal, was found to provide the major carbon source for these animals.

Two recent investigations of freshwater sponges have utilized clearance rates as a means of measuring feeding. In one of them (Willenz and Rasmont, 1979), the rate was determined by exposing small, gemmule hatched animals to polystyrene beads at concentrations of 3.9×10^7 to 3.0×10^8/ml. Although the initial retention of the beads is directly related to their concentration, the filtration (=clearance) rate becomes lower the higher the bead concentration (Table 6-11). This appears due to a saturation of the choanocytes with beads which leads to a lowered rate of water pumping. Such high concentrations of particulates probably rarely, if

Table 6-11 Ingestion of Polystyrene Beads and Filtration Rate in
Ephydatia fluviatilis[a]

Initial Concentration (beads/ml)	Ingestion of Beads in First 5 Min (beads/sec/sponge)	Filtration Rate[b] (ml/sec/ml sponge)
3.94×10^7	0.013×10^5	0.154
7.52×10^7	0.017×10^5	0.106
1.50×10^8	0.034×10^5	0.101

[a]Data taken from Willenz and Rasmont (1979) and presented in a modified form.
[b]Based upon the average volume of the sponges employed (1 sponge = 0.00022 ml).

ever, occur in nature so that one would not expect to find a lowering of filtration rate due to concentration. Frost (1978a,b, 1980a) has conducted a detailed set of experiments on *Spongilla lacustris* in which a radioactively labeled bacterium, an alga, and a yeast were fed to sponges in a feeding chamber, and the clearance rates were measured. Using a single food particle, there was no difference in rates over a concentration range of 3×10^4 to 4×10^6 cells/ml. However, clearance rates were found to increase with increasing temperature (15 to 25°C) but to decrease with increasing sponge size. Using a mixture of food types it was shown that the sponges could preferentially retain bacteria (Table 6-12), thus establishing a mechanism for selective feeding, the basis of which is still not clear. No differences in clearance rates were found at night versus day or in sponges that had few, if any, symbiotic algae. In a further study of *Ephydatia,* it was demonstrated that different types of particulate food are handled differently in terms of their intake through ostia and/or in terms of the rates at which they are digested (Frost, 1980b). Both of these variables significantly complicate what appear to otherwise be straightforward methods for determining retention rates.

Sites of Entrapment—Ingestion

That choanocytes are ingestive sites has never really been doubted (Fig. 6-22). The early, pioneering work of Vosmaer and Pekelharing (1898) clearly demonstrated that choanocytes and their collars act as ingestive sites. This and most other investigations up to the mid-1900s employed artificial food sources (carmine particles, milk, and the like) for identification of entrapment sites. Although skepticism concerning the use of such

Table 6-12   Simultaneous Clearance Rates of *Spongilla lacustris* Exposed to Yeast and Bacterial Cells[a]

Concentration (cells/ml)[b]	Clearance Rates (ml/sec/g dry wt)[c]	
	Of Yeast Cells	Of Bacteria
I. Yeast cells: 1.3×10^4 Bacteria: 1.7×10^5	$\begin{cases} 1.57 \pm 0.51 \\ 2.02 \pm 0.64 \\ 1.84 \pm 0.70 \end{cases}$	1.36 ± 0.93 2.61 ± 0.78 1.80 ± 0.63
II. Yeast cells: 1.7×10^6 Bacteria: 1.7×10^5	$\begin{cases} 0.18 \pm 0.25 \\ 0.20 \pm 0.18 \\ 0.35 \pm 0.26 \end{cases}$	1.20 ± 0.43 0.97 ± 0.42 1.31 ± 0.70

[a]Data taken from Frost (1978a, 1980a).
[b]Yeast: *Rhodotorula glutinis;* bacterium: *Aerobacter aerogenes.*
[c]Means ± standard deviations of three separate experiments for each of the two conditions. dry wt, dry weight.

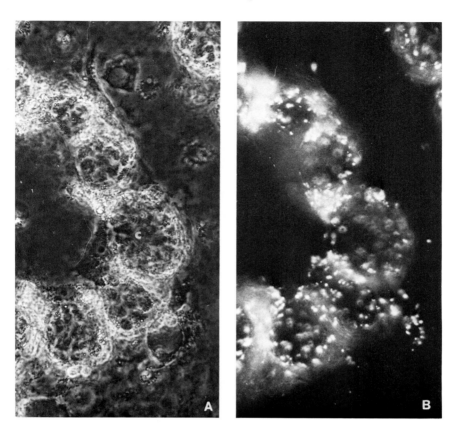

Figure 6-22 Ingestion of fluorescent casein by choanocytes of *Ephydatia fluviatilis* (living preparations). **A**. Phase-contrast micrograph of choanocytes chambers (*c*) 3 h after feeding casein (×510). **B**. The same chambers photographed with ultraviolet light showing the almost exclusive localization within the choanocytes (×510) (Schmidt, 1970a). (Courtesy Dr. I. Schmidt.)

artificial materials for determining the normal sites of entrapment and their ensuing digestion and transport has been expressed (Rasmont, 1968a), it now appears that, in general, the pathways for ingestion and transport are similar regardless of the nature of the particulates (Kilian, 1952). Their *size* is more important in determining alternative pathways of ingestion. Such a conclusion is not new, having been set forth in clear form by Van Weel (1949). Minchin (1900) had previously argued that the pathway taken by particulates depends upon the complexity of the canal system— in asconoid species ingestion occurs in collar cells, in more complex systems it occurs in the incurrent canals as well as in collar cells. In addition to the surfaces of the choanocytes, the prosendopinacoderm can also act as a site of ingestion (Van Tright, 1919; Van Weel, 1949; Kilian,

1952) and indeed, Metschnikoff (1879) had very early emphasized its probable role in ingestion, actually to the point of almost excluding choanocytes as ingestive sites. Similarly, Cotte (1902) expressed the view that *all* cell surfaces of sponges are capable of ingesting particulates. Further, Pütter (1909, 1914) contended that sponges absorb dissolved organic substances directly from the surrounding water. More recent investigations establish that all of these views are valid.

Vosmaer and Pekelharing (1898), employing *Sycon* and *Spongilla,* demonstrated that carmine or milk is intially taken up by choanocytes; the collars were viewed as a mechanical devise for entraining particulates on their inner surface; such particles are then ingested by the "protoplasm." Larger particulates were viewed by these workers and by Minchin (1900) as being entrapped in the incurrent system by "amebocytes" or in asconoid species by porocytes. It is interesting these early formulations—that wandering mesohyl cells can enter the incurrent canal—were put forth since there was at the time no known morphological basis of discontinuity of the prosendopinacoderm permiting such dynamic mobility. Van Tright (1919) also described choanocyte ingestion of carmine particles and algal cells but found that particules became trapped between cell bodies of the choanocytes and on the outer surfaces of the collars, particularly at their base. He also described, in *Spongilla,* the ingestion of larger particules by the cell(s) around the pinacocytic prosopyles. Such particles were seen to pass eventually into the mesohyl. Using india ink, Pourbaix (1933) further described particle entrapment by choanocytes of freshwater sponges; the particles were reported taken up outside the collar, generally at its base, and came to lie within vacuoles in the cytoplasm. Castro-Rodriguez (1930) observed the uptake of zoochlorellae by the same pathway. Pourbaix described particle uptake by endopinacocytes and occasionally also directly by exopinacocytes; choanocyte ingestion of bacteria was found similar to that of india ink (Pourbaix, 1933). Van Weel (1949) described a similar ingestive pathway via collar cells in *Spongilla proliferans* using carmine particles and india ink; however, vacuoles were rarely seen in the choanocyte cytoplasm, the particles appearing there "naked." Also, particles adhered to the collars externally and were then moved down them to the base for ingestion. Ingestion was additionally seen by cells in the incurrent canals some of which form web-like cytoplasmic bridges across the lumen. Less frequently, ingestion by exopinacocytes was observed. Higher ingestive rates by the endopinacocytes (as compared to exopinacocytes) were ascribed to the much higher transport rates of particles to the cell surfaces. In distinction to earlier studies, the following types of "food" were employed by Van Weel: carmine, india ink, blood cells, toad spermatozooids, diluted milk, and ferric saccharum. Some differences were found in the ingestion of these particulates. Spermatozooids were ingested by cells both in the incurrent canals and by choanocytes, and very few by exopinacocytes. Blood cells were ingested *only* by cells in the incurrent canals and exopinacocytes since they were too large to enter the choanocyte chambers; fat (=milk) was ingested by both choanocytes and incurrent canal cells. Results with ferric saccharum (in solution, no particles) were unimpressive, although small amounts of iron appeared in exopinacocytes, endopinacocytes, and "amebocytes." An important conclusion of these investigations was that the size of particulates determines the ingestive pathway (Van Weel, 1949).

In a detailed study of *Ephydatia fluviatilis,* Kilian (1952) confirmed the earlier studies of Van Tright (1919) and Van Weel (1949): particles larger than about 50 μm can be ingested directly by the exopinacoderm, those ranging in size between 5 and 50 μm are entrapped by the prosendopinacoderm, and those smaller than 5 μm (the approximate size of the pinacocytic prosopyles) are taken up by choanocytes appearing within digestive vacuoles in the cytoplasm. Kilian (1952) found that indigestible and digestible particles were treated in a similar manner, establishing the absence of discrimination in the ingestive process as well as the validity of employing indigestible materials to trace feeding pathways. All sized particles can be taken up by the exopinacoderm but larger ones rarely are. Kilian also observed that initial ingestion in the incurrent canals was primarily by collencytes, which seemed able to move freely onto and about the surfaces of the canals. When incurrent canals are viewed as being lined by a continuous layer of pinacocytes, it is difficult to visualize how collencytes can move about their surfaces. Some of these "collencytes" could be considered to be mobile pinacocytes as first suggested by Van Weel (1949), since the cytological features of both cell types are similar, only their position in the tissue differs (Chap. 3). It was not until recently that new light was shed on this problem. Both Weissenfels (1975) and De Vos (1979) have shown that the incurrent canals contain numerous porocytes as part of their surfaces; these openings provide a direct passageway from the lumen of the canal to the mesohyl which makes possible both cell movement into the incurrent canals and *direct* particle entrapment by mesohyl cells.

Using fluorescent-labeled materials and light microscopy, Schmidt (1970a) has shown that bacteria are primarily ingested by choanocytes and that casein (Fig. 6-22) and serum proteins are similarly ingested. Some limited ingestion of both of these food materials also occurs by pinacocytes. Employing bacteria and soluble protein, Weissenfels (1976) has found substantially the same results using transmission electron microscopy (Figs. 6-23, 6-24) and Willenz (1980) using latex beads (of about 0.8 μm diameter) and transmission electron microscopy has shown entrapment by choanocytes and exopinacocytes (Fig. 6-25) (Table 6-13). However, Weissenfels (1976) has reported a previously unknown pathway for bacterial ingestion. The pinacocytic prosopyles, each formed by a porocyte, were shown *not* to contact the choanocytes, and thus particles are able to directly enter the mesohyl in the vicinity of the chambers.

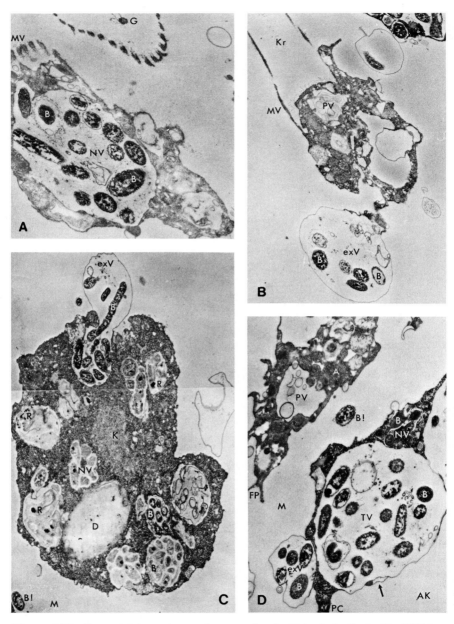

Figure 6-23 Bacterial ingestion and processing in *Ephydatia fluviatilis* (TEMs; all ×11,400). **A**. Bacteria (*B*) are initially taken up by choanocytes and collected in food vacuoles (*NV*). *MV,* collar; *G,* flagellum (Weissenfels, 1976). **B**. The food vacuoles are released into the mesohyl as exocytized vacuoles (*exV*) containing bacteria (*B*). *MV,* microvillus of collar (*Kr*); *PV,* contractile vacuole (Weissenfels,

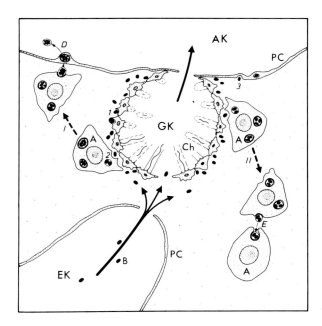

Figure 6-24 Schematic representation of the pathway of bacterial uptake and processing in *Ephydatia fluviatilis*. Bacteria (*B*) leaving the incurrent canals (*EK*) can be taken up by choanocytes (*Ch*) (*1*) or directly by archeocytes (*A*) (*2*) or they can enter the mesohyl directly without immediate ingestion. Some of the latter can be ingested by apendopinacocytes (*3*). Archeocytes that have directly ingested either bacteria or exocytized vacuoles from choanocytes (*II*) can transfer the vacuoles through exocytosis to other archeocytes (*E*) or they can migrate to the apendopinacoderm (*I*) and transfer the vacuoles which are then released (*D*) in the excurrent canals (*AK*). Many problems still remain to be worked out relative to the precise step-by-step transfer pathways. *PC*, pinacoderm; *GK*, choanocyte chamber (Weissenfels, 1976). (Courtesy Prof. N. Weissenfels.)

1976). **C.** Exocytized vacuoles (*exV*) containing bacteria (*B*) are taken up by archeocytes in which digestion occurs in the food vacuoles (*NV*) which give positive staining for acid phosphatase (*R*). *K*, nucleus. Some bacteria become extracellular (*B!*) in the mesohyl (*M*) (Weissenfels, 1976). **D.** Vacuoles still containing recognizable bacteria (*B*) are then transferred by exocytosis (*exV*) to apendopinacocytes (*PC*) lining the excurrent canals (*Ak*). Such transvacuoles (*TV*) are then released into the excurrent canal by the apendopinacocytes. Note the double nature of the membrane (*arrow*) of the vacuole. *A*, archeocyte; *PV*, contractile vacuole; *FP*, filopodia; *B!*, bacterium; *NV*, food vacuole; *M*, mesohyl (Weissenfels, 1976). (All courtesy Prof. N. Weissenfels.)

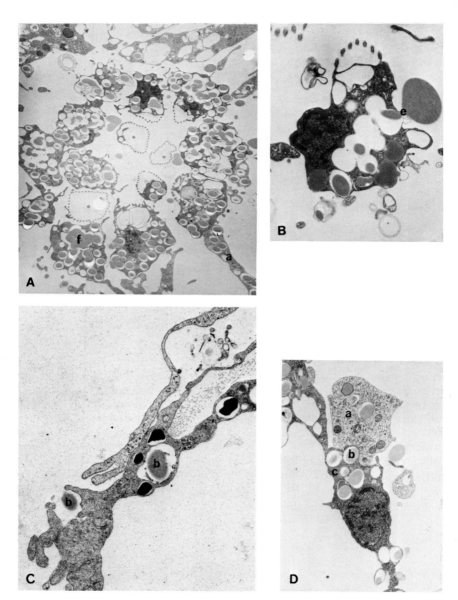

Figure 6-25 Ingestion and processing of latex beads by *Ephydatia fluviatilis* (TEMs). **A**. Five hours after feeding, choanocyte vacuoles are stuffed with the beads. A strange "fusion" (*f*) of intravacuolar beads occurs in some cells. Archeocytes (*a*) have also taken up the beads by this time through transfer from the choanocytes (see D.) (×1,045) (Willenz, 1980). **B**. Twelve hours after feeding, a bead is exocytised (*e*) to the mesohyl from a choanocyte (×8,370) (Willenz, 1980). **C**. Very soon after exposure to the beads (40 min) pinacocytes in the dermal membrane ingest them (*b*) (×11,180) (Willenz, 1980). **D**. Transfer of a bead (*b*) from a choanocyte (*c*) to an archeocyte (*a*) 2 h following feeding (×6,210) (Willenz, 1980). (Courtesy Dr. Ph. Willenz.)

Table 6-13 Sites of Ingestion of Polystrene (Latex) Beads by
Ephydatia fluviatilis[a]

Site of Ingestion[b]	Time of Continuous Exposure to Beads					
	5 min	10 min	20 min	30 min	40 min	1–12 h
Choanocytes		+	+	+	+	+
Dermal Membrane						
Exopinacocytes			+	+	+	+
Collagen Layer					+	+
Endopinacocytes					+	+
Archeocytes						+

[a]Data taken from Willenz (1980).
[b]The distribution of the beads was followed with transmission electron microscopy. When present inside cells beads occur within membrane-bound vacuoles.

Consequently, such particles can be directly ingested by archeocytes as is the case when they pass through the porocytes lining the incurrent canals and directly enter the mesohyl.

In a marine demosponge, *Suberites massa,* Diaz (1979a) has carried out a number of experiments in which he demonstrated the ingestion of yeast and bacteria by choanocytes and endopinacocytes; both kinds of food were phagocytized and appeared within vacuoles in the cytoplasm. In contrast to other studies, ingestion by choanocytes was found to occur both on the external and on the internal surfaces of the microvilli of the collar cells. Ferric saccharate was taken up by pinocytosis in choanocytes and endopinacocytes, whereas glycogen was ingested primarily (possibly exclusively) by choanocytes in the beta form (90 Å diameter particles). The latter apparently was pinocytosed by all surfaces of the collar cells although some of it appeared in the cytosol in a nonvesicular form (Fig. 6–26). Lévi (1965) has demonstrated ingestion of thorium oxide by the choanocytes of *Oscarella lobularis;* dense particle aggregates appeared within vesicles in the cytoplasm. Of some note in regard to glycogen ingestion in *Suberites* are the data of Reiswig (1971a), which demonstrate that a substantial portion of the organic diet of three marine demosponges in Jamaica is colloidal. It was conjectured by him that these colloids are ingested by choanocytes as now has been documented experimentally by Diaz (1979a) for glycogen. The microvilli and external coat of the collar appear crucial for such entrapment. In distinction to studies of freshwater species, Diaz (1979a) found that carmine and india ink are hardly ingested at all.

Harrison (1972a) has identified digestive vacuoles in *Corvomeyenia carolinensis* in basopinacocytes which were shown to contain acid phos-

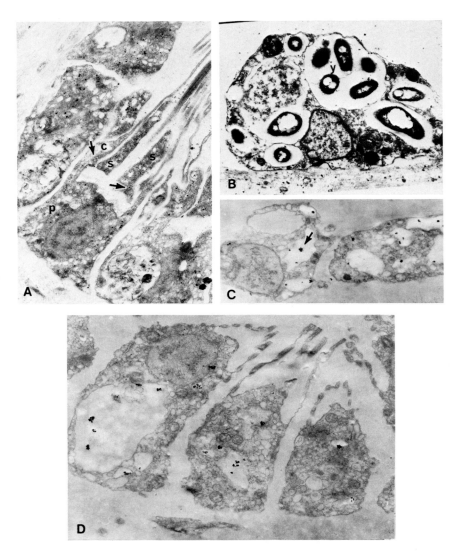

Figure 6-26 Ingestive sites in *Suberites massa* (TEMs). **A**. Ingestion of dissolved glycogen (*arrows*) (=black specks) by choanocytes. Note the uptake in the periflagellar sleeve (*s*), collar (*c*), and cytoplasm (*p*). TCH silver proteinate stain (×8,730) (Diaz, 1979a). **B**. Direct uptake of yeast cells (*y*) by an endopinacocyte (×6,355) (Diaz, 1979a). **C**. Direct uptake of solubilized iron saccharate (*arrow*) (black grains) by an endopinacocyte. Unstained section (×8,730) (Diaz, 1979a). **D**. Uptake and vacuolation of solubilized iron saccharate (black grains) by choanocytes. Unstained section (×12,400) (Diaz, 1979a). (All courtesy Dr. J-P. Diaz).

phatase; ingestion of bacteria by these cells was also directly observed. Although few other studies have been made of the feeding role of baso-pinacocytes, observations in marine species suggest that these cells are able to ingest particulates directly and in encrusting species, this pathway may be of much importance during active growth and spreading on the substratum (Simpson, 1963, 1968a). The mechanism whereby particles or colloids adhere to cell surfaces has not been documented but probably involves the organic matrix that constitutes the cell coat; this seems particularly clear in the case of choanocyte collars. Further, the thin pseudo-podia formed by choanocytes (see, for example, Diaz, 1979a) and the apparently static pseudopods encircling the base of collars in some species may act as "baskets" for particle collection. How particles that are trapped at or near the extremities of the collar microvilli are moved basally has not been established. The function of the ultrastructurally prominent strands of organic material connecting the choanocyte flagella to the surrounding microvilli is also not clear. Frost (1981) has developed a simple technique for determining the naturally occurring kinds of particulates that are ingested; this entails maceration of the sponge tissue and microscopic identification of the unicells. Using this technique and double labeling of two different unicells, Frost (1980b) has developed the view that two factors, clearance rate and retention time, interact in a complex manner to determine the overall selectivity of feeding in sponges. Different particle sources have different clearance rates and different retention times in the tissue.

A clear demonstration of at least one source of variability in retention times has been presented by Willenz and Van de Vyver (1982). In their study of *E. fluviatilis,* two sizes of latex beads were "fed" to the animals (Fig. 6-27). The beads were shown to be directly engulfed by exopinaco-cytes in a three-step process: adherence to the cell coat, formation of pseudopods, and uptake into the cytoplasm (endocytosis). In starved sponges exposed to the smaller beads (0.109 μm), the exopinacocyte plasmalemma formed ruffles in which bead ingestion took place. Also, the porocytes of the ostia immobilized the smaller beads through pseudopod formation, but they did not take them into cytoplasm. With the smaller beads it was also found that these are able to slip *between* the exopinaco-cyte junctions and enter the mesohyl of the dermal membrane. This study clearly documents the active role played by exopinacocytes in ingestion and further substantiates the diversity of pathways utilized for ingestion of particulates. Based on an earlier study (Willenz, 1980), the same beads can be taken up by choanocytes also, so that even with the same "food" different pathways are functional. Using yeast cells, Weissenfels (1983) has found that they are ingested at the *base* of choanocytes by means of extremely thin filopodia after passing *directly* into the mesohyl from the incurrent canals. Archeocytes also ingest them in the mesohyl as do apen-dopinacocytes. The size of the yeast cells apparently precludes their entrance *into* the chambers in distinction to smaller particles.

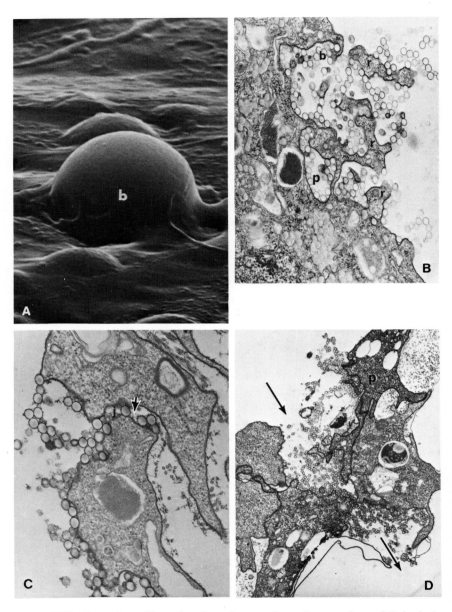

Figure 6-27   Ingestion of latex beads at the exopinacoderm surface of *Ephydatia fluviatilis*. **A.** A large (5.7 μm) bead (*b*) immobilized and surrounded by exopinacocyte pseudopods (SEM) (×5220) (Willenz and Van de Vyver, 1982). **B.** Ingestion of the smaller (0.109 μm) beads by an exopinacocyte through the formation of ruffles (*r*) at the cell surface. The beads (*b*) are immobilized by the cell coat. *p*, phagosome forming around ingested beads (TEM) (×16,650) (Willenz and Van de

Distribution and Digestion

Earlier as well as more recent investigations of living preparations in which pulsed exposure to particles was followed have shown that ingested particles in choanocytes are passed to cells in the mesohyl. Van Tright (1919) and Pourbaix (1933), for example, directly observed such transfer of carmine as did Castro-Rodriguez (1930) employing algae. Earlier, Vosmaer and Pekelharing (1898) found that immediately following exposure to carmine, the particles were present in choanocytes and that later (20 h) they appeared in the "parenchyma." Kilian (1952) obtained essentially the same results using india ink coated with albumen; the cells to which the particles were transported were invariably archeocytes. In a freshwater sponge which contains symbiotic algae, Van Weel (1949) also describes transfer of particles from choanocytes to mesohyl cells that lack symbionts. These cells he referred to as phagocytes, since symbiont containing cells received few particles from choanocytes. He also describes transport from endopinacocyte to phagocytes, but these data are not thoroughly convincing. The release into the mesohyl of particles previously taken up by phagocytes was also noted. Some sclerocytes were found to contain particles presumed to be transported to them by phagocytes. The observation of Van Weel (1949) that amebocytes (=archeocytes) containing many symbionts do not ingest many particulates is puzzling. Van Tright (1919) did not find this and no other reports of this phenomenon have appeared. Possibly, archeocytes may sometimes contain a superabundance of symbionts, which precludes further ingestion. Such a condition suggests that the number of occupied vacuoles in the cytoplasm is somehow involved in the regulation of the rate of uptake of additional particles, an idea which, although very interesting, is unsubstantiated.

Schmidt (1970a), employing pulsed exposure to fluoresent bacteria, found a sequential localization; the bacteria appear first in choanocytes and later in archeocytes (Fig. 6-28). Employing transmission electron microscopy, the freshwater sponge *Ephydatia fluviatilis,* and either latex beads (Willenz, 1980; 1983) or bacteria (Weissenfels, 1976), good evidence of the transport of whole digestive vacuoles or their contents from choanocytes to archeocytes has been presented (see Figs. 6-23, 6-24, 6-25). Such transfer includes a tight apposition of the cells, release of the vacuoles from the choanocytes, and their uptake by archeocytes

---

Vyver, 1982). **C.** Some smaller beads are able to slip between the exopinacocytye junctions (*j*) and are entrapped in cell coat materials (*arrow*) (TEM) (×27,585) (Willenz and Van de Vyver, 1982). **D.** Smaller beads can also enter through an ostium, shown here in tangential section. *Arrows* indicate the direction of water flow. Note that the beads adhere to the cell coat but are not taken up by the porocyte (*p*). This electron micrograph also indicates the complexity of the structure and of cell contacts in an ostium (TEM) (×7,020) (Willenz and Van de Vyver, 1982). (All courtesy Dr. Ph. Willenz.)

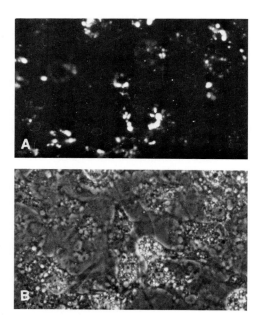

Figure 6-28 Demonstration of localization of ingested bacteria in archeocytes of *Ephydatia fluviatilis* 52 h after feeding (fluorescent antibody method). **A.** Ultraviolet fluorescene of intracellular bacterial uptake by archeocytes (×360). **B.** The same living tissue as in A., seen in phase contrast. The archeocytes are clearly present in the same locations as the fluorescence (×360) (Schmidt, 1970a). (Courtesy Dr. I. Schmidt).

(Willenz, 1980). Although the evidence is suggestive that whole digestive vacuoles including the phagosome membrane are transported (Weissenfels, 1976), it is difficult to follow precisely the membrane component, and further studies are required. Both of these studies as well as that of Weissenfels (1983) found that digestive vacuoles and their contents can be exocytized directly into the mesohyl by both choanocytes and archeocytes, thus supporting earlier observations of Van Weel (1949). Some beads that are not membrane bound are also released by choanocytes directly into the mesohyl.

Most investigations conclude that archeocytes (=phagocytes) are able to pass their digestive vacuoles on to "other" cells in the mesohyl, but no such transfer has actually been documented. Of interest in this context is the question of how special cell types, which never contain such vacuoles, receive nutrients. The presence of these cells in many species (Chap. 3) suggests the possibility of transport of solubilized nutrients. The nutrition of special cells requires investigation since no study to date has focused on this question. The transport of polystyrene beads, which were initially ingested by exopinacocytes, to the mesohyl in the dermal membrane and from there into prosendopinacocytes has been reported by Willenz (1980). This pathway involves release of the beads into the mesohyl (=collagen layer) and their uptake by endopinacocytes. It is not known how the beads are moved through the mesohyl which contains almost no cells. It is also not clear if the exocytized beads are membrane bound, but one published micrograph suggests this to be the case (Willenz, 1980). No further transport out of the endopinacocytes is to be expected, since their only remaining surface is that facing the lumen of the incurrent canals. In *Suberites massa,* particles ingested by choanocytes and endopinacocytes can be transferred to archeocytes, but in this species the "transport" appears to take place by a most unusual means, namely, metaplastic transformation of both cell types into archeocytes which then migrate into the adjoining mesohyl (Fig. 6-29) (Diaz, 1979a). Although of much interest, this conclusion is based upon minimal data and has previously been questioned (Pottu-Boumendil, 1975) (but, see Chap. 9).

There have been no really thorough investigations of the process of digestion. Earlier studies document a decrease in size of ingested particulates in mesohyl cells. For example, Van Tright (1919) observed the gradual breakdown of algal cells within "amebocytes." Van Weel (1949) observed a reduction in size of fat droplets in "phagocytes" and thus suggested the presence of a lipase. In the same study, ingested blood cells and spermatozoa were seen to become fragmented within the phagocytes after 3 to 8 h. Kilian (1952) emphasized that ingested particulates are accumulated primarily, if not exclusively, within archeocytes where they become digested. Such archeocytes, charged with digestive vacuoles, display exceptionally active movement (Kilian, 1952). Ingested bacteria within archeocytes undergo changes in shape indicative of their breakdown (Schmidt, 1970a; Weissenfels, 1976). Although changes in the morphology of *food* particles in phagosomes of choanocytes have been observed ultrastructurally (Diaz, 1979a; Pottu-Boumendil, 1975), the question of whether food is actually digested in them definitely requires further study; Weissenfels (1976) is of the opinion that digestion *per se* takes place only in archeocytes, and few investigations have suggested that choanocytes are a primary site of this process, particularly since the transport of particulates to archeocytes occurs rather quickly, in one to a few hours. However, since there have been no reports of the transport of nutrients *to* choanocytes from the mesohyl [Van Weel (1949) claims categorically that this does not occur] it seems likely that some digestion of particulates by them occurs prior to transport. The whole question requires thorough reevaluation.

In the only *in vitro* study of sponge digestive enzymes, broken cells consisting of moderately pure choanocytes displayed amylase, lipase, and protease activities; such activities were also demonstrated in archeocytes (Agrell, 1952). However, the activity of all three categories of lytic en-

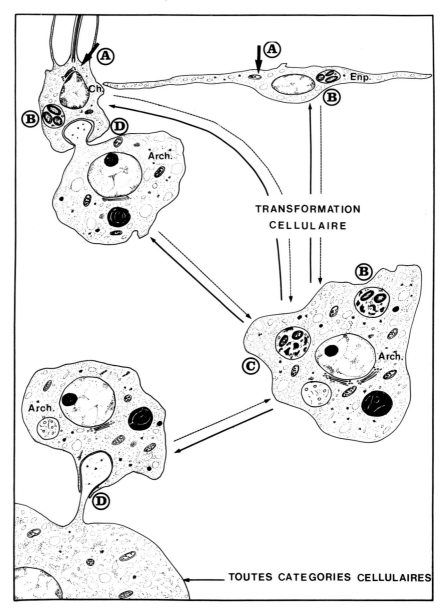

Figure 6-29 A scheme for nutrition in *Suberites massa*. A, ingestion of dissolved or particulate nutrients by endopinacocytes (*Enp*) and choanocytes (*Ch*). B, intracellular, vacuolar digestion of nutrients by choanocytes, archeocytes (*Arch*.), and endopinacocytes. C, cellular transport of nutrients within the mesohyl. D, transfer of nutrients by intercellular connections. Cell transformations (archeocyte–pinacocyte; archeocyte–choanocyte) account for an additional pathway for nutrient "transfer" (Diaz, 1979a). (Courtesy Dr. J-P. Diaz.)

zymes is 6 to 15 times higher in choanocytes than in archeocytes. The protease activity in both cell types displays two pH optima, one at 4.4 and the other at 6.8, suggesting the presence of, respectively, pepsin-like and trypsin-like enzymes (Hammen and Florkin, 1968). No indication of the presence of extracellular proteolytic enzymes was found in a recent study (Schmidt, 1970a).

A number of papers have appeared that report the presence of acid phosphatase in digestive vacuoles of choanocytes (Pottu-Boumendil, 1975; Diaz, 1979a), archeocytes (Fig. 6-30) (Thiney, 1972; Pottu-Boumendil, 1975; Diaz, 1979a; Weissenfels, 1976), endopinacocytes (Diaz, 1979a; Pottu-Boumendil, 1975), exopinacocytes and spherulous cells (Thiney, 1972), and in cystencytes (Tessenow and Kreutzmann, 1969; Pottu-Boumendil, 1975). Tessenow and Kreutzmann (1969, 1970) have also shown that following the hatching of gemmules of *Ephydatia mulleri,* there is a 14-fold increase in nonspecific esterase activity and a 5-fold increase in acid phosphatase activity as measured on broken cells *in vitro.* Such increases are correlated with the digestion of the vitelline platelets, a process which increases following hatching (Chap. 8). Further, some of the acid phosphatase and esterase activities are localized in small granules opposed to the outer surfaces of the platelet membranes and are likely lysosomes (Tessenow, 1969). Lysosomes containing acid phosphatase have also been identified near digestive vacuoles in archeocytes of *Hippospongia communis* (Thiney, 1972). In a cytochemical study

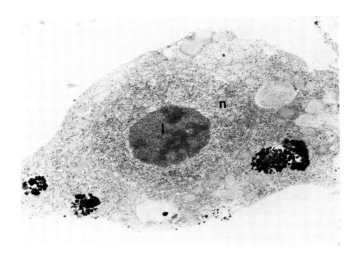

Figure 6-30 Demonstration of the localization of acid phosphatase (black deposits) within the phagosomes of an archeocyte of *Ephydatia mulleri. n,* nucleus; *l,* nucleolus (TEM) (×9,200) (Pottu-Boumendil, 1975). (Courtesy Dr. J. Pottu-Boumendil.)

of the breakdown of platelets following gemmule hatching, Tessenow (1968, 1969) describes the involvement of cystencytes that contain a single inclusion in which acid phosphatase and esterase activities are present. According to Tessenow (1969), this is an autophagic vacuole functioning in the digestion of platelets. However, Pottu-Boumendil (1975) disputes this conclusion, since cystencytes are present in adult animals and since following hatching, when these cells are abundant, there are hardly any vitelline platelets left in the tissue. Also, the appearance of acid phosphatase in the large vacuole occurs after most of the platelets have been digested (see further, Chap. 3).

Elimination

The elimination of particulates is probably an exceedingly complex phenomenon; relatively little of its basis is understood. Almost without exception, all reports that comment or provide data on the process conclude that elimination occurs in the excurrent canal system or at the surface of the sponge. Masterman (1894) reported the expulsion of carmine particles by mesohyl cells at both of these surfaces in *Grantia compressa,* and Cotte (1904) observed similar release and in addition reported that choanocytes can release particulates into the lumen of chambers. The latter study appears to be the first to suggest the release of vacuoles (=spherules) into the mesohyl by mesohyl cells and their eventual uptake by other cells and final expulsion into excurrent canals. Van Tright (1919) presents somewhat more detailed data in which he observed mesohyl cells at the surface of excurrent canals; these formed bubble-like protuberances that extended into the lumen; such vacuoles were then released into the canal. Foreshadowing Van Weel's distinction between "phagocytes" and amebocytes containing many symbiotic algae, Van Tright emphasized that amebocytes with few or no symbionts are the ones concerned with elimination. Van Tright also raised two questions that are of overwhelming importance relative to the process of elimination and that still remain totally unanswered: How do cells recognize an excurrent canal from an incurrent one? How do cells "know" that they have taken up food and not particulates that require elimination? The first of these brings to mind the question of cell recognition and leads one to the suggestion that there are fundamental differences in the surfaces of apendopinacocytes and prosendopinacocytes. The basis for such a difference has indeed been experimentally suggested by Mergner (1970) (Chap. 9). The second question may not be as complex as appears at first sight, since all cells that ingest particulates appear to exocytize them and thus the retention time within a particular cell may be the controlling mechanism for elimination. However, nothing is known concerning the control of retention time other than that choanocytes appear to have a much shorter one than archeocytes.

Van Weel (1949) briefly commented on elimination following exposure to carmine or india ink; the particles appear in endopinacocytes and phagocytes bordering the excurrent canals and vacuoles of these cells were observed protruding into the canal lumen. Kilian (1952) has confirmed other findings by observing archeocytes, collencytes, and pinacocytes extruding blister-like vacuoles into excurrent canals. By following fluorescent bacteria, Schmidt (1970a) has further supported the view that archeocytes exocytize solid wastes into excurrent canals (Fig. 6-31). Finally, Weissenfels (1976; 1983) has presented convincing evidence of this, but the vacuoles are released first into the mesohyl by archeocytes and are then taken up and expelled by apendopinacocytes (see Fig. 6-23). Willenz (1983) has also observed the release of exocytotic vesicles into excurrent canals. In the homoscleromorph, *Plakina trilopha,* some choanocytes accumulate dense inclusions and these cells are apparently released into the chamber lumen (Donadey, 1978, 1979) (Chap. 3).

In a comparative study of central cells, Reiswig and Brown (1977) have suggested that at least in *Aplysina (Verongia), Tethya,* and *Merlia* these cells carry out an egestive function; the eliminated wastes apparently are released into the chambers near the apopyle (downstream) where they are swept out of the sponge. Central cells in the orders Haplosclerida, Poecilosclerida, and Halichondrida are considered able to stop water flow

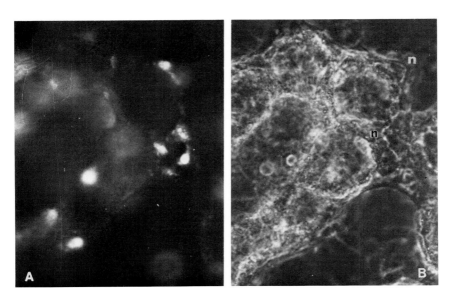

Figure 6-31 Elimination of ingested bacteria in *Ephydatia fluviatilis* (fluorescent antibody method). **A.** Fluorescence of bacteria in ultraviolet light within the endopinacocytes that line the excurrent canal ($\times 505$). **B.** Phase-contrast micrograph of the same living cells as in A., demonstrating the localization of the bacteria in apendopinacocytes (n) ($\times 505$) (Schmidt, 1970a). (Courtesy Dr. I. Schmidt.)

through the chambers permitting "cells" to clear particulates from the prosopyles. While highly suggestive and of probable importance, these views are very conjectural and now require corroboration. As pointed out by these workers, some species (freshwater sponges) do not possess central cells and in others their morphology and distribution do not fit any present interpretation. Comparative ultrastructural studies combined with feeding experiments would provide new and much needed data. Reiswig (1971b) has demonstrated in three marine demosponges that detritus is actively produced by them. On the average these species release 2.7 times the number of detrital particles as they take in. It is not clear if some of the detritus produced passes through the feeding system unchanged.

CHAPTER SEVEN

Gamete, Embryo, Larval Development

This chapter presents descriptions of the origin, structure, and differentiation of gametes, larval development, and larval metamorphosis. Recent reviews of sponge reproduction have appeared or will shortly, and reference can be made to them for other points of view (Fell, 1974a, 1983, in press; Reiswig, in press; Sara, in press; Simpson, in press; Tuzet, 1973a; Brien, 1973; Sara and Vacelet, 1973).

General Features of Sexual Reproduction

The development of gametes involves the differentiation of choanocytes and/or archeocytes. Eggs are either fertilized *in situ* in the mesohyl and undergo development there (viviparity) or are released and undergo development in the water. Gonochorism and hermaphroditism occur in different species. Fertilization in viviparous species involves the transport of spermatozoa to the egg which then undergoes cleavage and, in most species, results in the formation of a solid morula stage. Flagellated larvae then develop without gastrulation and become free swimming. However, some events in development can be, and have been, considered comparable to gastrulation. Fertilization requires a degree of synchrony of gamete production and release in order to ensure the production of a new generation of animals. The distribution and settlement of larvae are, in turn, dependent upon their response to environmental stimuli and more significantly upon physical parameters in the environment such as currents. Although numerous reports have appeared dealing with sexual reproduction, specific events such as those dealing with fertilization and the timing of egg maturation still require further elucidation.

Table 7-1 presents selected examples of modes of reproduction in the phylum. Three types of free-swimming larvae can now be recognized: coeloblastulae characteristic of calcineans and tetractinomorphs; hollow amphiblastulae characteristic of calcaronean species; and parenchymellae characteristic of ceractinomorphs, sclerosponges, and hexactinellids. Most species reproduce seasonally during a specific time of the year; *Haliclona ecbasis* and *Ochridaspongia rotunda* are among the exceptions, both are reproductively active throughout the year.

Table 7-1 Representative Reproductive Profiles

Taxon (Class, subclass)	Species	Locality	Habitat
Calcarea			
Calcaronea	*Sycon ciliatum*	Mediterranean Italy	Littoral Marine
	Leucosolenia botryoides	Bay of Naples Italy	Littoral Marine
Calcinea	*Clathrina coriacea*	Bay of Naples Italy	Littoral Marine
	Clathrina coriacea	Pacific California	Littoral Marine
	Clathrina blanca	Pacific California	Littoral Marine
Pharetronida	*Petrobiona massiliana*	Mediterranean France	Grottos Marine
Sphinctozoidia	*Neocoelia crypta*	Indian Ocean Iles Glorieuses	Benthic Marine
Sclerospongiae			
Ceratoporellida	*Stromatospongia vermicola*	Caribbean	Benthic Marine
Demospongiae			
Tetractinomorpha	*Aaptos aaptos*	Pacific New Zealand	Subtidal Marine
	Agelas sp.[c]	Caribbean	Benthic Marine
	Agelas oroides[c]	Adriatic, Ionian, Italy	Littoral Marine
	Ancorina alata	Pacific New Zealand	Subtidal Marine
	Chondrilla nucula	Adriatic, Ionian, Italy	Littoral Marine
	Chondrosia reniformis	Mediterranean France	Benthic Marine
	Chondrosia reniformis	Adriatic, Ionian, Italy	Littoral Marine
	Erylus discophorous	Adriatic Italy	Littoral Marine
	Geodia cydonium	Adriatic Italy	Littoral Marine
	Hemectyon ferox	Caribbean	Benthic Marine
	Polymastia hirusta	Pacific New Zealand	Subtidal Marine

[c]Reiswig (1976) has suggested placing *Agelas* in the Tetractinomorpha while Liaci and Sciscioli (1975b) have kept the genus in the Ceractinomorpha.

Reproductive Period	Form of Sexual Reproduction[a]	Type of Larva	References
All Year	Viviparous Hermaphroditic	Amphiblastula	Sara and Rellini-Orsi (1975)
Feb–Mar	Viviparous	Amphiblastula	Sara (1955b)
Sep–Nov	Viviparous	Coeloblastula	Sara (1955b)
Jul–Oct	Viviparous	Coeloblastula	Johnson (1978b)
Apr–Aug	Viviparous	Coeloblastula	Johnson (1978b)
May–Dec	Viviparous	Amphiblastula	Vacelet (1964)
Apr	Viviparous	Parenchymella	Vacelet (1979a)
?	Viviparous	Probably Parenchymella	Hartman (1969)
Sep–Oct	Oviparous Gonochoristic?	Unknown	Ayling (1980)
Jul	Oviparous Gonochoristic	Unknown	Reiswig (1976)
Jun–Jul	Oviparous Gonochoristic	Unknown	Liaci and Sciscioli (1975b)
Feb–Jun	Oviparous Gonochoristic	Unknown	Ayling (1980)
Jul–Oct	Oviparous	Unknown	Liaci et al. (1971a)
Jul–Aug	Oviparous	Coeloblastula	Lévi and Lévi (1976)
May–Sep	Oviparous Gonochoristic	Unknown	Liaci et al. (1971a)
Sep–Dec	Oviparous Gonochoristic	Unknown	Liaci and Sciscioli (1970)
Jun–Oct	Oviparous Gonochoristic	Unknown	Liaci and Sciscioli (1969)
Aug	Oviparous Gonochoristic	Parenchymella?	Reiswig (1976)
May–Oct	Oviparous Gonochoristic	Unknown	Ayling (1980)

[a]Many sponges have been found to be labile in terms of sex determination. Listings give the predominant type of sexuality if known; see references for additional information.

Table 7-1 Representative Reproductive Profiles (*Continued*)

Taxon (Class, subclass)	Species	Locality	Habitat
Demospongiae Tetractinomorpha (*cont.*)	*Polymastia robusta*	N. Atlantic France	Intertidal Marine
	Raspailia topsenti	Pacific New Zealand	Subtidal Marine
	Stelleta grubii	Adriatic Italy	Littoral Marine
	Suberites carnosus	Adriatic Italy	Littoral Marine
	Suberites massa	Mediterranean France	Benthic Marine
	Tethya aurantium	Adriatic, Ionian, Italy	Littoral Marine
	Tethya citrina	Adriatic, Ionian, Italy	Littoral Marine
	Tethya crypta	Caribbean Jamaica	Littoral Marine
	Tetilla japonica	Pacific Japan	Benthic Marine
	Tetilla sp.	Adriatic Italy	Littoral Marine
Ceractinomorpha	*Adocia varia*	Adriatic Italy	Littoral Marine
	Anchinoe sp.	Pacific New Zealand	Subtidal Marine
	Aplysina (*Verongia*) *aerophoba*	Adriatic, Ionian, Italy	Littoral Marine
	Aplysina (*Verongia*) *cavernicola*	Mediterranean France	Benthic Marine
	Aplysina (*Verongia*) *gigantea*	Caribbean Jamaica	Benthic Marine
	Crambe crambe	Adriatic, Ionian, Italy	Littoral Marine
	Ephydatia fluviatilis	Bruxelles Belgium	Littoral Freshwater

Reproductive Period	Form of Sexual Reproduction[a]	Type of Larva	References
Sep	Oviparous	Coeloblastula	Borojevic (1967)
Jan–Jun	Oviparous Gonochoristic	Unknown	Ayling (1980)
Jul–Dec	Oviparous	Unknown	Liaci and Sciscioli (1967)
Jun–Sep	Oviparous Gonochoristic	Unknown	Liaci et al. (1971c)
Apr–Jul[b]	Oviparous Gonochoristic	Unknown	Diaz (1973, 1979a)
Jul–Oct	Oviparous Gonochoristic	Unknown	Liaci et al. (1971c)
May–Nov	Oviparous Gonochoristic	Unknown	Liaci et al. (1971c)
Nov–Jan	Oviparous Gonochoristic	Unknown	Reiswig (1973)
Jul–Sep	Oviparous Gonochoristic	None, direct development	Watanabe (1978a)
May–Aug	Oviparous Hermaphroditic	Unknown	Liaci et al. (1976)
May–Oct	Viviparous Gonochoristic	Parenchymella	Liaci et al. (1973)
Feb–Nov	Viviparous Hermaphroditic	Parenchymella	Ayling (1980)
Jun–Jul	Oviparous Hermaphroditic	Unknown	Liaci et al. (1971b)
Apr–Aug	Oviparous	Unknown	Gallissian and Vacelet (1976)
Feb–Mar	Oviparous Gonochoristic	Unknown	Reiswig (1973)
Apr–Jul	Viviparous Hermaphroditic	Parenchymella	Liaci and Sciscioli (1975b)
Nov–Jul[d]	Viviparous Gonochoristic	Parenchymella	Van de Vyver and Willenz (1975)

[a]Many sponges have been found to be labile in terms of sex determination. Listings give the predominant type of sexuality if known; see references for additional information.
[b]Two forms of this species were studied. The digitate form reproduces from April to May and the massice form from May to July.
[d]Young oogonia overwinter; reproduction begins in the spring.

Table 7-1   Representative Reproductive Profiles (*Continued*)

Taxon (Class, subclass)	Species	Locality	Habitat
Demospongiae Ceractinomorpha (*cont.*)	*Gellius fibulatus*	Adriatic Italy	Littoral Marine
	Halichondria sp.	L.I. Sound Connecticut	Littoral Estuarine
	Haliclona elegans	Adriatic Italy	Littoral Marine
	Haliclona loosanoffi	L.I. Sound Connecticut	Littoral Estuarine
	Haliclona permolis	Pacific Oregon	Intertidal Marine
	Halisarca dujardini	N. Atlantic France	Intertidal Marine
	Halisarca nahantensis	N. Atlantic Massachusetts	Intertidal Marine
	Hamigera hamigera	Adriatic, Ionian, Italy	Littoral Marine
	Hippospongia communis	Mediterranean Tunisia	Littoral Marine
	Hymeniacidon caruncula	Mediterranean France	Benthic Marine
	Hymeniacidon perleve	N. Atlantic England	Littoral Marine
	Ircinia fasiculata	Adriatic Ionian, Italy	Littoral Marine
	Ircinia variabilis	Adriatic, Ionian, Italy	Littoral Marine
	Microciona prolifera	L.I. Sound Connecticut	Intertidal Marine
	Mycale sp.	Caribbean Jamaica	Littoral Marine
	Ochridaspongia rotunda	Lake Ochrid Yugoslavia	Benthic Freshwater
	Ophlitaspongia seriata	N. Atlantic England	Intertidal Marine
	Petrosia ficiformis	Adriatic, Ionian, Italy	Littoral Marine

Reproductive Period	Form of Sexual Reproduction[a]	Type of Larva	References
Apr–Nov	Viviparous? Gonochoristic	Unknown	Liaci et al. (1973)
Apr–Jul	Viviparous Gonochoristic	Parenchymella	Fell and Jacob (1979) Lewandroski and Fell (1981)
May–Aug	Viviparous Gonochoristic	Parenchymella	Liaci et al. (1973)
May–Aug	Viviparous Gonochoristic	Parenchymella	Fell (1976b)
Feb–Aug	Viviparous Gonochoristic	Parenchymella	Elvin (1976)
Apr–Sep	Viviparous Hermaphroditic	Parenchymella	Lévi (1956)
Nov–May[d]	Viviparous Hermaphroditic	Parenchymella	Chen (1976)
Apr–Sep	Viviparous Hermaphroditic	Parenchymella	Liaci and Sciscioli (1975b)
Mar–Jun	Viviparous Gonochoristic	Parenchymella	Tuzet and Pavans de Ceccatty (1958)
Apr–Jun	Viviparous Hermaphroditic	Parenchymella	Diaz (1973)
Jul–Sep	Viviparous Hermaphroditic?	Parenchymella	Stone (1970a)
Mar–Jan	Viviparous Hermaphroditic	Parenchymella	Liaci et al. (1971b)
Mar–Dec	Viviparous Hermaphroditic	Parenchymella	Liaci et al. (1971b)
May–Aug	Viviparous Hermaphroditic	Parenchymella	Simpson (1968b)
May–Oct	Viviparous Hermaphroditic	Parenchymella	Reiswig (1973)
All year	Viviparous Gonochoristic	Parenchymella	Gilbert and Hadzisce (1977)
Jul–Sep	Viviparous	Parenchymella	Fry (1971)
Apr–Nov	Oviparous Gonochoristic	Unknown	Liaci et al. (1973)

[a]Many sponges have been found to be labile in terms of sex determination. Listings give the predominant type of sexuality if known; see references for additional information.
[d]Young oogonia overwinter; reproduction begins in the spring.

Table 7-1 Representative Reproductive Profiles (*Continued*)

Taxon (Class, subclass)	Species	Locality	Habitat
Demospongiae Ceractinomorpha (*cont.*)	*Spongia officinalis*	Adriatic, Ionian, Tyrrehenian Italy	Littoral Marine
	Spongilla lacustris	New Hampshire USA	Littoral Freshwater
	Spongilla semispongilla	Gunma Japan	Littoral Freshwater
	Stylopus sp.	Pacific New Zealand	Subtidal Marine
	Trochospongilla (=*Tubella*) *pennsylvanica*	New Hampshire USA	Littoral Freshwater
Homoscleromorpha	*Octavella galanguai*	Atlantic France	Littoral Marine

Gametogenesis

Spermatogenesis

The development of sperm cells involves (1) the differentiation of stem cells, spermatogonia; (2) the formation of spermatogenic cysts; and (3) the development of mature sperm. Data on these processes are limited almost exclusively to the Demospongiae. Adult sponges have no tissue that can be identified structurally as reproductive, and the development of male gametes is the result of the differentiation of a stock of adult cells into spermatogonia, which then give rise to sperm cysts. During the reproductive period, groups of spermatogenic cells form within the mesohyl (Lévi, 1956; Tuzet and Pavans de Ceccatty, 1958; Liaci and Sciscioli, 1967; Simpson, 1968b; Fell, 1970; Tuzet *et al.*, 1970a,b; Diaz *et al.*, 1973; Simpson and Gilbert, 1973; Gilbert and Hadzisce, 1977; Van de Vyver and Willenz, 1975; Diaz, 1979a; and many others). Recent investigations by Tuzet and Paris (1964) on *Octavella galanguai*, by Tuzet *et al.* (1970a,b) on *Aplysilla rosea*, by Tuzet and Pavans de Ceccatty (1958) on *Hippospongia communis*, by Vacelet (1979a) on *Neocoelia crypta*, and by Diaz *et al.* (1973) and Diaz and Connes (1980) on *Suberites massa* establish that

Reproductive Period	Form of Sexual Reproduction[a]	Type of Larva	References
Mar–Dec	Viviparous Hermaphroditic	Parenchymella	Liaci *et al.* (1971b)
Apr–Jul	Viviparous Gonochoristic	Parenchymella	Simpson and Gilbert (1973)
Jul–Sep	Viviparous Gonochoristic	Parenchymella	Mukai (1980)
Jan–Apr	Viviparous Hermaphroditic	Parenchymella?	Ayling (1980)
May–Jul	Viviparous Gonochoristic	Parenchymella	Simpson and Gilbert (1973)
May–Sep	Viviparous Hermaphroditic	Coeloblastula (?Amphiblastula)	Tuzet and Paris (1964)

[a]Many sponges have been found to be labile in terms of sex determination. Listings give the predominant type of sexuality if known; see references for additional information.

in these species choanocytes directly form spermatogonia; in *Aplysilla* all of the choanocytes of a single chamber have been observed simultaneously undergoing transformation into a spermatogenic cyst. In other demosponges, spermatogenic cysts appear too large to have developed directly from single choanocyte chambers (Fig. 7-1). The latter condition in particular has led some investigators to suggest that mesohyl cells (? archeocytes) aggregate and form the cysts (Lévi, 1956; Fincher, 1940; Okada, 1928). The establishment of a choanocyte origin of spermatogenic cysts in some demosponges raises the possibility that these cells are also the origin of cysts in all other species. Sara (1974) and Lemche and Tendal (1977) have recently championed this view. If this is the case, however, a number of different choanocyte chambers would have to fuse together in order to form the larger cysts reported in many species, or a reasonably high level of mitoses of each chamber would have to be initiated prior to formation of the definitive cyst. The latter is a real possibility, since choanocytes have been reported to have relatively high mitotic activity (Shore, 1971). An alternative explanation is that the origin of cysts is different in different species—in some they are derived from choanocytes and in others from mesohyl cells which form aggregates.

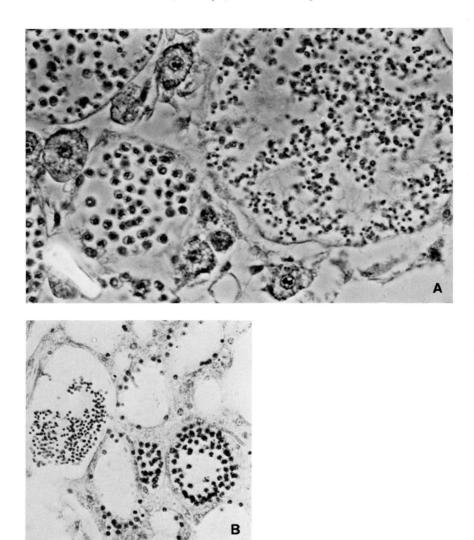

Figure 7-1 Examples of spermatogenesis in demosponges (light micrographs).
A. Large spermatogenic cysts of *Ochridaspongia rotunda* in which two synchronized developmental stages are present. The one on the right contains spermatids
and developing spermatozoa; the other is in division (×520) (Gilbert and Hadzisce, 1977). **B**. Small spermatogenic cysts in *Spongia officinalis*, each of which
could, based upon size, be derived directly from single choanocyte chambers.
The cyst on the left contains spermatids (×550) (Liaci *et al.*, 1971b). (**A**, courtesy
Prof. J. J. Gilbert; **B**, courtesy Prof. L. Scalera-Liaci.)

Leveaux (1942) suggests that choanocytes both migrate into the mesohyl and form cysts; such appears the case in *Suberites* where, however, small, not large, cysts develop (see following).

Two detailed ultrastructural studies of spermatogenesis have appeared; one is that of Tuzet *et al.* (1970a,b) in *Aplysilla rosea.* In this species, mature sperm contain abundant glycogen, a highly condensed nucleus, and two large mitochondrial masses, but an acrosome is absent. In other species, however, such as *Hippospongia communis,* acrosomes have been described (Tuzet and Pavans de Ceccatty, 1958), but this and other light microscopic reports of them require ultrastructural reevaluation in view of their absence in species that have been so studied. Each sperm in *Aplysilla* is uniflagellated and contains at the base of the flagellum two centrioles, one of which is part of the flagellum. All stages in spermatogenesis in this species—spermatogonia, spermatocytes, spermatids, and sperm—are uniflagellated (Figs. 7-2, 7-3). Spermatogonia developing directly from choanocytes *in situ* do not undergo mitoses but proceed directly to sperm development. The transformation of choanocytes into spermatogonia involves loss of the collar, extrusion of cytoplasm and phagosomes at the base of the cell, and the migration of the cell into the lumen of the chamber. The cysts thus formed become limited by a highly flattened, unicellular epithelium derived from mesohyl cells. Tuzet *et al.* (1970a,b) conclude that spermatogenesis in *Aplysilla* involves two successive divisions based upon an observed reduction in nuclear size and the finding of synaptonemal complexes. Decrease in cell and nuclear size also led Tuzet and Pavans de Ceccatty (1958) to the same conclusion in *Hippospongia,* and Diaz and Connes (1980) report this also in *Suberites* (see below). However, it must be emphasized that no study to date has established a halving of chromosome number or has reported or pictured tetrad formation. In many light microscopic studies, two distinct size classes of dividing cells within cysts have been routinely reported and/or pictured and are obvious (Simpson, 1968a; Simpson and Gilbert, 1973; Gilbert and Hadzisce, 1977; Tuzet and Pavans de Ceccatty, 1958; and others); but, since spermatogonia have also been reported to divide mitotically (Diaz and Connes, 1980) prior to the supposed reduction divisions, the two size classes may indeed not be part of a meiotic division but rather two mitotic divisions leading to smaller cell and nuclear sizes. In point of fact, the so-called second meiotic division is very poorly documented even on an ultrastructural level. Tuzet *et al.* (1970a,b) and Diaz and Connes (1980) had extreme difficulty in observing it at all. Until an unequivocal determination of chromosome number is made, it is possibly best to keep an open mind regarding this question.

The second detailed ultrastructural study of spermatogenesis deals with the hadromerid, *Suberites massa,* in which the following developmental sequence has been reported (Diaz and Connes, 1980; see also Diaz, 1979a). Individual choanocytes within chambers undergo growth, become nucle-

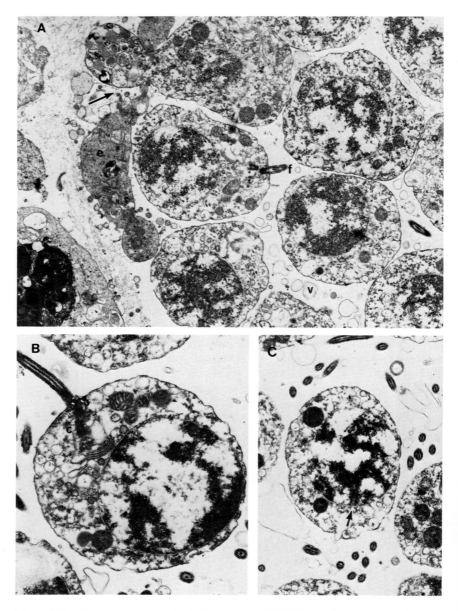

Figure 7-2 Spermatogenesis in *Aplysilla rosea* (TEMs). **A**. Choanocyte chamber being converted to a spermatogenic cyst. Flagella (*f*) are retained. Empty intercellular vesicles (*v*) are probably remnants of the collars. *e,* developing epithelial cell surrounding the cyst; *arrow,* cell migration possibly into the cyst (×8,100) (Tuzet *et al.,* 1970a). **B**. Spermatocyte I with flagellum. *c,* centriole (×12,150) (Tuzet *et al.,* 1970a). **C**. Prophase I showing axial structure in the chromatin (*arrow*) (×8,370) (Tuzet *et al.,* 1970a). (All, courtesy Prof. M. Pavans de Ceccatty.)

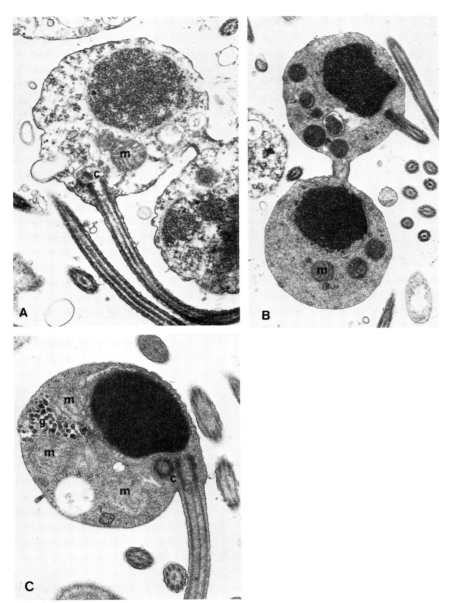

Figure 7-3 Later stages of spermatogenesis in *Aplysilla rosea* (TEMs). **A**. Telophase I with cells still attached. Note retention of flagellum and centrioles. The mitochondria (*m*) have an enlarged size. *c*, centriole (×15,300) (Tuzet *et al.*, 1970a). **B**. Telophase II with cells still attached and flagellated. *m*, mitochondrion (×12,600) (Tuzet *et al.*, 1970a). **C**. Sperm cell with two, perpendicular centrioles (*c*). *m*, mitochondria; *g*, glycogen (×23,760) (Tuzet *et al.*, 1970a). (All, courtesy Prof. M. Pavans de Ceccatty.)

olate, lose their collars and flagella, and move into the mesohyl where, with some limited mitoses, they form cysts (Figs. 7-4, 7-5). Archeocytes form a limiting epithelium around the cysts, which are somewhat larger than the original choanocyte chambers and fewer in number. The limiting epithelial cells may ingest so-called "defective" spermatogonia. An incidental observation of such phagocytic activity by the epithelial cells has also been noted by Garrone (1978, p. 31) in *Aplysilla*. Small numbers of choanocytes, still within chambers, also appear to enter spermatogenesis *in situ* as in *Aplysilla*, but additional details of these are not presented. The spermatogonia develop into spermatocytes I, in which the chromatin is closely applied to the inner surface of the nuclear membrane; in the cytoplasm there are moderate amounts of glycogen, and dense, Golgi-derived vesicles; in larger vesicles lipid is possibly present. Synaptonemal complexes have been observed in these cells when they are dividing. Spermatocytes II were neither clearly identified nor observed and it is *assumed* that the second division is very rapid. The resulting spermatids

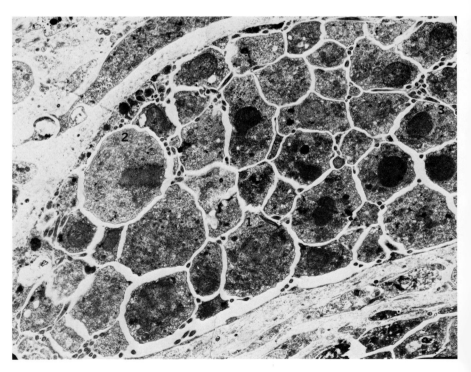

Figure 7-4 Spermatogenic cyst in *Suberites massa* in which the cells are not synchronized, but there appears to be a gradient (from left to right) of differentiation. *1*, spermatocyte I in prophase; *2*, spermatocyte I in metaphase; *3*, spermatocyte II (TEM) (×3,905) (Diaz, 1979a). (Courtesy Dr. J-P. Diaz.)

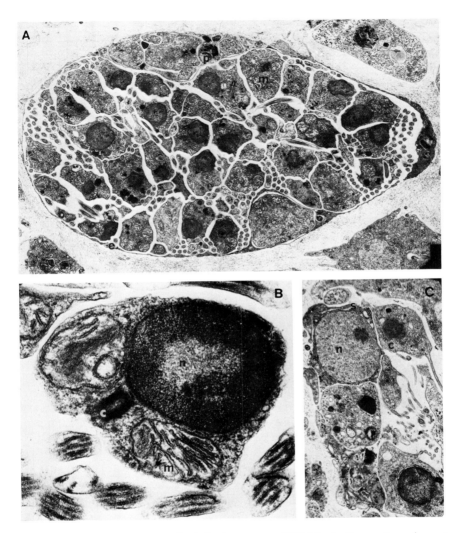

Figure 7-5 Spermatogenesis in *Suberites massa* (TEMs). **A**. Spermatogenic cyst limited by an epithelium (*e*). Some apparently deficient cells are phagocytized (*p*) by epithelial cells. Many cells possess large mitochondria (*m*) suggesting that they are spermatids (×3,665) (Diaz and Connes, 1980). **B**. Mature sperm cell showing two of the three large mitochondria (*m*) and one of the two, parallel centrioles (*c*). *n*, nucleus (×25,920) (Diaz and Connes, 1980). **C**. A choanocyte that is evolving into a spermatogonia (*s*) with a large nucleolate nucleus (*n*). Other normal choanocytes (*c*) are present in the chamber (×6,635) (Diaz and Connes, 1980). (All, courtesy Dr. J-P. Diaz.)

possess a nucleus in which the chromatin is all peripheral leaving a less dense core. Glycogen occurs just below the plasmalemma except in the small cleft between the nucleus and cell membrane where small, dense vesicles are present; these are apparently the same as those elaborated earlier by the Golgi. Supposed mitochondrial fusion occurs leading to the formation of exceptionally large organelles (~ 1.0 μm). Autophagic vacuoles are presumably responsible for reducing the cytoplasmic volume. A pair of parallel centrioles occurs at the pole opposite the nucleus and a flagellum arises from one of them (Fig. 7-5). In the mature sperm cell there are three mitochondria, suggesting a bilateral arrangement. There is no true intermediate (middle) piece; the nucleus is small (~ 1.5 μm) and the sperm head is rounded with largest dimensions of about 2.0 μm. Mature sperm thus possess primitive structure except for bilaterality.

Sperm cysts and spermatids of the sphinctozoid *Neocoelia* have also recently been observed ultrastructurally; the latter contain large mitochondria and the cysts are said to be derived from choanocytes that initially develop larger (3.0–4.0 μm), nucleolate nuclei. Each cyst, which is limited by a flattened epithelium, apparently forms from the merger of several chambers; cells within each cyst are synchronized (Vacelet, 1979a). In *Sycon ciliatum*, Sara and Rellini-Orsi (1975) have reported the possible transformation of choanocytes into spermatogenic cysts, which are found at the distal end (nearest the oscule) of the choanocyte chambers. However, because of the limited number of observations of spermatogenesis in the Calcarea, it is best at present to accept choanocyte transformation as a likely possibility rather than as a generality (but, see Sara, 1974). Spermatogenesis among calcareous species is apparently a very rapid process and/or is highly localized leading to great difficulties in observing the process despite very frequent sampling and extensive microscopic examination (Sara and Rellini-Orsi, 1975; Johnson, 1979a).

According to Fell (1974a), spermatogenesis in the phylum occurs in three different patterns: (1) all cells in all of the cysts of an individual are synchronized, or (2) all cells in any one cyst are synchronized but different cysts are in different stages, or (3) no synchrony occurs within or between cysts. Reiswig (1976) has recently reported synchronized sperm release in a number of Caribbean demosponges in which it can be inferred that spermatogenesis of type 1 occurs; among the sponges recorded are members of *Aplysina* (*Verongia*), *Ianthella, Xestosponiga, Agelas,* and *Geodia.* Although the concept of synchrony (versus asynchrony) is of much interest relative to the stimulation of specific cell differentiation (formation of spermatogonia), it should be realized that no completely thorough studies have been conducted. The best indication of synchrony is the simultaneous release of sperm by whole populations (Reiswig, 1976) in which it is clear that at the time of release all cells are mature; but, even in this case their development need not have been synchronous if storage of mature sperm occurs. There are no definitive data dealing with the question of storage of mature sperm in sponges. Okada (1928) has observed the presence of spermatogenic cysts in the hexactinellid, *Farrea sollasii*. Among the sclerosponges only a single observation of type 3 spermatogenesis has been reported (Reiswig, in press).

There is reasonably good evidence that spermatogenesis is temperature related, requiring increased ambient temperatures in many species. However, it is unclear whether an increase in temperature acts as a stimulus for cell differentiation and mitoses or whether higher temperature is required for spermatogenesis to proceed, or both. It is possible that increased temperature could lead to an increased mitotic rate in choanocytes thus disturbing the equilibrium between the number of choanocytes and the number of mesohyl cells (Connes *et al.,* 1974b). Such a perturbation in cell number may be causally related to the formation of polyblasts from choanocytes and thus to the onset of spermatogenesis. At least such a hypothetical view can lead to a meaningful structure for the design of experiments which otherwise are not obviously of importance.

Oogenesis

Diaz, Connes and Paris (1973, 1975) and Diaz (1979a) have reported that oogonia are derived from choanocytes in the demosponge *Suberites massa*. Korotkova and Aisenstadt (1976) make a similar claim in *Halisarca*. Other workers, however, have attributed their origin to archeocytes (Lévi, 1956; Simpson, 1968b; Leveaux, 1941). Among the Calcarea, a number of reports have appeared which indicate a choanocytic origin (see Sara, 1974; Gallissian, 1981), although in *Ascandra minchini* pinacocytes are considered as the stem cells (Borojevic, 1969). As is the case with spermatogonia, it is not possible at this writing to discern whether all species produce oogonia through choanocyte transformation or whether there are species differences with regard to this important differentiative event.

The evidence for a choanocyte origin of oogonia in demosponges, while extremely suggestive, is not conclusive and raises a number of important problems. Not least among them is how one and the same stem cell, namely, the choanocyte, is able to give rise to both spermatogonia and oogonia, a process in hermaphroditic species which would have to take place in randomly adjoining regions of the same mesohyl. Second, the occurrence of larger, nucleolated choanocytes in and of itself is not proof of a transformation into oogonia since these cells could also be archeocytes developing into choanocytes (see Borojevic, 1966). Further, the close physical association of an archeocyte-type cell with a choanocyte chamber is likewise not proof of the migration into the mesohyl of a choanocyte-derived oogonium. However, and similarly, there is also no direct proof of the development of oogonia from archeocytes, although there is no question that cells with archeocyte features are the initial oogonia. Thus, the question becomes: What is the ultimate origin of the archeocyte-type cells that are oogonia? Only experimental approaches, using selective cell labeling, will finally answer this question.

A very detailed light and electron microscopic study of oogenesis has been recently conducted by Diaz (1979a) and Diaz *et al.* (1975) and can serve as an example of the process. In *Suberites massa,* cells considered to be choanocytes develop large, nucleolate nuclei and increase cell size while retaining their collars and flagella. These presumptive oogonia then lose both of the latter structures as well as their phagosomes and migrate into the adjoining mesohyl where they undergo growth into oocytes. Typically, these cells have a reduced cytoplasmic volume and thus are identical to polyblasts (=hyalin archeocytes) (Chap. 3, 9). As growth occurs, they accumulate glycogen, increase their number of mitochondria which form clusters, acquire a few phagosome-like inclusions, and greatly increase the number of dictyosomes. Dense material is frequently seen being extruded from the nucleus. The mature oocyte is some 50 μm in diameter and contains a nucleus ($\sim$17 μm) with a prominent, single nucleolus ($\sim$5.0 μm), which has an outer dense region and a less dense core. Exceedingly well-developed dictyosomes, each with an average of 12 stacked lamellae occur just outside the nucleus; around them is a zone that contains few organelles. Peripheral to this begins an outer zone containing, proximally, clusters of mitochondria and, distally, numerous yolk inclusions and glycogen; rough endoplasmic reticulum and ribosomes are abundant. Archeocytes then form a limiting (=follicle) epithelium around the oocyte. The process whereby nutrients are supplied to the oocyte is varied and includes initially phagocytosis of gray cells and fragments of other unknown mesohyl cells. According to Diaz (1979a) phagocytosis plays only a minor role in the nutrition of the oocyte of *Suberites.* More importantly, short, thin pseudopods or microvilli, in which the cytoplasm generally lacks organelles, make intimate contact with choanocytes, gray cells, other oocytes with arrested development, follicle cells, and, most importantly, archeocytes. In some cases, cytoplasmic bridges are present which are presumed to act as points of transfer for complex, nutrient molecules. These nutrient pathways lead to the accumulation of glycogen, small vesicles containing pepsin-sensitive material, and larger, internally heterogeneous yolk (vitelline) inclusions. Golgi-derived vesicles have been observed to fuse with developing yolk inclusions further supporting the view that the contents of the latter are assembled *de novo* through the synthetic activity of the oocyte itself. No meiotic divisions were described in *Suberites.*

Oocyte growth in some other species differs especially as concerns nutrition. In *Spongilla lacustris* there are, according to Leveaux (1941), two phases of growth, the first of which involves the uptake of soluble materials and the second of which, "le grand accroissement," involves the phagocytosis of nurse cells (variously identified as trophocytes and spherulous cells) (Gilbert, 1974; Simpson and Gilbert, 1973). Direct phagocytosis of other cells (Fig. 7-6) by oocytes has also been reported in *Clathrina coriacea* (Sara, 1955a; Johnson, 1979a), *Haliclona ecbasis* (Fell, 1969), *Leucosolenia botryoides* (Sara, 1955a), *Ascandra minchini* (Borojevic, 1969), *Halisarca dujardini* (Aisenstadt and Korotkova, 1976), and *Tetilla* (Watanabe, 1978a). On the other hand, as in *Suberites,* a purely nonphagocytic process appears to lie at the basis of nutrition in *Aplysina (Verongia) cavernicola* (Gallissian and Vacelet, 1976), *Chondrosia reniformis* (Lévi and Lévi, 1976), and *Reniera elegans* (Tuzet, 1947). In *Grantia compressa,* although nurse cells are in very intimate contact with the growing oocyte, ultrastructural observations establish that they are not phagocytized and this may be the case in other calcareous species in which, however, "phagocytosis" has been reported on a light microscope level (Gallissian, 1981). In this calcareous species, and apparently in others, there are two growth phases of the oocytes: (1) the petit accroissement during which oocytes gain nutrients from choanocytes (without collars and flagella) through pseudopod interdigitation and (2) the grand accroissement which occurs deeper in the mesohyl and where a complex of cells becomes associated with the oocyte including follicle cells, a special nurse cell, and an "additional cell" occurring within a depression of the oocyte plasmalemma. Discrete yolk inclusions only appear during the grand accroissement. In both *Chondrilla* and *Chondrosia,* a layer of nurse cells surrounds developing eggs; these nurse cells (of unknown type but possibly archeocytes) extend long, thin filopodia to the egg surface suggesting direct, nonphagocytic transfer of nutrients (Fig. 7-7) (Liaci *et al.,* 1971a). However, regardless of these nutritional differences, all egg cells come to contain large numbers of membrane-bound yolk inclusions with heterogeneous contents. Also, in literally all cases examined in some detail, developing eggs in the mesohyl eventually become surrounded by a flattened epithelium (follicle) and thus the problem of how other nurse cells are able to migrate within the cavity for ingestion by, or transfer of soluble nutrients to, oocytes presents itself. The timing of formation of the follicle epithelium is poorly studied and thus appears variable among different species. In at least three cases in which uncleaved eggs are shed [*Aplysina (Verongia) cavernicola, Tetilla japonica,* and *Polymastia robusta*], there is no surrounding follicular epithelium although in *Tetilla* and *Aplysina (Verongia)* nurse cells are associated with maturing oocytes in the mesohyl (Watanabe, 1978a; Gallissian and Vacelet, 1976).

Supposed meiotic divisions in oocytes are, in general, poorly documented but have been reported, primarily in calcareous species: *Sycon raphanus, Grantia compressa, Petrobiona massiliana, Leucosolenia botryoides, Clathrina coriacea* (Dendy, 1915; Tuzet, 1964; Vacelet, 1964). However, in *C. coriacea,* Sara (1955b) did not report them nor did Borojevic (1969) in *Ascandra minichini.* In *Sycon ciliatum,* Sara and Rellini-Orsi (1975) have reported only a single division, which is also the case in a

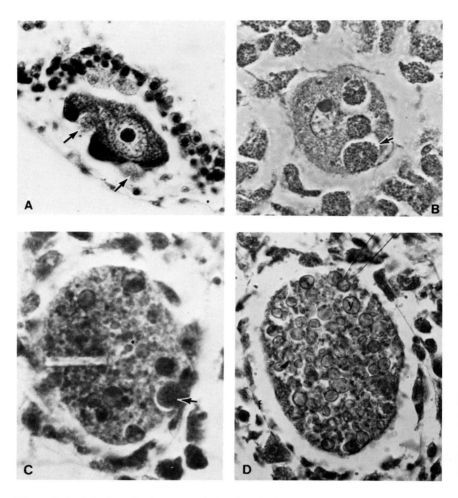

Figure 7-6 Whole cell phagocytosis by developing oocytes (light micrographs). **A**. Phagocytosis (*arrows*) of nurse cells in *Clathrina blanca* (×1,125) (Johnson, 1979a). **B**. Phagocytosis (*arrow*) of archeocytes in *Haliclona ecbasis* (×720) (Fell, 1969). **C**. Phagocytosis (*arrow*) of archeocytes in *Spongilla lacustris* (×630) (Simpson and Gilbert, 1973). **D**. Mature egg cell in *Spongilla lacustris* showing the large yolk inclusions (*y*) and follicular epithelium (*f*) (×450) (Gilbert, 1974). (**A**, courtesy Dr. M. Fischel Johnson; **B**, courtesy Dr. P. E. Fell; **D**, courtesy Prof. J. J. Gilbert.)

few demosponges: *Reniera elegans* (Tuzet, 1947), *Halisarca dujardini* (Lévi, 1956), *Hippospongia communis* (Tuzet and Pavans de Ceccatty, 1958), and *Octavella galangaui* (Tuzet and Paris, 1964). Two possible divisions are reported in *Halisarca nahatensis* (Chen, 1976) and *Baikalospongia bacillifera* (Gureeva, 1972). In general, these divisions have been

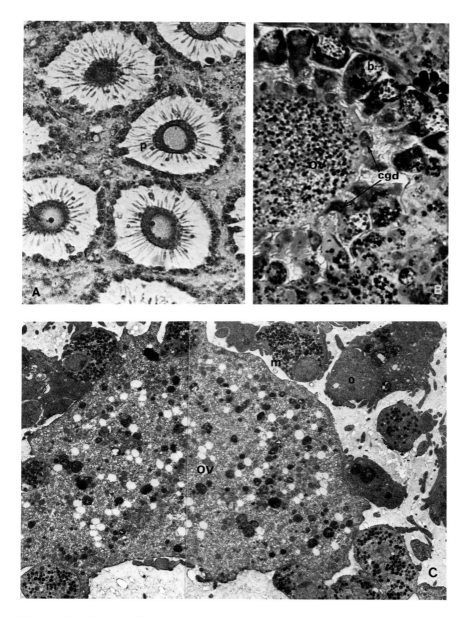

Figure 7-7 Nurse cells of developing oocytes in *Chondrosia reniformis*. **A.** Young oocytes with a halo of cell processes (*p*) extending to the oocytes. A layer of large, follicular cells (*f*) surrounds them (light micrograph) (×225) (Liaci *et al.* 1971a). **B.** Semithin section of a later stage in oogenesis. The oocyte (*OV*) is surrounded by microgranular cells (*cgd*) and more distally by bacteriocytes (*b*) (light micrograph) (Lévi and Lévi, 1976). **C.** Transmission electron micrograph of an oocyte as in B. The surrounding microgranular cells (*m*) are numerous but other cells (*o*) are also present. The oocyte (*OV*) contains many developing yolk inclusions (×3,600) (Lévi and Lévi, 1976). (**A**, courtesy Prof. L. Scalera-Liaci; **B**, **C**, courtesy Prof. C. Lévi.)

reported to take place at the end of the growth of the oocyte and supposedly prior to fertilization. The data on so-called oocyte reduction divisions require much reevaluation and extention on the ultrastructural level.

Of some interest are reports of the extrusion of nuclear material to the oocyte cytoplasm in species other than *Suberites massa* [in *Aplysina* (*Verongia*) *cavernicola,* Gallissian and Vacelet, 1976; in *Stelleta grubii,* Liaci and Sciscioli, 1967; in *Petrobiona massiliana,* Vacelet, 1964; in *Grantia compressa,* Gallissian, 1980; in *Reniera elegans,* Tuzet, 1947]. This process and the resulting presence of the extruded material just outside the nucleus may serve as useful markers for developing oocytes as may also the general increase in mitochondrial number and their clustering. As in *Suberites,* in *Tetilla* (Watanabe, 1978a), *Grantia* (Gallissian, 1981), and *Aplysina* (*Verongia*) (Gallissian and Vacelet, 1976) the Golgi bodies are extremely well developed.

In *Aplysina* (*Verongia*), pseudopods of the egg cell secrete a surrounding collagen matrix also enclosing spherulous cells (Fig. 7-8); the egg itself further ingests and retains bacteria within cytoplasmic vacuoles (Gallissian and Vacelet, 1976). Diaz (1979a) has also recorded limited collagen fibrilogenesis by developing oocytes within the mesohyl of *Suberites.* In *Tetilla,* the mature, released egg is surrounded by a prominent layer of fibrous material which in *T. serica* displays 17 nm fibril banding (Endo *et al.,* 1967). Similar fibers surround the egg of *T. japonica* (Watanabe, 1978a). In *Chondrosia reniformis,* on the other hand, symbiont-containing somatic cells and microgranular cells become incorporated within the follicle surrounding the egg and there are no fibrils associated with them (Lévi and Lévi, 1976).

Developing oocytes may have a very specific localization in the mesohyl. For example, in *Sycon ciliatum* and *Grantia compressa,* the choanocyte-derived oogonium becomes closely associated with a choanocyte forming a so-called "oocyte-nurse cell satellite complex" (Sara and Rellini-Orsi, 1975; Gallissian, 1981). The egg then is reported to ingest the choanocyte (but see Gallissian, 1981) and migrates into the mesohyl. Such precise localizations may be of future developmental significance as in *Sycon raphanus* where the mature oocyte comes to lie beneath an area of the choanoderm in such a manner that the proximal half (closest to the coanocytes) of the egg is predetermined to form the flagellated epithelium of the larva and the distal half, the nonflagellated cells (Tuzet, 1973a). The former has been referred to as the animal or anterior pole and the latter, the vegetal or posterior pole (Tuzet, 1963; Lévi, 1963a). It is not known whether the choanocytes act as an inducer for this predetermination, which is not known to occur in the phylum outside of the calcaronean calcareous sponges. Some clustering of oocytes in the mesohyl has also been recorded, but not frequently (in *Hymeniacidon caruncula,* Diaz, 1973; *Halichondria* sp., Fell and Jacob, 1979; *Halisarca dujardini*

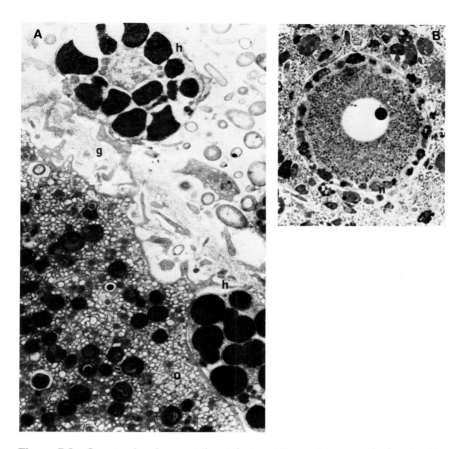

Figure 7-8 Oocyte development in *Aplysina (Verongia) cavernicola*. **A.** The peripheral zone of an oocyte is pictured in which numerous yolk inclusions are developing. The oocyte secretes a collagenous matrix (*g*) around itself in which are spherulous cells (*h*). Later development involves the uptake by the oocyte of bacteria (not shown) (TEM) (×4,320) (Gallissian and Vacelet, 1976). **B.** Semithin section of a developing oocyte. A layer of nurse cells (*n*) (spherulous cells) surrounds the oocyte, but their role in oocyte nutrition does not involve their phagocytosis (light micrograph) (×605) (Gallissian and Vacelet, 1976). (Both, courtesy Dr. J. Vacelet.)

and *Oscarella lobularis,* Lévi, 1956). There is no apparent correlation between the size of mature egg cells and the ovipository behavior (incubation versus release). In some cases, eggs are considerably smaller than the resulting embryos which they form (Simpson, 1968b; Liaci *et al.,* 1973; Tuzet and Pavans de Ceccatty, 1958), and thus some mechanism for an increase in biomass is necessary; such a mechanism is unknown, although in one case there are indications that somatic cells may directly become incorporated into the developing embryo (Simpson, 1968b).

Diaz (1979b) has described the degeneration of oocytes in *Suberites massa* in which the nucleus and cytoplasmic organelles undergo disintegration and the cytoplasm often becomes vacuolated. The degenerated oocytes are released from the sponge. The significance of such degeneration is not clear and has rarely been reported to occur naturally in other species. In *Sycon raphanus*, Colussi (1958) also reports the degeneration of some oocytes, particularly those that migrate deeper within the mesohyl. Such migration may result in the absence of fertilization and thus degeneration. On the other hand, in *Spongilla lacustris*, the development of eggs during periods when no sperm cells are available leads to their degeneration (Fig. 7-9) with the release of their contents, particularly the yolk, into the mesohyl (Gilbert, 1974).

Nurse Cells

The precise mechanism for the transfer of nutrients to developing oocytes is not known and therefore it is not presently possible to indicate the roles played by mesohyl cells, choanocytes, and the surrounding follicular epithelium. Consequently, all somatic cells associated either transitorily or long term with the growing oocyte are referred to here as "nurse cells".

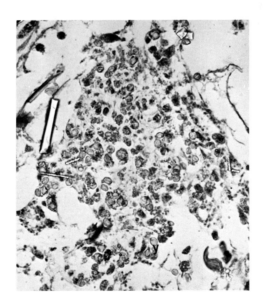

Figure 7-9   A degenerating egg cell in *Spongilla lacustris*. The yolk (*y*) is being dispersed in the mesohyl. Such degenerating cells occur in animals not able to secure sperm cells (light micrograph) (×210) (Gilbert, 1974). (Courtesy Prof. J. J. Gilbert.)

This broad category includes a variety of known, specific cell types (Table 7-2) and thus cannot be defined structurally. Further, follicular epithelial cells which appear derived from archeocytes can also generally be considered as nurse cells. Although their role in nutrition is ill-defined, their

Table 7-2   Nurse Cells[a]

Cell Type Acting as Nurse Cell	Species	References
Archeocyte	*Ascandra minchini*	Borojevic (1969)
	Halisarca nahantensis	Chen (1976)
	Suberites massa	Diaz (1979a)
	Hymeniacidon heliophila	Fincher (1940)
	Hymeniacidon caruncula	Diaz (1973)
	Haliclona ecbasis	Fell (1969)
	Spongilla lacustris	Gilbert (1974)
	Petrosia ficiformis	Liaci *et al.* (1973)
Spherulous cells	*Spongilla lacustris*	Leveaux (1941)
	Aplysina (*Verongia*) *cavernicola*	Gallissian and Vacelet (1976)
Microgranular cells	*Chondrosia reniformis*	Lévi and Lévi (1976)
Gray cells	*Suberites massa*	Diaz (1979a)
Eosinophilic amebocytes	*Clathrina coriacea*	Johnson (1979a)
	Clathrina blanca	Johnson (1979a)
Oocyte-like cells	*Leucosolenia botryoides*	Sara (1955b)
	Suberites massa	Diaz (1979a)
Follicular epithelium	*Haliclona ecbasis*	Fell (1969)
	Hippospongia communis	Tuzet and Pavans de Ceccatty (1958)
	Hymeniacidon heliophila	Fincher (1940)
	Octavella galangaui	Tuzet and Paris (1964)
	Spongilla lacustris	Leveaux (1941)
	Suberites massa	Diaz (1979a)
Choanocyte	*Tetilla*	Watanabe (1978a)
	Suberites massa	Diaz (1979a)
	Halisarca dujardini	Korotkova and Apalkova (1975)
	Ascandra minchini	Borojevic (1969)
	Petrobiona	Vacelet (1964)
	Sycon	Sara and Rellini-Orsi (1975)
	Clathrina coriacea	Sara (1955b)
	Grantia compressa[b]	Gallissian (1981)

[a]The term *nurse cell* as used here includes all cells associated with developing eggs; see text for further discussion.

[b]Follicle, nurse and other cells are associated with the oocyte in later growth.

specific localization and pinacocyte-like structure render them easily identifiable. Some confusion in the use of the term "nurse cell" arises from the fact that in some cases somatic, parental cells become associated with and/or incorporated into developing embryos (see later section). It is not clear whether these cells have as their primary function nutrition and thus the use of the term nurse cell to refer to them is problematical. In order to temporarily simplify this important problem in terminology, the term nurse cell is used here to refer to any somatic cell type physically associated with developing oocytes and egg cells, and the term somatic cells or parental cells is used to refer to cells so associated with developing embryos, bearing in mind that in some instances somatic parental cells in, or associated with embryos, may play a nutritional role during embryogenesis. Sara (1974) has suggested that growing oocytes may induce their surrounding nurse cells to develop characteristics like those in archeocytes, especially among calcareous species where it appears that nurse cells are derived from choanocytes.

The pathway of development of yolk and other stored nutrients in eggs is poorly documented. Two possibilities exist: (1) *de novo* synthesis and (2) conversion of preformed materials supplied by nurse cells (see Oogenesis). Stored nutrients occur in the form of membrane-bound lipid, membrane-bound, structurally complex yolk granules, and cytoplasmic glycogen (see, for example, Gallissian and Vacelet, 1976; Diaz *et al.*, 1975; Diaz, 1979a; Lévi and Lévi, 1976; Watanabe, 1978a; Aisenstadt and Korotkova, 1976). Although *Grantia compressa* oocytes appear to lack glycogen they possess small, cytoplasmic, dense masses which uniquely are not membrane-bound (Gallissian, 1981). Glycogen and lipid are also usually found within the yolk inclusions which rarely occur in the area surrounding the nucleus. In at least one case, *Aplysina* (*Verongia*) *cavernicola,* there is reasonably good evidence that yolk is synthesized *de novo,* but based upon the diversity of types of nurse cells in other species this may not universally be the case. The Golgi bodies may play an important role in such *de novo* synthesis (Diaz *et al.*, 1975).

Factors Influencing Gametogenesis

Temperature

Although there has only been a single demonstration of the direct effect of temperature on gametogenesis (Elvin, 1976) field data are highly suggestive of such a role (Table 7-3), and additional laboratory experiments in which the temperature was manipulated further support the view that gametogenesis is correlated with increasing temperature (Fry, 1971; Simpson, 1968b). Studies of gametogenesis in numerous species in the Adriatic and Ionian Seas establish that this occurs during the warmer months, spring to autumn [see Liaci and Sciscioli (1975a) for a review of their data]. However, observations of *Spongilla officinalis, Ircinia fasiculata*, and *I. variabilis* (Liaci *et al.*, 1971b) establish that gametogenesis can occur for 8 to 10 months of the year, thus making it difficult to correlate temperature with gamete development. Further, in *Ochridaspongia rotunda*, gametogenesis occurs all year, although under relatively constant temperature conditions (Gilbert and Hadzisce, 1977) and in *Sycon ciliatum* oogenesis occurs throughout the year despite fluctuation in temperature (Sara and Rellini-Orsi, 1975). In *Halisarca dujardini* both in the United States and France, oogenesis begins while water temperature is decreasing (Lévi, 1956; Chen, 1976); oocytes in *Ephydatia fluviatilis* may also appear during the cooler autumn months (Van de Vyver and Willenz, 1975). Decreasing water temperature also precedes gametogenesis in *Desmacidon fructicosum* (Lévi, 1956) and in *Tethya crypta* and *Aplysina* (*Verongia*) *gigantea* (Reiswig, 1973).

Although the latter observations greatly complicate any overall conclusion relative to the control of gametogenesis by temperature, the majority of studies do suggest such control. Apparently some species have become adapted to (or respond to) other temperature regimes (*Tethya*) or have become independent of temperature (*Ochridaspongia*). Further, it has now become clear that even in those species in which a positive correlation exists, gametogenesis can also take place under a completely different set of temperature conditions. In newly metamorphosed larvae of *Spongilla lacustris* (Simpson and Gilbert, 1973) and *Halichondria* sp. (Fell and Jacob, 1979), gametes develop after the normal gametogenic period of the parental population under different temperature conditions. Further, young sponges, issuing from gemmules that were hatched *in habitat* following the normal period of gamete development undergo gametogenesis (only oogenesis was studied) (Gilbert *et al.*, 1975; Gilbert, 1974). In some studies of larval settling, two discrete periods of larval production have been discovered (Ayling, 1980; Wells *et al.*, 1964), suggesting that young, newly metamorphosed larvae enter gametogenesis and give rise to a third generation of animals as clearly documented in one case (Fell and Jacob, 1979; Fell *et al.*, 1979). These data strongly indicate an endogenous (environment-independent) control of gametogenesis. If such is indeed the case, temperature may actually be more critical for supporting gametogenesis rather than initiating it. These two possibly separate roles of temperature—as a trigger for gametogenesis and as a factor supporting the ensuing development of gametes—will have to be carefully examined under controlled conditions before a thorough understanding is possible. The complexities of such investigations are indicated by a study of gametogenesis in *Haliclona permolis* (Elvin, 1976) in which it was found that although water temperature is relatively constant throughout the year the tissue temperature of the animals varies due to exposure to the air at low tides. Such exposure also increases light penetration and it is thus exceedingly difficult to separate these factors. In that

Table 7-3 Reports of Temperature Increase Prior to Gametogenesis

I. Field Data

Class, Order, and Species	Habitat and Locality	Spermatogenesis Occurs Later Than Oogenesis[a]	References
Demospongiae			
Haplosclerida			
Haliclona loosanoffi	Estuarine and marine, Atlantic and L.I. Sound, USA	?	Fell (1976b) Wells *et al.* (1964) Hartman (1958a)
Haliclona palmata	Marine, Atlantic, USA	—[b]	Wells *et al.* (1964)
Spongilla lacustris	Freshwater pond, New England, USA	Yes	Simpson and Gilbert (1973)
Trochospongilla pennsylvanica	Freshwater pond, New England, USA	Yes	Simpson and Gilbert (1973)
Poecilosclerida			
Lissodendoryx isodictyalis	Marine, Atlantic, USA	—[b]	Wells *et al.* (1964)
Microciona prolifera	Marine, L.I. Sound, USA	Yes	Simpson (1968a)
Mycale cecilia	Marine, Atlantic, USA	—[b]	Wells *et al.* (1964)
Ophlitaspongia seriata	Marine, England	—[b]	Fry (1971)
Halichondrida			
Halichondria sp.	Marine, L.I. Sound, USA	Yes	Fell and Jacob (1979)
Halichondria bowerbankii	Marine, L.I. Sound, and Atlantic, USA	—[b]	Wells *et al.* (1964) Hartman (1958a)
Hymeniacidon caruncula	Marine, Mediterranean	Yes	Diaz (1973)
Hymeniacidon perleve	Marine, England	—[b]	Stone (1970a)

			References
Hadromerida			
Cliona celata	Marine, L.I. Sound, USA	—[b]	Hartman (1958a)
Cliona lobata	Marine, Atlantic, USA	—[b]	Wells *et al.* (1964)
Prosuberites microsclerus	Marine, Atlantic, USA	—[b]	Wells *et al.* (1964)
Suberites carnosus	Marine, Ionian Sea	Yes	Liaci and Sciscioli (1979)
Suberites massa	Marine, Mediterranean	Yes	Diaz (1973, 1979a)
Dictyoceratida			
Hippospongia lachne	Marine, Caribbean	—[b]	Storr (1964)
Calcarea			
Clathrinida			
Clathrina blanca	Marine, Pacific	—[b]	Johnson (1978b)
Clathrina coriacea	Marine, Pacific	—[b]	Johnson (1978b)

II. Experimental Data on Demosponges

Species	Temperature (°C)	Results	References
Haliclona permolis	4.0	No Gametogenesis	Elvin (1976)
	7.0	Gametogenesis; eggs develop first	
	9.5	Gametogenesis	
	13.0	Gametogenesis; higher spermatogenic activity	
Ophlitaspongia seriata	Increased from 15 to 18	Larvae released 4–5 weeks later	Fry (1971)
Microciona prolifera	10.0	No larval development	Simpson (1968b)
	15.0	Few larvae develop	
	20.0, 25.0	Numerous larvae develop and are released	

[a]See text for additional discussion.
[b]Not recorded.

study, increased tissue temperature can be correlated with the onset of gametogenesis.

There are now considerable data indicating that oogenesis precedes spermatogenesis even in dioecious animals, thus further suggesting a dependency of the latter upon higher temperatures, a result experimentally obtained by Elvin (1976) (Table 7-3).

Size of Animals

Recent studies of newly metamorphosed larvae (Fell and Jacob, 1979; Fell et al., 1979; Simpson and Gilbert, 1974) and of newly hatched gemmules (Gilbert et al., 1975; Gilbert, 1974) establish that even the smallest animals are capable of gametogenesis, although in some cases (Haliclona loosanoffi, Spongilla lacustris) larvae may not develop. Despite these observations, smaller animals of some species apparently do not initiate gamete development. For example, in Raspailia topsenti sponges having branches less than about 1.0 cm in diameter do not develop eggs, whereas above this thickness all sponges do (Ayling, 1980). In Halichondria sp. larger, postlarval sponges are more likely to contain gametes than smaller ones and the former possess a higher density of gametes (Table 7-4) (Lewandrowski and Fell, 1981). In Hippospongia lachne, Mycale sp., and Tetilla serica smaller sponges either do not initiate gamete development or produce few of them (Storr, 1964; Reiswig, 1973; Watanabe, 1978a). Alternatively, in Ochridaspongia rotunda and Clathrina, all sizes of animals are reproductively active (Gilbert and Hadzisce, 1977; Johnson,

Table 7-4 Relationship of Size to Oogenesis in Halichondria sp.[a]

Size of Sponge (mm)	Number Examined	Percentage of Sponges Containing Large Oocytes or Eggs
<3	680	0.6
3.5–10.0	799	17.5
10.5–50.0	832	58.2
50	103	97.1

	Number of oocytes or eggs/cm^2 in 10 μm sections[b]	
	July	August
<10	35.9	50.3
10.5–30.0	188.9	190.5
>30	235.9	402.4

[a]Data taken from Lewandrowski and Fell (1981).
[b]Means.

1978b). Excluding small postlarval animals, all sizes of *Haliclona loosanoffi* also initiate gametes (Fell, 1976b). In *Ophlitaspongia seriata,* Fry (1971) found that the level of gametogenesis (as indicated by larval release) can be highly variable and is not size dependent; in *Suberites massa,* Diaz (1979a) has reported a similar situation.

Age and Other Factors

No thorough investigations of age dependency of gametogenesis have appeared. In the only available study dealing with nutrition, Elvin (1976) has, surprisingly, found no correlation between ambient nutrient levels and gametogenesis, suggesting that a minimally essential diet is all that is required. In that study also, light was found to possibly influence oogenesis but could not be separated from temperature effects. In *Suberites massa,* changes in salinity are without apparent effect (Diaz, 1973, 1979a), but in *Haliclona permolis* freshwater runoff may temporarily inhibit oogenesis (Elvin, 1976).

Two extremely interesting cases of induced oogenesis have been reported; in one of them mechanical trauma to the tissue (see Fig. 9-6) and in the other the presence of virus particles (see Fig. 3-1D) resulted in the development of cells resembling eggs (Diaz, 1977; Vacelet and Gallissian, 1978). It is of more than just passing interest that gametogenesis has been reported to occur immediately following mechanical trauma, larval metamorphosis, gemmule hatching, and the initiation of growth and development from overwintering tissue. The initiation of development and growth may possess an intrinsic signal leading to gametogenesis. Such a notion is inherent in the position taken by Connes *et al.* (1974b). Their view emphasizes the equilibrium between archeocytes and choanocytes as a major controlling factor for cell activities. The specific changes that occur in this equilibrium at the onset of development may thus lead directly to gametogenesis which, according to these researchers, is a function of the choanocytes.

Two biochemical analyses indicate that shifts in metabolism may be correlated with gametogenesis. In *Hymeniacidon perleve,* lipid content apparently increases prior to gametogenesis and decreases after larval release (Stone, 1970b). In *Haliclona permolis,* changes in lipid, protein, and RNA content vary with sex. In males, all three decline or are minimal prior to gametogenesis while in females they are all increasing (Elvin, 1979). In males, lipid, RNA, and protein then increase *during* spermatogenesis. These shifts may reflect an underlying endogenous component related to the control of gametogenesis as suggested by Reiswig (in press).

In *Ephydatia fluviatilis,* combined field and laboratory data suggest that sexual reproduction occurs only in those animals in which tissue disorganization rather than gemmule formation takes place during the winter months (Van de Vyver and Willenz, 1975). On the other hand, all individuals of *Spongilla lacustris* form gemmules in the late fall and overwinter as gemmules which, upon hatching in the spring, form animals all of which are sexually reproductive (Simpson and Gilbert, 1973; Gilbert, 1974). The significance of this difference is not known and substantially more data are required to elucidate its basis. In species in which the whole tissue is converted to gemmules (Chap. 8), newly developing tissue derived from their hatching initiates gametogenesis (Simpson and Gilbert, 1973; Gilbert, 1974; Fell, 1976a; Fell et al., 1979). Although newly metamorphosed larvae of these species initiate gametogenesis prior to forming gemmules (Simpson and Gilbert, 1974; Fell et al., 1979), it may still be that older, gemmule-producing sponges have a dependency upon gemmulation prior to their initiation of gametogenesis. Investigation of this proposition presents a number of technical difficulties.

Sex Determination

Recent investigations clearly establish that sex determination in sponges is highly labile and is therefore possibly physiologically rather than genetically determined. In otherwise gonochoristic species, a small number of hermaphroditic individuals have been reported (Fell, 1970; Diaz, 1973; Liaci and Sciscioli, 1967; Elvin, 1976). Further, abortive oocytes have been reported in male sponges of *Hymeniacidon sanguinea* (Sara, 1961), *Stelleta grubii* (Liaci and Sciscioli, 1967), *Haliclona loosanoffi* (Fell, 1976b), and *Haliclona permolis* (Elvin, 1976). In *Halichondria* sp., which may be a contemporaneous hermaphrodite, separate male and female individuals are sometimes present in the population as well as some in which only a few scattered oocytes are found (Lewandrowski and Fell, 1981) (Table 7-5). However, these data are not susceptible to any simple explanation, since in one year the later species was predominantly dioe-

Table 7-5 Occurrence of Separate Sexes and Hermaphrodites in *Halichondria* sp.[a]

| History of Sponges | Year | Total Examined | Number of | | | |
			Male	Female	Hermaphrodites	With Few Oocytes
Postlarval (recently metamorphosed larvae)	1977	68	1	6	61	0
Postdormant (having overwintered)	1969	117	0	6	59	52
	1970	55	25	26	4	—
	1975	15	0	1	14	—
	1979	40	1	1	23	15

[a]Data taken from Fell and Jacob (1979) and Lewandrowski and Fell (1981).

cious and in a later year it was mostly hermaphroditic (Fell and Jacob, 1979). *Spongilla lacustris* (Gilbert and Simpson, 1976a), *Suberites massa* (Diaz, 1973), and *Ephydatia fluviatilis* (Van de Vyver and Willenz, 1975) have been reported to be dioecious and a change in sex (either from male to female or female to male) has been observed (Table 7-6). This change occurred from one year to the next, such that in any given year an individual was either male or female and in the following year it was the other sex, with, however, only some individuals displaying sex reversal. In *Spongilla* it has been conjectured that such sex reversal could be highly adaptive if new ecological habitats were colonized by asexual means (Gilbert and Simpson, 1976a). In such a case, the introduction of one individual into a new habitat could result in the eventual establishment of a heterosexual population.

As reviewed by Fell (1974a) the distinction between sponges which are gonochoristic and those which display successive hermaphroditism during the same breeding season is difficult to establish. In *Suberites massa,* the digitate form is possibly protogynous, although the data are not completely convincing (Diaz, 1973). On the other hand, *Ochridaspongia rotunda* is clearly dioecious based upon exhaustive analyses (Gilbert and Hadzisce, 1977). The problem of distinguishing between gonochorism and successive hermaphroditism is severe and there is no apparent, simple means of analysis (Fell, 1976a). In *Tetilla serica,* which is gonochoristic, the growing together of individuals of different sexes does not result in an induction of either sex, possibly indicating an absence of any humoral influence on sex determination (Egami and Ishii, 1956). In *Ephydatia fluviatilis* a number of different strains have been identified on the basis of the absence of fusion between different individuals grown in close proximity (Van de Vyver, 1970) (Chap. 9). Although strains of different sex display nonfusion, two known strains, both of which are females, also display nonfusion establishing that the lack of compatibility of strains may not simply be sex related. Elvin (1976) has suggested that sex determination may be thermally controlled in *Haliclona permolis,* such that those individuals physiologically able to form gametes at low temperatures develop oocytes and others form spermatocytes later at higher temperatures. In dioecious species, oogenesis or some other factor would have to inhibit spermatogenesis in female (oocyte producing) individuals, and, in males, oogenesis would have to be suppressed.

A now almost routine observation during the reproductive season in some dioecious species is the finding of some individuals that do not form gametes (Diaz, 1979a; Elvin, 1976; Ayling, 1980; Gilbert and Hadzisce, 1977; Liaci et al., 1971c; Liaci and Sciscioli, 1969). However, some of these indifferent sponges may simply be out of phase with the rest of the population (Gilbert and Hadzisce, 1977). In some studies, particularly those dealing with calcareous species, spermatogenesis has not been observed despite thorough sampling (Vacelet, 1964; Johnson, 1979a; Ayling,

Table 7-6 Changes in Sexual Status of Two Demosponges[a]

Species	Sponge Number	1970	1971	1972	1973	1974	1975	Reference
Spongilla lacustris	1	—	—	—	—	E	E	Gilbert and Simpson (1976a)
	4	—	—	—	—	S	E	
	9	—	—	—	—	E	S	
	10	—	—	—	—	E	E	
	11	—	—	—	—	E	S	
Suberites massa	1	N	N	N	N	—	—	Diaz (1979a)
	2, 3	E	E	—	—	—	—	
	4	N	H	—	—	—	—	
	5	S	E	E	E	—	—	
	8	—	S	E	S	—	—	
	9	—	N	N	N	—	—	
	10	—	E	E	—	—	—	
	11, 15, 17	—	E	E	S	—	—	
	12, 13, 14	—	E	E	E	—	—	
	18, 19	—	N	N	E	—	—	
	22	—	—	N	E	—	—	
	24	—	—	N	S	—	—	
	25	—	—	S	N	—	—	
	26	—	—	E	E	—	—	
	27, 29	—	—	E	N	—	—	
	28	—	—	N	N	—	—	

[a]Symbols: E, eggs only formed; S, sperm only formed; H, both eggs and sperm form; N, neither eggs nor sperm formed; —, no record.

1980; see Johnson, 1979a, for a brief review of earlier literature). In a year-round sampling of *Sycon,* Sara and Rellini-Orsi (1975) were able to observe spermatogenesis only once in a single animal. These data have led to the view that sperm development in calcaronean, calcinean, and pharetronid species is an exceedingly rapid, isolated event. In distinction, sperm development has been easily observed in the sphinctozoid, *Neocoelia crypta* (Vacelet, 1979a).

There are no data suggesting a chromosomal basis for sex determination and if indeed there is such a basis, it is obviously susceptible to modulation. Sex ratios in many gonochoristic species are either highly variable or are far from 1 : 1, or both (Table 7-7), further implying that sex determination is primarily under physiological rather than genetic control (Elvin, 1976). On the other hand, Elvin (1979) has found that the protein and lipid content of females of *Haliclona permolis* is sufficiently characteristic, such that females of this species can be distinguished from males.

Gonochorism is the predominant form of sexuality among tetractinomorphs while both it and hermaphroditism occur in ceractinomorphs. Little definitive data are available for other classes (Table 7-1). Oviparity is clearly linked to a gonochoristic condition but the reverse is not the case. In distinction, viviparity occurs in both gonochoristic and hermaphroditic animals (Table 7-1). In this regard it should be noted that very few cases of true oviparity (=egg release) have been reported. Rather, many of these involve release of young embryos (Reiswig, 1976) or fertilized eggs (Borojevic, 1967; Lévi and Lévi, 1976).

Gamete Release

Observations and studies of gamete release are restricted to field data and laboratory observations of spontaneous release. In most of the reported cases of so-called egg release, it appears that the sexual product released is actually a zygote as in *Polymastia robusta* (Borojevic, 1967) and *Chondrosia reniformis* (Lévi and Lévi, 1976), or a young embryo (Reiswig, 1976). These observations thus suggest that the fertilization event itself may be involved as a triggering mechanism for the release event. *Tetilla serica* appears to be the only known sponge in which the release of unfertilized eggs has been documented (Watanabe, 1978a). Sudden release of large numbers of spermatozoa (Fig. 7-10) have been recorded in Caribbean demosponges (Reiswig, 1970, 1976) and release occurs in many instances only during July and August indicating a seasonal relationship; some correlation between time of day (sperm release) and lunar cycle (egg release) also exists as well as the suggestion that a diffusable, release-stimulating factor may be involved. There are no data dealing with the cellular events in gamete release, although sperm have sometimes been observed in excurrent canals (Simpson, 1968b). Field observations of

Table 7-7 Sex Ratios and Absence of Reproductive Activity[a]

Species	Total No.	Reproductively Active Sponges				Percentage Indifferent (Of all sponges)	References
		Percentage Males	Percentage Females	Percentage Hermaphrodites	Sex Ratio (female/male)		
Adocia varia	13	61.5	38.5	0	0.63	67.5	Liaci *et al.* (1973)
Axinella damicornis	91	14.3	85.7	0	5.99	60.7	Siribelli (1962)
Axinella verrucosa	154	11.0	89.0	0	9.1	54.6	Siribelli (1962)
Chondrilla nucula	72	16.7	83.3	0	4.98	86.9	Liaci *et al.* (1971a)
Chondrosia reniformis	113	14.2	85.8	0	6.04	80.1	Liaci *et al.* (1971a)
Erylus discophorus	150	34.7	65.3	0	1.88	30.5	Liaci and Sciscioli (1970)
Gellius fibulatus	14	21.4	78.6	0	3.67	66.7	Liaci *et al.* (1973)
Geodia cydonium	267	19.8	80.2	0	4.05	58.2	Liaci and Sciscioli (1969)
Halichondria sp.	228	11.8	17.5	62.7	1.48	0	Fell and Jacob (1979), Lewandroski and Fell (1981)

Species							Reference
Haliclona ecbasis	56	28.6	62.5	8.9	2.18	10.9	Fell (1970)
Haliclona elegans	69	39.1	60.9	0	1.56	37.8	Liaci *et al.* (1973)
Haliclona permolis	84	41.7	58.3	0.7[b]	1.39	10.6	Elvin (1976)
Ochridaspongia rotunda	274	31.4	68.6	0	2.18	9.6	Gilbert and Hadzisce (1977)
Petrosia ficiformis	519	1.7	98.3	0	57.8	65.6	Liaci *et al.* (1973)
Stelleta grubii	85	20.0	80.0	0	4.0	26.1	Liaci and Sciscioli (1967)
Suberites massa	48	16.7	81.2	2.1	4.86	27.3	Diaz (1979a)
Tethya aurantium	86	6.9	93.1	0	13.5	85.3	Liaci *et al.* (1971c)
Tethya citrina	41	14.6	85.4	0	5.85	90.0	Liaci *et al.* (1971c)

[a]Data (for all years available) compiled *only* for the breeding season of each species. The breeding season is here defined as that period during which some sponges possess gametes and/or embryos. See references for further details.

[b]Percentage hermaphrodites in 147 specimens.

Figure 7-10   Underwater photo of massive, natural sperm release in *Aplysina (Verongia) crassa* (×0.1) (Reiswig, 1976). (Courtesy Dr. H. M. Reiswig.)

gamete release strongly suggest that the excurrent canals act as passageways, but it is also possible that there is a remodeling of the mesohyl and canals prior to and during release. Synchronous release events (Reiswig, 1970) suggest a level of integration previously unknown in sponges. There appears to be no known agent that is able to artificially stimulate gamete release, although experiments of this kind are now conceivable with certain species in which the timing of natural gamete release is both known and restricted to a short period (Reiswig, 1976).

Fertilization

Precious little data are available on fertilization and there has been only a single ultrastructural investigation of the process due to the servere difficulties encountered in manipulating gametes and thus timing the process. There appears to be only a single instance in which it has been demonstrated that fertilization occurs after release of the egg cell; this is in a species of *Tetilla* in which Watanabe (1978a) has observed the event on a light microscope level. In other so-called oviparous species, *Polymastia robusta* (Borojevic, 1967), *Chondrosia reniformis* (Lévi and Lévi, 1976), and *Agelas* sp. (Reiswig, 1976), the female cells released appear to be zygotes and young embryos indicating that fetilization had occurred internally and prior to gamete release.

In *Tetilla* (Fig. 7-11), immediately following fertilization, the vitelline membrane expands forming a fertilization membrane and the bundles of fibers of unknown composition occurring between the egg and the membrane change their arrangement, swell, and loose their integrity. In viviparous and oviparous species with internal fertilization, the details of fertilization have been documented ultrastructurally only in *Grantia*

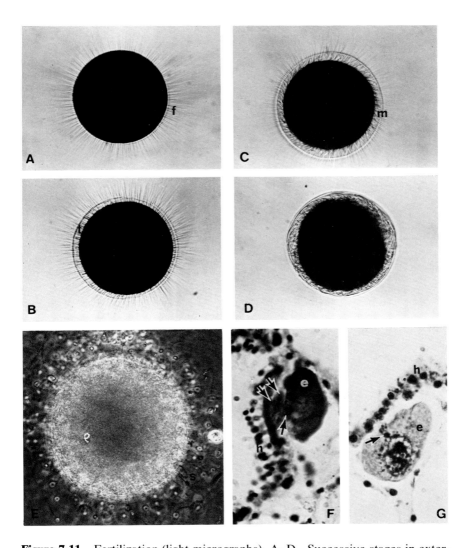

Figure 7-11 Fertilization (light micrographs). A–D., Successive stages in external fertilization in *Tetilla serica,* living cells (all ×180) (Watanabe, 1978a). **A.** Unfertilized egg with radiating fiber bundles at the surface (*f*). **B.** Ten seconds after fertilization. A fertilization membrane is forming. **C.** Thirty seconds after fertilization. The fiber bundles are being withdrawn into the perivitelline space. *m*, fertilization membrane. **D.** Four minutes after fertilization. All fiber bundles are withdrawn. **E.** Phase contrast micrograph of a living, released egg of *Chondrosia reniformis* with surrounding sperm cells (*s*) (×450) (Lévi and Lévi, 1976). **F.** Entrance of spermiokyste (*arrow*) into an egg (*e*) of *Sycon ciliatum.* Note the presence of accessory cells (*double arrow*). *h*, choanocytes (×585) (Sara and Rellini-Orsi, unpubl.). **G.** Spermiokyste (*arrow*) entrance in *Sycon ciliatum* without the intervention of accessory cells. *e*, egg; *h*, choanocytes (×585) Sara and Rellini-Orsi, unpubl.). (**A–D**, courtesy Dr. Y. Watanabe; **E**, courtesy Prof. C. Lévi, **F**, **G**, courtesy Prof. M. Sara.)

compressa. Gallissian (1980) has presented ultrastructural evidence of the presence of a carrier cell (cellule-charriante) that contains a modified sperm cell, called a spermiocyst, within a cytoplasmic vacuole (Fig. 7-12). The carrier cell makes contact with the egg cell surface and the speriocyst is then introduced into the egg cell cytoplasm. Such a sequence was long ago reported, especially in calcareous species (Tuzet, 1932; Duboscq and Tuzet, 1937; see Tuzet, 1973a, for a review). Other light microscope studies of the carrier cell–spermiocyst system have been carried out on *Sycon ciliatum* (Sara and Rellini-Orsi, 1975) and *Petrobiona massiliana* (Vacelet, 1964) and are further considered by Sara (1974). In these studies, the following transport sequence has emerged; the sperm enters the incurrent canals and is ingested by a choanocyte; the latter then migrates into the mesohyl where it contacts the egg surface and transfers the spermiocyst. This intriguing sequence raises many questions of intense interest which will doubtless be investigated in the not too distant future. The events suggest a crucial role for cell recognition of the sperm cell by the choanocyte and of the egg cell by the carrier cell; further, a precise guidance system for the location of the mature egg cell must also be operative.

The relationship of fertilization to the meiosis of female gametes appears diverse, but it should be emphasized that there are few, if any, cases in which meiosis has clearly been documented and the data require keen scrutiny as well as thorough reevaluation. In *Clathrina coriacea* and *Octavella galangaui,* the spermiocyst is reported to enter the oocyte which then undergoes growth followed by meiosis (Tuzet, 1947; Tuzet and Paris, 1964). In *Sycon elegans* and *raphanus,* meiosis occurs first and the spermiocyst then enters the egg (Duboscq and Tuzet, 1944), while in *Hippospongia communis* the spermiocyst enters the oocyte followed by, respectively, meiosis and then growth (Tuzet and Pavans de Ceccatty, 1958). After entry in the egg cytoplasm, the spermiocyst swells, loses its mitochondria, and develops a nucleolus (Gatenby, 1927; Duboscq and Tuzet, 1937, 1944). Korotkova and Apalkova (1975) claim that in *Halisarca dujardini* only a single polar body forms and that the egg develops parthenogenetically.

Cleavage

In all cases where cleavage is clearly visible it is total and generally equal (see, for example, Gilbert and Hadzisce, 1977; Gilbert, 1974; Reiswig, 1976; Johnson, 1979a; Fell and Jacob, 1979; Okada, 1928; Lévi and Lévi, 1976; Borojevic, 1969; Watanabe, 1978a; and for a review, Fell, 1974a, in press). There are a number of cases in which early cleavage has been reported to be highly unequal and difficult to interpret—in *Adocia simulans* (Lévi, 1956), *Ephydatia fluviatilis* (Brien and Meewis, 1938), *Micro-*

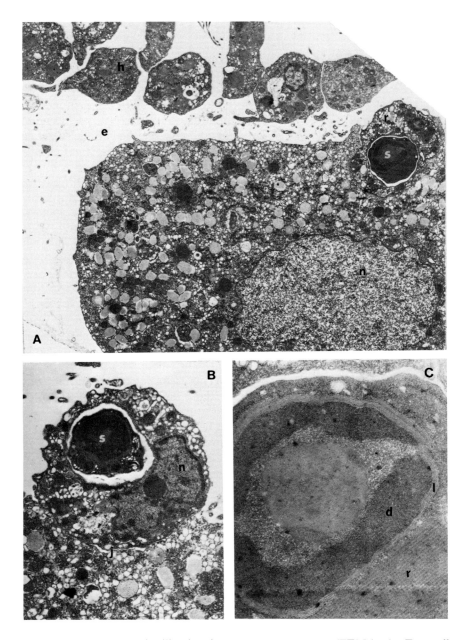

Figure 7-12 Internal fertilization in *Grantia compressa* (TEMs). **A**. Egg cell
enveloping a carrier cell (*r*) containing a spermiokyste (*s*). *n*, egg cell nucleus; *h*,
choanocytes; *e*, mesohyl. Note the numerous yolk inclusions in the egg (×3,330)
(Gallissian, 1980). **B**. Carrier cell which possesses a nucleolate nucleus (*n*) and
contains the spermiokyste (*s*). *j*, junction between carrier and egg cell (×9,810)
(Gallissian, 1980). **C**. The spermiokyste. Striated material (*r*) lies outside of the
sperm head and a lamellar capsule (*l*) surrounds the chromatin which occurs as a
dense annulus (*d*) and internal, less dense zone which is heterogeneous (×31,500)
(Gallissian, 1980). (All, courtesy Dr. M-F. Gallissian.)

ciona prolifera (Simpson, 1968b), *Haliclona ecbasis* (Fell, 1969), and in a number of other demosponges (Bergquist *et al.*, 1970). In some of these, plurinucleate blastomeres have been reported. As suggested by Fell (in press), all of these cases may be artifactual, a result of the presence of large amounts of yolk which make it impossible to identify individual cells. For example, in *Haliclona ecbasis* embryos of about 1,000 cells clearly are cellular while in earlier stages it is impossible on a light microscope level to identify individual cells (Fell, 1969).

Some workers have emphasized differences in cell size resulting from early cleavage (Tuzet, 1963) and thus recognize micromeres and macromeres (Brien and Meewis, 1938; Lemche and Tendal, 1977). In calcaronean species this distinction signals the formation of the two cell types present in the larva. In most sponge blastulas, however, no such distinction exists or if it does is not prominent and has not been noted. In distinction, there are pronounced differences in cell size in many larvae. There have been no studies of the synchronization of the cleavage divisions, but based upon available published figures there does appear to be synchronization at least in early stages.

Cleavage results in the formation of either a solid stereoblastula stage, as in hexactinellids, most ceractinomorphs, and probably sclerosponges, or a cavity-bearing coeloblastula stage, as in calcareous species and at least some tetractinomorphs. In calcineans (Borojevic, 1969; Johnson, 1979a), calcaroneans (Tuzet, 1963; Lemche and Tendal, 1977), pharetronids (Vacelet, 1964), and tetractinomorphs (Borojevic, 1967; Lévi and Lévi, 1976) the coeloblastula is also the final stage in embryogenesis and leads directly to the formation of a hollow larva which, however, in some cases becomes secondarily solid. Uniquely, in the sphinctozoid, *Neocoelia,* a coeloblastula stage is converted to a solid, incubated stereoblastula which continues development (Vacelet, 1979a).

Lemche and Tendal (1977) have presented a unique and thoroughly interesting view of cleavage in *Scypha* (Figs. 7-13, 7-14). According to them the egg cell is presumed to be derived from a choanocyte and thus possesses regional differences in its plasmalemma which correspond to those in the original choanocyte; basal surface, contact (lateral) surface, digestive surface, and intracollar surface. Following cleavage, each of these regions is hypothesized to be specifically localized in the coeloblastula such that the digestive surface characterizes the macromeres, the contact surface occurs between micromeres and between micromeres and macromeres, the basal surface borders the external surface of the micromeres, and the intracollar surface borders the internal surface of the micromeres. According to this view, the digestive surface functions, during growth and development of the coeloblastula, as a nutritive surface. However, it is difficult to envisage how such surface differences in eggs could be portioned out to the blastomeres in other sponges in which no inversion (see later) of a coeloblastula stage takes place and, indeed, in

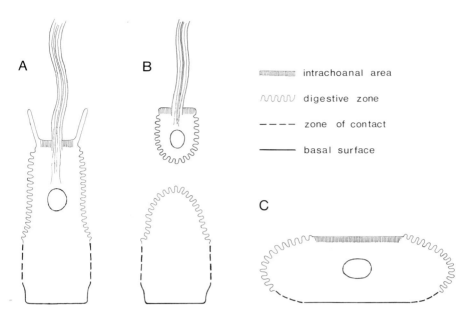

Figure 7-13 Hypothetical model of the development of gametes from choano-cytes emphasizing the heterogeneity of regions of the choanocyte plasmalemma. **A.** Supposed surface activity pattern of the plasmalemma of a choanocyte. **B.** Origin of a sperm cell (above). **C.** Origin of an egg cell. See Fig. 7-14 (Lemche and Tendal, 1977). (Courtesy Dr. O. S. Tendal.)

some of which no coeloblastula stage occurs at all. Regardless, this view is of much importance in focusing attention upon the question of the origin of oocytes and upon the possible role of surface specialization in cleavage.

In *Ascandra,* Borojevic (1969) has found that during cleavage, the mitotic spindles are always oriented tangentially so that the division products are added to the surface and are not moved to the interior of the embryo. He considers this orientation as the underlying basis for the formation of a coeloblastula rather than a stereoblastula. One could assume that the plane of division in other coeloblastula producing species is of similar fundamental importance.

Somatic Cells Associated with Embryos

The identification of a surrounding, flattened epithelium that produces a cavity in which cleavage occurs in viviparous species is a routine observation. Such an epithelium has been referred to as a placental membrane in calcareous sponges where it is said to be derived from migrating choanocytes, although other views have been expressed (Lufty, 1957a). In the latter study, it was also reported that a second flattened epithelium sur-

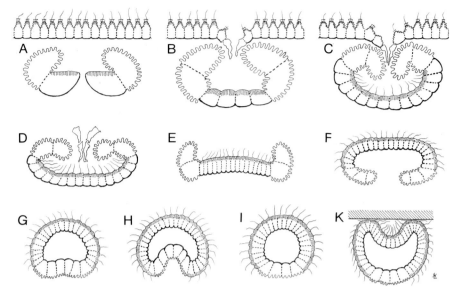

Figure 7-14 Hypothetical pattern of embryonic development of the amphiblastula larva in *Scypha*. The surface specializations are denoted in the same manner as in Fig. 7-13. **A**. Four-cell stage. **B, C, D**. Formation of the stomoblastula. **E, F**. Inversion of the embryo. **G, H. I**. Formation of the amphiblastula. **K**. Settlement of the amphiblastula (Lemche and Tendal, 1977). (Courtesy Dr. O. S. Tendal.)

rounds the placental membrane, but no other similar observations have appeared. The relationship of the placental membrane to the follicular epithelium that earlier surrounds *eggs* (see previous discussion) is unknown and the simplest view is that they are the same structure.

A few, well-documented cases of the incorporation of somatic cells into developing embryos exist. In *Chondrosia reniformis,* such cells surround the egg, are released with it and in later stages of cleavage come to occupy the blastocoel. Two types of cells are present—nucleolate bacteriocytes (? archeocytes) and microgranular cells (Lévi and Lévi, 1976). In *Hemectyon ferox,* somatic cells are similarly released with the developing embryo and invade the blastocoel (Reiswig, 1976). Warburton (1961) also described such incorporation of somatic cells into embryos of *Cliona celata*.

During the course of embryonic development in *Grantia,* somatic cells have been observed to migrate into the blastocoel [see Lufty (1957b) for a review of earlier observations]. Four categories of such cells are identified—choanocytes, granular cells (=eosinophilic cells), yolk cells (=archeocytes), and vacuolated cells. All of them may be derived directly or indirectly (via the placental membrane) from choanocytes, and some of them, at least, undergo degeneration acting as nutritive sources. The final fate of those cells that are released with the larva is not clear. They are clearly not mesodermal (Lufty, 1957b), but it is possible that they persist during metamorphosis as do the microgranular cells and bacteriocytes in *Chondrosia* thus producing a chimera (Lévi and Lévi, 1976). The latter finding suggests that such cells in other embryos (and larvae) may not have a nutritive, or solely nutritive, function.

Polarity, Micromeres, Macromeres

Tuzet (1970) has reviewed the early data indicating that the mature oocyte of *Sycon* and *Grantia* possesses a predetermined polarity (Fig. 7-15). The egg surface closest to the choanocytes will ultimately form the animal pole—nonflagellated, ectoblastic cells—and that farthest away the vegetal pole—flagellated, endoblastic cells. The short axis (perpendicular to the choanocytes) is the plane of the first division and the long axis is the plane in which the polar bodies form. The point of entrance of the spermiocyst is along the short axis or at least approximately so in *Leucandra*. The clumped vesicular material in the egg cytoplasm lies at the vegetal pole and becomes localized in four symmetrically placed cells at the equator of the embryo; these are the future cellules en croix of the mature amphiblastula larva. The fusion of the pronuclei is reported to occur at the point of intersection of the short and long axes. The fourth cleavage produces an embryo with eight ectoblastic and eight endoblastic cells. Four of the latter possess vesicular material and can be recognized as the anlage of the cellules en croix. In *Leucosolenia,* the penetration of the spermiocyst and formation of the polar bodies are less well defined relative to the short and long axes of the egg. The egg and embryo of the pharetronid, *Petrobiona,* possess a symmetry similar to that of the calcaronean species described above.

The polarity of eggs and embryos in other groups remains unstudied and indeed, in some cases, there well may be no polarity as in the embryo and larvae of *Polymastia* and *Ascandra* (Borojevic, 1970) where no predetermination of the cells occurs until after attachment, during metamorphosis. Lévi (1963a) has presented the view that in most sponges the larva has a reverse polarity with the endoblastic cells (choanoblastic) being anterior and ectoblastic ones (pinacoblastic) posterior. It is still not at all clear how one can relate the ectoderm–endoderm of metazoans to the pinacoderm–choanoderm of sponges. The kind of polarity suggested by Lemche and Tendal (1977) (see previous section) circumvents this problem by employing the functional nature of the cells themselves rather than their relationship to eumetazoan embryos.

In amphiblastula-producing species, one can distinguish micromeres as distinct from macromeres by the 16-cell stage. The former are destined to form flagellated cells of the anterior hemisphere of the mature larva and the latter nonflagellated cells. In species that form parenchymellae larvae, the terms micromeres and macromeres have been used in a parallel

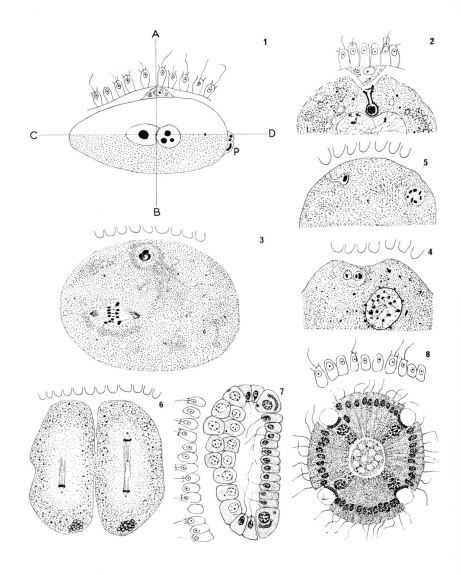
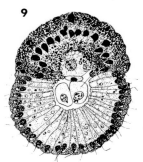

fashion in the late stereoblastula to refer to the development of, respectively, the flagellated line of cells and the nonflagellated line (see, for example, Harrison and Cowden, 1975b). However, in the latter embryos, the flagellated cells take up an epithelial position at the surface and the nonflagellated cells an internal position (although in many mature parenchymellae larvae a few polar, nonflagellated cells are also surficial), such that the distinction between anterior placement and posterior placement is not really applicable. Thus, the terms micromere and macromere have different meanings in different types of sponge embryos and, as pointed out above, they cannot readily be equated with the same terms as applied to other eumetazoan embryos (see later, The Problem of Polarity of the Larva).

Larval Formation

Larval Structure

The structure of mature larvae is now known to be highly diverse and it has become increasingly difficult to establish categories of larvae based upon their structure (see, for example, Fell, in press). Despite this, it is still possible and necessary to tentatively recognize three more or less discrete morphological types: amphiblastula, parenchymella, and coeloblastula. Amphiblastulae larvae are well characterized by (1) possession of four, equatorially placed, distinctive cells, called cellules en croix, (2) the presence of an internal cavity, (3) the presence of externally directed flagellae on the cells of only the anterior hemisphere where the cell size is slightly smaller (=micromeres), (4) the presence of a single layer of cells which constitute the larva, and (5) viviparous development (see Fig. 7-15). Such larvae are typical of the Calcaronea and Pharetronida such as *Leucosolenia botryoides* (Tuzet, 1948) and *Petrobiona massiliana* (Vacelet, 1964). Larvae possessing *all* of these features have not been described in other groups, although the term amphiblastula has been used to refer to some larvae that are here categorized as coeloblastulae larvae (Lévi and

---

Figure 7-15 (opposite)   Embryonic development in calcaronean calcareous species. **1.** Fusion of pronuclei in *Sycon raphanus*. *AB,* principal axis; *CD,* long axis; *p,* polar bodies. Stippled area will give rise to the flagellated cells. **2.** Entrance of the spermiokyste in *Sycon raphanus*. **3.** First maturation division of the egg in *Grantia compressa;* spermiokyste above. **4.** Penetration of the spermiokyste in *Leucandra nivea*. **5.** First polar body metaphase in *Leucandra aspera*. Spermiokyste entrance to the left. **6.** Telophase of a two-cell embryo of *Sycon raphanus*. The inclusions that will be segregated in the cellules en croix are at the lower pole in each cell. **7.** Stomoblastula of *Sycon ciliatum* with flagella directed inward. Embryo lies below the choanocytes. **8.** Cross section of an amphiblastula of *Sycon raphanus* showing the cellules en croix. **9.** The amphiblastula of *Petrobiona massiliana* (Tuzet, 1970).

Lévi, 1976; Lévi and Porte, 1962; Borojevic, 1970). In comparison, parenchymellae larvae possess (1) a pseudostratified epithelium of narrow (1.0
to 3.0 μm), elongate (10 to 15 μm), uniflagellated cells that completely, or
almost so, cover their surface, (2) internal cells which are derived during
embryogenesis from cleavage and are usually cytodifferentiated—in spicule-bearing species, sclerocytes routinely secrete spicules within the
larva, and (3) viviparous development (Fig. 7-16). The third category is
coeloblastulae larvae which undoubtedly represent a heterogeneous assemblage of types, but appropriate data are not available bearing on this
question. Morphologically these larvae are characterized by (1) a retained
blastocoel which is either fluid filled or contains somatic (parental) cells
and in which neither spicules nor cytodifferentiated, embryonically derived cells are present, (2) a flagellated epithelium which is usually simple
(cuboidal or columnar), covers all or almost all of the surface, and contains large cells, (3) the absence of cellules en croix, and (4) oviparous
development. Regional differences in the flagellated epithelium of some
coeloblastular larvae such as *Oscarella lobularis* (Lévi and Porte, 1962)
and *Octavella galangaui* (Tuzet and Paris, 1964) have led to the view that
these are "amphiblastulae" larvae, a term also used to refer to them by
Fell (in press) in his recent review of sponge larvae. However, since these
larvae lack cellules en croix, are almost totally flagellated (Fig. 7-17), and
since there are no experimental data establishing a differential fate at
metamorphosis of different regions of the flagellated epithelium, there is
little basis at present for including them within the amphiblastula category,
although they probably should be considered as a special case within the
coeloblastular category. The flagellated cells constituting the locomotory
tissue of larvae do not possess collars as are typical of choanocytes.
Although descriptions of cytoplasmic sleeves around larval flagella have
appeared (Bergquist and Green, 1977b), these should not be confused
with the microvillus collar characteristic of choanocytes.

The internally positioned cells present in *some* larvae appear to act as
nutrient sources. In *Oscarella* (Lévi and Porte, 1962), some of these cells
slowly disintegrate supplying nutrients to the surrounding cells while
others are incorporated into the flagellar epithelium. Similarly placed
somatic, parental cells in *Chondrosia* do not disintegrate but actually take
part in metamorphosis (Lévi and Lévi, 1976). In maturing, incubated
amphiblastulae larvae, the so-called mesoblast cells are nutritive and are
derived from the parental tissue (Lufty, 1957b). In the homoscleromorphs, *Oscarella* and *Octavella,* at least some internal cells in the larva
become part of the flagellated epithelium leaving behind an internal, acellular cavity. This sequence of development appears to be both unique and
restricted to the Homoscleromorpha. Regional differences in the flagellated epithelium in both of these species further support the notion that
these larvae should possibly be placed in a category of their own.

The sexual products of some demosponges have been reported to de-

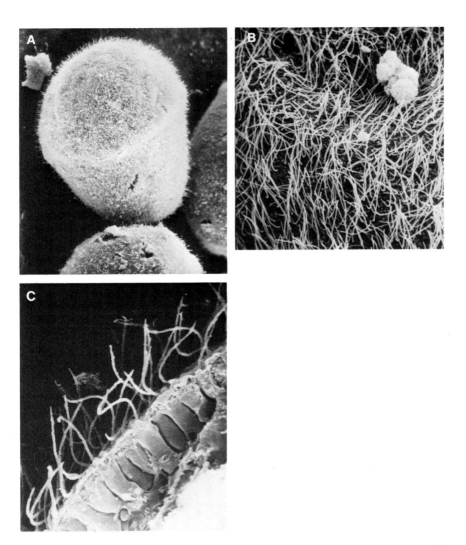

Figure 7-16 The parenchymella larva of *Ephydatia fluviatilis* (SEMs). **A**. Whole larva (×270) (De Vos, unpubl.). **B**. Surface of the larva showing flagellation (×1,305) (De Vos, unpubl.). **C**. Fractured, outer portion of a larva showing the elongate shape of the flagellated cells and their flagella (×1,800) (De Vos, unpubl.). (All, courtesy Dr. L. De Vos.)

velop directly into adults without an intervening larval stage. This is well documented in *Tetilla serica* and *japonica* (Watanabe, 1957, 1960, 1978a), in which the *attached* zygote undergoes cleavage and directly forms a young sponge (Fig. 7-18). In distinction, Burton (1931), Sollas (1888) and Bergquist (1968) describe the direct development of young adults from

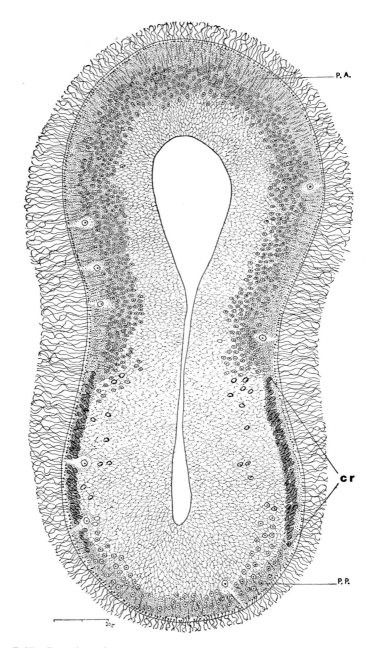

Figure 7-17 Drawing of a longitudinal section of the larva of *Oscarella lobularis*.
The differential structure of the flagellated epithelium into "anterior" pole (*P.A.*),
"posterior" pole (*P.P.*) and a region of cells containing refractile inclusions (*cr*)
has been compared to the amphiblastula larva of calcaroneans. The flagellated
epithelial cells are, however, morphologically similar to those in parenchymellae
and the internal cavity is similar to that in coeloblastulae larvae (×1,035)
(Meewis, 1939a).

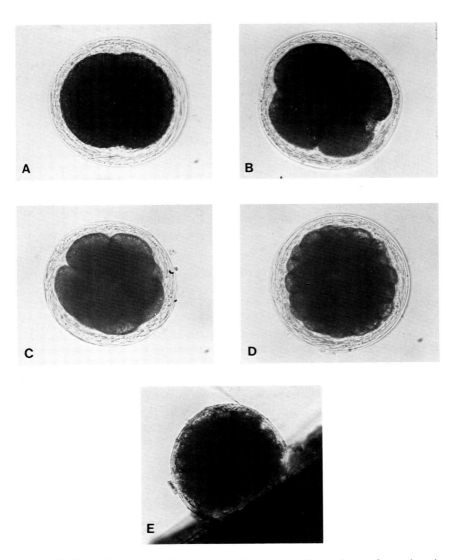

Figure 7-18 Oviparous embryonic development without larva formation in *Tetilla serica*. All stages are attached to the substratum. (light micrographs, living preparations) (all ×200 except E. which is ×180). (All, Watanabe, 1978a.). **A.** Two-cell stage. **B.** Four-cell stage. **C.** Eight-cell stage. **D.** Morula. **E.** Side view of the attached embryo. (All courtesy Dr. Y. Watanabe.)

embryos within the parental tissues of, respectively, *Tetilla cranium, T. schmidtii,* and *T. australe.* Bergquist (1978) has treated this as a separate type of larval metamorphosis. As emphasized by Fell (in press) and reiterated here, the details of this process, if indeed it occurs, are far from clear and its basis could be related to asexual bud formation. Thorough, sequential analyses of development in these species are absolutely mandatory to extend and verify these observations.

Processes in Larva Formation

The specific processes responsible for the development of the mature larva from the embryo are, with few exceptions, not well documented. The absence of such data is related to the difficulty of obtaining a timed sequence of events in development. Despite the deficiencies, which are most glaring in the development of parenchymellae larvae, the major features are known in the structurally less complex amphiblastulae larvae and in a few coeloblastular ones.

Development of Amphiblastulae Larvae.　The formation of these larvae was early described by Duboscq and Tuzet (1941, 1942, 1944) and more recently reviewed by Tuzet (1970) and Lemche and Tendal (1977). At the sixteen cell stage there are eight smaller micromeres and eight larger macromeres. Four of the micromeres can be identified as the progenitors of the cellules en croix, containing the anlage of the distinctive vesicular structures. At the 32 or 64 cell stage, the four definitive cellules en croix have formed by loss of their flagella and the remaining micromeres are uniflagellated, with flagella pointing inward into the blastocoel; the macromeres lie closer to the choanoderm. The embryo then inverts to produce the definitive amphiblastula with its anterior hemisphere externally flagellated and posterior one nonflagellated (see Fig. 7-14). The four cellules en croix lie at 90° to one another at the equator. According to Duboscq and Tuzet (1942), the Golgi bodies have a very regular, predictable orientation as in *Oscarella* (see later). The cellules en croix are discharged from the larva after its release and take no part in later development. During larval development, nurse cells wander into the blastocoel and a few may be retained here even after the larva is released. A similar developmental sequence occurs in *Petrobiona* (Vacelet, 1964).

Development of Coeloblastulae Larvae.　In *Polymastia robusta,* cleavage leads directly to a flagellated blastula stage, the coeloblastula larva, in which the blastocoel is small and the larva creeps on the substratum (Borojevic, 1967); development in *Raspailia* appears comparable to that in *Polymastia* (Lévi, 1956). In *Chondrosia reniformis,* cleavage similarly leads to the formation of a completely flagellated coeloblastula larva whose blastocoel, however, contains numerous, somatic (parental) cells (Fig. 7-19). The epithelium of the posterior pole is somewhat flattened while the remainder is cuboidal. The somatic cells migrate into the blasto-

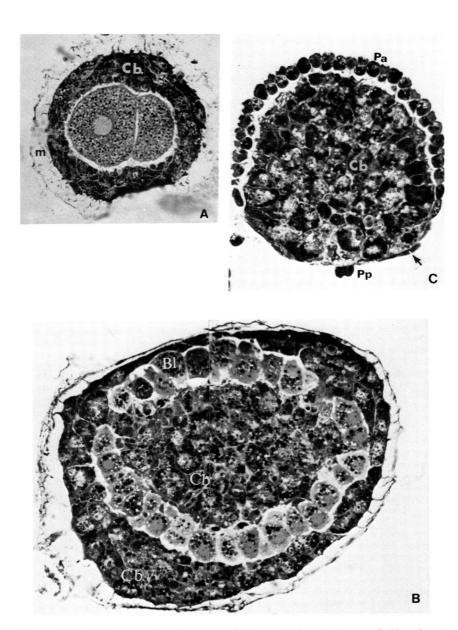

Figure 7-19 Oviparous development of the coeloblastula larva of *Chondrosia reniformis* (light micrographs, semithin sections). **A.** Two-cell stage surrounded by a constellation of parental follicular cells (*Cb*) (bacteriocytes) outside of which is a coat of mucoid material (*m*) (×470) (Lévi and Lévi, 1976). **B.** Blastula stage in which some of the parental bacteriocytes (*Cb*) have migrated within the single layer of blastomeres (*Bl*) and have filled the blastocoel. Other bacteriocytes still remain outside of the embryo (×900) (Lévi and Lévi, 1976). **C.** Mature coeloblastula larva in which the blastocoel is packed with bacteriocytes (*Cb*). The "anterior" pole (*Pa*) contains cuboidal, uniflagellated cells while the "posterior" pole (*Pp*) possesses squamous, flagellated cells (*arrow*) (×630) (Lévi and Lévi, 1976). (All courtesy Prof. C. Lévi.)

coel during cleavage. Development in *Cliona celata* has been described to follow a course similar to that in *Chondrosia* with the formation of a coeloblastula larva containing internal, somatic cells; however, some of the internal cells may be blastomeres (Warburton, 1961). On the other hand, Nassonow (1883) originally described larvae of *Cliona stationis* as hollow, coeloblastula larvae. It is presently not settled as to whether the larvae of *Cliona celata* should be considered as coeloblastulae with internal parental cells (as is clearly the case in *Chondrosia*) or whether they should be considered as parenchymellae with internal blastomeres as in *Tethya* and *Agelas* (see later). In *Clathrina, Ascandra,* and other calcineans, cleavage results in a flagellated coeloblastula larva with a spacious blastocoel (Fig. 7-20). A few nonflagellated cells (granular cells) are present at the posterior pole (Borojevic, 1969; Johnson, 1979a). Nurse cells, sometimes many of them, may become trapped in the blastocoel during cleavage (Borojevic, 1969). The nonflagellated, granular cells have been considered to be blastomeres that are retarded in their development and they are even absent in some larvae. In *Clathrina reticulum* and *Ascandra falcata,* these cells appear to be derived, by loss of flagella, from the flagellated epithelium (Borojevic, 1969). In *Clathrina blanca* and *coriacea,* some embryonic blastomeres migrate into the blastocoel (Johnson, 1979a; Tuzet, 1948). However, in these larvae, it is not a simple matter to distinguish between nurse cell and blastomere migration into the blastocoel.

In *Octavella,* a solid morula stage develops a surrounding columnar epithelium into which the internal cells then migrate leaving a spacious blastocoel. Each columnar cell develops a flagellum, with the exception of a few posterior cells and the coeloblastula larva is released (Tuzet and Paris, 1964). The sequence in *Oscarella* is similar, except that many internal cells act as a nutrient supply as previously discussed (Meewis, 1938). Through relatively unknown events, the flagellated epithelium then becomes regionally differentiated: in the anterior hemisphere, the cells occur in five to six tiers, those at the posterior in two to three tiers. The Golgi bodies in each cell have a predictable orientation with the forming face "anterior" and the maturing face "posterior." Toward the presumed posterior pole, epithelial cells are present which contain an intranuclear inclusion (Meewis, 1939a). Also, in this region are flask-shaped cells with numerous vesicles; these cells do not take part in metamorphosis, since they are eliminated from the larva (Lévi and Porte, 1962). The similarities of *Oscarella* larvae to the amphiblastula larva of the Calcaronea are obvious according to these authors. The larva of another homoscleromorph, *Plakina,* is also a coeloblastula with a spacious blastocoel (Bergquist *et al.*, 1979). The ultrastructure of the flagellated epithelium has not been elucidated in this case.

Development of Parenchymellae Larvae. The development of typical parenchymellae larvae occurs in three stages: formation of a solid, non-

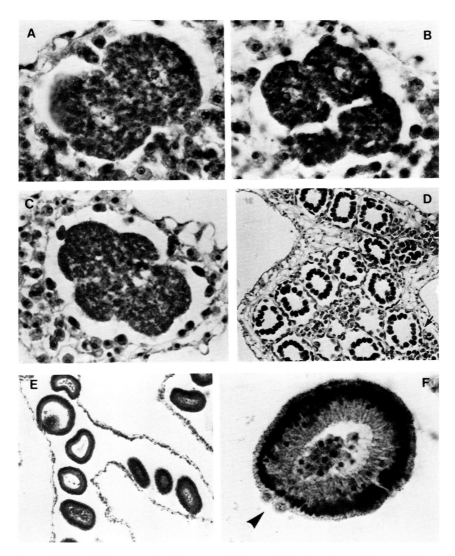

Figure 7-20   Viviparous development of the coeloblastua larva of the calcinean species, *Clathrina blanca* and *C. coriacea* (light micrographs). **A, B, C.** Two, four, and eight cell stages, respectively, of *Clathrina blanca* (all ×900) (Johnson, 1979a). **D.** Thirty-two to sixty-four cell stages of *Clathrina coriacea*. Note follicular epithelium around each (×180) (Johnson, 1979a). **E.** Maturing coeloblastulae larvae within the anastomosing tubes of *Clathrina blanca* (×180) (Johnson, 1979a). **F.** Mature, coeloblastula larva of *Clathrina blanca* with a few internal cells which are derived from the flagellated epithelium (see text) and two posterior cells (*arrow*) whose significance is still unclear (×900) (Johnson, 1979a). (All courtesy Dr. M. Fischel Johnson.)

flagellated stereoblastula; differentiation of a surrounding, usually pseudostratified, flagellated epithelium; cytodifferentiation of usually some, and often many, of the internal cells (Fig. 7-21). The specific processes (changes in cell and nuclear size, differential mitoses, formation of special cytoplasmic organelles) involved in this developmental sequence are complex and not thoroughly documented, although the overall sequence of development is well recorded in a number of species (Fell, 1969; Fell and Jacob, 1979; Gilbert and Hadzisce, 1977; Harrison and Cowden, 1975b; Brien and Meewis, 1938; Lévi, 1956; Okada, 1928; Simpson and Gilbert, 1973; Simpson, 1968b; Meewis, 1939b). The presence of archeocytes, sclerocytes, special cells, and collencytes within these larvae (Fig. 7-22) has also been clearly documented, although not all of the same cell types are present in all larvae; archeocytes appear universally present (Boury-Esnault, 1976a; Lévi, 1964; Evans, 1977; Evans, 1899). In some haplosclerid larvae, the internal cell mass may even precociously form choanocyte chambers (Harrison and Cowden, 1975b; Meewis, 1939b; Brien, 1970; Brien and Meewis, 1938; Efremova and Efremov, 1979) and in freshwater species the larvae develop a moderately large, secondary cavity lined by pinacocytes (Fig. 7-22C) (Brien and Meewis, 1938; Harrison and Cowden, 1975b; Gilbert and Hadzisce, 1977; and others). This cavity has been referred to as a floatation cavity, but there is no real evidence that it is an organ for buoyancy; because it occurs only in freshwater sponges there is a good possibility that it is involved in osmoregulation.

In distinction, the larvae of *Tethya aurantium* (Lévi, 1956) and *Agelas* sp. (Reiswig, 1976) develop internal cells some of which, in the former, disintegrate and provide nutrients and none of which in either species appears to be highly cytodifferentiated; as previously pointed out, this may also be the case in *Cliona celata*. Larvae in these three sponges are thus somewhat transitional between coeloblastulae and parenchymellae larvae as is also signaled by the presence of a simple cuboidal or columnar flagellated epithelium in *Tethya* and *Agelas* rather than a pseudostratified one typical of parenchymellae. Consequently, these larvae are problematical in terms of their categorization, and further studies are clearly required.

Development in *Neocoelia crypta* follows the same general sequence as in other parenchymellae with the important exception that in early cleavage a coeloblastula is formed which is then, through cell migration, converted into a stereoblastula (Fig. 7-23) (Vacelet, 1979a).

There are few comprehensive studies of the processes whereby the stereoblastula is transformed into a parenchymella and there are severe difficulties in tracing cell lineages due to the absence of specific, coordinated cell movements and formation of discrete cell groups characteristic of embryogenesis in most multicellular animals. Although a number of

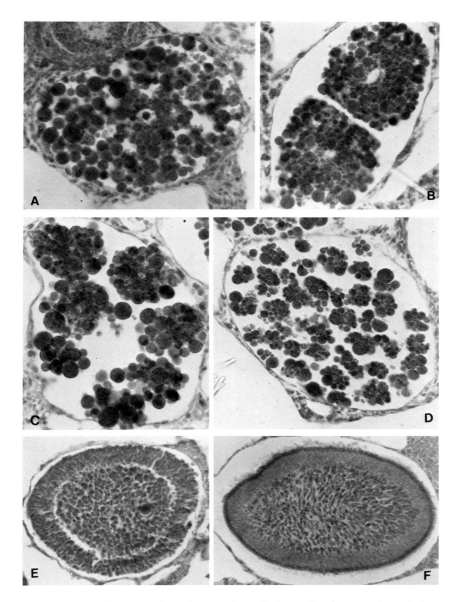

Figure 7-21 Embryogenesis and parenchymella larva development in *Halichondria* sp. (light micrographs). **A.** Mature egg packed with yolk inclusions (×360) (Fell and Jacob, 1979). **B, C.** Two cell and eight cell stages, respectively (both ×360) (Fell and Jacob, 1979). **D.** Morula stage (×215) (Fell and Jacob, 1979). **E.** Early differentiation of the parenchymella with segregation of peripheral and internal cells (×215) (Fell and Jacob, 1979). **F.** Mature parenchymella larve with flagellated epithelium and solid mass of internal cells (×215) (Fell and Jacob, 1979). (All courtesy Dr. P. E. Fell.)

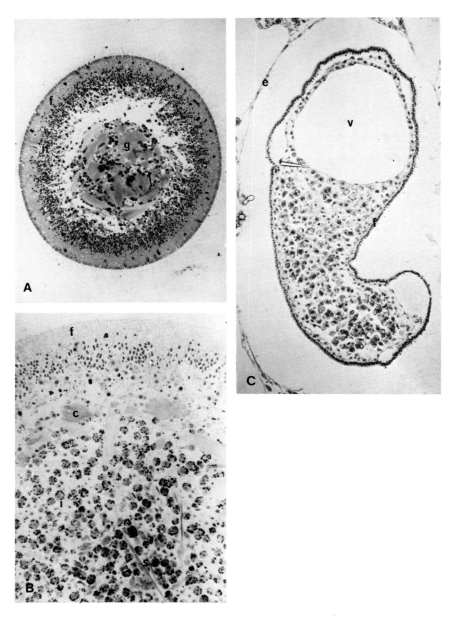

Figure 7-22 Two examples of demosponge parenchymellae larvae (light micrographs). **A.** Semithin section of the whole larva of *Hamigera hamigera* showing the flagellated epithelial cells (*f*) and their internally positioned nuclei. Further internally there is a mass of cells and collagen (*g*) (×205) (Boury-Esnault, 1976a). **B.** Semithin section of a portion of the surface and internal region of the parenchymella larva of *Hamigera hamigera*. *f,* flagellated epithelial cells; *i,* internal cells

workers have recorded the presence of two cell populations in the stereoblastula, micromeres and macromeres, and have presented data indicating cell lineages based upon this, there still is no conclusive evidence of the validity of these views. The formation of the flagellated epithelium apparently involves repeated divisions of peripherally positioned blastomeres leading to smaller nuclear and cell size. However, in *Haliclona limbata* and *Adocia cinerea* (Meewis, 1939b, 1941), smaller cells destined to become flagellated epithelial cells appear intermixed with other cells internally, further pointing out the difficulties involved in establishing cell lineages. Brien and Meewis (1938) and Meewis (1939b) describe the formation of a subepithelial layer of collencytes below the flagellated epithelium but this has not been confirmed by more recent ultrastructural observations, although Harrison and Cowden (1975b) also report its presence based, however, primarily on cytochemical staining patterns. In the latter study of *Eunapius fragilis,* the mobilization of food reserves in the blastomeres was found to be a major developmental process during larval development and equally impressive changes in the cytochemistry of the chromatin of the developing cell types were observed. In this species, the anlage of the large anterior cavity forms prior to the development of the flagellated epithelium. The timing of appearance of siliceous spicules is variable: In *Haliclona ecbasis* they appear in the late stereoblastula, peripherally, and are later moved internally (Fell, 1969). In *Haliclona limbata* spicules do not appear until after the definitive larva has formed when they first occur in a bundle internally (Meewis, 1939b). In *Ephydatia fluviatilis,* spicules appear internally (Brien and Meewis, 1938) at a comparable stage to that in *Haliclona ecbasis.* The types of spicules secreted in the larva, relative to those formed in the adult tissue, are the same but frequently some spicule types are missing and/or their dimensions are significantly different (Simpson, 1968b; Bergquist and Sinclair, 1973; Borojevic, 1966; Lévi, 1956). In an extreme case, *Halichondria moorei,* no spicules are present in the larva until after metamorphosis (Bergquist and Sinclair, 1968). In all cases where ultrastructural data are available, collagen fibrils are secreted within the larva (Vacelet, 1979a; Boury-Esnault, 1976a; Lévi, 1964; Bergquist and Green, 1977b), and based upon staining patterns, small

---

including a sclerocyte (*s*); *c,* collagen (×305) (Boury-Esnault, 1976a). **C.** Parenchymella of *Ochridaspongia rotunda* showing the large epithelial-lined cavity (*v*) typical of freshwater larvae. The flagellated epithelium (*f*) is clearly demarcated and the larva is surrounded by an epithelium (*e*). Note that the nuclei of the flagellated epithelial cells are not internally placed as in *Hamigera* (×115) (Gilbert and Hadzische, 1977). (**A, B,** courtesy Dr. N. Boury-Esnault; **C,** courtesy Prof. J. J. Gilbert.)

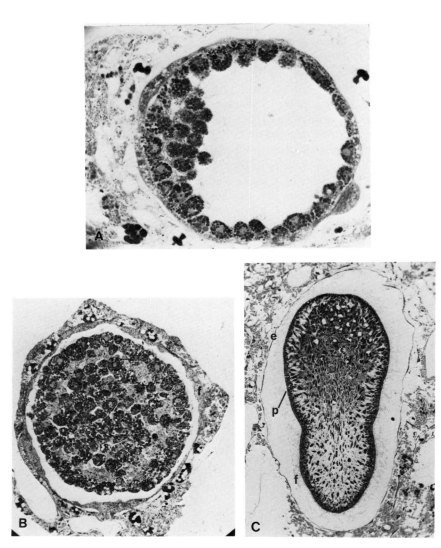

Figure 7-23 Development of the parenchymella larva of the sphinctozoid, *Neocoelia crypta* (light micrographs, semithin sections). **A**. Coeloblastula stage which is unique in parenchymella forming species (×450) (Vacelet, 1979a). **B**. Morula stage resulting from the infilling of the cavity in the coeloblastula. Note well-developed follicular layer (*f*) (×225) (Vacelet, 1979a). **C**. Mature parenchymella showing flagella (*f*), internal cells (*i*), flagellated epithelium (*p*), and surrounding squamous epithelium (*e*) (×160) (Vacelet, 1979a). (All courtesy Dr. J. Vacelet.)

quantities of spongin are elaborated around the larval spicules (Simpson, 1968b; Harrison and Cowden, 1975b). Precise knowledge of the origin of flagellated epithelial cells, collencytes, sclerocytes, special cells, collagen, and other differentiated products and cells during the embryogenesis of parenchymellae larvae is subject to the same deficiencies as knowledge of their origin during somatic growth and regeneration (Chap. 9).

The final pattern and distribution of flagella is variable (Bergquist *et al.*, 1979): parenchymellae may be uniformly and totally flagellated or the posterior and/or anterior poles may lack flagellation and in some instances a ring of longer flagellae may occur at the posterior pole. In other cases flagellation may be lost at one of the poles (Meewis, 1939b). The distribution and length of flagella may differ even within species of the same genus. Bergquist *et al.* (1979) have conducted an excellent, descriptive investigation of the patterns of flagellation in a substantial number of demosponges and this work should be consulted.

In mature larvae of *Eunapius fragilis,* archeocytes and sclerocytes are characterized by diffuse chromatin and are rich in RNA, suggesting high synthetic activity while the flagellated epithelial cells possess very condensed chromatin, no cytochemically detectable nuclear RNA, and little cytoplasmic RNA, both typical of terminally differentiated cells; collencytes and the pinacocytes lining the large larval cavity are similar to the flagellated epithelial cells but contain mildly diffuse chromatin (Harrison and Cowden, 1975b). In the structurally similar larva of *Baikalospongia bacillifera* the flagellated epithelial cells, eosinophilic cells, and sclerocytes were found nonproliferative, whereas the precocious choanocytes, archeocytes, and collencytes actively divide (Efremova and Efremov, 1979).

The cell types present in the majority of parenchymellae larvae are strikingly similar to those in the corresponding adult tissue (Table 7-8). Among freshwater forms where precocious choanocyte chambers and a pinacocyte-lined cavity are formed, the correspondence is close to absolute. In the majority of species with parenchymellae larvae, choanocytes and pinacocytes are not present; nevertheless, the remaining basic contingent of adult cell types are present (see particularly Simpson, 1968b; Borojevic, 1966; Boury-Esnault, 1976a), although sometimes not every type (Boury-Esnault, 1976a). Such data support the view that these larvae are essentially nonattached adults. In comparison, coeloblastulae larvae typically possess only a single cell type (the flagellated epithelium) not corresponding to any adult type. Amphiblastulae larvae on the other hand possess the two rudimentary cell types necessary for structuring the adult, pinacocytes and flagellated cells, but do not possess spicules or sclerocytes which are present in the adult. It is therefore interesting to view the three larval types as representing progressive stages of premetamorphic cytodifferentiation—coeloblastulae are least advanced and in-

Table 7-8 Cellular Features of Larval Types[a]

Genus	Cell Types Present in Larva	Occurrence of Spicules in Larva When Also Present in Adult[b]	References
I. Coeloblastulae larvae			
Plakina		Absent	Bergquist *et al.* (1979)
Polymastia	Flagellated blastomeres	Absent	Borojevic (1967)
Raspailia		Absent	Lévi (1956)
Chondrosia	Flagellated blastomeres; Somatic, parental cells	—	Lévi and Lévi (1976)
Cliona		Absent	Warburton (1961)
Oscarella	Flagellated blastomeres with regional differences	—	Lévi and Porte (1962)
Ascandra	Flagellated blastomeres; Posterior granular cells; Somatic, parental cells (sometimes absent)	Absent	
Clathrina		Absent	Borojevic (1969)
II. Amphiblastulae larvae			
Sycon	Flagellated epithelial cells (anterior hemisphere),	Absent	
Grantia	Nonflagellated epithelial cells (posterior hemisphere),	Absent	Tuzet (1970, 1973a)
Leucandra	Cellules en croix (eventually lost from larva)	Absent	

III. Parenchymellae larvae

	Cell types		Reference
A. With few cell types			
Tethya	Flagellated epithelial cells, Internal archeocytes, Internal smaller cells	Absent	Lévi (1956)
B. Marine, with diverse cell types			
Hamigera	Flagellated epithelial cells, Archeocytes, Collencytes, Sclerocytes, Nonflagellated epithelial cells (posterior), Cellulaes spheruleuses, Cellules à vacuoles, Cellules en urne (not present in adult)	Absent[c]	Boury-Esnault (1976a)
Microciona	Flagellated epithelial cells, Archeocytes, Gray cells, Globoferous cells, Rhabdiferous cells	Present	Simpson (1968b)
Mycale	Flagellated epithelial cells, Archeocytes, Collencytes, Cellules vacuolaire, Sclerocytes, Cellules globiferes (?spheruleuses), Pinacocytes (nonflagellated epithelium)	Present	Borojevic (1966)
C. Freshwater, with choanocyte chambers and large cavity			
Baikalospongia	Flagellated epithelial cells, Archeocytes, Collencytes, Sclerocytes, Eosinophilic Cells (two types), Choanocytes, Pinacocytes (lining cavity)	Not recorded[c]	Efremova and Efremov (1979)
Eunapius	Flagellated epithelial cells, Archeocytes, Sclerocytes, Collencytes, Pinacocytes (lining cavity), Choanocytes	Not recorded[c]	Harrison and Cowden (1975b)

[a]See also Borojevic (1970).
[b]___ indicates the absence of spicules in the adult.
[c]Although not present or recorded, spicules can be considered to be incipiently present since their sclerocytes are.

deed are free-swimming blastulae; amphiblastulae have attained the next stage in which the essential adult cell types are present but no others; marine parenchymellae possess in general the full complement of adult cell types in which their physiological functioning has already developed (spicule secretion, collagen fibrilogenesis), and freshwater larvae are essentially adults with an incomplete canal system. While there is good evidence to support such a scheme, it is not clear how (or whether) these stages are related to evolution—in particular if coeloblastulae are truly "primitive" and parenchymellae are actually "advanced." In this context, the case of *Neocoelia crypta* is both intriguing and suggestive since, in its development, this sponge passes through coeloblastular, stereoblastular, and parenchymellar stages and the adults possess cellular features like those in demosponges but skeletal features (calcareous skeleton) possibly related to early calcareous sponges.

Reports of Asexually Formed Larvae

Since the description by Wilson (1894, 1902) of what he concluded was the asexual formation of larvae in *Tedania brucei* (?=*ignis*), other similar reports have appeared sporadically (Sivaramakrishnan, 1951; Bergquist *et al.,* 1970; Evans, 1977). In his investigation, Wilson (1894) describes the aggregation of mesohyl cells which then form what he refers to as "gemmule." These "gemmules" then were considered to develop into parenchymellae larvae. There is little convincing evidence of such a transformation and the large-sized groups of cells that are present in this species are most certainly not gemmules in the strict sense since they are not encapsulated, nor directly known to become encapsulated, by a surrounding, acellular, collagenous coat (Simpson, 1968a). While the origin and formation of these cell aggregates are not known, their developmental significance is still of much interest. It is, for example, possible they are dormant stereoblastulas; cursory histological examination has suggested a significant level of mitosis in them (Simpson, 1968a).

Based upon observations similar to those of Wilson (1894), Sivaramakrishnan (1951), and Ijima (1901, 1903), Bergquist *et al.* (1970) have concluded that one general form of larval development in sponges is asexual and involves the formation of a "gemmule" stage, and Fell (1974a) has included in an earlier review of sponge reproduction a listing of species in which gemmules give rise to larvae. It is to be emphasized that such "gemmules" have poorly documented origins and they have no clear relationship to the encapsulated gemmules of haplosclerid and hadromerid species (Chap. 8). Such *un*encapsulated structures should simply be referred to as cell masses until more definitive data become available. Brien (1973) categorically rejects and refutes both the conclusion and the point of view that sponge larvae can be produced asexually, as do most workers.

Embryo and Larva Release

The cellular events involved in the release of embryos and larvae can only be discussed on a hypothetical level since there are no detailed studies. Although such release is usually considered to occur via the excurrent canals, there are no truly convincing data on the point (Fig. 7-24). For example, while it is clear that release in *Hemectyon, Agelas,* and a number of other Caribbean demosponges (Reiswig, 1976) occurs via the secondary oscule, it is not actually known whether they enter the secondary atrial cavity via the primary oscules or otherwise. Similarly, although oscular chimneys and excurrent canals have been observed to become enlarged during the period of spawning (Lévi, 1956), the entrance of sexual products into the excurrent system is undocumented. The release of sexual products in the excurrent stream of species with secondary oscules is not proof that they are released into the secondary atrium via the primary oscules; their release into this cavity by a different pathway would still result in their expulsion from the sponge via the excurrent stream emitted from the secondary oscules. One aspect of these release events is clear: in some species, the events can be highly synchronized throughout the tissue of each individual, thus clearly pointing to an underlying mechanism of coordination (Reiswig, 1976). Following larval release, individual larvae have been reported to fuse, producing larger

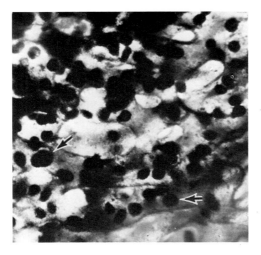

Figure 7-24 Whole mount of a portion of an individual of *Clathrina blanca* showing the numerous mature coeloblastulae larvae (*arrows*) within the interconnecting tubes just prior to release (×30) (Johnson, 1976). (Courtesy Dr. M. Fischel Johnson.)

structures that are then able to attach and metamorphose (Warburton, 1958d; Fry, 1971; Van de Vyver, 1970; Wilson, 1910). The cellular processes involved in such fusion are uninvestigated.

Attachment of Larvae to the Substratum

Larval attachment is the beginning of metamorphic processes and involves the interaction of larval cell surfaces with the substratum. The chemical nature of the substratum appears to be of little significance in general and a bewildering array of types of substrata for attachment have been reported including glass, plastics, rocks, wood, metals, mollusc shells, paraffin, agar, Epon, and others (Wilson, 1935; Brien and Meewis, 1938; Hartman, 1958a; Wells *et al.*, 1964; Bergquist and Sinclair, 1968, 1973; Fell, 1976b; Evans, 1977; and others). The precise cellular events initiating attachment are not known, but the newly forming basopinacocytes secrete a complex layer of material between themselves and the substratum. These materials include two sizes of fibrils in *Mycale contarenii,* one of which (125 Å in diameter) is banded and appears to be collagen while the other is more abundant (Borojevic and Lévi, 1967). In addition, granular material, electron dense bodies, and what appears to be cell debris may also be present (Bergquist and Green, 1977a). This basal lamella can be up to 1.0 μm or more thick and forms an organic substratum to and in which the basopinacocytes are attached. It is tempting to conclude that the apparent nonspecificity of larvae for substrata is due in part to the rapid formation of a buffering and anchoring layer of organic matrix (Evans, 1977), such that the cell surfaces never actually contact the environment. Larvae have been observed "attaching" upside down to the surface film of undisturbed water (Lévi, 1956), which further suggests that attachment involves cell produced matrix–substratum interaction and not a direct cell surface–substratum one.

The cellular dynamics at the earliest stages of larval attachment appear complex and there is a scarcity of detailed observations which, admittedly, are exceedingly difficult to obtain since three-dimensional views of living larvae as they interact with the substratum are required. In at least some coeloblastulae (*Ascandra, Polymastia*), all of the flagellated cells lose their flagellae and some of them then form the attachment layer of basopinacocytes (Borojevic, 1969, 1970). The precise sequence of events are not known, but in the case of *Polymastia* the flagellated larva is a creeping stage suggesting that, although flagella are still present, there is already a "preattachment" mechanism at work possibly involving flagellated cell–substratum interactions (Borojevic, 1967). In *Oscarella* also, flagellated cells form some type of initial preattachment with the substratum; they then migrate inward into the blastocoel and other flagellated cells that have lost their flagella then attach to the substratum (Meewis,

1938). In amphiblastulae larvae, such as in *Sycon,* the flagellated cells of the anterior hemisphere form a preattachment followed by their movement inward into the blastocoel resulting in contact (due to flattening of the larva) of the nonflagellated, posterior cells with the substratum, thus establishing the definitive attachment layer (Jones, 1971).

In parenchymellae, also, flagellated cells have been described as initially making contact with the substratum, at least for brief periods. In *Halichondria moorei, Ulosa* sp., and *Microciona rubens,* larvae creep on the substratum prior to attachment and here also flagellated cells may form transitory, initial attachments and are later replaced by collencytes which develop into basopinacocytes (Bergquist and Green, 1977b). In *Mycale syrinx,* flagellated cells attach to the substratum but are rapidly or contemporaneously replaced by what appear to be collencytes (Wilson, 1935). On the other hand, Meewis (1939b) describes the attachment of larvae of *Haliclona limbata* directly by nonflagellated cells which appear to migrate to the larval surface displacing the flagellated cells. But, just prior to attachment the larvae rotate in close contact with the substratum and the flagellated cells doubtless make some contribution to the ensuing attachment. Brien and Meewis (1938) describe the replacement of flagellated cells by collencytes, with the latter making initial contact; a similar sequence is reported in *Spongilla lacustris* by Evans (1899). In *Halisarca,* flagellated cells initially make contact and then are replaced by what appear to be archeocytes which form the basopinacocytes (Lévi, 1956). In the latter, new basopinacocytes can take on the form of T-shaped exopinacocytes (Chap. 2) with most of their mass located as much as 12 μm internally from the attachment surface.

As reviewed above, the flagellated cells of sponge larvae are intimately involved in the very early events of larval attachment and may "condition" the substratum for the ensuing definitive attachment by basopinacocytes. Further, in parenchymellae, some special cells can sometimes be found partially within the epithelial layer (urn cells, cellules vacuolaire, secretory cells) and they, as well as the flagellated cells, may release special matrix substances aiding in the preliminary attachment events. Indeed, Evans (1977) views larval attachment as a two-step process: secretion of a "ground mat" by larval cells and then attachment of the ground mat to the substratum.

The Problem of the Polarity of the Larva

Only the anterior pole of amphiblastulae larvae is flagellated and thus the smaller cells constituting it can be readily distinguished and followed during metamorphosis; these cells make initial contact with the substratum. In parenchymellae larvae and the coeloblastula of *Oscarella,* particular emphasis has been placed upon the conclusion that these larvae also attach by their anterior pole (Lévi, 1956; Brien and Meewis, 1938; Bergquist and Green, 1977b; Meewis, 1939b; Evans, 1899). However, this conclusion is difficult to support. First, in the development of these larvae, there is no clearly defined cleavage stage at which one can, as in amphiblastular development, identify an anterior hemisphere of smaller cells destined to become flagellated. Second, even if such an identification is made, it is not possible to equate unequivocally this same pole in the embryo with one produced during later larval development. Third, there has been no demonstration in these larvae that the forward directed pole of the free-swimming larva is equivalent to the anterior hemisphere of amphiblastulae. The view that all sponge larvae attach by their anterior pole is highly simplistic and obscures the absolute necessity for additional cell lineage studies in order to decide if the concept of polarity, based upon the morphological position of cells, is at all valid in comparisons of sponge larvae. Indeed, some parenchymellae have been found to preferentially attach on their "sides" (Wilson, 1935; Evans, 1899). In other cases, free-swimming larvae of some demosponges lack flagellated cells at both of their poles (Bergquist *et al.,* 1979) and although an "anterior" *swimming* pole can be readily identified, its lineage is unknown. The critical nature of this problem is exemplified by the larvae of *Oscarella,* which are both very interesting and potentially important in terms of an understanding of sponge larval development. In these larvae, Meewis (1938) and Lévi (1956) maintain that since the definitive basopinacocytes originate from flagellated cells of the *posterior* pole and choanocytes from those of the anterior pole the larva is an amphiblastula. However, in these larvae it is not really established which pole is anterior and which posterior in the sense of embryogenesis and cell lineage.

Larval Metamorphosis

The metamorphosis of sponge larvae involves the following morphogenetic processes: formation of the basopinacoderm and exopinacoderm, development of choanocyte chambers (or a choanoderm in asconoids), development of canal spaces and their connections with choanocyte chambers, formation of ostia and oscules, and the laying down of collagen fibrils, spongin, spicules, and matrix substances (Fig. 7-25). The specific sequence in which these events occur has not been established in very many species, may vary somewhat from species to species (Lévi, 1956), but always is initiated by the attachment of the larva and formation of the basopinacoderm and exopinacoderm. The origin of these pinacoderms varies depending upon the type of larva. In amphiblastulae the nonflagellated epithelium forms them (Tuzet, 1970, 1973a). In coeloblastulae (except *Oscarella* and *Octavella*) the epithelial cells that come to lie against the substra m or on the larval surface form these pinacoderms, such that

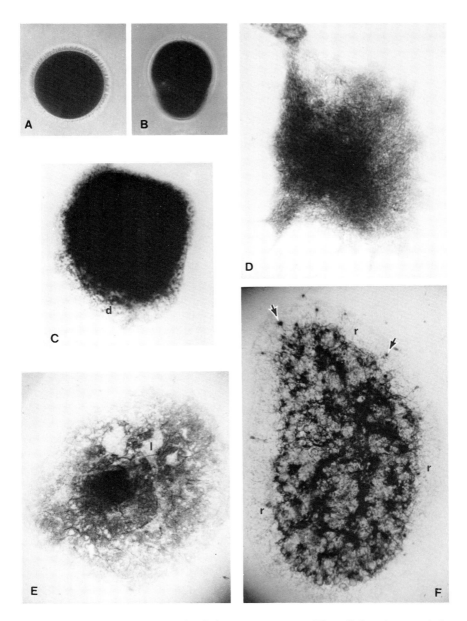

Figure 7-25 Larval metamorphosis in *Microciona prolifera* (light micrographs).
A. Phase contrast micrograph of a living, free-swimming parencymella. Note flagella (×50) (Simpson, 1968b). **B**. Phase contrast micrograph of a living larva showing the bulged area that can develop at one end of the larva (×45) (Simpson, 1968b). **C**. Whole mount of newly attached larva showing developing pinacoderm (*d*) (×65) (Simpson, 1968b). **D**. A later stage in metamorphosis in which substantial spreading has occurred. Whole mount (×70) (Simpson, 1968b). **E**. Initial formation of lacunae (*l*) and choanocyte chambers (small circles) (×45) (Simpson, 1968b). **F**. Fully metamorphosed larva (whole mount) in which a functional canal system has formed. Note the thin marginal region (*r*) lacking canal elements. *arrows,* spongin deposition around megascleres (×70) (Simpson, 1968b).

there is no predetermination of a cell lineage destined to develop into pinacocytes and the position of a cell at metamorphosis will determine its fate (Borojevic, 1969). In the homoscleromorphs, *Oscarella* (Meewis, 1938; Lévi, 1956) and *Octavella* (Tuzet and Paris, 1964), some of the flagellated cells lose their flagella and form the pinacoderms. According to these workers, these cells are derived from the posterior hemisphere of the larva and thus have a specific cell lineage; but as discussed previously, polarity in these larvae is not completely clear. Since this pattern of pinacoderm formation differs from that in amphiblastulae, in parenchymellae, and in other coeloblastulae, it should probably be considered a separate developmental pathway, at least until more detailed and comparative studies are available. In parenchymellae larvae, there is no suggestion of a flagellated cell origin of the pinacoderms. The cells forming them are part of the internal cells of the larva and during attachment they migrate to the surfaces, flatten, and develop typical pinacocyte features. In these metamorphosing larvae two types of cells are reported to give rise to the pinacoderms—collencytes and archeocytes—depending upon the species. In *Mycale contarenii,* a species which has been thoroughly studied experimentally, a large stock of collencytes is present internally in the larva; during attachment and early metamorphosis they form the pinacoderms (Borojevic, 1966). This also appears to be the case in *Halichondria moorei, Ulosa* sp., and *Microciona rubens* (Bergquist and Green, 1977b). In other parenchymellae such as *Halisarca,* archeocytes form the pinacoderms and in *Microciona prolifera* this also appears the case (Simpson, 1968b). The developmental significance of the presence or absence of collencytes in parenchymellae larvae (and in adult sponges) remains unclear (see Chap. 3).

The origin of choanocytes during metamorphosis may also be variable and in some cases is highly disputed. In amphiblastulae, they develop from the invaginated flagellated cells of the anterior pole and in homoscleromorphs they are *considered* to have the same origin. In other coeloblastulae (*Polymastia, Ascandra,* possibly *Cliona* and *Chondrosia*) they are derived from cells whose position in the attached, cellular mass (which is sometimes referred to as the "pupa") (Borojevic, 1969) is internal. In parenchymellae larvae the origin of choanocytes is highly problematical and conflicting views dominate the literature. Among *freshwater* species, the larval flagellated cells are described as being phagocytized by archeocytes and thus they are considered as playing no role in choanocyte formation or any other developmental process (Brien and Meewis, 1938). In direct conflict with this conclusion are the highly detailed observations of Evans (1899). He describes the migration of the flagellated cells inward where they form aggregates; during this process, striking changes occur in their chromatin, which eventually becomes more diffuse. Reported phagocytosis of all flagellated cells at metamorphosis was extended to *marine* haplosclerids by Meewis (1939b) in her study of *Haliclona lim-*

bata, and Brien (1973, p. 363) considers this to be the case generally in all freshwater parenchymellae while in marine species he leaves open the possibility that a few of these cells may persist as choanoblasts which then give rise to choanocytes. In the metamorphosis of freshwater species and *Haliclona limbata,* two origins of developing choanocytes are reported: (1) from archeocytes, and (2) from the precocious choanocytes already present in the free-swimming larva. In *Haliclona,* archeocytes are reported to be the origin of the developing choanocytes—those that both develop prior to metamorphosis as well as appear during it. In freshwater species, Brien and Meewis (1938) described the formation of *new* choanocyte chambers through cell division of existing choanocytes followed by subdivision of these larger newly formed chambers. The conflicting views of, on the one hand, Evans (1899) and, on the other hand, Brien and Meewis (1938) continue up to the present. Using electron microscopical techniques, Bergquist and Green (1977b) report that the flagellated epithelium is completely sloughed off—a truly amazing observation which, because of its uniqueness, requires further verification. Their results substantially extend the conclusions of Brien (1973) and Meewis (1939b) to include demosponge groups in addition to the haplosclerids. In distinction, Boury-Esnault (1976a) has clearly described the formation of choanocytes and choanocyte chambers directly from the flagellated epithelial cells in *Hamigera hamigera.* In the experimental studies of the larvae of *Mycale contarenii,* Borojevic and Lévi (1965) and Borojevic (1966) conclude that while some larval flagellated cells are phagocytized during metamorphosis, the remainder form choanocytes; their ultrastructural data are thoroughly convincing and leave little doubt of their conclusions. However, due to the continuing conflict on this question, and as recently commented upon by Fell (in press), a resolution of it requires a method for specifically labeling larval flagellated cells and following their fate during metamorphosis in parenchymellae larvae. Interestingly, Boury-Esnault (1976a, 1977) has reported the absence of gray cells in the parenchymella of *Hamigera hamigera* and their development from flagellated epithelial cells during metamorphosis. This is the first report of the origin of a special cell during metamorphosis and of the capacity of larval flagellated cells in a parenchymella to form any cell type other than choanocytes.

The migration of the flagellated cells inward to form choanocytes during the metamorphosis of amphiblastulae and of at least some parenchymellae is considered by some workers as gastrulation (Brien, 1967a) and thus is used as an argument for placing the sponges, along with the Cnidaria, at the base of the phylogeny of the Eumetazoa. The detailed, comparative data presented by Lévi (1956) certainly more than support such a notion.

The formation of canal spaces, canals, ostia, and oscules is discussed in Chapter Six. All of these studies indicate an archeocyte or collencyte origin of endopinacocytes, which then enter into complex morphogenetic interactions to produce a functional canal system. These processes are poorly understood and represent a significant challenge for future investigations. The initial canal system formed during metamorphosis appears quite simplified and synconoid-like leading to the so-called rhagon stage for metamorphosing coeloblastulae and parenchymellae (Lévi, 1956; Brien, 1973) and to the olynthus stage for metamorphosing amphiblastulae (Tuzet, 1973a). Beginning with the attachment of the larva and continuing throughout metamorphosis, the skeleton progressively develops by processes discussed in Chapters Four and Five (see especially Garrone and Pottu, 1973).

Experimental Embryology

While the number and kinds of reported experimental manipulations of sponge larvae are very limited, those which have been carried out provide highly significant results. The dissociation of mature parenchymellae larvae of *Mycale contarenii* and *Adocia elegans* results in the reaggregation of the cells into a mass and their development into a young sponge (Borojevic and Lévi, 1964a, 1965). That these aggregates do not reform a larva is further evidence of their adult nature. Similarly, dissociated larval cells of *Microciona prolifera* respond to aggregation factor in roation-mediated aggregation in a manner comparable to adult cells and there is no reformation of the larva (Burkart *et al.,* 1978, 1979). In the reaggregated larval cells of *Mycale,* some flagellated cells are phagocytized while the remainder form choanocyte chambers.

In a further, elegant study of *Mycale,* Borojevic (1966) has mechanically isolated three regions of the larva and then followed their fate. Cultures containing mostly flagellated epithelial cells and some collencytes and archeocytes rapidly form numerous choanocyte chambers if they first attach; some flagellated cells are phagocytized in these cultures. Attachment depends upon the presence of sufficient numbers of collencytes. Cell groups with too few of them round up and degenerate. Cultures of the internal cells alone—collencytes, archeocytes, globoferous cells, vacuolar cells, but not flagellated cells—develop into functional sponges with choanocyte chambers. The choanocytes are formed by the aggregation, in groups of three or four, of archeocytes which then divide. Cultures of the small, nonflagellated, posterior region neither attach nor survive. These results clearly demonstrate the potential of larval flagellated cells to form choanocytes, the regulative capacity of archeocytes to replace choanocytes, the essentiality of collencytes for attachment, the essentiality of attachment for development, and the absence of any obvious role of special cells in early development. Further, the flattened "pinacocytes" at the posterior pole of these larvae are not able to replace collencytes—they do not attach to the substratum. These results confirm the presence of two larval cell "layers" that form the basic structures of the adult—pinacoderms and flagellated epithelium.

Many years ago, Maas (1906) performed similar experiments on the amphiblastulae of *Sycon* which he mechanically transected yielding anterior, flagellated halves and posterior nonflagellated halves. The former rounded up and failed to develop while the nonflagellated halves attached and formed a functional sponge. These results thus establish that the two poles of amphiblastulae are comparable to the two cell "layers" in parenchymellae. Further, the regulative capacity of the nonflagellated cells to functionally replace the flagellated cells by forming choanocytes is completely comparable to the results with *Mycale* larvae and comparable to the development of a functional sponge by the internal cells alone in freshwater parenchymellae.

Most coeloblastulae possess only one cell type that is a flagellated blastomere lacking any predetermination (Borojevic, 1969). These whole larvae are thus developmentally comparable to the posterior cells of amphiblastulae and the internal cells of parenchymellae. The coeloblastulae of the homoscleromorphs appear regionally differentiated, but there are no experimental data to support this view. Mechanical separation of the "posterior" flagellated cells from the "anterior" ones and observations of their development are required in order to decide finally if they are functionally coeloblastulae (in the sense of *Polymastia*) or amphiblastulae (in the sense of *Sycon*). If indeed the "posterior" cells are regulative and form a functional sponge and the "anterior" cells do not, then this would be clear and strong evidence of their amphiblastular nature. If, on the other hand, *both* halves are regulative and form functional sponges, then these larvae could clearly be considered coeloblastular in nature.

CHAPTER EIGHT

Buds, Gemmules, Tissue Regression

A number of naturally occurring, asexual, propagative, developmental processes are known in the phylum. The most widespread and important of these is somatic growth, which is dealt with in Chapter Nine. Of the remaining, gemmule formation and hatching are best studied. In addition, some species develop and release buds, although this phenomenon is not especially common. A special case of "budding" involves fragmentation of the tissue and sometimes its dispersal. Some animals undergo tissue disorganization, usually on a seasonal basis, followed by cellular reorganization and development. Such disorganization has been reported following sexual reproduction in some species.

Buds

Fragmentation: A Special Case of Budding

Two distinct types of fragmentation have been reported; one of them involves the fragmentation of the substratum to which the animals are attached as in *Haliclona loosanoffi* and *Halichondria* sp. where the eel grass substratum undergoes breakage and the resulting fragments with attached sponge tissue become dispersed, primarily by waves and currents (Fell, 1976a; Fell and Lewandrowski, 1981). Further, pieces of tissue can be mechanically broken away from individuals, primarily due to heavy wave action following storms (Burton, 1949b). Recent field observations in Jamaica, West Indies, indicate that the dispersal of such sponge fragments can result in their reattachment and establishment of new individuals (Hartman, personal communication). In distinction, Fell and Lewandrowski (1981) consider substratum fragmentation as leading to the mortality of the fragments. These types of fragmentation, while not involving specific cellular processes for their occurrence, demonstrate the ability of tissue fragments to reconstitute new functional animals as can be experimentally accomplished in a parallel manner by cuttings and explants (Chap. 9).

A second type of fragmentation probably does involve cellular dynamics in its initiation. This kind of fragmentation is characterized by the "pinching off" of part of encrusting sponges so that two or more smaller individuals result. Such a process has been recently documented in *Clathrina coriacea* and *blanca* through underwater photography by Johnson (1979b) (Fig. 8-1) and followed in *Hymeniacidon perleve* by Burton (1949b) and Stone (1970a). Although detailed cellular studies of the process have yet to be undertaken, the phenomenon itself is of much interest developmentally. The areas of tissue that become isolated could form due

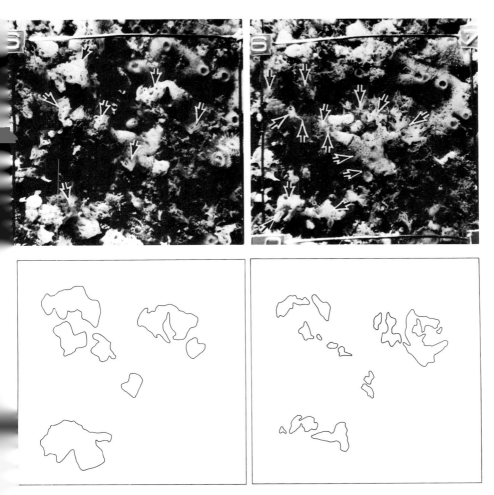

Figure 8-1 Above: Underwater photographs of fragmentation in *Clathrina coriacea*. Both photographs are of the same marked quandrant (×1.1). Left: Photograph taken in June 1975. Arrows designate seven individuals. Right: Photograph taken in July 1975. Arrows designate 14 individuals, a net increase of 7 due to fragmentation of the original animals. **Below**: Outline drawings prepared from enlarged prints of the sponges pictured above (Johnson, 1976). (Courtesy Dr. M. Fischel Johnson.)

to a streaming of cells into an outgrowth region followed by contraction or dissolution of the bridge between it and the rest of the animal. However, such fragments appear to have a high mortality possibly because the number of cells and/or their density are too low, or because sufficient numbers of essential cell types are not present.

Budding

Asexual buds (Fig. 8-2) which are released, become free floating, and eventually attach to a substratum and initiate a new animal are relatively uncommon. They have been investigated most thoroughly in *Tethya lyncurium* where they can be experimentally induced and have been initially described histologically in *Axinella damicornis* and *Mycale contarenii;* in the latter two cases no data are available on their release and further development. Highly unique, planktonic buds, which are probably formed by individuals of *Alectona,* have been described ultrastructurally, but the mechanism of their formation and their fate are unknown. Other examples of budding have been observed but remain essentially uninvestigated (Burton, 1949a; Schulze, 1887).

Budding is best known in *Tethya,* and the following description is based upon the pioneering work of Connes (1967, 1968). In *T. lycurium,* buds begin as thin filaments which contain one or a few spicules in their core (Fig. 8-3). These filaments then develop a distal swelling, some 5.0 mm in diameter, forming a definitive bud which can drop off and round up. Free buds can then attach to a substratum and undergo development or they may degenerate after attachment. The formation of buds in Mediterranean populations tends to be seasonal; from September to January the percentage of budding individuals is highest (40–80%) and drops to 10 to

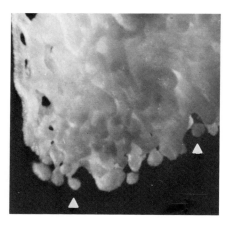

Figure 8-2 Budding in *Clathrina blanca*. The buds (*arrows*) are superficially similar to those formed in demosponges. No data are available on their cellular nature (×15) (Johnson, 1978b). (Courtesy Dr. M. Fischel Johnson.)

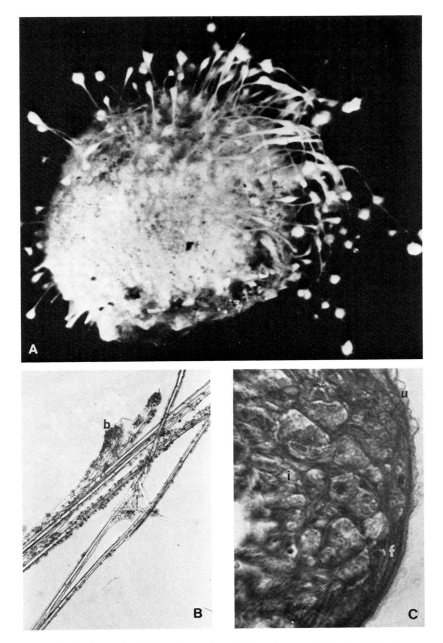

Figure 8-3 Budding in *Tethya lyncurium* (light micrographs). **A**. Buds form on thin stalks attached to the parent and then drop off and become free (×1.9) (Connes, 1968). **B**. Whole mount of young buds (*b*) attached to the shafts of spicules. The small spheres are microscleres (asters) (×95) (Connes, 1967). **C**. Histology of a bud showing the fibrous superficial area (*f*), cuticle (*u*), and densely packed internal cells (*i*) (×950) (Connes, 1967). (All courtesy Dr. R. Connes.)

30% for the remainder of the year. During the period of greatest budding, the number of buds per individual is also higher and budding tends to occur in larger sponges. The pigmentation of the sponge is also related to the level of budding, with unknown significance (Table 8-1).

In the initial filament, the pinacoderm is unusually fibrous and its structure is not clear; possibly a cuticle is present. Below it is found a layer of lophocytes. Internally archeocytes and spherulous cells are present as well as numerous microscleres (asters), many of them newly secreted and others apparently derived from the parent tissue through movement of preformed spicules. As the filament develops into a bud, the spherulous cells form groups, some of which are located more peripherally, and archeocytes and lophocytes elaborate collagen fibrils, with the latter cells becoming highly flattened below the bud surface. During maturation there is also a large increase in ground substance. The principal cell types present in the bud are archeocytes, whose density is much higher than that in parental tissue, spherulous cells, and lophocytes. The fully formed bud contains an outer cortex limited by pinacocytes and containing numerous lophocytes and more internally a layer of microscleres. Internal to the bud cortex is an intermediate zone containing abundant collagen, spherulous cells, microsclerocytes, and polyblasts. The central core contains megascleres, archeocytes, spherulous cells, and lophocytes. Mature tissue of *Tethya* possesses an outer cortex and inner medulla, and the zones within the bud are a reflection of such a morphology; however, choanocytes and canals are wanting and thus the bud as a whole more closely resembles the parental cortex than the medulla.

Following attachment and prior to the development of the canal system, many spherulous cells and archeocytes lose their characteristic cytoplasmic inclusions and some collencytes appear within the core. Spherulous cells are considered to give rise to microsclerocytes, although this very tentative conclusion requires additional supporting data (Connes, 1967). The bud cortex comes to contain few cells, but much ground substance and is now distinctive while in the core there is less collagen secretion and archeocytes form choanocytes by one of two methods: (1) they divide, forming a group of choanocytes within which a lumen develops; or (2) they aggregate around preformed lacunae and differentiate directly into choanocytes. The significance of these two separate processes is unknown and demands further investigation. Exceedingly few mitotic figures are recorded, and the suggestion was made that cell division may occur by binary fission. Such a view has little support from the data and it may be that there is very little cell division altogether. Canal spaces (lacunae) develop in the cortex and become lined by endopinacocytes which appear to be derived from archeocytes or possibly lophocytes. The major processes in the development of the bud include (1) cell migration and ground substance elaboration, (2) formation of a fibrous cortex containing few cells, (3) secretion of numerous microscleres, (4)

Table 8-1 Formation of Buds in *Tethya lyncurium*[a]

Month	Percentage Sponges with Buds	Mean Number of Buds/Sponge	Diameter (mm) of Sponges		Percentage Sponges with Buds	
			With Buds	Without Buds	Yellow Sponges	Yellow-Orange, Orange Sponges
Jan	68	16	40.6	37.3	58.1	78.3
Feb	30	7.5	41.9	36.8	30	29.4
Mar	26	6	38	36.5	22.2	31.8
Apr	17	4.5	40	37.8	17.9	18.1
May	5	3.8	42.5	38.4	0	9.5
June	6	3	22	38.1	0	14.3
July	4.5	4	38.3	34.5	2.8	8.3
Aug	14	6	33	32.5	12.5	25
Sept	43	9	43.6	39.5	31.6	52.2
Oct	72	16	40.1	36.2	64.1	76.1
Nov	54	22.5	38.4	33.6	68.6	52.6
Dec	75	17	35.7	30.2	75	73.7

[a]Data taken from Connes (1968).

development of new exo- and endopinacocytes, (5) development of canal spaces, and (6) formation of new choanocytes and chambers. These processes establish in a relatively clear fashion the central role played by archeocytes in development and further point to our continuing ignorance of the role of special cells (spherulous cells) in these processes. Both of these conclusions also emerge from experimental studies of *Mycale* larvae (see Chap. 7).

Bud formation in *Tethya* can be experimentally stimulated by cutting individuals (which have a spherical shape) in half. The mechanical trauma acts as a stimulus for the migration of many archeocytes to the outermost portion of the cortex (Chap. 9). The development of experimentally induced buds into functional sponges is completely comparable to that of naturally formed ones, except that the former are very delayed in their development, requiring some ten months of dormancy before rapidly forming canals and choanocyte chambers. During the dormant period, many cells are phagocytized, a process not apparent during normal bud development. This result is viewed as suggesting that the proportions of cell types present in the experimentally induced buds must be readjusted before development can proceed. In naturally produced buds, such cell ratios are apparently established during bud formation.

Connes (1967) has also described in *Tethya* the occurrence of so-called cortical protuberances which are surface swellings a few millimeters in height. When detached from the parent tissue, they are able to attach and begin development by forming choanocytes but do not progress beyond this stage. The normal function of these protuberances is not known and they do not appear related to budding. Possibly they are a result of tissue remodeling (Chap. 9).

In *Axinella damicornis,* Boury-Esnault (1970) has described buds observed in 75% of the animals from May to September and several individuals containing them were recorded in February suggesting that, as in *Tethya,* budding may occur throughout the year (Fig. 8-4). Buds of *Axinella* are swellings in the walls of oscules or in the excurrent dermal membrane covering over highly inflated, spherically bulged areas of the superficial excurrent canals. Their continuity, sometimes on short stalks, with the mesohyl contained within the dermal membrance gives them an appearance similar to *Tethya* buds. *Axinella* buds are covered by exopinacocytes except at the attachment point. Internally they contain collencytes, archeocytes, and spherulous cells—the same cell types as in the dermal membrane. Cell counts indicate that the density of archeocytes is significantly higher in buds than in the mesohyl, also similar to *Tethya* buds. No spicules are present in these buds and the ground substance does not appear especially dense. Although data on their release and further development are not available, if they do so, choanocytes would have to be derived *de novo* as in *Tethya.*

De Vos (1965) has described buds in the marine demosponge *Mycale*

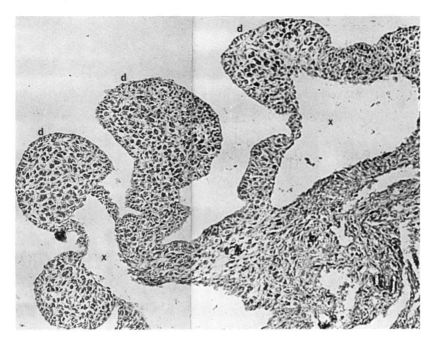

Figure 8-4 Budding in *Axinella damicornis* (light micrograph). The buds (*d*) are groups of cells which form above the superficial excurrent canals (*x*) (×125) (Boury-Esnault, 1970). (Courtesy Dr. N. Boury-Esnault.)

contarenii, which contain all of the cell types found in the parent: pinaco-cytes, collencytes, lophocytes, archeocytes, choanocytes, spherulous cells, cellules fuchsinophile (=granular cells), sclerocytes, and cellules "V". The latter appear completely comparable to spherulous cells that have released the contents of their inclusions as described by Connes (1966b) and Thiney (1972). These buds possess fully developed canals and choanocyte chambers, although some have only few of the latter. De Vos considers the latter condition as a stage in development, since intermedi-ates were also observed. The buds occur in depressions on the surface of the parent and are held in place by bundles of parental spicules. The depressions may also be partially roofed over by spicule tracts. No infor-mation is available on their release and further development. The nature of *Mycale* buds is in strong contrast to that in *Tethya* and *Axinella* and some consideration should be given to the possibility that they are derived from larvae which have failed to be completely released from the parent and come to lie at, or near, the surface where they undergo development. On the other hand, their complex structure is reminiscent of buds de-scribed below.

Tregouboff (1942) has described free-floating, planktonic buds from

Villeurfranche-sur Mer in the Mediterranean Sea which he originally referred to as larvae ("larves cuirassees") and later as "gemmules armees" (Tregouboff and Rose, 1957). One type described is most certainly derived from *Tethya* as originally suggested (Tregouboff, 1942). A second type, which Tregouboff and Rose (1957) consider to be derived from the clionid, *Alectona millari,* has recently been reexamined and further studied ultrastructurally by Garrone (1974). In the latter study, the buds were found to possess astonishingly unique structures (Figs. 8-5, 8-6). They are spherical and measure about 300 μm in diameter. A number of thin, stalk-like structures protrude from the surface and each contains a centrally located spicule. The central mass of the bud is covered by highly unusual siliceous scales, which Tregouboff (1942) considers to be modified microscleres (discotrienes) which are thin, disk-shaped siliceous deposits with a vague three-rayed structure. The central mass of the bud contains three more or less distinct layers: (1) a superficial (10 μm thick) layer bordered by T-exopinacocytes below which are the siliceous scales and a few spherulous cells; (2) an intermediate layer (60 μm thick) containing nucleolate, fusiform cells with very abundant cytoplasmic glycogen, small, homogeneous osmophilic inclusions, and similarly sized inclusions containing collagen fibrils (which sometimes have a tubular aspect). The fibrillar inclusions sometimes open to the extracellular space and are more numerous in cells deeper in the intermediate layer. Bacteria are present in vacuoles in these cells, which are referred to as gray cells, although fibrillar inclusions and bacteria are not usual features of this cell type (Chap. 3). Archeocytes are also present in this zone and contain intravacuolar bacteria, much cytoplasmic glycogen, fibrillar inclusions, and highly unusual membrane-bound glycogen accumulations. A third cell type present is a nucleolate, microgranular cell with glycogen and numerous microvesicles; (3) a central zone containing choanocytes organized into chambers. The choanocyte nucleus is not in the same plane as the collar, a completely unique arrangement except for hexactinellids. Other cells in the central zone appear to be degenerating within a matrix containing abundant collagen fibrils.

In these buds, there is a striking similarity between gray cells and archeocytes, with the exception of the osmophilic granules in the former which, based upon the presence of intermediate structured granules, may be forerunners of the fibrillar inclusions (Fig. 8-6A). These granules do not react to peroxide and thus do not contain melanin, although they may be lipid. The elaboration of collagen by gray cells has also been reported by Connes *et al.* (1972) and dense inclusions similarly occur in other collagen-secreting cells (Garrone, 1978) (Chap. 4). Future studies of these unique buds, particularly of their attachment and further development hold much promise for a more comprehensive understanding of the role of gray cells in development. According to Boury-Esnault (1977) and Boury-Esnault and Doumenc (1979), gray cells are a key source of metabolic energy for regenerative and growth processes (Chap. 9).

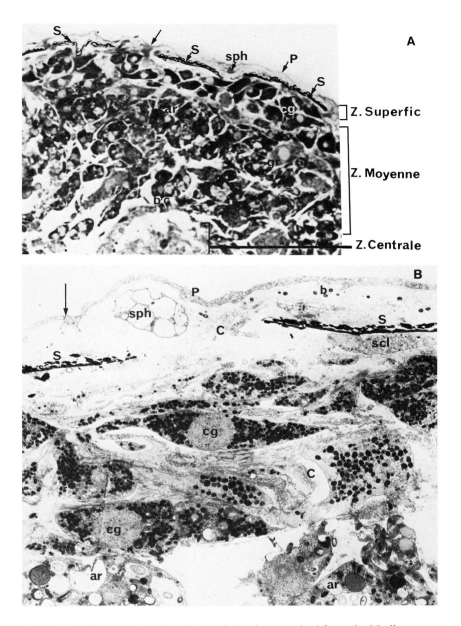

Figure 8-5 Free-floating clionid (possibly *Alectona*) bud from the Mediterranean.
A. Semithin section demonstrating the zonation: *Z. Superfic.*, superficial zone; *Z. Moyenne*, middle zone; *Z. Centrale*, central zone. The surface is covered by a pinacoderm (*P*) below which are siliceous sclaes (*S*) and spherulous cells (*sph*). *arrow*, exopinacocyte cell body. More internally are gray cells (*cg*), archeocytes (*ar*), granular cells (*gr*), and bacteriocytes (*bc*) (light micrograph) (×765) (Garrone, 1974). **B**. Superficial and middle zones of a bud. *sph*, sperulous cells; *P*, pinacocyte; *S*, siliceous scales; *scl*, sclerocyte of a scale; *b*, mesohyl bacteria; *C*, collagen; *cg*, gray cells; *ar*, archeocytes; *arrow*, intercellular junction of pinacocytes (TEM) (×3,310) (Garrone, 1974). (Both courtesy Dr. R. Garrone.)

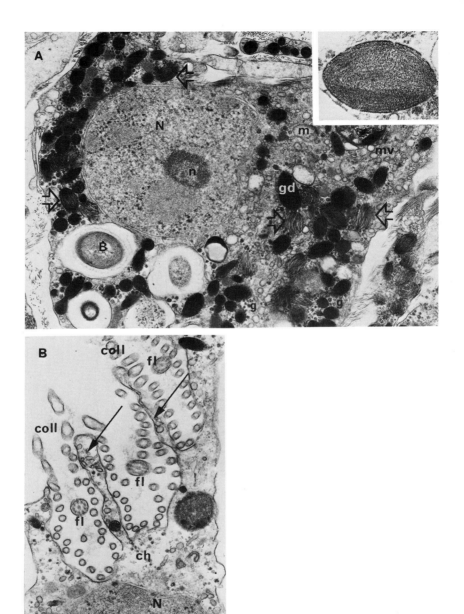

Figure 8-6 Gray cell and choanocyte of free-floating clionid bud (TEMs). **A.**
Gray cell located in the central zone. The cell possesses amazing organelle complexity in addition to the usual presence of dense granules (*gd*) and glycogen (*g*).
N, nucleus; *n*, nucleolus; *B*, intravacuolar bacterium; *m*, mitochondrion; *mv*,
microvesicles; *arrows*, fibrillar inclusions (×10,800). **Inset:** An inclusion intermediate between the dense granules and the fibrillar inclusions (×37,800) (Garrone,
1974). **B.** Choanocyte in the central zone. Note the unusual morphology, which
includes cell processes (*arrows*) that partially encircle the collars (*coll*) and flagella (*fl*). *N*, nucleus. There are possibly multiple collars and flagella on each such
cell (×16,200) (Garrone, 1974). (Both courtesy Dr. R. Garrone.)

Schulze (1887) has recorded the presence of relatively large, bud-like structures attached to the surface of the hexactinellid, *Lophocalyx,* and Burton (1949a) has observed small cell masses clinging to spicules at the surface of *Geodia barretti* which he considers to be buds that are released. In a three year *in situ* study of the antarctic hexactinellid, *Rosella racovitzae,* Dayton (1979) has shown that budding is a routine process at least in smaller (50 to 2,800 ml volume) individuals further substantiating this process in deep-water glass sponges. However, in the same study, no budding was reported in two other hexactinellids, *Rosella nuda* and *Scloymastra joubini,* the latter of which grow to an immense size (2.0 × 1.3 m). In *Rosella racovitzae,* animals less than about 15 ml in volume did not bud during three years despite very substantial growth of as much as 253% increase in volume. Based upon earlier reports that larvae may be retained and undergo metamorphosis within the parental tissue (but see Chap. 7), Dayton (1979) has emphasized the unknown origin (asexual versus sexual) of the buds in this species. Buds have also been described in *Polymastia* sp. (Ayling, 1980) and in *Clathrina blanca* (Johnson, 1978b). In the former, they are considered to be the major form of reproduction. In none of these studies are there data dealing with microstructure or further development. Similar observations of what is presumed to be budding have been reported in other species of *Tethya* and in *Stelleta arenaria* (Bergquist, 1978).

A process that is undoubtedly closely related to budding and that is frequently referred to as such is, in reality, a special case of somatic growth (see Fig. 9-1). This involves the formation of tissue masses at the base (*Sycon*) or along thin stolons (*Tethya*) that develop *without detachment* into new functional portions of the animals. This process is discussed in Chapter Nine as a category of somatic growth.

Gemmules

The development and hatching of encapsulated gemmules (Fig. 8-7) are highly ordered processes, which have been extensively investigated in freshwater spongillids and more recently in marine species. Fully developed gemmules, which range in size from about 300 to 400 μm up to 1000 μm, all have in common an outer collageneous coat, which generally contains spicules, and an inner mass of yolk-laden cells. In some cases, the type of siliceous spicules fused into the coat or its surface only occur in this location and such spicules are generally referred to as gemmoscleres, although the term has also been used in a more loose fashion to refer to any spicules which are so located (Brien, 1973). Many spongillids, possibly some potamolepidids, and the marine species, *Haliclona loosanoffi,* annually pass through a stage in their life cycles when the only cells present are those within the gemmules. Gemmule formation in these

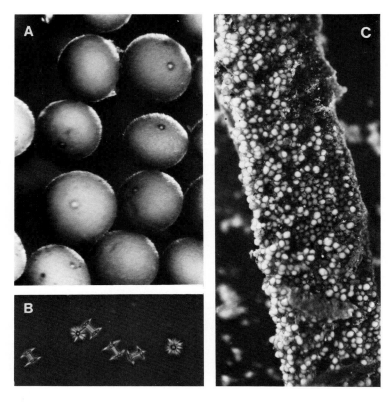

Figure 8-7 Freshwater and marine gemmules. **A**. A group of freed gemmules of *Ephydatia mulleri* var. *japonica* showing the single micropyle in each gemmule (×30) (Mukai, 1980). **B**. Freed gemmoscleres which were incorporated into the gemmule coat of *Ephydatia mulleri* var. *japonica* (phase contrast micrograph). (×270) (Mukai, 1980). **C**. Gemmules of the marine species *Haliclona loosanoffi* attached to a blade of eel grass. Note the close packing of the gemmules whose coats are fused (×5.0) (Simpson and Fell, 1974). (**A**, **B**, courtesy Dr. H. Mukai; **C**, courtesy Dr. P. E. Fell.)

animals thus takes on an essential role in their survival and appears obligatory in distinction to other gemmule producing species in which these asexually formed structures always occur within the fully developed tissue of the parent. In distinction to buds, gemmules do not appear to have a routine role as dispersive agents and are poorly adapted for such a function (Simpson, in press). However, they are structures that are presumed to function *sporadically* in the dispersion of a population (see, for example, Annandale, 1915; Poirrier, 1976) through wind or animal vectors. However, it is to be emphasized that there appears not to be a single case in which dispersion to a new habitat has been unequivocably documented. Presently available data which most closely approximate such documentation are those for *Haliclona loosanoffi* in which the fragmentation of the eel grass substratum to which gemmules are attached possibly results in a dispersive role for them (Fell, 1976a). In species displaying nonobligatory gemmule formation, it is not clear whether their capacity to form these structures is a sign of a newly developed ability or whether it is a remnant of their evolution.

Occurrence of Gemmule Producing Species

Gemmule formation has been reported in two orders of the Demospongiae—the Haplosclerida and Hadromerida (Table 8-2)—incidentally suggesting that these groups may represent a link between the Ceractinomorpha and the Tetractinomorpha. Among marine species, only *Haliclona loosanoffi* is known to form gemmules in an obligatory fashion. In species that are encrusting in growth form, gemmules are routinely produced basally in a single pavement layer and their collagenous coats are, more often than not, directly fused to the parental, basal collagen layer (Brien, 1973). The coats of adjacent, basally located gemmules are also frequently fused together as in *Haliclona loosanoffi* (Hartman, 1958a; Simpson and Fell, 1974), *Suberites domuncula* (Connes *et al.*, 1978), *Potamophloios symoensi* (Brien, 1967c), *Laxosuberites lacustris* (Annandale, 1915), *Spongilla fragilis* (Langenbruch, 1982). In branching individuals, the gemmule coats become lightly fused with the spongin enrobing the spicule tracts (Simpson and Fell, 1974).

Some note should be taken of the complexity of the relationship of the freshwater habitat to gemmule formation. There are now three distinct families that contain freshwater species. Members of one of them, the Lubromirskiidae, which is endemic in Lake Baikal, do not form gemmules. A second, the Potamolepididae occurring in Africa and South America, contains some species that are gemmule producing (*Potamophloios*) and some that are not (*Potamolepis*) (see Brien, 1970), as is also the case in a third family, the Spongillidae, which has worldwide distribution and is thus best known. In the latter family, for example, *Ochridaspongia rotunda* does not form gemmules (Gilbert and Hadzisce, 1977) nor does an unidentified species in New Hampshire (Gilbert and Allen, 1973b). Adding to this systematic diversity, some freshwater sponges have also been placed in the family Adociidae (Brien, 1970). Further, the family Potamolepididae may actually belong in the order Hadromerida rather than in the Haplosclerida (Volkmer-Ribeiro and Rosa-Barbosa, 1979). The current uncertainties of the systematic placement of some freshwater, gemmule producing species should be duly noted and considered; future revisions can certainly be expected.

Life Cycles Involving Gemmules

Obligatory gemmule formation is typified by spongillids such as *Spongilla lacustris* and *Trochospongilla (Tubella) pennsylvanica* (Simpson and Gilbert, 1973) and *Ephydatia mulleri* (Rasmont, 1970). However, one spongillid, *Ephydatia fluviatilis* can be either obligatory or not, depending upon the severity of winter conditions. When not too severe, disorganized tissue is maintained along with gemmules through the winter; when severe, only gemmules are present (Van de Vyver and Willenz, 1975). Aside from *Haliclona loosanoffi* in Long Island Sound, U.S.A. (Hartman, 1958a; Fell, 1974b) in other marine gemmule producing species and in potamolepidids, fully formed gemmules are found at all times of the year within the parental tissue (Fell, 1974b; Herlant-Meewis, 1948b; Brien, 1970). In *Spongilla lacustris, Trochospongilla pennsylvanica, Haliclona loosanoffi,* and *Ephydatia fluviatilis,* sexual reproduction occurs very soon after gemmule hatching, and since these species are obligatory gemmule producers, sexual reproduction only takes place in individuals that have recently hatched from gemmules. A causal link between dormancy and sexual reproduction might therefore be suggested. However, it is now also known that young sponges recently developed from larval metamorphosis also enter sexual reproduction very quickly (Fell *et al.*, 1979; Simpson and Gilbert, 1974; Lewandrowski and Fell, 1981) as do overwintering species (see later section) which redevelop functional canals (Simpson, 1968b; Fell and Jacob, 1979). Thus, a number of forms of active development appear possibly as stimuli for sexual reproduction with gemmule hatching as one of them (Simpson, 1980).

The time of year when gemmules are formed in obligatory species is highly variable and cannot easily be related to any single environmental factor; thus on a comparative basis it appears that endogenous physiological states, such as osmoregulatory efficiency, are of more importance (Simpson and Fell, 1974). This appears also to be true for gemmule hatching, except it is clear that minimal temperatures are required (Fell, 1974b). The biological function of gemmules in nonobligatory species is puzzling, although suggestions have been made that they serve as a means of survival when massive damage occurs to the animal (Herlant-Meewis, 1948b; Fell, 1974b). However, in one case, *Haliclona oculata,* it is not possible to induce any gemmule germination and hatching (Fell, 1974b). The almost routine occurrence of gemmules in the older (basal) parts of marine sponges suggests an age–substratum-dependent relationship.

The Gemmule Envelope

Structure. The structure of the surrounding envelope, or coat, of gemmules is variable but within relatively narrow limits. The two basic types of coats are characterized by (1) the single-layered coat of *Suberites domuncula,* which at the light microscope level consists of a relatively homogeneous capsule some 10 to 15 μm thick and which generally does not

Table 8-2 Gemmule Formation[a]

	Habitat[b]	Gemmule Coat	Cells	Micropyle	References
Order Hadromerida					
Family Suberitidae					
Suberites domuncula	M	"Bilayered", no spicules	Mononucleate	One	Topsent (1888), Herlant-Meewis (1948b), Hartman (1958a), Prell (1915), Carrière et al. (1974)
Suberites ficus	M	"Bilayered", no spicules	NR[c]	Absent	Hartman (1958a), Müller (1914)
Suberites sericeus	M and B	"Bilayered", no spicules	NR	Absent	Annandale (1915)
Suberites carnosa	M	NR	NR	NR	Burton (1949a)
Prosuberites microsclerus	M	NR	NR	NR	Wells et al. (1964)
Laxosuberites aquaedulcioris	M and B	Single, no spicules	NR	Absent	Annandale (1915)
Laxosuberites lacustris	B and FW	Single, spicules	NR	Absent	Annandale (1915)
Family Clionidae					
Cliona vastifica	M and B	NR, no spicules	NR	Absent	Topsent (1888), Wells et al. (1960), Annandale (1915)
Cliona lampa	M	Single, no spicules	NR	NR	Rutzler (1974)
Cliona trutti	M	NR	NR	NR	Wells et al. (1964)

Table 8-2 Gemmule Formation[a] (*Continued*)

	Habitat[b]	Gemmule Coat	Cells	Micropyle	References
Order Haplosclerida					
Family Haliclonidae					
Haliclona loosanoffi	M	Single, spicules	Mononucleate	Absent	Wells *et al.* (1964), Hartman (1958a), Fell (1974a,b)
Haliclona oculata	M	Single, spicules	Mononucleate	Absent	Topsent (1888), Fell (1974a,b)
Haliclona ecbasis	M	Single, spicules	Mononucleate	Absent	Fell (1970)
Haliclona gracilenta	M	NR, spicules	NR[c]	Absent	Topsent (1888)
Haliclona permolis	M	NR	NR	NR	Elvin (1976)
Haliclona sp.	M	NR	NR	NR	Burton (1949a)
Family Potamolepididae					
Potamophloios	FW	Double, spicules	Mononucleate	Absent	Brien (1970)
Uruguaya	FW	Single, spicules	?	One or two	Volkmer-Ribeiro and Rosa-Barbosa (1979)

Family Spongillidae
Eighteen genera including[d,e]

Genus		Coat	Nuclei	Number	References
Spongilla	FW	Single, no spicules; Double, spicules; Triple, spicules	Binucleate	One to several	Jorgensen (1946), Penney and Racek (1968), Rasmont (1956), Simpson et al. (1973), Gilbert and Simpson (1976a)
Ephydatia	FW	Triple, spicules	Binucleate	One	Rozenfeld (1970), Evans (1901), Rasmont (1956), Leveaux (1939), De Vos and Rozenfeld (1974)
Corvospongilla	FW	Single or double, spicules	NR	One	Penney and Racek (1968)
Eunapius	FW	Triple, spicules	NR	One	Penney and Racek (1968), Harrison and Cowden (1975a)
Trochospongilla	FW	Triple, spicules	Binucleate	One	Penney and Racek (1968), Simpson and Gilbert (1973)

[a] Based upon Simpson and Fell (1974). See text.
[b] M, marine; FW, freshwater; B, brackish.
[c] NR, not recorded
[d] According to Penney and Racek (1968).
[e] Not all freshwater spongillids produce gemmules (see Gilbert and Allen, 1973b; Gilbert and Hadzisce, 1977).

contain embedded spicules (Herlant-Meewis, 1948b), although occasionally megascleres become accidentally enrobed in it during formation (Fig. 8-8) (Connes and Artiges, 1980); and (2) the triple-layered coat characteristic of most spongillids such as *Ephydatia* and *Trochospongilla* (see Penney and Racek, 1968) in which three distinct layers are present—external (or outer), alveolar (or middle), internal (or inner)—and in which spicules (sometimes uniquely localized only here) are embedded within the alveolar layer (Fig. 8-9). In the potamolepidids, special, smaller versions of megascleres are routinely embedded in the coat and in many they form a veritable armour at its surface (Brien, 1970). An intermediate type of two-layered coat is sometimes present in spongillids, as in *Spongilla lacustris* (Gilbert and Simpson, 1976b), in which only the internal and alveolar layers are present. These doubtless are stages in the formation of triple-

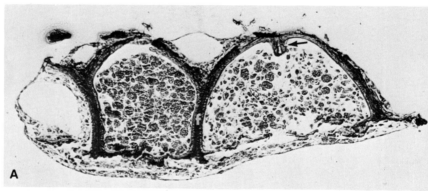

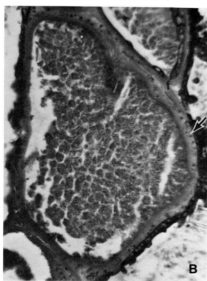

Figure 8-8 Marine gemmules (light micrographs). **A.** *Suberites domuncula* gemmules with fused coats (*f*) and micropyle (*arrow*) (×170) (Connes *et al.*, 1978). **B.** *Haliclona loosanoffi* gemmules also with fused coats (*f*) and with spicules (*arrow*) embedded in the coat (×180) (Simpson and Fell, 1974). (**A**, courtesy Dr. R. Connes; **B**, courtesy Dr. P. E. Fell.)

layered coats which are either incomplete or are prematurely complete (Simpson and Fell, 1974). However, the usual structure of the coat in some species can routinely be two layered as in *Umborotula borgorensis* (Rutzler, 1978). The so-called "bilayered" coats of suberitids and the "double" coats of the potamolepidids actually now appear to be single-layered coats in which inner and outer zones are distinguishable but continuous (Connes and Artiges, 1980; see following ultrastructural description of *Suberites* coat). The gemmules in some potamolepidids have an irregular, lobate shape, suggesting fusion of adjoining cell aggregates during their formation (Brien, 1967c). The coats of neighboring gemmules can be firmly fused together as in *Suberites domuncula, Haliclona loosanoffi*, and *Spongilla fragilis* (Fig. 8-8).

Gemmule coats routinely possess a special structure called the micropyle, which is usually a slightly raised, single, tubular protuberance with a closed base. In some spongillids, the micropyle is very long and forms an elevated tube (see later Fig. 8-20) (Langenbruch, 1982). Reports of the occurrence of gemmule coats without micropyles require reevaluation since in *Suberites domuncula,* micropyles are now known to have exceedingly small diameters (5–6 μm) and could easily be overlooked. Gemmules of a particular species are exceedingly uniform relative to their coat structure with the exception of some populations of *Spongilla lacustris* (Jorgensen, 1946). In this case, in individuals with large-diameter branches, single- and triple-layered (and a few double-layered) gemmules are found together in the same animal; the triple-layered ones occur more internally in the branch while the single-layered gemmules occur more superficially (Gilbert and Simpson, 1976b). In individuals with smaller branch diameters only single-layered gemmules are formed (Simpson and Gilbert, 1973). Jorgensen also noted that the triple-layered gemmules occur only in the basal portions of encrusting animals. There appear to be no other reports of such gemmule polymorphism, aside from those experimentally induced in *Spongilla lacustris* (Brønsted and Brønsted, 1953; Rasmont, 1954; Brønsted and Løvtrup, 1953).

Ultrastructure. Ultrastructural investigations of gemmule coats have been carried out on *Ephydatia fluviatilis* (De Vos, 1972; De Vos and Rozenfeld, 1974; Langenbruch, 1981), *Suberites domuncula* (Carrière *et al.*, 1974), and *Spongilla lacustris* (Simpson *et al.*, 1973) (see also later, Gemmule Formation). In all of these studies, a large part of the structure of the coat was found to consist of banded fibrils generally oriented parallel or tangentially to the surfaces of the coat. The inner layer of *E. fluviatilis* coats contains alternating dark bands of fibrils and lighter bands of "amorphous" material—two bands of each (see Fig. 5-6). In the darker bands, there are giant collagen fibrils (Chap. 5) (De Vos, 1972). The inner border of this layer of the coat consists of a distinctive, dense, thin band of material which clearly differs from the rest of the collageneous layer in

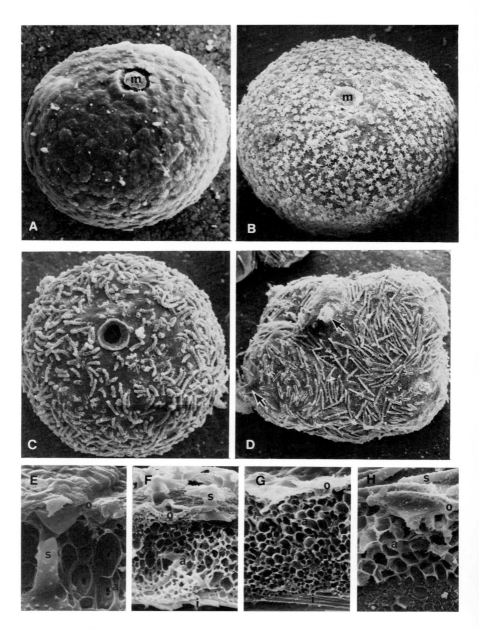

Figure 8-9 Whole gemmules (A.–D.) and fractured gemmule coats (E.–H.) of four freshwater species (SEMs). **A**. *Ephydatia fluviatilis* gemmule with a closed micropyle (*m*). The ends of the gemmoscleres are covered by the collagen in the outer layer of the coat (×165) (De Vos, unpubl.). **B**. *Ephydatia mulleri* gemmule with closed micropyle (*m*). Gemmosclere ends (star-shaped surface structures) are not covered by collagen (×125) (De Vos, unpubl.). **C**. *Spongilla lacustris* gemmule with three layers in the coat (see text). The micropyle is wide open (hole) and the gemmoscleres are visible at the coat surface (×120) (De Vos,

which there are small, spherical deposits that also clearly differ from the surrounding collagen. A similar structure of the inner coat layer has now been described in this species during its formation (Langenbruch, 1981; see later) and the single-layered coats of *Spongilla lacustris* have a completely comparable structure (see Fig. 5-7), except they are thinner (2.0 μm) and there do not appear to be any alternating bands of fibrils and amorphous material (Simpson *et al.*, 1973). In distinction, the single-layered coat of the marine species, *Suberites domuncula,* contains neither dense inclusions nor an internal dense band (Carrière *et al.*, 1974; Connes and Artiges, 1980). However, these coats do possess light and dark bands, and based upon the distance between bands, two zones can be recognized, an internal one and an external one (Fig. 8-10). In the internal zone, which is about 4.5 μm wide, there are six or seven dark bands alternating with light ones, and in the external zone there are fewer and wider bands. According to Carrière *et al.* (1974) the dark bands contain banded (10–15 nm periodicity) fibrils which are frequently tubular (15–25 nm diameter). However, in a later study of the synthesis of the coat, in which fibril morphology is more easily discerned, it was found that most of the coat consists of *microfibrils* (see Chap. 5), 5 to 7 nm in diameter and that the dark bands are regions where microfibrils are parallel and thus packed more tightly. The light bands are regions where the microfibrils are not as dense or are oriented in a different plane. Possibly, microfibrils of the dark band bend out of their central plane laterally and thus form the light bands; the microfibrils in the dark bands were reported to be spiral in tangential section, which supports this view to some extent (Connes and Artiges, 1980). Such an arrangement brings into question the amorphous nature of the light bands in the inner layer of *Ephydatia fluviatilis* coats and suggests that it too is fibrillar but the fibrils are differently oriented. The alveolar layer of the coats of the latter species consists of membranous remnants of the secretory cells. These remnants are large (4.0 μm) vacuolar spaces that give the layer its "open" structure (see Fig. 8-9). There are many giant collagen fibrils between the vacuoles and much amorphous material. In some areas the vacuoles can clearly be seen to be membrane bound (De Vos and Rozenfeld, 1974). The outer layer of the coat of these gemmules also contains giant fibrils, but there are no alter-

unpubl.). **D.** *Spongilla fragilis* gemmules grouped together with a common outer coat layer. Gemmoscleres visible at surface. The tubular micropyles are indicated by *arrows* (×83) (De Vos, unpubl.). **E.** *Ephydatia fluviatilis* coat. Inner coat layer not visible. *s,* gemmosclere spanning the middle layer (×1,360) (De Vos, unpubl.). **F.** *Ephydatia mulleri* gemmule coat. *s,* gemmosclere protruding from the surface (×800) (De Vos, unpubl.). **G.** *Spongilla lacustris* coat (×1,245) (De Vos, unpubl.). **H.** *Spongilla fragilis* coat. *s,* gemmosclere at surface of outer coat layer; inner coat layer lost (×475) (De Vos, unpubl.). Key for E.–H.: *o,* outer coat layer; *a,* alveolar (middle) coat layer; *i,* inner coat layer. (All courtesy Dr. L. De Vos.)

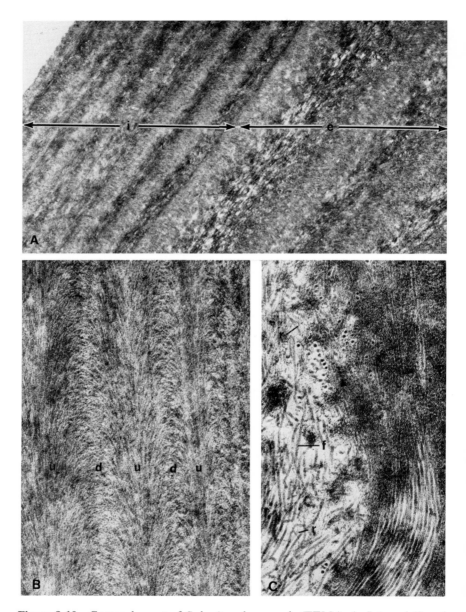

Figure 8-10 Gemmule coat of *Suberites domuncula* (TEMs). **A**. Internal (*i*) and external (*e*) regions of the coat with banding patterns in both (×10,620) (Carrière *et al.*, 1974). **B**. Substructure of the coat showing plumose bundles (*u*) of collagen separated by fibrils oriented in a different plane (*d*) (×36,900) (Carrière *et al.*, 1974). (**A** and **B** Copyright Archives de l'Académie des Sciences de Paris.) **C**. Collagen fibrils (*f*) and microfibrils (*r*) which are visible during the assembly of the coat (×42,750) (Connes and Artiges, 1980). (All courtesy Dr. R. Connes.)

nating bands; the structure generally appears more random and the layer is considerably thinner (2–3 μm) than the inner layer of these same coats. Further, there are no dense spherical deposits nor a dense limiting band.

The micropyle of *E. fluviatilis* has been shown to be formed by the fusion of the inner and outer layers of the coat producing a thin (1.0 μm) membrane-like structure. Surrounding this "membrane" is a short rim in which the fibrils are oriented obliquely to those in the inner and outer layers (De Vos and Rozenfeld, 1974). Langenbruch (1981) has recently concluded that the portion of the coat that forms the micropyle is not comparable in its origin to any of the layers in the remainder of the coat (see later section), although he too finds direct continuity between the collagen in the micropyle and the surrounding collagen in the coat. In *Suberites domuncula,* the micropyle is closed by a "plug" of collagen which, in its development, is also not comparable to the rest of the coat (Carrière *et al.,* 1974).

Chemistry. X-Ray diffraction data and amino acid analyses (Table 5–2) of *E. fluviatilis* (Huc and De Vos, 1972; De Vos, 1972, 1974) and of *S. domuncula* (Connes and Artiges, 1980) coats clearly establish that collagen is the major protein present as originally demonstrated using paper chromatography by Rasmont (1956). In *E. fluviatilis,* it theoretically constitutes 26% of the dry weight of the coat, most of the remainder being siliceous spicules (De Vos and Rozenfeld, 1974). In *S. domuncula,* collagen can account for as much as 77% of the coat which, however, contains few spicules (Connes and Artiges, 1980). In both species the glycine content is considerably lower than expected for sponge collagens, possibly suggesting the presence of other proteins. Also, the apparent absence of hydroxyproline in *Suberites* and of hydroxylysine in both species may indicate a significant departure from the usual collagens. Metachromatic staining of *Suberites* coats also suggests the presence of glycosaminoglycans (acid mucopolysaccharides). Jeuniaux (1963) reports the presence of chitin in gemmule coats, and in *Spongilla lacustris,* at least, the dense inner band of material in the inner layer makes up an appropriate mass to be this polysaccharide (Simpson *et al.,* 1973). However, it is to be emphasized that earlier statements that most of the coats of *Ephydatia* (Leveaux, 1939) and *Suberites* are chitinous are no longer tenable.

The triple-layered coats of *Spongilla wagneri* have been preliminarily examined for their lipid content which makes up 8.7% of the dry weight of the coats (Laseter and Poirrier, 1970). Of the lipid, 18.5% are fatty acids (Table 8-3). It is tempting to conjecture that at least some of these are present in the vacuolar remnants in the alveolar layer, thus helping to form an impermeable barrier protecting the gemmules from desiccation (see later section). In *Eunapius fragilis,* the inner layer, based on cytochemical data, is clearly heterogeneous and contains fibers (=spongin) embedded within a homogeneous matrix possibly consisting in part of

Table 8-3 Free Fatty Acids in the Gemmule Coats of
Spongilla wagneri[a]

Number of Carbons	Number of Double Bonds	Percentage of Total Free Fatty Acids[b]
10	0	0.10
12	0	0.41
13	0	0.36
14	0	1.35
14	1	trace
15	0	1.35
16	0	19.20
16	1	0.20
17	0	2.04
17	1	1.04
18	0	7.84
18	1	1.00
18	2	0.50
18	3	0.11
19	0	1.26
19	1	0.30
20	0	9.39
20	1	1.30
21	0	6.80
21	1	1.09
22	0	23.30
22	1	1.49
23	0	9.31
23	1	1.35
24	0	5.70
24	1	3.16

[a]Data taken from Laseter and Poirrier (1970).
[b]Free fatty acids represent 18.5% of the total lipids in the coat.

acid mucins (Harrison and Cowden, 1975a). In a number of freshwater species, Harrison (1974a) has demonstrated the presence of both DNAase and RNAase activity in the gemmule coat by substrate film enzymology. Such a finding is most surprising and requires additional investigation. The origin of such enzymatic activity could originate in the alveolar layer where cell remnants abound. Further studies of enzyme activity in gemmule coats would be most useful particularly in terms of the process of micropylar opening which must precede hatching (see following sections).

The Gemmular Cells—Thesocytes

Structure.   The cells that constitute fully formed, mature gemmules are referred to as thesocytes (Fig. 8-11). In all gemmules, the cytoplasm of thesocytes is packed with numerous spherical to elipsoidal yolk inclu-

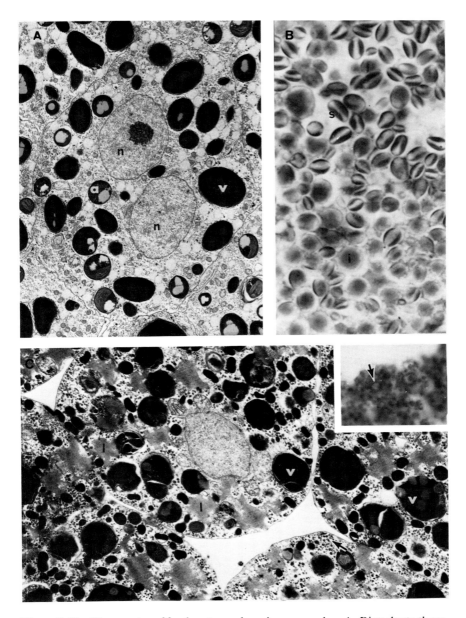

Figure 8-11 Thesocytes of freshwater and marine gemmules. **A**. Binucleate thesocyte of *Spongilla lacustris*. *v,* vitelline platelet; *a,* symbiotic zoochlorella; *n,* nuclei (TEM) (×3,330) (Williamson, 1979). **B**. Vitelline platelets of *Ephydatia mulleri* var. *japonica* stained for RNA which forms valve-like structures (*s*) when the platelet is viewed from the side. Spherical inclusions (*i*) are platelets seen in polar view (light micrograph) (×1,350) (Mukai, 1980). **C**. Mononucleate thesocytes of the marine species *Suberites domuncula*. *v,* vitelline platelets; *arrow,* glycogen; *l,* lipid (TEM) (×5,625)(Carrière *et al.,* 1974). (**C**, Copyright Archives de l'Académie des Sciences de Paris.) **Inset:** For comparison, a light micrograph of the mononucleate thesocytes of *Haliclona loosanoffi. Arrow,* nucleus (×900) (Simpson and Fell, 1974). (**A**, courtesy Dr. C. E. Williamson; **B**, courtesy Dr. H. Mukai; **C**, courtesy Dr. R. Connes; **C**, inset, courtesy Dr. P. E. Fell.)

sions called platelets. In those cases where symbiotic zoochlorellae are present these also occur throughout the cytoplasm. Thesocyte platelets of marine gemmules are generally smaller than those of freshwater ones (Carrière et al., 1974; Simpson and Fell, 1974) and thesocytes of marine gemmules and of the freshwater potamolepidids are mononucleate while those of spongillids are binucleate (Table 8-1). However, the description of potamolepidid thesocytes as mononucleate (Brien, 1967b) deserves reexamination since no further studies of them have appeared since their original description. The cells constituting gemmules appear to be a morphologically homogeneous population, although Carrière et al. (1974) have noted the sporadic presence of smaller archeocytes in *Suberites domuncula* along with the large (15 μm) thesocytes; thesocytes of *Haliclona loosanoffi* also measure in this range. In a parallel fashion to platelet size, thesocyte dimensions and those of their nuclei in spongillids are about twice those of the marine counterparts (Table 8–4). In distinction to most other thesocytes and the earlier description of Herlant-Meewis (1948b), many of the thesocytes of *S. domuncula* have been reported to lack nucleoli (Carrière et al., 1974). The latter author has also described the presence of highly flattened thesocytes just internal to the coat, but these appear in other respects to be morphologically similar to the more internally located cells. Thesocytes of gemmules appropriately examined microscopically are very tightly packed together within the coat but lack special junctional complexes (Ruthmann, 1965; Carrière et al., 1974).

Ultrastructure and Cytochemistry.   Ultrastructural information on thesocytes is available in spongillids, *Spongilla lacustris* (Ruthmann, 1965; Simpson et al., 1973; Simpson and Fell, 1974; Williamson, 1979), *Ephydatia fluviatilis* (Ruthmann, 1965; De Vos, 1971), *E. multidentata* (Simons and Müller, 1966), and in a marine species, *Suberites domuncula* (Carrière et al., 1974; Connes, 1975, 1977). Based on these observations, some general features are common in thesocytes of both freshwater and marine species. There are two types of membrane-bound, cytoplasmic inclusions, smaller lipid inclusions, and larger platelets. Internally within the platelets are also lipid inclusions except in *Spongilla fragilis* (Ruthmann, 1965), but this latter claim should be reinvestigated. The cytoplasm contains ribosomes, some rough endoplasmic reticulum, mitochondria, and Golgi complexes. While the cytoplasm of thesocytes of marine gemmules contains exceptionally abundant glycogen, little has been noted in that of freshwater forms.

The platelets of spongillid thesocytes (Fig. 8-12A,B) are ordered and highly complex, consisting of a somewhat less dense "core" around which are mitochondria. External to the mitochondria is a more dense "valve" region constituting about one half of the platelet. Surrounding the core equatorially is a belt of lipid inclusions and enclosing the whole structure is a multilayer, myelin-like membrane system. The platelet

Table 8-4 Comparison of Gemmules in Marine and Freshwater Forms[a]

	Marine (*Suberites domuncula*)	Freshwater (*Ephydatia fluviatilis*)
Thesocytes		
Cell size	14–22 μm	25–40 μm
Nuclear size	2.8 μm	6.0 μm
Cytoplasm		
Lipid inclusions	1.0 μm	0.8 μm
Lysosomes	0.4 μm	Few or none
Glycogen	Abundant	Rare
Platelets	1.2–3.15 μm	3.0–8.0 μm
Glycogen	Abundant	Little or none
Lipid inclusions	0.4 μm	0.4 μm
Ribosomes (RNA)	+	+
Reticulum	+	+
Basic protein	+	+
Mitochondria	+	+
Multiple surrounding membranes	+	+
Coat		
Internal layer	12 μm	6 μm
Alveolar layer	None	20–30 μm
External layer	None	2–3 μm
Internal dense band	None	+
Collagen microfibrils and fibrils	+	+
Special spicules	None	+ (Amphidiscs)
Micropyle	5–6 μm	25 μm
Fusion of adjacent coats	+	None

[a]Data taken from text and figures of Connes (1975), Carrière *et al.* (1974), Ruthmann (1965), De Vos (1977), Rosenfeld (1970), De Vos and Rozenfeld (1974).

valves were originally found to contain RNA in *Ephydatia fluviatilis* (Kauffold and Spannhof, 1963) and later the RNA was shown to be present in ribosomes which are tightly packed in the valves (Simons and Müller, 1966). The valves also contain isolated patches of rough reticulum similar to that in the cytoplasm. The core appears unstructured and contains basic proteins (De Vos, 1971; Harrison and Cowden, 1975a) and glycoproteins (Simons and Müller, 1966) as originally reported many years ago by Pourbaix (1934). Harrison and Cowden (1975a) have also found substantial levels of neutral mucins (polysaccharides) in platelet cores of *Eunapius fragilis,* although in that same study no RNA (using RNAase for localization) was demonstrable in the valves at the light microscope level. Such a result is possibly due to the dense packing of the ribosomes and the employment of thick rather than semithin sections.

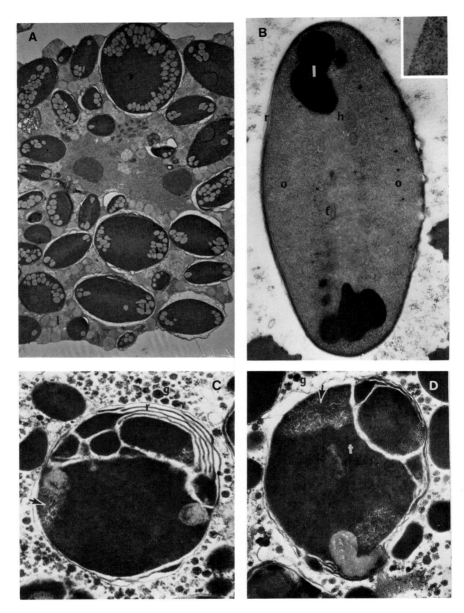

Figure 8-12   Vitelline platelets of freshwater and marine thesocytes (TEMs). **A**. Platelets in the binucleate thesocyte of *Ephydatia fluviatilis*. Note lipid (*l*) inclusion in the platelets and also in the cytoplasm (×4,050) (De Vos, unpubl.). **B**. Platelet of *Ephydatia fluviatilis* enlarged and showing lipid (*l*), surrounding membranes (*r*), internal mitochondria (*h*) and reticulum (*t*) and the valves containing ribosomes (*o*) (×24,300)(De Vos, 1971). **Inset:** Ribosomes specifically stained for

The lipid inclusions within platelets, also examined by Pourbaix (1934), contain neutral fat and acid phosphatase activity (Kauffold and Spannhof, 1963), although De Vos (1971) finds acid phosphatase activity is eventually lost when the platelets mature. Ruthmann (1965) suggests the fats may be, in part, unsaturated. In addition to RNA, the valves contain basic protein which according to some workers only stains well following RNA extraction (Ruthmann, 1965). Simons and Müller (1966) suggest that the ribosomes are actually attached to these basic proteins. The extreme density of the valves and core make ultrastructural observation difficult and although much glycogen is present in young, developing platelets (which are incidentally much easier to visualize) probably little or none is present in the mature structure (De Vos, 1971).

Although Simons and Müller (1966) indicate the possible presence of cytoplasmic DNA (Feulgen reaction), there are no clear data supporting this (De Vos, 1971) and the platelets do not appear to contain this nucleic acid (Harrison and Cowden, 1975a). Air-dried platelets exhibit strong spherite cross birefringence due to the orderly array of the surrounding membranes and their phospholipid components (Ruthmann, 1965). In addition, in water, the membranes bordering the cytoplasmic lipid inclusions and nuclear membranes as well as those around platelets also display birefringence indicating highly ordered structures. De Vos (1971) and Simons and Müller (1966) report the infrequent presence of nuclei within platelets referred to by the latter authors as dense bodies. As discussed by De Vos (1971), these "nuclei" are remnants of phagocytized cells that have not, for unknown reasons, been converted to the more usual storage state of other nutrients; they do not appear to retain their DNA, however (Simons and Müller, 1966).

The thesocyte platelets of the marine sponge *Suberites domuncula* appear significantly less uniform than those of spongillids (Fig. 8-12C,D). They too are surrounded by multiple membrane systems and contain lipid inclusions of neutral fats and, uniquely, carotenoids, which give the whole gemmules their yellow-orange color. Internally and frequently centrally located in their platelets is a large mass containing RNA apparently in the form of ribosomes, and basic proteins as well as some rough reticulum with attached ribosomes. In distinction to spongillids, these platelets also contain aggregates of glycogen rosettes with some platelets more rich in them than others (Carrière *et al.*, 1974). The largest internal masses

---

RNA ($\times 44,100$) (De Vos, 1971). **C, D.** Two platelets of marine thesocytes (*Suberites domuncula*) showing the variability in structure. *r,* multiple surrounding membranes; *arrows,* glycogen; *t,* reticulum. Note abundant cytoplasmic glycogen (*g*) (C: $\times 23,850$; D: $\times 22,050$) (Carrière *et al.,* 1974) (**C** and **D** Copyright Archives de l'Académie des Sciences de Paris.) (**A, B,** courtesy Dr. L. De Vos; **C, D,** courtesy Dr. R. Connes.)

contain the lipid inclusions, ribosomes, and glycogen; peripherally are smaller, similar masses, some of which consist only of glycogen. Mitochondria are present in the larger masses and at the surface of the platelet there is typically a finger-like protuberance of the surrounding membrane system (Connes, 1975). Some young platelets contain a whole nucleus derived from the cell which was phagocytized (see following section) and also contain small masses which give positive staining for acid phosphatase. Similar appearing membrane-bound inclusions also occur in the thesocyte cytoplasm where they have been tentatively identified as lysosomes. There is a clear absence of a discrete core and valve region in these marine platelets and their structure is consequently less uniform and more difficult to generalize. The heterogeneity of *S. domuncula* platelets is apparently due to an admixture of both young and old stages in platelet formation, both of which are stabilized. In this species, the thesocyte cytoplasm can be literally packed with glycogen. The platelets in potamolepidids are also less uniform in size and appearance and thus more closely resemble marine platelets than spongillid platelets (Brien, 1967b).

Symbionts.   Many spongillids possess symbiotic zoochlorellae and are green, and the question can be raised as to how the symbionts are transmitted in the gemmule stage. Most green species have not been appropriately examined and only for *Spongilla lacustris* are there any difinitive data and even these are incomplete. This species is now known to form three different types of gemmules: (1) green with single-layered coats, (2) white with single-layered coats, and (3) brown with triple-layered coats (Jorgensen, 1946; Simpson and Gilbert, 1973; Gilbert and Simpson, 1976b; Williamson, 1977, 1979). Only the first two of these have been studied relative to their zoochlorellae content, and it has been considered that the triple-layered type lacks, or possesses very few symbionts (Brønsted and Brønsted, 1953; Brønsted and Løvtrup, 1953). Williamson (1977, 1979) has compared the white gemmules produced by white sponges growing in shaded microhabitats with the green ones produced by green individuals growing in well-lighted areas (see Fig. 3-14); both types of gemmules possess intracellular, membrane-bound, zoochlorellae but in significantly different numbers. Green gemmules possess approximately forty times more symbionts, which, however, do not reproduce in either type of gemmule. The ultrastructue of the zoochlorellae is similar in both types of gemmule but differs from the structure of active symbionts in adult, green sponges in the following manner: the gemmular symbionts contain loosely rather than tightly packed chloroplast membranes, they generally lack chloroplast starch grains and they lack lipid granules (see Fig. 3-14). This modification in structure appears to be a result of the relative inactivity of the symbionts within gemmules, although Gilbert and Allen (1973b) have shown that the symbionts within thesocytes are photosynthetically active, and even pass some of their photosynthate to the sponge cells. In that study, it was also demonstrated that the chlorophyll a content of gemmules is higher than that in adult green sponges (1.44 μg versus 1.13 μg/mg ash-free dry weight) and that there is no significant change in this value in the gemmules during their dormancy (winter months).

Gemmule Formation in Spongillids

In comparison to budding, regeneration, reorganization of overwintering tissue, and growth, the process of gemmule formation is much more ordered and predictable, and specific stages in the process have been proposed using time-lapse microcinematography (Rasmont and De Vos, 1974). Such a sequence of events was originally worked out using histological procedures on a number of spongillids, most especially in the genus *Ephydatia* (Evans, 1901; Leveaux, 1939; Rasmont, 1956), and more recently by employing electron microscopy (De Vos, 1971, 1977) and semithin sections and phase-contrast microscopy (Langenbruch, 1981). The overall process (Table 8-5) involves the aggregation of mesohyl cells into a mass that becomes limited by a collagen-secreting epithelium. Two sets of dynamic interactions can be recognized—those occurring within the aggregate and those occurring within the surrounding epithelium. In both cases, determination of the origin of specific kinds of cells, the nature of their interactions, and their final fate emerge as major focal points in the elucidation of gemmule morphogenesis. There is considera-

Table 8-5 Gemmule Formation in *Ephydatia fluviatilis*[a]

24 h	72 h	120 h	168 h	216 h	264 h
Spongocytes loosely arranged in the aggregate	Spongocytes form columnar epithelium		Spongocyte epithelium becomes squamous		
	Primitive membrane forms				
		Primitive membrane lost			
	Secretion of inner coat layer				
		Amphidiscs moved into epithelium			
			Amphidiscs released from cells		
			Secretion of alveolar layer of coat		
					Secretion of outer coat layer
			Secretion of micropylar membrane		
Migration of archeocytes and trophocytes					
			Thesocytes become binucleate		

[a]Taken from Langenbruch (1981); gemmule formation stimulated by theophylline.

bly more data and understanding of cell interactions and their fate than of
their origin.

Initial Phase of Aggregation.   The first sign of the initiation of gemmule
formation is a localized increase in cell density (Fig. 8-13), which is due to
the directed movement of cells toward a specific locality in the mesohyl;
this process appears analogous to a chemotactic one in which cells move
continuously toward a specific center (Rasmont and De Vos, 1974) and
indeed, Rozenfeld *et al.* (1979), using time-lapse photography, have established that the cell movements are directed and thus chemotactic in
nature.

There are three types of cells that eventually constitute the aggregate—
trophocytes, archeocytes, and spongocytes (see Fig. 3-2) (Leveaux, 1939;
Rasmont, 1956; De Vos, 1971, 1977; Langenbruch, 1981). In reality, all
three of them possess typical archeocyte features, but either their eventual position and/or structure differs. According to Leveaux (1939), the
initial aggregate consists only of archeocytes which contain a few phagosomes and otherwise hyaline cytoplasm. These are then joined progressively by trophocytes containing numerous small granules occurring in a
cytoplasm which appears vacuolated. More recent studies do not support
the idea that trophocytes begin arriving after an initial aggregation of
archeocytes forms; rather, the initial aggregate seems to contain both
types of cells from the beginning. According to De Vos (1971) and
Langenbruch (1981), the earliest aggregates possess all three types of cells
which have the following common features: large (6.0 μm) nucleolate
nucleus, numerous Golgi bodies, abundant ribosomes and mitochondria.
The three types are distinguishable on the basis of the relative abundance
of organelles that they possess rather than on their exclusive presence (De
Vos, 1971). Trophocytes contain numerous membrane-bound lipid inclusions (0.5 μm), very abundant *free* ribosomes (which make the cytoplasm
very electron dense), many microvesicles (0.1 μm), and very abundant
but dispersed glycogen; very few phagosomes are present. Possibly,
tightly packed groups of lipid inclusions or microvesicles are what led
Leveaux (1939) to describe trophocyte cytoplasm as "vacuolated." Both
she and Rasmont (1956) indicate that the size of trophocytes is larger than
that of archeocytes, but more recent investigations do not emphasize or
record such a difference. As the trophocytes are phagocytized (see following), they possibly become flattened and thus appear larger. Archeocytes contain fairly abundant phagosomes with variable contents, sometimes including membranous material; lipid inclusions and glycogen are
also present but are much less abundant than in trophocytes. According
to De Vos (1971), archeocytes always possess a centriole. Spongocytes
are distinguished by exceptionally well-developed rough endoplasmic reticulum in addition to free ribosomes; lipid inclusions and phagosomes are
not plentiful.

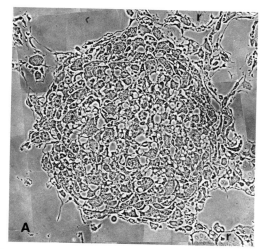

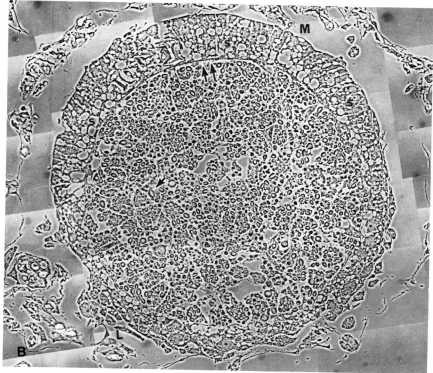

Figure 8-13 Gemmule formation in *Ephydatia fluviatilis* (phase contrast micrographs, semithin sections). **A.** Initial cell aggregation. *r*, choanocyte chambers (×285) (Langenbruch, 1981). **B.** Later aggregation in which the peripheral spongocytes (*s*) have differentiated and the inner coat layer (*double arrows*) is appearing. Platelets (*arrow*) are also appearing in the internal cells. Note the polarity of development which is most advanced at the pole marked *M* and least advanced at the pole marked *L*. At the latter pole, the micropyle will form (×335) (Langenbruch, 1981). (Both courtesy Dr. P-F. Langenbruch.)

It is still not clear whether these three cell types arrive in the aggregate already cytodifferentiated or if they differentiate during and after arrival (Fig. 8-13B). Leveaux (1939) considers the latter to be the case and concludes that cell position determines cytodifferentiation, whereas Rasmont (1956) considers it possible that their prior differentiations direct their final positions. He found that archeocytes arriving early are phagocytic and those arriving later are not. The former develop into thesocytes and the latter into spongocytes. Also, the late arriving cells were found to undergo some limited mitoses, an observation not recorded by other investigators. Weissenfels and Langenbruch (personal communication) find that trophocytes occur in the mesohyl outside of the aggregates thus supporting the view of their differentiation prior to their migration within aggregates.

Vitellogenesis and Early Coat Formation. The following processes occur in general contemporaneously and lead to the final phases of morphogenesis. The internally located archeocytes elaborate platelets through nutrients provided by the trophocytes (Fig. 8-14). Leveaux (1939) and Rasmont (1956) describe two mechanisms for nutrient accumulation: (1) the trophocytes undergo slow histolysis and lobes of cytoplasm are taken up by the archeocytes, (2) some trophocytes are phagocytized whole. On an ultrastructural level only the latter has been reported and the young archeocyte phagosomes contain whole trophocyte nuclei and other organelles (De Vos, 1971). The early view of Evans (1901) that trophocytes pass nutrients to archeocytes by diffusion and then return to the surrounding mesohyl has been largely abandoned. It will be very difficult to distinguish between trophocyte histolysis followed by phagocytosis and initial phagocytosis resulting in histolysis and then further phagocytosis. In any case, there is an inverse relationship between the number of trophocytes present in the aggregate and the numbers of platelets being assembled (Langenbruch, 1981). Using histochemical procedures, Pourbaix (1935) found that protein appears first in the newly developing platelets and the lipid appears later. In *Eunapius fragilis,* the RNA content in the valves of mature platelets is significantly greater than that in newly formed ones (Harrison and Cowden, 1975a). Newly forming platelets can also be identified by their spherical shape; as they mature they become ellipsoidal and their contents then become stratified (Rasmont, 1956; De Vos, 1971). Initial platelets contain trophocyte organelles, sometimes whole remnants of nuclei, as well as lipid, ribosomes, glycogen, and mitochondria (De Vos, 1971). Almost as soon as the phagosomes form, the young platelet becomes stratified with the lipid inclusions equatorial, ribosomes peripheral, glycogen in a central core surrounded by a layer of mitochondria. Even at this early stage, multiple membranes are present surrounding the structure but are not as regularly arranged. The contents of the platelet then become condensed, particularly the presumptive valves, and the

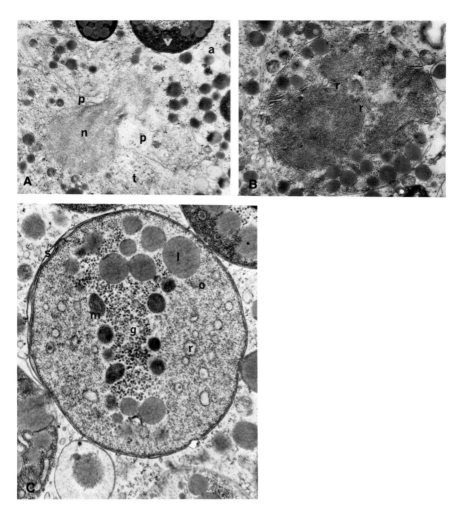

Figure 8-14 Nutrient procurement and platelet formation during gemmule formation in *Ephydatia fluviatilis* (TEMs). **A**. Phagocytosis of a portion of a trophocyte (*t*), including the trophocyte nucleus (*n*), by an archeocyte (*a*). The archeocyte pseudopods (*p*) appear to be pinching off the trophocyte nucleus and surrounding cytoplasm. *v*, developing platelet in the archeocyte (×6,750) (De Vos, 1971). **B**. An archeocyte phagosome containing remnants of a trophocyte nuclear envelope (*r*) and other nuclear and cytoplasmic fragments (×9,000) (De Vos, 1971). **C**. A developing platelet containing glycogen (*g*), mitochondria (*m*), lipid (*l*), rough reticulum (*r*), ribosomes (*o*), and surrounding membranes (*s*). Glycogen disappears in the mature platelet (×16,560) (De Vos, 1971). (All courtesy Dr. L. De Vos.)

glycogen in the core forms large aggregates. Later, glycogen becomes more dispersed and slowly disappears leaving a homogeneous core slightly less dense than the valves (De Vos, 1971). The structure then becomes ellipsoidal and the surrounding unit type membranes of about 100 nm thickness form a very regular arrangement with each membrane layer separated by about 20 nm (Ruthmann, 1965). According to De Vos (1971) each "membrane" may consist of two closely applied, 75 nm membranes.

As phagocytosis and platelet development are progressing the cell aggregate becomes surrounded by two epithelia—internally by the so-called primitive membrane of Leveaux (1939), which consists of highly flattened archeocytes with few platelets, and externally by the spongocyte epithelium. These epithelia form beginning at one pole of the aggregate and progress around the whole cell mass. The area at which the forming epithelia meet at the opposite pole later undergoes a special development to form the micropyle (see Fig. 8-13). There is now completely convincing evidence of the reality of the internal epithelium (primitive membrane) (Langenbruch, 1981) (Figs. 8-15, 8-16). External to it, spongocytes, which lack platelets, form a simple columnar epithelium in which cells are joined by very numerous interdigitations and septate-like junctions (De Vos, 1977). As the spongocytes arrange themselves, microsclerocytes, each carrying a fully formed microsclere (in *Ephydatia* an amphidisc), migrate from the surrounding mesohyl and push their way in between the spongocytes at very regular intervals in the epithelium (Evans, 1901). Recent, detailed study of semithin and ultrathin sections reveals that additional cells are closely applied to and wrapped around the microsclerocyte and apparently aid in the movement of the spicule into the epithelium (Fig. 8-17). Langenbruch (1981) has called them "companion cells". Harrison and Cowden (1975a) describe the presence of a granular cell within the spongocyte epithelium which releases its inclusions. This observation is unique and among others led these workers to consider that gemmule formation in *Eunapius fragilis* does not conform to that in other spongillids. A thin layer of collagen begins to be laid down between the spongocytes and the primitive membrane. At the junction of the external border of the flat archeocytes constituting the primitive membrane and the newly synthesized collagen of the internal layer, a dense band of material appears and is possibly secreted by the cells of the primitive membrane (De Vos, 1977; Langenbruch, 1981). The formation of the coat of potamolepidids appears to differ from spongillids in that no primitive membrane has been described (Brien, 1967b), although a columnar epithelium does form and secretes the coat. Sclerocytes were described moving spicules into the newly forming coat.

Later Stages in Coat Formation.   As the spongocytes secrete collagen microfibrils which form the internal layer, some of them, at least in *Ephydatia fluviatilis,* are assembled into the giant fibrils found in the mature

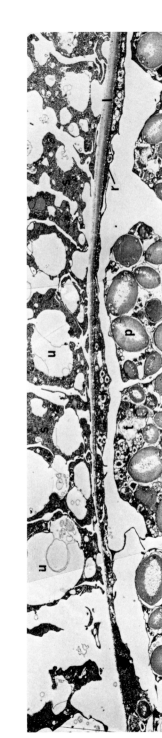

Figure 8-15 Early secretion of the inner layer (*l*) of the gemmule coat of *Ephydatia fluviatilis*. *s*, spongocytes beginning to form large vacuoles (*u*) which participate in the laying down of the alveolar layer of the coat. *t*, thesocytes; *p*, platelets; *r*, primitive membrane; *l*, inner coat layer. (×3,000) (Langenbruch, 1981). (Courtesy Dr. P-F. Langenbruch.)

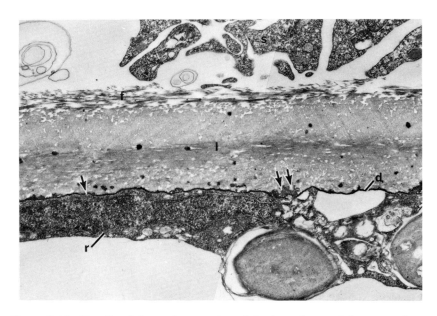

Figure 8-16   Details of the early secretion of the inner layer of the gemmule coat (*l*) in *Ephydatia fluviatilis* (TEM). A cell that is part of the primitive membrane (*r*) is very tightly applied to (*arrow*) and surrounds parts of (*double arrow*) the inner, thin dense band of limiting material (*d*). *s,* spongocyte; *f,* newly secreted collagen fibrils (×14,000) (Langenbruch, 1981). (Courtesy Dr. P-F. Langenbruch.)

coat (De Vos, 1977). The cells in the primitive membrane "disappear" soon after the internal collagen layer has begun to appear; their fate is unknown. The laying down of the alveolar layer has been thoroughly studied by the latter author and the holes that are produced are a result of the release of vacuoles from the spongocytes forming "ghost membranes." These are then surrounded by collagen microfibrils that stabilize the membrane system resulting in holes which are sometimes interconnected by pores (De Vos and Rozenfeld, 1974) as a result of the fusion of adjoining ghost membranes (see Fig. 5-12) (De Vos, 1977). In *Spongilla fragilis,* Langenbruch (1982) also finds such pores and further reports that the collagen secreted in the alveolar layer can appear at the junctions of the spongocytes (Fig. 8-18). Thus, the holes and interconnecting pores appear to form in a different manner in this species (Langenbruch, personal communication). Outside the alveolar layer, the external coat layer is then secreted by the spongocytes as they migrate slowly outward away from the aggregate (Fig. 8-19); they eventually flatten and form an apparently continuous squamous epithelium around the whole gemmule and then secrete an exceedingly thin, extra layer of collagen around the gemmule, the "husk" (Langenbruch, 1981).

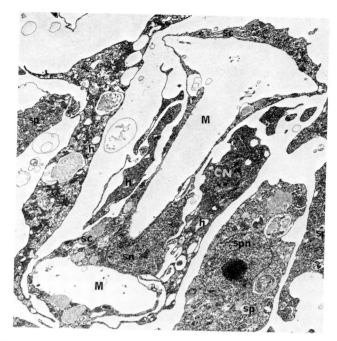

Figure 8-17 Insertion of a microsclere (M) into the developing gemmule coat of *Ephydatia fluviatilis* (TEM, desilicified). *sc*, microsclereocyte; *h*, companion cell reported to aid in the movement of the sclerocyte with its spicule into the coat; *sp*, spongocyte; *sn*, sclerocyte nucleus; *CN*, companion cell nucleus; *spn*, spongocyte nucleus (×4,900) (Langenbruch, 1981). (Courtesy Dr. P-F. Langenbruch.)

The micropyle is covered by a "membrane" of collagen which, as in the inner coat layer, possesses a thin dense band on its innermost surface; its secretion therefore probably also involves the primitive membrane. The spongocytes that secrete the micropylar membrane are oriented in a swirl at the point where the spongocyte epithelia meet (Fig. 8-19B). Langenbruch (1981) claims, therefore, that the membrane is not comparable to either the internal or the external layers of the rest of the coat; it does not contain an alveolar layer or spicules (De Vos, 1977). It is clear, however, that this structure is indeed physically continuous with both the internal and the external layers and it is even continuous with a small portion of the alveolar layer. The difference in orientation of the spongocytes that secrete it is doubtless the basis for the altered orientation of the collagen fibrils at its edges where they are continuous with the rest of the coat.

Toward the end of the secretion of the coat, the internal, platelet-laden archeocytes become binucleate by a process that has yet to be documented. The mature gemmule contains only these binucleate thesocytes

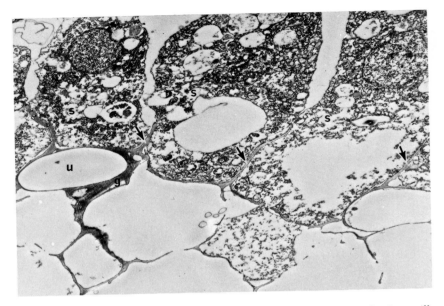

Figure 8-18   Secretion of the alveolar layer of the gemmule coat in *Spongilla fragilis* (TEM). The large vacuoles (*u*) surrounded by collagen (*g*) are released as the cell moves outward (toward the top of the photo). At least some of the collagen in this species is secreted *between* the spongocytes (*arrows*), *s*, spongocytes (×4,500) (Langenbruch, 1982). (Courtesy Dr. P-F. Langenbruch.)

and apparently the flat archeocytes in the primitive membrane are transformed into them also, although it is also possible that they are phagocytized late in gemmule formation; they are not a constituent of the mature structure.

The formation of the gemmule coat in *Spongilla fragilis* has been recently described by Langenbruch (1982). In this, and some other species, a number of gemmules form in close proximity and the alveolar and outer coat layers are continuous around the group of gemmules while each has its own separate inner coat layer (Fig. 8-20). After the inner layer has formed around the separate masses of developing thesocytes, the spongocytes of different gemmules intermingle and form a common alveolar layer around all gemmules in a localized area. They then elaborate a common outer coat layer. The micropyle is tubular and formed by a special group of spongocytes around a "plug" of other spongocytes. The micropylar membrane is at the bottom of the tube and is similar to that in *Ephydatia,* but the top of the tube is also covered by a thin layer of collagen not unlike the husk. The inner surface of the tube is similar to the inner surface of the micropylar membrane—it is limited by a thin band of dense material. This dense band may be secreted by the plug of spongo-

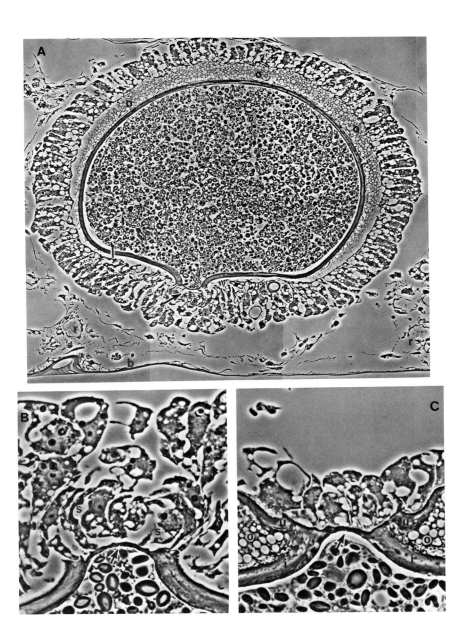

Figure 8-19 Later stages of gemmule formation in *Ephydatia fluviatilis* (phase contrast micrographs, semithin sections). **A.** Whole gemmule nearing completion. Note polarity of maturation—fastest at top, slowest below where the micropyle is forming (*arrow*). *s,* spongocytes; *l,* inner layer of coat; *o,* alveolar layer of the coat; *b,* basal layer of spongin in the animal. Note the persistence of some choanocyte chambers (*r*) (×270) (Langenbruch, 1981). **B.** Early stage in the formation of the micropyle (*arrow*). Note curved, rather than columnar shape of the spongocytes (*s*) secreting the micropyle (×945) (Langenbruch, 1981). **C.** Final stage of micropyle (*arrow*) secretion. The inner (*i*), alveolar (*o*), and outer (*u*) layers are seen adjacent to the micropyle (×945) (Langenbruch, 1981). (All courtesy Dr. P-F. Langenbruch.)

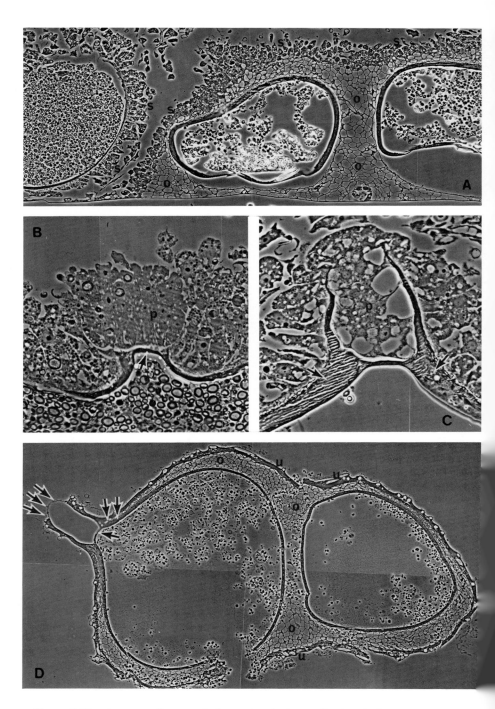

Figure 8-20 Aspects of gemmule formation in *Spongilla fragilis* in which a number of gemmules are grouped together and possess common alveolar and outer coat layers in which the micropyle is tubular (phase contrast micrographs,

cytes making them comparable to the primitive membrane. The tube wall is consequently secreted between two layers of spongocytes.

Morphogenetic and Developmental Aspects. There is still no resolution of the question of whether the position of a cell in the initial aggregate determines its fate or whether the cells are predetermined. Although recent reports favor the latter view, there have been no detailed studies of the mesohyl cells in the outlying areas around the initial aggregation center to determine if cytodifferentiation precedes migration. The mechanism of determination of the cells that come to form the primitive membrane could well be an inductive one involving influences at the surfaces of the aggregate. In addition to the question of predetermination versus positional determination, there is the problem of the origin of trophocytes, spongocytes, and even archeocytes, since the cell and nuclear sizes of all of them are well above those for vegetative archeocytes and other cells. At a minimum, cell growth must precede cell migration and, further, there must be a prior set of inductive events that stimulate the development of these large cells. This is possibly why when gemmule formation is stimulated experimentally by treatment with methyl xanthines, it takes at least 16 to 24 h before cell aggregation is maximal. Contraction of the exopinacoderm and tissue in general can temporarily stop cell movements, but it has no overall effect upon the rates of movement of the aggregating cells or on their orientation (Rasmont and De Vos, 1974). Such a time dependency establishes a requirement for cell mobilization and differentiation (at least in terms of cell size), which would not be the case if the cells were already competent to aggregate when the stimulus is applied. A thoroughly intriguing question is how a "center" for aggregation develops and what its nature is. There are no data or even hints that relate to this question other than the known involvement of cyclic nucleotides (see later).

Gemmule formation in the wild frequently occurs in older (usually more basal) areas of the mesohyl first [see particularly Pourbaix (1934)], and

---

semithin sections). **A.** An intermediate stage in gemmule formation. The two developing gemmules on the right are forming a common alveolar layer (*o*), while that on the left has its own gemmular epithelium of spongocytes (*s*) (×200) (Langenbruch, 1982). **B.** Early micropyle (*arrow*) development in which a "plug" of spongocytes (*p*) occurs above the newly forming micropyle (*arrow*) (×600) (Langenbruch, 1982). **C.** Later micropyle formation in which the "plug" of cells (*p*) is trapped within a developing tube of collagen. Note the alveolar layer of the coat is absent to the sides of the micropyle (*arrows*) (×600) (Langenbruch, 1982). **D.** Fully formed gemmules sharing common alveolar (*o*) and outer (*u*) coat layers. The micropyle possesses *two* "membranes," and inner one (*arrow*) comparable to that in nontubular types except the alveolar layer is missing lateral to it (*double arrows*) and an outer one (*triple arrow*) at the summit of the tube (×150) (Langenbruch, 1982). (All courtesy Dr. P-F. Langenbruch.)

thus aging possibly acts to trigger the development of such a center. Rasmont (1962) has suggested that a certain higher density of archeocytes is necessary to initiate gemmule formation. If such a density increase occurred locally, it might then serve as a center for aggregation. In laboratory cultures, young sponges will only produce gemmules if they are of a sufficient size (Rasmont, 1963), an observation compatible with the necessity for a threshold in archeocyte density for gemmule formation to commence. The real problem, however, remains the mechanism by which a center develops, since one there, it could then become self-sustaining, both stimulating and supporting the programmed interrelationships of the cells entering the aggregate. Possibly all areas of the mesohyl have the capacity to develop into such centers, but one specific area develops more rapidly, thus overshadowing the potential of adjoining as well as distant areas. However, in sponges growing in the wild, numerous gemmules form simultaneously and one is struck by the regularity of spacing between them at least in certain instances. Consequently, the centers for aggregation must also be regularly spaced; if they overlap sufficiently then coat fusion occurs between adjacent gemmules, which is indeed the case as discussed above in *Spongilla fragilis*.

The process of phagocytosis raises many interesting questions and it can be conjectured that the trophocyte cell surface is recognized as foreign by the archeocytes. The process is very similar to that of oocyte growth, which in some species includes the phagacytosis of nurse cells (Chap. 7). Since the spongocytes are not involved in phagocytosis and because they function at the surface of the aggregate, it is simpler to consider that they arrive later in the aggregate than the archeocytes and trophocytes. The other alternative, namely, sorting out, is also possible but has never really been clearly demonstrated, despite statements to the contrary. The spongocytes apparently degenerate after flattening and forming the extragemmular collagen husk, but the fate of the microsclerocytes and companion cells is far less clear. The companion cells appear to be carried outward with the spongocyte epithelium and may return to the mesohyl (Langenbruch, 1981). Choanocytes appear to play no part in aggregate formation and later development since they are maintained even during later stages of gemmule development (see Fig. 8-19A). On the other hand, there have been no specific studies of choanocytes, or pinacocytes, during gemmule development.

In theophylline-stimulated gemmule formation, the micropyle forms closest to the basopinacoderm (Langenbruch, 1981) suggesting that the mesohyl may directly influence morphogenesis. In branching individuals of *Spongilla lacustris,* two or three micropyles can develop in *each* gemmule with a single-layered coat (Jorgensen, 1947) indicating that there may be no polarity in the formation of the gemmule in these animals. There have been no detailed studies of gemmule morphogenesis in these multimicropylar forms.

Gemmule Formation in Marine Species

Histological Features.   Herlant-Meewis (1948b) studied gemmule formation in *Suberites domuncula* where aggregates develop in the basal, older
parts of the mesohyl. Initially there is a disorganization of the choanocyte
chambers and canals and groups of cells appear. These groups contain a
variety of cell types—archeocytes, eosinophilic cells (=gray cells), collencytes, and choanocytes. There are only two functional cell categories
in terms of gemmule formation: cells that eventually develop into thesocytes of the mature gemmule and cells that provide nutrients for thesocyte
development. The primary nutritive cells are gray cells which progressively disappear as the cytoplasmic inclusions within the developing
thesocytes increase in number. At the surface of the aggregate, two epithelial layers develop, a peripheral one and an internal one; the collagenous coat is secreted between them. The peripheral epithelium eventually
histolyses but the internal one is maintained, at least for a time. A second
method whereby gemmules were reported to develop involves the encir-
clement by spongin of portions of the basal mesohyl in areas in contact
with the coats of other previously formed gemmules. The initial contents
of these gemmules include choanocyte chambers, canals, collencytes,
archeocytes, gray cells, and occasionally spicules. This tissue is then
converted to thesocytes through the phagocytosis and uptake of nutrients
by archeocytes in a manner comparable to that described above. Finally,
a third method of gemmule formation is reported, which entails the subdivision of a previously formed one; no details of this process are given and
since there have been no recent investigations of the latter two methods of
gemmule formation, which are highly unusual, some caution is required in
accepting the interpretation as presented. In *Haliclona loosanoffi,* also,
two discrete epithelia are involved in the elaboration of the coat (Simpson
and Fell, 1974) and in both species (Fig. 8-21) gemmules form very close
to one another and the coats of neighboring gemmules are shared in
common such that when newly forming gemmules appear they utilize a
portion of the older coats. This results in the formation of a "network" of
collagenous gemmule coats quite unlike most spongillids. In *H.
loosanoffi,* adult spicules are routinely incorporated into the coat (Hartman, 1958a) unlike the coats of *S. domuncula* in which they rarely are.
The definitive thesocytes in both species are mononucleate and there is no
suggestion that a binucleate condition exists during their development
(Herlant-Meewis, 1948b; Connes, 1977; Simpson and Fell, 1974).

Ultrastructural Analyses.   Connes (1977) has conducted an ultrastructural investigation of gemmule formation in *S. domuncula* dealing only
with the first described method of their formation, and this recent work
corroborates the earlier study of Herlant-Meewis (1948b). The origin of
the thesocytes was traced to larger archeocytes, which are derived from
two sources—from the immediate area in which the gemmule is forming

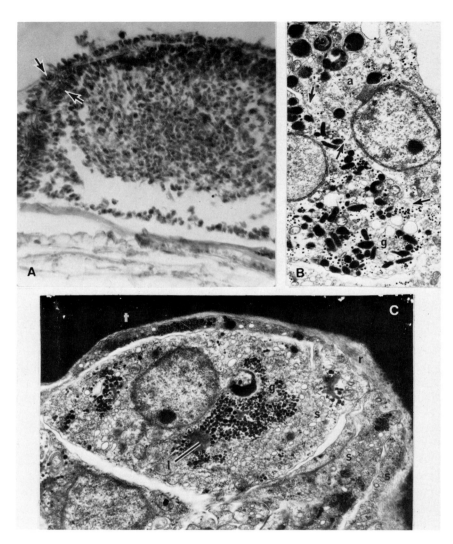

Figure 8-21 Aspects of gemmule formation in marine species. **A**. Early gemmule formation in *Haliclona loosanoffi* showing the two spongocyte epithelia (*arrows*) between which the coat is secreted (light micrograph) (×180) (Simpson and Fell, 1974). **B**. Fusion (*arrows*) of a gray cell (*g*) and an archeocyte (*a*) during the socyte development in *Suberites domuncula*. The gray cell is considered to diffuse nutrients to the archeocyte (TEM) (×6,300) (Connes, 1977). **C**. Secretion of the coat (*t*) in *Suberites domuncula* by spongocytes (*s*). *r*, newly secreted collagen microfibrils; *g*, glycogen; *l*, lipid (TEM) (×9,000) (Connes and Artiges, 1980). (**A**, courtesy Dr. P. E. Fell; **B**, **C**, courtesy Dr. R. Connes.)

and from more distant adjoining regions of the mesohyl. Some of them from both localities are described as being derived directly from choanocytes that grow in size, develop a nucleolus, lose their collars and flagella, and develop a cytoplasm enriched in dense inclusions, ribosomes, and Golgi bodies. In the immediate area of cell aggregation, whole choanocyte chambers appear to be transformed into archeocytes. In some instances, the transformation involves an intervening polyblast stage (Chap. 2). Thus, in the area of aggregation there is a complete disorganization of the chambers, as originally described (Herlant-Meewis, 1948b). According to Connes (1977), archeocytes migrating from distant localities contain numerous inclusions, whereas those from the immediate area do not and have instead an elevated nuclear : cytoplasmic ratio similar to polyblasts. The aggregate thus consists primarily of archeocytes, gray cells, and choanocytes which have not been transformed into archeocytes. Nutrients are secured by archeocytes from choanocytes, gray cells, and other archeocytes by four methods: (1) diffusion of soluble nutrients, (2) pinocytosis, (3) formation of junctions between cells in which the membranes temporarily lose their integrity (Fig. 8-21B), and (4) phagocytosis of cell fragments, sometimes of whole cells; the latter two predominate. The formation of platelets in developing thesocytes has been given special attention (Connes, 1975). Newly formed phagosomes contained mitochondria, ribosomes, sometimes a nucleus, vesicles, glycogen, endoplasmic reticulum, and cytosol. This material is then converted, by unknown but highly interesting processes, to a dense mass containing one or more aggregates of glycogen, numerous closely packed ribosomes, patches of reticulum, and lipid inclusions. The glycogen and lipid seem to be partially derived through chemical conversion of the initial material phagocytized. The developing platelet comes to contain usually one larger mass and a few smaller ones and is surrounded by multiple membranes which appear to some extent *de novo*. In addition to this method of platelet formation, the developing thesocytes also contain and acquire endogenous materials—glycogen, lysosome-like bodies, Golgi-derived dense inclusions, and lipids—which fuse together to form platelets. Cytoplasmic lipid inclusions characteristic of mature thesocytes may develop through the accumulation of fat within cisternae of the endoplasmic reticulum, which then appears to progressively expand and form lobe-shaped, membrane-bound inclusions.

Connes and Artiges (1980) have studied the formation of the coat ultrastructurally. As the central mass of cells becomes more compact, lophocytes and collencytes form an irregular "barrier" around it. Then at the surface of the aggregate, thesocytes that contain few inclusions form an internal pseudoepithelium. External to the "barrier," spongocytes derived from mesohyl archeocytes form a columnar epithelium. Between these two epithelia, the coat is elaborated and apparently both layers of cells are active in secreting collagen. The external spongocytes possess typical structure (Chap. 5) but also contain much glycogen and sometimes dense inclusions and phagosomes (Fig. 8-21C). The assembly of the coat is discontinuous with patches of collagen appearing irregularly around the perimeter in strong contrast to the highly polarized process in spongillids.

Developmental Aspects. Gemmule formation in *S. domuncula* differs significantly from that in spongillids in a number of respects, especially in the cellular source of nutrients and the active role of both spongocyte epithelia in collagen biosynthesis. The cellular origin of trophocytes in *S. domuncula* includes apparently all cell types in the animal and thus, although it does not pose an outstanding question, presents numerous problems. As concerns the origin of the thesocytes and the two epithelia, all of which originate from archeocytes, the problem of predetermination versus positional determination is unresolved and there is no information at all on the morphogenesis of the micropyle. Although spongillid theso- cytes differ significantly by being binucleate, a recent study of gemmule hatching (see later section) in *S. domuncula* reports the finding of some binucleate cells. The chemistry of storage products in both types of theso- cytes is similar with the major exception of glycogen which persists in marine thesocytes (Connes *et al.*, 1978), suggesting a difference in carbo- hydrate metabolism in the final maturation of the platelet. In this regard, the amount of cytoplasmic glycogen present in marine thesocytes appears much greater than that in spongillids. A striking aspect of marine gem- mule formation is the claim that many thesocytes ultimately are derived from choanocytes. Such a conclusion is of much basic importance to our views of development in sponges and, although generally treated with skepticism, there are now sufficient data that demand serious consider- ation of the role of choanocytes in developmental processes; such data are further considered in Chapter Nine. The absence of nucleoli in many marine thesocytes implies a modification in RNA metabolism in compari- son to spongillids.

Determinants of Gemmule Formation

Physiological and Ecological Factors. Rasmont (1963) has carried out an exhaustive study of gemmule formation in *Ephydatia fluviatilis* under laboratory conditions. The results of that investigation establish that the size of the sponges and their nutrition directly influence gemmule forma- tion; larger sponges and those fed more heat-killed bacteria form more gemmules. However, the type of bacterium, either *Escherichia coli* or *Staphylococcus aureus,* is critical to obtain these results. The latter bacte- rium when fed at higher concentration results in fewer but larger gem- mules in comparison to this same food supply at lower concentration. On the other hand, with *E. coli* there is a direct relationship with the number of gemmules formed (Table 8-6). Under these experimental conditions, very small animals fail to form gemmules and slightly larger ones do so if

Table 8-6 Effects of Food and Size on Gemmule Formation in *Ephydatia fluviatilis*[a]

	Percentage of sponges forming gemmules					
Sponge size[b]:	×	2×	3×	4×	5×	6×
No Food	0	12.6	53.9	87.2	95	100
10 µg nitrogen[c]						
E. coli	1.1	51	93.3	100	100	100
S. aureus	1.1	47.9	72.8	95.7	100	100

	Number of gemmules per 100 sponges when fed			
	S. aureus		E. coli	
	10 µg N	50 µg N	10 µg N	50 µg N
Sponge size[b]: 6×	100	90.9	115	150

	Sponge size[b]			
	3×	4×	3× + implant[d]	4× + implant[d]
Percentage of sponges forming gemmules	11.1	31.4	62.5	80.0

[a]Data taken from Rasmont (1963) and presented in a modified, abbreviated form.
[b]× = Sponge hatched and grown from one gemmule; 2× from two gemmules; etc.
[c]Per feeding.
[d]Implant = a new gemmule was experimentally implanted into the hatched, young sponges and it then hatched, adding more cells to the sponge. Sponges were unfed.

fed or left in unchanged media. The percentage of small sponges forming gemmules can be increased by implanting gemmules into them (Table 8-6). The results are interpreted to mean that in order for gemmulation to occur a minimum number of cells and a sufficient amount of an inducer are essential. Fed sponges produce more inducer which also builds up in the medium if unchanged. Further, gemmules stored for different lengths of time at 3°C showed differences in their ability to support later gemmule formation after they had hatched, suggesting the involvement of an endogenous component which has yet to be identified. Such an endogenous component has also been clearly demonstrated by Gilbert (1975) through implantation of cold-stored gemmules back into their natural habitat at varying times of the summer and autumn. Sponges derived from gemmules implanted after mid-June did not form gemmules or formed them late despite the presence of environmental conditions which are known to support gemmule formation in the wild populations of sponges and in those derived from gemmule implants prior to mid-June. Additional data supporting the importance of endogenous factors are the observations of Rasmont (1956) on gemmule formation in very small individuals of *E. fluviatilis* during early spring when the new, young sponges have just emerged from the overwintering gemmules. Further, different species in the same habitat initiate gemmule formation at different times (Simpson and Gilbert, 1973) as do different individuals of the same species in some localities (Rasmont, 1975). Other field observations indicate that a wide array of differing environmental conditions exist prior to and during gemmule formation in different species, thus further emphasizing the role of endogenous factors (Simpson and Fell, 1974). However, this does not exclude the intimate involvement in some cases of such factors or of their importance. For example, it has been experimentally demonstrated that constant illumination completely inhibits gemmule formation in one strain of *E. fluviatilis* (Rasmont, 1970). Increasing the dark period from 0 to 16 h per day substantially increases gemmulation. Temperature can also interact with illumination in a complex fashion (Table 8-7). It is important to keep in mind, however, that such experimental conditions are far removed from filed conditions.

The discovery that larger and better-fed sponges form larger gemmules is an important one, since it demonstrates that the determination of size is rather liable and that gemmules do not necessarily have to contain a certain number of cells. Obviously there must be a lower limit but this is not known. In this regard, Peetermans-Pé *et al.* (1975) have reported an amazing effect of lowered silicic acid content of the medium. At very low levels (0.2 mg SiO_2/liter) approximately twice as many gemmules are formed and they are about one half the usual size of those formed in media with 15 mg SiO_2/liter. Although the coats lack spicules, they are the same

Table 8-7   Effect of Light on Gemule Formation in *Ephydatia fluviatilis*[a]

Illumination (h/24 h)		Temperature (h/24 h)		Number of Gemmules Formed Per 100 Sponges
Dark	Light[b]	20°C	23°C	
—	24	24	—	0
8	16	24	—	90
16	8	24	—	135
24	—	24	—	68
24	—	16	8	73
24	—	8	16	127
24	—	—	24	20

[a]From Rasmont (1970).
[b]25 lux.

thickness and have the same morphology, but the total volume of theso-cytes is halved (Table 8-8). The authors suggest that the absence of spic-ules in the mesohyl may permit more aggregation centers to develop due to increased space and diffusion. Also, the presence of sclerocytes which do not secrete spicules may make available an additional stock of cells permitting more numerous localities of high cellular density.

The reasons for the formation of single-layered coats, rather than triple-layered ones, by *Spongilla lacustris* are not clear, but it is possible that if gemmule formation does not occur until autumn, as is the case in one population which almost exclusively forms single-layered coats (Simpson and Gilbert, 1973; Gilbert and Simpson, 1976b), the falling temperatures may inhibit the activity of the spongocytes and thus suspend coat forma-tion prematurely. This possibility should be tested experimentally. The white rather than green single-layered gemmules formed by this species are due to the loss of most (but not all) of their symbiotic algae due to lowered illumination (Williamson, 1979).

Cyclic Nucleotides. In 1974, Rasmont discovered that theophylline, an inhibitor of cyclic nucleotide phosphodiesterases, stimulated the rapid formation of gemmules in newly developed, young sponges. Significantly, it also increased the number of gemmules produced in each sponge from one large gemmule to two smaller ones, thus implying that a specific local process was effected in addition to a possible general effect upon cell metabolism and mobility. The time required for gemmule formation in petri dish cultures stimulated with theophylline is about 240 h (Rasmont and De Vos, 1974); Langenbruch (1981) reports essentially the same tim-ing in much older sponges (98 and 127 day-old cultures). In both studies, the initial appearance of cell aggregates occurs at three days after expo-sure to this substance. However, in specially constructed chambers for

Table 8-8 Effect of Silicon Content on Gemmule Size and Number in *Ephydatia fluviatilis*[a]

	Amount of SiO_2 in Medium/liter	
	15 mg	0.2 mg
Number of gemmules		
Three weeks	32	67
Five weeks	36	84
Gemmule diameter (μm)	348	298
Gemmule coat thickness (μm)	28	28
Gemmule radius minus coat (μm)	146	121
Gemmule volume minus coat (mm^3)	0.013	0.007

[a]Data from Peetermans-Pé *et al.* (1975).

microcinematography, the time for gemmule formation is about halved, specifically the time for cell aggregation to take place is reduced from 4 to 1 day, while the time for coat elaboration is not substantially affected (Rasmont and De Vos, 1974). It is still not clear why the time for aggregation is shortened under these conditions. Theophylline-stimulated aggregation was found to be a continuous process of cell migration and does not occur in waves.

Although it was not possible to stimulate gemmule formation in *Ephydatia fluviatilis* using cyclic nucleotides directly (Rasmont, 1974), this has proven possible in *Spongilla lacustris* with continuous exposure to them as well as to aminophylline (a closely related substance to theophylline) (Simpson and Rodan, 1976a). Furthermore, it was found possible under these conditions to stimulate the formation of a new gemmule from a newly hatched sponge derived from just a single gemmule, a result not achieved under any other known culture conditions. The time for such formation is very much in line with that reported for theophylline in *E. fluviatilis*—twelve days, which includes the time for establishment of the new sponge (3–4 days) and the formation of the gemmule (8–9 days). In the latter study, aminophylline was also shown *in vitro* to inhibit phosphodiesterase activity. These results make it highly likely that the process of gemmule formation has as its basis an alteration of cyclic nucleotide metabolism which leads to cell aggregation and the ensuing process of gemmule morphogenesis. Many outstanding problems still require elucidation. It is not clear what the role of cGMP is in the process, since both it as well as cAMP are effective in stimulating gemmule formation. Similarly, aminophylline may stimulate the process through inhibition of either or both phosphodiesterases. A question of much interest is that of how the cyclic nucleotides are involved in stimulating the formation of aggregation centers whose nature is totally unknown. It is possible that they are involved only in the stimulation of aggregation centers, but alternatively, they could also effect cell migration and possibly even the cytodifferentiation of the four cell types that eventually constitute the developing aggregates. The apparent requirement for continuous exposure to theophylline (Rasmont and De Vos, 1974; Rasmont, 1974) suggests cell migration is directly involved in the response. Various environmental factors now require evaluation in terms of their possible effect upon cyclic nucleotide metabolism. In some strains of *E. fluviatilis,* continuous illumination cancels theophylline stimulation in unfed sponges, whereas feeding under these same conditions restores it. One strain of this species was even reported unresponsive to theophylline unless it was provided with food (Rasmont, 1974). The hypothetical relationship between osmoregulatory activity and gemmule formation (Simpson and Fell, 1974) also requires further consideration particularly in view of the known localization within the plasmalemma of the enzymes that synthesize the cyclic nucleotides.

Gemmule Dormancy

Fully formed gemmules are kept in a quiescent, or dormant, state by (1) low temperature (3–4°C), (2) the presence of an inhibitor which is apparently produced by the parent tissue, or (3) an endogenous condition within the gemmule which prevents its germination but which can be overcome by cold treatment. Gemmules whose dormancy is a result of either of the first two factors are referred to as nondiapausing and those which are characterized by the third are called diapausing. However, in all known cases and regardless of the basis of dormancy, low temperature is effective, at least for a period of months, in maintaining gemmules in an inactive state. In one known case, that of *Haliclona oculata,* gemmules remain dormant regardless of temperature and thus can be considered to be unhatchable (Fell, 1974b), although more comprehensive studies are still required.

Diapausing and Nondiapausing Gemmules. Rasmont (1954, 1955a) established that the germination and hatching of gemmules of *Ephydatia mulleri* and *Spongilla fragilis* are stimulated by prior cold treatment. The length of time of the cold treatment and the specific temperature employed directly effect the subsequent rate of percentage hatching of the gemmules as does the incubation temperature following cold treatment (Rasmont, 1955a, 1962). Cold treatment (3°, 8°C) for about four weeks followed by incubation at 20°C results in 90% germination and hatching while a temperature of 12°C for four weeks results in only 60% hatching and no cold treatment (18°C) yields 25% hatching. But, maintenance of the gemmules at 18°C for forty-four days and then incubation at 20°C results in close to 90% hatching. Thus, these gemmules require maturation which is accelerated by cold but not absolutely dependent upon it. Mukai (1980) has reported that low temperature also enhances the hatching of gemmules of these species as well as those of *Heteromeyenia baileyi* and *Ephydatia crateriformis*. However, low-temperature storage actually inhibits subsequent hatching in *Spongilla semispongilla* and in this species storage at room temperature (25°C) for about three months results in about 90% hatching. In temperate habitats, gemmules are routinely exposed to the cold during the winter months and gemmules employed in diapause studies must therefore be collected prior to the cold weather.

The gemmules of the marine sponge *Haliclona loosanoffi* similarly display diapause but appear more dependent upon cold treatment than their freshwater counterparts (Fell, 1974b). Early autumn gemmules of this species maintained for 55 or 77 days at 20°C display some germination and hatching while prior cold treatment (5°C) for 30 days results in maximal germination. Shifting of gemmules from 20 to 5°C for about 40 days and then back to 20°C results in maximal hatching. There is, however, little effect upon germination by low temperature treatment beyond 28 to 63 days and cold treatment for short periods, 7 to 14 days is not fully effective in stimulating maximal germination.

In distinction, the single-layered, green gemmules of *Spongilla lacustris* and those of *Ephydatia fluviatilis* are little effected in their germination rates or percentage hatching by prior cold treatment and thus are considered to be nondiapausing (Mukai, 1980; Rasmont, 1962). On the other hand the triple-layered brown gemmules of the former species appear to be diapausing (Rasmont, 1962).

The Nature of Gemmule Dormancy. It is still not known what processes are effected by the cold treatment of diapausing gemmules, although it is clear that they are able to proceed at higher temperatures given appropriate time (Rasmont, 1962). In *E. mulleri,* there is some suggestion that low-temperature treatment for three and one half months results in a higher glycogen level of 0.8 μg/gemmule than does storage at higher temperature (18°C) which results in 0.6 μg glycogen/gemmule (Rasmont, 1961a). The possible significance of this difference is not known but could be related to the involvement of cyclic nucleotides in dormancy. In cold-stored nondiapausing, green gemmules of *S. lacustris,* there is a high level of cAMP which is abruptly reduced during the first few hours of germination at 20°C (Simpson and Rodan, 1976a,b). Thus, if this cyclic nucleotide is involved in gemmular glycogen metabolism, there may be a dependency upon an initial burst of glycogen utilization for germination to proceed; higher glycogen levels may thus support such a step. Alternatively, the achievement of a high cAMP level itself may be the specific step which occurs faster at lower temperatures and thus the diapause period is required in order to accumulate this substance. In *S. lacustris* green gemmules inhibitors of phosphodiesterase activity inhibit the initiation of germination through maintaining cAMP at the higher, dormant level. Exposure of these gemmules to cAMP in the medium, at appropriate temperature (15°C), also inhibits germination. Although no data are presently available, one could suppose that cold treatment of diapausing gemmules accelerates the buildup in concentration of this nucleotide. Of some interest in this regard is the finding that the high-affinity cAMP phosphodiesterase activity in *S. lacustris* cold-stored gemmules is about 20 to 25% lower at 5 and 10°C than at 15 and 25°C, which may be causally related to such a buildup of cAMP. However, the adenylate cyclase activity is also similarly lower at 5 to 10°C so that the *relative* activities of these enzymes *in vivo* must on balance favor cAMP accumulation.

An earlier investigation of *S. lacustris* nondiapausing gemmules demonstrated that fully formed gemmules develop high internal hydrostatic pressure, possibly due to the accumulation of a low-molecular-weight (142) substance (Zeuthen, 1939). The identification of this material still awaits further analysis, but it does not appear to be glycerol and/or sorbitol

(Rasmont, 1961a). Experimental reduction of the internal hydrostatic pressure through the use of sodium chloride solutions results in an inhibition of germination (Simpson *et al.*, 1973). It is conceivable that in diapausing gemmules, cold treatment accelerates the development of hydrostatic pressure possibly through the elaboration of a low-molecular-weight molecule either independently or coupled with cyclic nucleotide metabolism.

Thesocytes in dormant gemmules are osmotically unstable and undergo lysis in water. When removed from their coats, these cells can be experimentally stabilized by placing them in 115 mM NaCl (Schmidt, 1970b). Since in the later stages of germination and at hatching these same cells are stable in water, it is clear that the nature of the thesocyte plasmalemma is very different in dormant gemmules and that the tight packing of the cells within the coat is necessary in order to stabilize them *in situ;* loose packing would permit swelling and eventual lysis while tight packing results in mechanical stability under high hydrostatic pressure. However, freeze fracture data do not establish a difference in particle density and arrangement when comparing thesocytes to archeocytes (Lethias and Garrone, personal communication). The gemmule coat thus acts as an osmometer in which water balance is achieved through high internal hydrostatic pressure (Simpson *et al.*, 1973).

Nondiapausing gemmules can be kept in a dormant state by low temperature as occurs during the winter months in their environment or through refrigeration in the laboratory. In *E. fluviatilis*, which has been studied extensively, gemmules form during the summer months and are exposed to maximal temperatures (25°C), but during this period they are surrounded by functional tissue and do not hatch. Other species, such as *Trochospongilla pennsylvanica* similarly form gemmules during the warm summer months (Simpson and Gilbert, 1973). Upon removal from the parent sponge, *E. fluviatilis* gemmules are able to undergo germination without prior cold treatment (Rasmont, 1962). It has been shown that a diffusable substance, called gemmulostasin, produced by the parent tissue inhibits the germination of these gemmules *in situ* (Rasmont, 1965). This low-molecular-weight (dialysable) material is inactivated by boiling but can be concentrated through boiling under vacuum. Addition of gemmulostasin to incubating gemmules inhibits their germination at an early stage such that incubation in control medium for 48 h *or less* followed by transfer to the same medium but containing gemmulostasin results in a significant inhibition of germination and subsequent hatching (Table 8-9); the effect is, however, freely reversible (Rozenfeld, 1970). This factor is released by young sponges into the incubation medium by *Ephydatia fluviatilis* and *Spongilla lacustris* but not by *E. mulleri*. However, its action is nonspecific in sponges; gemmulostasin derived from either of these species is able to inhibit the germination of any of them (Rozenfeld, 1970). Although not directly demonstrated, there is a good possibility that

Table 8-9 Time Course of Gemmulostasin Inhibition of Gemmule Germination in *Ephydatia fluviatilis*[a]

	Time (days) of incubation (20°C) in control medium						
	0	0.5	1.0	1.5	2.0	2.5	3.0
	Subsequent time (days) of incubation in gemmulostasin						
	14	13.5	13	12.5	12	11.5	11
Percentage hatching	0	0	23	44	69	92	95
Percent inhibition (Adjusted for nonhatching in control medium only)	100	100	76	53	27	3	0

	Time (h) of preincubation (20°C) in gemmulostasin				
	0	12	24	36	60
Time (h) for hatching following transfer to control medium[b]	240	240	264	288	312

[a]From Rozenfeld (1970).
[b]Estimated from graphed data.

the gemmulostasin produced by the parental tissue is cAMP or an inhibitor of phosphodiesterase (Simpson and Rodan, 1976a) (see later section). More recently, Rasmont (1975) has suggested the gemmules of *E. mulleri* themselves contain gemmulostasin, since when gemmules are incubated in clusters their germination is inhibited in the center of the cluster but not at the periphery (see also, Kilian, 1964). Further, when these gemmules are punctured with a small hole, they no longer require cold treatment in order to germinate (Rasmont, 1975), indicating that an inhibitor of germination diffuses out of the gemmules during their germination.

Treatment of *E. mulleri* gemmules for 1 h in saturated aqueous solutions of toluene and bromobenzene accelerates their time for germination (Rasmont, 1955b) possibly through effecting the permeability properties of either the thesocytes and/or the coat. In either case, the diffusion of substances from the gemmule into the medium would be accelerated. On the other hand, xylene is without effect and chloroform completely inhibits germination. Xylene, toluene, and bromobenzene retarded the germination of the nondiapausing gemmules of *E. fluviatilis,* further demonstrating fundamental differences between diapausing and nondiapausing gemmules.

The permeability of the single-layered coat of green *S. lacustris* gemmules has been studied using hyperosmotic solutions of a number of low-molecular-weight organic compounds (Table 8-10). Carbohydrates (glycerol and glucose) display very slow diffusion through the coat and sucrose is impermeable. Alcohols with higher partition coefficients are freely permeable and some even support germination and hatching possibly because they are metabolized (Simpson *et al.*, 1973). Sodium and potassium are also permeable but at high concentration inhibit germination. The innermost, thin dense band of electron opaque material in the coat (see previous section) may represent the primary barrier to diffusion, although it is clear that water and some solutes are able to cross it. The plasmalemma of the thesocytes also appears more permeable to substances with higher partition coefficients. As implied above and discussed more fully later, the permeability properties of the gemmule coat may be the primary controlling factor in gemmule dormancy, particularly in view of the unpublished observations of Rozenfeld (as quoted in Rasmont, 1975) that if the coat of diapausing gemmules is punctured, the gemmules germinate even though they have not been cold treated.

Although it is clear that the coats must have some permeability to water, some freshwater gemmules are able to withstand complete drying (Annandale, 1915; Kilian, 1964; Poirrier, 1969) while others are not (unpub. observ.). The mechanism whereby some gemmules can withstand

Table 8-10 Diffusion of Solutes Through the Gemmule Coat of *Spongilla lacustris*[a]

Solution (230 mOsmolar)	Molecular Weight	Partition Coefficient	Folding of Coat[b]	Recovery[c]
Methanol	32	0.14	No	
Ethanol	46	0.26	No	
2-Propanol	60	0.64	No	
1-Propanol	60	1.9	No	
1-Butanol	74	7.7	No	
Ethyl acetate	88	8.5	No	
Urea	60	0.00047	No	
Ethylene glycol	62	0.0053	No	
1,2-Propanediol	76	0.018	Yes (+)	Yes
1,4-Butanediol	90	0.029	Yes (+)	Yes
Glycerol	92	0.00066	Yes (++)	Yes, very slow
Glucose	180	Negligible	Yes (++)	Yes, very slow
Sucrose	342	Negligible	Yes (++)	No
NaCl	58.5	Negligible	Yes (+)	Yes
KCl	74.5	Negligible	Yes (+)	Yes

[a]From Simpson *et al.* (1973).
[b]Due to water withdrawal.
[c]Water reenters due to entrance of solute.

drying is not known but may be due either to the complete impermeability of the coat to water (an unlikely possibility) or to the formation of substances that can substitute for water as in other dormant systems in which carbohydrates play such a role (Rasmont, 1968b). Such substances may thus play a dual role by permitting drying and causing high internal osmotic pressure in water. The gemmules of the marine sponge *Haliclona loosanoffi* show little resistance to drying when they are initially blotted free of seawater (Table 8-11) (Fell, 1975). *Spongilla lacustris* green gemmules can be lyophylized, stored, and then germinated if, for the latter, they are first placed in 115 mM NaCl for rehydration followed by slow reduction of the salt concentration down to habitat levels (Gilbert and Simpson, 1976b). Kilian (1964) has reported that *S. lacustris* gemmules even survive short-term freezing (2 days); longer-term freezing of the single-layered gemmules, however, results in no viability (unpub. observ.).

Gemmules of *H. loosanoffi* are able to withstand drastically lowered salinity (5–10‰) even at 20°C for a period of at least fifteen days and are subsequently able to hatch (at 25‰) (Fell, 1975), while those of *S. lacustris* when exposed to NaCl solutions of 115 milliosmolar or greater at 20°C are unable to germinate when placed back in pond water (Simpson *et al.*, 1973). But, the latter gemmules when exposed to the same range of NaCl but at 4°C are able to germinate at 20°C in the absence of NaCl (Table 8-12). Thus, in marine gemmules, higher temperature coupled with lower salinity are tolerable, but in freshwater ones higher temperature coupled with higher salt concentration are inhibitory. In *H. loosanoffi* a salinity of 45‰ at 20°C inhibits germination but is reversible at 25‰. Thus the gemmules of these two species appear to act similarly in respect to solute (or water) concentration relative to their natural environment, par-

Table 8-11   Effect of Desiccation on the Hatching of Gemmules of *Haliclona loosanoffi*[a]

	Germination index[c]	
Hours of Desiccation[b]	Unblotted Gemmules	Blotted Gemmules
0	5.0	5.0
1	4.95	5.0
4	4.45	3.78
12	5.0	1.75
24	4.6	0

[a]From Fell (1975).
[b]At 20°C in 80% relative humidity.
[c]Five (5) is maximal hatching.

Table 8-12 Effect of Sodium Chloride upon Hatching of *Spongilla lacustris* Gemmules[a]

Five-day preincubation in NaCl (mOsmolar)	Percent Hatching	
	At 17 Days after Transfer to Pond Water (20°C) on Day 6	At 17 Days When Left in Original NaCl Solution and Brought to 20°C
460–276 at 20°C	0	—
460–276 at 4°C	0	0
230 at 20°C	7	—
230 at 4°C	94	0
184 at 20°C	13	—
184 at 4°C	79	0
115 at 20°C	13	—
115 at 4°C	85	7
23 at 20°C	80	—
23 at 4°C	100	15

[a]From Simpson *et al.* (1973).

ticularly in view of the fact that *S. lacustris* gemmules are able to germinate in water alone (Simpson *et al.*, 1973).

Although the initial oxygen uptake upon warming (to 20°C) of green (algal containing) nondiapausing and of brown (algal-deficient) diapausing gemmules of *S. lacustris* is significantly different, with the green ones displaying higher levels of respiration both in the dark and in the light (Brønsted and Løvtrup, 1953), it is clear that the presence of symbiotic zoochlorellae is *not* related to the diapause condition. In *Ephydatia*, there are no symbionts but *mulleri* is diapausing and *fluviatilis* is not (Rasmont, 1968b). In *S. lacustris*, the difference in oxygen uptake between green and brown gemmules is not significantly affected by the absence of light and thus the respiration of the green ones does not appear strongly influenced by the symbionts. Initial measurements of oxygen consumption of *E. mulleri* gemmules has demonstrated that cold treatment for six months increases uptake by about threefold (Rasmont, 1962). Further, cold treatment results in more sensitivity to cyanide, suggesting that diapausing gemmules have less reliance upon oxidative metabolism. The previously mentioned difference in glycogen content between cold-stored gemmules and those stored at 18°C cannot be easily interpreted in view of the results on oxygen uptake because the experimental conditions were significantly different. Simultaneous measurements of oxygen uptake and glycogen content are required and would be most enlightening. Also, light conditions must be carefully controlled in these types of measurements since Rasmont and Schmidt (1967) have reported that light increases the respiration of *E. fluviatilis* gemmules, although they do not contain symbionts. This result has yet to be explained.

Gemmule Germination

The processes in germination include those which occur up to the time at which the internal cells migrate through the open micropyle and begin to establish a new functional sponge. It is not clear when they are set in motion. Specifically, it is not known in diapausing gemmules whether cold treatment accelerates the attainment of a physiological condition, which then supports the initiation of germination or whether cold treatment results in the initiation of a required germinative event which then supports further processes. Similarly, in nondiapausing gemmules, cold storage may support germinative process but at a very low level. In any case, the first half of germination is a set of slow events with few morphological changes. This suggests the presence of one or more limiting biochemical steps which themselves require many hours.

Morphological Events: Freshwater Species. Berthold (1969) and Rozenfeld (1970) have investigated the very early stages in gemmule germination in *Ephydatia fluviatilis* which are stimulated by warming the gemmules. It is essential to keep in mind that the incubation temperature utilized is different in these two studies—25°C in the former and 20°C in the latter—and thus the absolute timing of events does not correspond (Rozenfeld, 1970). The latter worker considers that the lower temperature employed has the advantage of slowing germination, thus making analyses more precise. A further study of germination and hatching utilizing the higher incubation temperature has also appeared (Höhr, 1977) but this focuses upon later germinative and hatching events.

The earliest known morphological event in germination is the moving apart (separation) of the two nuclei present in each thesocyte (Berthold, 1969; Rozenfeld, 1970). At 25°C this occurs in all cells within 5 h but at 20°C only 35 to 60% of the thesocytes display separation after 24 h and Rozenfeld (1970) indicates that there is much variability in the timing of the process. In the former study, by 24 h a significant number of thesocytes have divided to produce mononucleate archeocytes, which aside from their mononucleate condition are essentially like the thesocytes from which they are derived (Table 8-13). The events leading to the formation of these cells include (Fig. 8-22): (1) nuclear separation, (2) karyokinesis to yield tetranucleate cells, and (3) cytokinesis which results in four mononucleate cells from each thesocyte which is so dividing. According to Berthold (1969) a few archeocytes appear within 12 to 17 h, and as suggested by Wierzejski (1935), these may be derived from thesocytes that undergo cytokinesis without prior karyokinesis although there is no direct evidence for this. Between 24 and 48 h of incubation, most thesocytes have completed division and the gemmule comes to contain archeo-

Table 8-13 Cellular Events During Gemmule Germination in *Ephydatia fluviatilis*[a]

Hours of Incubation	Binucleate Cells[b]			Prohistoblasts	Mononucleate Cells[b]				Tetranucleate Cells[b]	
	Nuclei Not Separated	Nuclei Separated	In Mitosis	Histoblasts	Archeocytes	Prohistoblasts	Histoblasts	Mitosis	Nondividing	In Mitosis
0	83.8	16.1								
5	9.0	90.0								
12	10.8	89.0			0.2					
17	8.8	90.8			0.5					
24	6.4	75.7	2.5	0.2	14.2	1.1			0.1	
29	2.2	28.8	2.5	1.6	19.0	39.6	1.0	1.3	3.7	
36	2.4	11.6	0.7	1.6	15.7	18.6	43.8	1.0	4.8	
48	0.7	11.6	0.7	0.1	35.5	29.5	16.8	1.1	3.5	0.4

[a]Data taken from Berthold (1969).
[b]In percentage of total cells.

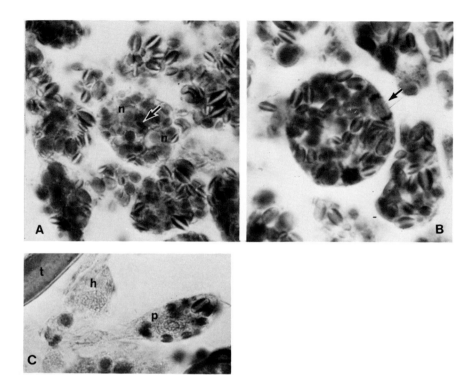

Figure 8-22   Germination events in gemmules of *Ephydatia fluviatilis* (light micrographs). **A**. Nuclear separation in a thesocyte. The arrow indicates the area of separation between the two nuclei (*n*) (×540) (Rozenfeld, 1970). **B**. Mitosis (*arrow*) in a germinating thesocyte (×1,170) (Mukai, 1980). **C**. Formation of a histoblast (*h*) and a prohistoblast (*p*). Note, respectively, loss of platelets and reduction in platelet number. *t,* inner layer of gemmule coat (×900) (Rozenfeld, 1970). (**A, C**, courtesy Dr. F. Rozenfeld; **B**, courtesy Dr. H. Mukai.)

cytes and histoblasts. The latter cells possess anucleolate nuclei and few, if any, platelets. In addition, many prohistoblasts are present (Fig. 8-22C); these cells possess a small nucleolus and have reduced numbers of platelets. In Berthold's study, some prohistoblasts and histoblasts appear early (24–36 h) and are binucleate. This author favors the view that the latter cells are derived from the early-formed mononucleate archeocytes that undergo a karyokinesis and are then delayed in entering cytokinesis. Alternatively, they may be derived directly from the binucleate thesocytes. From 36 to 48 h of incubation, a small number of tetranucleate cells appear which undergo karyokinesis and cytokinesis to produce eight archeocytes (Berthold, 1969). The overall result of all of the thesocyte divisions is the formation of two categories of mononucleate cells—archeocytes and histoblasts—both of which are themselves able to divide mitotically. Such mitoses are much more prevalent in archeocytes and prohistoblasts and few histoblasts have been observed dividing (Table 8-14). There is a specific gradient relative to the distribution of histoblasts; they are most numerous beneath the micropyle and although their migration to this position is possible (Berthold, 1969) it is more likely, because of the tight packing of the cells, that their differentiation takes place *in situ;* numerous histoblasts occur below the micropyle even before the latter is open (Höhr, 1977). This author also reports that histoblasts come to form a complete pinacoderm around the germinating cells within the gemmule prior to hatching and even prior to the opening of the micropyle. Such a condition is also suggested by the data of Rozenfeld (1970). Höhr (1977) has quantitatively investigated the appearance of archeocytes and histoblasts and finds that parallel numbers of both cell types appear but that even at and following hatching there are still some binucleate thesocytes present within the cell mass as also noted by Rozenfeld (1970).

The breakdown of the vitelline platelets occurs in the thesocytes to some extent as well as in the histoblasts and includes a shrinkage of the platelet contents and development of multiple limiting membranes around each of them. The platelet lipid inclusions disappear and the RNA-rich valves collapse into the core. Progressively, more membrane appears at the periphery and eventually the whole platelet is converted to a membranous, lamellar body (Fig. 8-23) (Höhr, 1977). Thesocyte cytoplasm contains extensive, small empty spaces (electron lucent) that may be artifactual; alternately, they may be related to water uptake and balance. There is a significant reduction in the number of these spaces in the resulting archeocytes and histoblasts (Höhr, 1977), and the latter come to possess extensive membrane systems in the cytoplasm which possibly correlate with the onset of osmoregulatory activity. Collagen fibrils appear between cells particularly in the region of the micropyle where at hatching they can extend in and through the opening (Höhr, 1977).

In an experimental study, Schmidt (1970b) removed thesocytes from their coats and followed their behavior in culture (Fig. 8-24). She confirmed that they become tetranucleate before undergoing cytokinesis but also observed these cells adhering directly to the substratum forming "pinacocytes." Apparently they have a delayed cytokinesis but are able to proceed toward differentiation, a result similar to that achieved with puromycin (see later).

It seems likely that the temporary existence of binucleate histoblasts and tetranucleate cells is due to the random inability of some cells to complete cytokinesis due to the presence of the abundant and closely packed platelets. The high concentration of histoblasts below the micropyle and at the periphery of the gemmular cell mass may be a direct result of the stimulation of platelet breakdown due to increased exchange with the environment, particularly of water. A strong piece of evidence sug-

Table 8-14 Distribution of Cell Division During Gemmule Germination[a]

Hours of Incubation	Percentage Mitoses in Each Category[b]				Number of Mitoses in Eight Gemmules			
	Mononucleate Cells	Binucleate Cells	Tetranucleate Cells		Archeocytes	Prohistoblasts	Histoblasts	
24	0.0	3.0	0.0					
29	2.2	8.1	0.0		143	5	0	
36	1.3	4.6	0.0		94	47	5	
48	1.3	5.7	11.4		54	22	2	

[a]Data taken from Berthold (1969).
[b]The total number of cells in each category is counted as 100%.

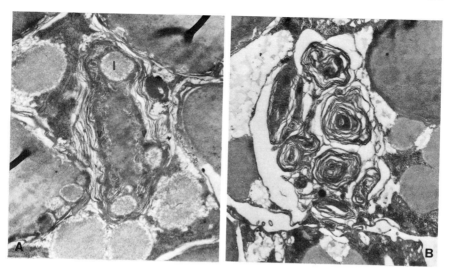

Figure 8-23 Platelet digestion during germination of *Ephydatia fluviatilis* (TEMs). **A**. Early digestion involving the inward collapse of the valves (*v*). *l*, lipid (×15,750) (Höhr, 1977). **B**. Final disposition of a platelet that has undergone breakdown. The whole platelet is converted to a lamellar body filled with membrane (×15,750) (Höhr, 1977). (Both courtesy Dr. D. Höhr.)

gesting that this is actually the case is the finding that when the gemmule coat is punctured prior to germination, hatching (histoblast migration) occurs through the artificial hole not through the micropyle which, however, is wide open (Rozenfeld, 1970). Such artificial holes will obviously greatly enhance water and solute exchanges locally.

The opening of the micropyle appears to be a direct result of germination, not a cause of it, and does not occur mechanically as suggested earlier by Jaffe (1912). Two pieces of evidence support this conclusion: the edges of the open micropyle are absolutely smooth, not ragged as expected if mechanically opened, and during germination, prior to the opening of the micropyle, there is a decrease in internal hydrostatic pressure (Zeuthen, 1939), thus effectively eliminating this factor as a causative agent (Kilian, 1964; Rozenfeld, 1970). Its opening then is most likely due to an enzymatic process which raises the interesting possibility of the synthesis of a collagenase by the histoblasts (Fig. 8-25). A specific sponge collagenase has yet to be identified and its availability would greatly facilitate biochemical studies of sponge collagen (Garrone, 1978) (Chap. 5).

Morphological Events: Marine Species. In *Suberites domuncula*, the only marine gemmule system in which germination has been microscopically investigated, by the sixteenth day of incubation the mononucleate thesocytes contain fewer inclusions, their nuclei become larger and they

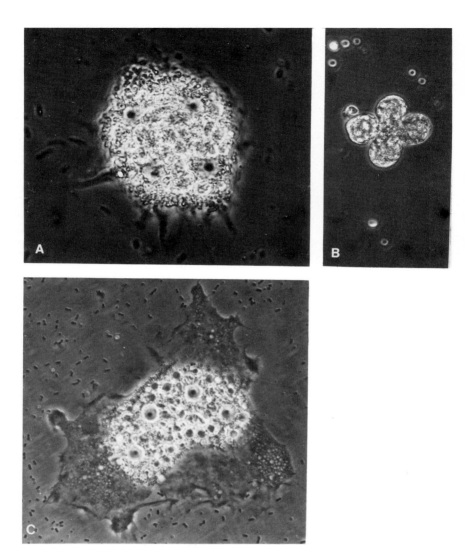

Figure 8-24 *In vitro* germination events in *Ephydatia fluviatilis* thesocytes extracted from their gemmule coats (phase contrast micrographs, living cells). **A.** Formation of tetranucleate cell from a binucleate thesocyte (×765) (Schmidt, 1970b). **B.** Cytokinesis of a tetranucleate cell to form four mononucleate, platelet-laden archeocytes (×460) (Schmidt, 1970b). **C.** Precocious attachment and spreading of a tetranucleate cell on a glass substratum (×630) (Schmidt, 1970b). (Copyright Archives de l'Académie des Sciences de Paris.) (All courtesy Dr. I. Schmidt.)

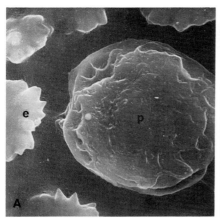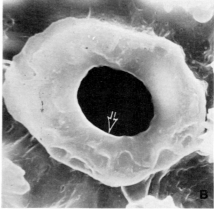

Figure 8-25   The micropyle of gemmules of *Ephydatia fluviatilis* (SEMs). **A.** Micropyle (*p*) in the closed condition prior to germination. Edges (*e*) of gemmoscleres are visible around the micropyle (×495) (Rozenfeld, 1971). **B.** Fully open micropyle with completely smooth edges around the opening (*arrow*) suggesting a chemical rather than a mechanical basis for its opening (×450) (Rozenfeld, 1971). (Both courtesy Dr. F. Rozenfeld.)

develop prominent nucleoli (Connes *et al.*, 1978). Although mitoses are very difficult to observe, some thesocytes are transitorily binucleate prior to cytokinesis, thus having an unexpectedly similar morphology to freshwater thesocytes. Some of the divisions that occur during the next 72 h are very unequal (Fig. 8-26A), each giving rise to one much smaller cell which may or may not be nucleolated. The breakdown of the vitelline platelets can involve rupture of the platelet membranes and release of some of the contents, or *in situ* hydrolysis and conversion to lamellar bodies, or aggregation of a number of platelets into a large autophagic inclusion (Fig. 8-26B). Although the amount of cytoplasmic glycogen appears to decrease slightly, the lipid inclusions persist while the small osmophilic granules (? lysosomes) disappear rather rapidly. Golgi-derived granules, which are possibly primary lysosomes, are frequently found fusing to platelets. Some cells retain considerably more platelets than others and those that do not are prevalent in the region of the micropyle and correspond to the histoblasts of freshwater gemmules. Substantial quantities of collagen fibrils appear between the histoblasts but not between the more internally located, platelet-laden cells. At hatching, the histoblasts migrate through the micropyle and, as in *Ephydatia fluviatilis,* a hole punctured in the gemmules of *Suberites domuncula* results in cell migration through the hole rather than through the micropyle. The ultrastructure of the open micropyle in the latter species is unknown.

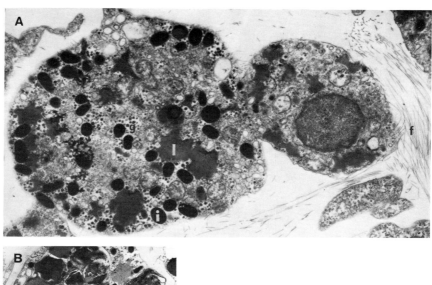

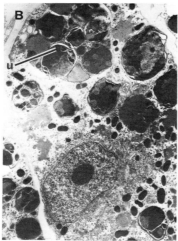

Figure 8-26 Germination events in a marine gemmule (*Suberites domuncula*) (TEMs). **A**. Unequal cell division of a thesocyte producing one small and one large cell. Note also the apparent segregation of glycogen (*g*) and dense inclusions (*i*) in the larger cell. *l*, lipid; *f*, collagen fibrils (×8,100) (Connes *et al.*, 1978). **B**. Aggregation and breakdown of platelets within a large autophagic vacuole (*u*) of a thesocyte (×4,950) (Connes *et al.*, 1978). (Both courtesy Dr. R. Connes.)

Temperature, Light, and Respiration. The rate of germination is strongly influenced by temperature as early reported by Brien (1932) and more recently by Kilian (1964), Rasmont (1962), and Rozenfeld (1970) in *Ephydatia fluviatilis*, by Benfey and Reiswig (1982) in *Ephydatia mulleri*, by Strekal and McDiffett (1974) in *Spongilla fragilis*, and Fell (1974b) in

Haliclona loosanoffi (Table 8–15). In *Spongilla lacustris* temperatures of 25 and 30°C substantially increase the germination rate (as compared to 15°C) while 37°C is inhibitory (unpub. observ.). In *H. loosanoffi* a temperature of 34°C is irreversibly inhibitory while 10°C is reversibly inhibitory. The slowing of germination at low temperature is of much interest ecologically, since germination (and hatching) is able in some cases to take place *in habitat* and in the laboratory at 5°C (Simpson and Gilbert, 1973; Brønsted and Brønsted, 1953; Jorgensen, 1946; Zeuthen, 1939). The presence of zoochlorellae in single-layered gemmules of *S. lacustris* is correlated with their ability to germinate at lower temperatures in the field (Brønsted and Brønsted, 1953).

Although the symbiont containing gemmules germinate faster, the presence of light does not significantly affect their respiration (Brønsted and Brønsted, 1953), suggesting that the algal contribution to the system involves an increase in some essential metabolite rather than a general increase in metabolism. Upon warming, the initial respiration of the brown gemmules is lower than the green ones further suggesting a rate-limiting step that is compensated for by the presence of symbionts. In the newly formed green gemmules, at least some of the carbon dioxide that is photosynthetically fixed by the algae is transferred in an organic form to the platelets and thesocyte nuclei establishing a biochemical interrelationship between the algae and the thesocytes (Gilbert and Allen, 1973b). No comparable studies have been carried out on germinating gemmules but nutrient transfer from symbiotic cyanobacteria to adult sponge cells has also been demonstrated (Wilkinson, 1979a).

In *Ephydatia fluviatilis,* the oxygen consumption of germinating gemmules is effected by light. In the presence of daylight, or an artificial source, oxygen uptake is more than double that in the dark (Rasmont and

Table 8-15 Effect of Temperature on the Germination of *Haliclona loosanoffi* Gemmules[a]

Temperature (°C)	Time (in days) for Maximal Germination	Germination Index[b]
10	No germination	—
15	22	5.0
20	10	4.96
25	12	5.0
30	10	3.96[c]
34	No germination	—

[a]From Fell (1974b). Gemmules were stored at 5°C for 30 to 43 weeks before use.
[b]Five (5) is maximal germination.
[c]Variable from culture to culture.

Schmidt, 1967). Light–dark cycles result in an oscillation of oxygen uptake directly related to the presence of light. Since the thesocytes of these gemmules do not contain symbionts, apparently light energy directly effects respiration through an unknown mechanism. Based upon these results, the conclusion of Brønsted and Brønsted (1953) that light does not significantly affect oxygen uptake in the symbiont containing gemmules of *S. lacustris* requires further comment. In the latter system, it is possible that light reduces algal respiration but increases thesocyte respiration and that dark stimulates the former while reducing the latter. Such a dual effect would result in approximately equal oxygen uptake under light and dark conditions. Further studies of the specific site of action of light on both these gemmule types are now required. Investigations of photoperiod effects on gemmule *hatching* may be complicated by intraspecific variation of such effects as recently shown by Benfey and Reiswig (1982) in *E. mulleri*.

The possible involvement of light in gemmule germination has also been reported by Strekal and McDiffett (1974) in *Spongilla fragilis*. The germination of these gemmules in distilled water in the dark is strongly inhibited by the absence of light, whereas in environmental water or a synthetic medium no such inhibition occurs in the dark (Table 8-16). Possibly, light is somehow involved in preventing the loss of essential ions, which can be compensated for by their presence in the incubation medium. Although *S. fragilis* gemmules also lack symbionts, it is clear that the lower oxygen uptake in the dark of *E. fluviatilis* gemmules is not similarly related to ions, since there is little difference in respiration when germination occurs in distilled water rather than in synthetic media (Rasmont and Schmidt, 1967). Thus, it is very unlikely that the lowering of oxygen uptake in the dark is due to a mineral deficit.

Table 8-16 Effect of Light on the Germination of *Spongilla fragilis* Gemmules[a]

Culture Medium	Conditions[b]	Percentage Germination[c]
Distilled water	L–D	58
	D	3
Enviromental water	L–D	80
	D	88
Synthetic medium	L–D	78
	D	80

[a]From Strekal and McDiffett (1974).
[b]L–D: 12 h light, 12 dark cycle. D, no light.
[c]Data approximated from figures.

Ions and Water.   Although the absence of ions in the incubation medium has been reported to inhibit germination (Brønsted, 1936; Rasmont and Schmidt, 1967), this has not been found to be the case by other workers (Strekal and McDiffett; Simpson *et al.*, 1973). Possibly the former results are due to very weak *hatching* in water, since this was used as the criterion for germination; hatching is known to be strongly influenced by the ionic content of the medium (see later section). Alternately, the absence of light or the time of prior storage of the gemmules may be the source of these conflicting data. In *S. fragilis,* the percentage germination is somewhat lower (60%) in distilled water than in enviromental or synthetic water (80%) (Strekal and McDiffett, 1974), while in *S. lacustris* green gemmules there is no difference (Simpson *et al.*, 1973).

Rasmont (1961b) has established a synthetic germination medium and based upon his formulation, Strekal and McDiffett (1974) have employed a similar although much less concentrated one (Table 8-17). The latter workers have carried out a detailed investigation of the effects of ions on germination. When diluted even to 1:1000 the percentage germination is little affected, which is also the case when single ions (Ca, Mg, CO_3, SO_4) are omitted from the medium. Despite earlier reports, all of these data establish that essential ions are already present within the thesocytes and gemmular fluid and are sufficient to support germination.

A number of divalent cations have been shown to be inhibitory to germination, but their inhibition in many cases can be overcome by appropriate concentrations of calcium (Table 8-18), suggesting that calcium is essential for germination, specifically for cell division. Magnesium cannot substitute for calcium in overcoming inhibition, but at low concentration it is not inhibitory (Ostrom and Simpson, 1978, 1979). During early germination, a relocation of total calcium within the thesocytes takes place; the $600 \times g$ pellet of broken cells (platelets, nuclei, algal symbionts) has a twofold increase in calcium and the supernatant (organelles) has a comparable decrease (Table 8-19). Further support of the view that calcium

Table 8-17   Synthetic Media Employed in the Germination of Freshwater Gemmules[a]

Rasmont (1961b)		Strekal and McDiffett (1974)	
$CaCl_2$	1.0	$CaCO_3$	0.05
$MgSO_4$	0.5	$MgSO_4$	0.08
$NaHCO_3$	0.5	Na_2SiO_3	0.02
Na_2SiO_3	0.5	KCl	0.01
KCl	0.05		

[a]Concentration of salts in millimolar.

Table 8-18   Effect of Divalent Cations on Gemmule Germination in *Spongilla lacustris*[a]

Divalent Cation	Minimum Inhibitory Concentration (mM)	Cell Size (μm) at 72 h Incubation (15°C) in 1.0 mM Solution[b]	Calcium Overcomes Inhibition[c]
None (water)	Not inhibitory	16.0 ± 0.5	—
Ca	Not inhibitory[d]	15.4 ± 0.8	—
Mg	10.0	17.1 ± 1.1	Unknown
Sr	0.1	25.2 ± 0.8	Yes
Zn	0.1	27.7 ± 0.6	Yes
Mn	0.1	28.8 ± 0.6	Yes
Ba	1.0	26.3 ± 0.6	Yes
Ni	0.001	27.9 ± 0.7	Yes
Co	0.01	25.4 ± 0.7	Yes
Cd	0.01	23.0 ± 0.8	Yes
Fe	0.1	24.9 ± 0.7	Yes
Cu	0.01	23.5 ± 0.7	No
Cr	0.1	24.2 ± 0.6	No
Pb	0.001	24.2 ± 0.7	No
Hg	0.001	25.2 ± 0.6	No

[a]Data compiled from Ostrom and Simpson (1979).
[b]In ungerminated, dormant gemmules the cell size is 25.3 ± 0.5μm. Cell division (=germination) reduces cell size as above in water. Measurements given are means ± SEM. See also Ostrom and Simpson (1978).
[c]In most cases, 1.0 mM Ca overcomes the minimum inhibitory concentration.
[d]Germination occurs in 10 mM Ca. Higher concentrations not tested.

Table 8-19   Changes in Calcium Content During Germination of *Spongilla lacustris* Gemmules[a]

Hours of Incubation (15°C)	Micrograms of Calcium Per Milligram of Protein[b]		
	Supernatant (600 × g)	Pellet[c] (600 × g)	Total
0	3.58	0.36	1.97
24	2.40	0.75	1.20
48	1.41	0.76	1.03

[a]From Ostrom and Simpson (1979).
[b]The cells were mechanically broken open then centrifuged.
[c]Pellet contains platelets, algae, nuclei.

relocation is critical for germination is the important observation that the calcium chelator, EGTA, stimulates germination at 4°C (Ostrom and Simpson, 1978) while not effecting it at 15°C.

In addition to many divalent cations, sodium in sufficient concentration also inhibits germination (*S. lacustris*), but its inhibitory effects are to a large extent reversible if exposure occurs at low temperature (Table 8-12). The effect of higher sodium concentrations, however, may be a result of their effect upon water availability, since nonpenetrating sugars at high concentration are also inhibitory (Simpson *et al.*, 1973). Similarly, in the marine gemmules of *Haliclona loosanoffi*, increased salinity inhibits germination but so also does decreased salinity (Table 8–20). Thus, in the latter gemmules both increased and decreased water availabilities are inhibitory, but the effects of both at incubation temperature (20°C) are freely reversible (Table 8–20) in distinction to *S. lacustris* (Table 8-12). If the gemmules of *H. loosanoffi* are able to develop high hydrostatic pressure in order to osmoregulate, then adaptation to lower salinity would be possible in the same fashion as in *S. lacustris* (Zeuthen, 1939; Simpson *et al.*, 1973).

Water balance in *S. lacustris* gemmules changes drastically during germination; the internal hydrostatic pressure is sharply reduced (Zeuthen, 1939) (Table 8-21). This reduction is directly correlated with the onset of the ability of the thesocytes to osmoregulate as originally discovered by this worker, but not emphasized. Thus the "loose consistency" of the

Table 8-20   Effect of Salinity on the Germination of *Haliclona loosanoffi* Gemmules[a]

Salinity (‰)	Germination at Day 15 (20°C)		Subsequent Germination at 25‰	
	Germination Index[b]	Percentage Cultures with Maximal Germination	Germination Index[b]	Percentage Cultures with Maximal Germination
5	0	—	4.99	98
10	0	—	5.0	100
15	0	—	4.96	95
20	4.61	55		
25	4.97	99		
30	4.91	95		
35	4.71	85		
40	4.67	60		
45	0	—	4.88	86

[a]From Fell (1975).
[b]Five (5) is maximal germination.

Table 8-21   Changes in Internal Osmotic Pressure of Gemmules of *Spongilla lacustris*[a]

Incubation Time (days) (22°C)	Gemmules[b]			
	Newly formed	Older	Maturing	Mature
0	20	61	117	146
2.5	59	81	—	152
4.5	—	64	110	176
8.5				178
12.5				96
14.5				15
16.0				Hatched

[a]From Zeuthen (1939). Average osmotic pressure is expressed as mM NaCl equivalents.
[b]Only the forming and mature brown, thick-walled gemmules were investigated.

thesocytes when removed from the coat is due to their swelling and lysis prior to germination, and the "coherent" cell consistency is due to the initiation of osmoregulation by the cells which no longer swell and lyse in water (Schmidt, 1970b). The development of osmoregulation is time dependent and thus appears to be a direct result of the initiation of cell division. It is not known if there are differences in the osmoregulatory abilities of tetranucleate versus mononucleate cells. When removed from the gemmule coat, the thesocytes can be stabilized by placing them in 115 mM NaCl. During the following 24 h, its concentration can then be slowly lowered (Schmidt, 1970b) and the cells are able to adapt, thus experimentally demonstrating a change in osmoregulatory behavior. Although there is no known appearance of contractile vacuoles at this very early stage in germination, the development of an extensive membrane system in the thesocytes may signal the onset of water balance (Höhr, 1977). Gemmule germination is remarkably tolerant to pH; it takes place over the range of 5.5 to 8.0 and some limited germination even occurs at a pH of 9.0 (Kilian, 1964).

Gemmulostasin.   As indicated earlier, gemmulostasin is produced by young sponges, is released into the incubation medium, and is able to nonspecifically inhibit the germination of gemmules. Rozenfeld (1970) has established that its inhibitory effect occurs early during germination, within 24 to 48 h of incubation at 20°C (Table 8-9) and that nuclear separation is prevented by its action. Biochemically, gemmulostasin stimulates an earlier than normal round of both RNA and protein synthesis at 24 h while inhibiting the large peak in DNA synthesis, which begins at about 36 h and is sustained for at least an additional 36 h (Rozenfeld, 1974). It is not known how or whether these events are causally related. Although Rozenfeld (1974) suggests that gemmulostasin may even affect the permeability of the thesocyte plasmalemma thereby influencing the intracellular availability of isotopes for incorporation studies, this seems unlikely, since one can directly observe the absence of karyokinesis caused by gemmulostasin under conditions in which no thymidine is present in the medium (Rozenfeld, 1970). When the gemmule coat is punctured in the presence of gemmulostasin, the latter is no longer inhibitory and germination takes place (Table 8-22) including the opening of the micropyle, although the cells migrate through the artificial opening rather than the micropyle, which is also the case with punctured gemmules incubated in control media (Rozenfeld, 1971). Both Rozenfeld (1971) and Rasmont (1975) suggest that this release from inhibition is due to the diffusion out of the gemmule of a substance, which is necessary in order for gemmulostasin to exert its inhibitory effect. They further suggest that such a substance may be synthesized during the early round of protein synthesis induced by gemmulostasin. This, however, is not the only possible explanation of the puncture experiments. The artificial hole certainly results in a rapid entry of water, which could in turn result in sufficient cell lysis and the release of hydrolytic enzymes within the gemmule which break down gemmulostasin. Indeed, 2 to 5% of the thesocytes undergo lysis due to the puncture (Rozenfeld, 1971).

There is, on the other hand, a completely different kind of explanation of the results whose basis is presented by Rasmont (1975) in his latest paper on the subject. This explanation fits very well with the data on cyclic nucleotides to be discussed below and assumes that gemmulostasin is also synthesized by the thesocytes themselves and is present within the

Table 8-22 Effect of Gemmulostasin on Punctured Gemmules of *Ephydatia fluviatilis*[a]

	Incubation Medium		
		Gemmulostasin	
Gemmules	Control	2 Units	4 Units
Intact			
Percentage germination	95–96%	12%	0%
Hours to develop an oscule	144 h	216 h	—
Punctured[b]			
Percentage germination	95%	92%	70%
Hours to develop an oscule	144 h	168 h	240 h

[a]From Rozenfeld (1971).
[b]The hole produced by a needle was approximately 40 μm in diameter, comparable to the size of the micropyle.

gemmule but is able to diffuse out. Under control conditions, its diffusion outward could result in a decrease of intragemmular concentration and thus in release from dormancy. When present in the medium, the intragemmular concentration of gemmulostasin remains high as a result of lowered outward diffusion and thus there is an inhibition of germination. This agrees well with the observation that at a given concentration of gemmulostasin, the germination of *some* gemmules is *slowed,* while the remainder germinate on time (Rasmont, 1965). Those that are slowed may contain a higher concentration of gemmulostasin than those that germinate at the normal rate. A hole punctured in the coat could result in an immediate equilibrium of the gemmulostasin concentration, resulting in a rapid lowering of its intragemmular concentration and thus the initiation of germination. Specifically, the *rate* of reduction of the intragemmular concentration would be critical. In intact gemmules incubated in gemmulostasin, although a lowering of its intragemmular concentration is possible through diffusion, its synthesis may keep up with the concentration gradient and little concentration reduction occurs. In the absence of gemmulostasin, its synthesis would not keep up with its more rapid diffusion and thus a lowering of concentration occurs. This equilibrium hypothesis can similarly explain why puncturing diapausing gemmules of *Ephydatia mulleri* results in an immediate release from dormancy, that is, if gemmulostasin is considered to be the diapause factor (Rasmont, 1975). Cold treatment of these gemmules is viewed as permitting a shift in equilibrium to occur so that upon warming a sufficient lowering of intragemmular gemmulostasin concentration is possible. This view is essentially the same as that presented by Rasmont (1975), but does not include the presence of an additional inhibitor which is assumed produced due to gemmulostasin action; rather, the concentration gradient of gemmulostasin is the prime factor.

Rasmont (1975) has also suggested an involvement of gemmulostasin in the development of high intragemmular osmotic pressure. There are, however, no compelling data to support this view, and indeed there are even no recent corroborating data that support the view that this osmotic pressure is a result of the accumulation of a specific organic metabolite as concluded by Zeuthen (1939). The extremely high concentration of cytoplasmic inclusions in the thesocytes is certainly sufficient to act in this capacity in parallel with the very tight packing of cells in the coat. That the cells themselves are able to react osmotically is clearly demonstrated by their rapid lysis when removed from the coat (Schmidt, 1970b). It is thus possible that the low-molecular-weight molecule found by Zeuthen (1939) adds to, but is not the primary component in, the osmotic activity of the system.

The formation of a mass of histoblasts (due to cell division) below the micropyle may be the result of a more rapid diffusion of gemmulostasin through the micropyle than through the rest of the coat, thus releasing dormancy there sooner than in the more centrally and distantly located cells. When gemmules are punctured, the thesocytes lying below the artificial hole develop into histoblasts indicating that a rapid, local decrease in gemmulostasin has occurred in that area. Indeed, it can be assumed that the change is more rapid here than below the micropyle itself. An investigation of the distribution of histoblasts in germinating, punctured gemmules would be of much interest in this regard since no such data are presently available.

Cyclic Nucleotides.   The effects and *in vivo* changes of cyclic adenosine monophosphate during the germination of green gemmules of *Spongilla lacustris* closely parallel those of gemmulostasin as do the effects of inhibitors of phosphodiesterase (Simpson and Rodan, 1976a,b). While this is the case, it should be borne in mind that the chemical identification of gemmulostasin still remains unknown and until this is accomplished it can only be conjectured that it is cyclic AMP. Alternately, it may be an inhibitor of phosphodiesterase (Simpson and Rodan, 1976a) or it may even possibly act by stimulating adenylate cyclase. The phosphodiesterase inhibitor, aminopylline, at appropriate concentration, inhibits the division of the thesocytes (Table 8-23). Unfortunately, it is not known if it also inhibits nuclear separation as does gemulostasin. Similarly, isobutyl methylxanthine inhibits germination as does cAMP. The effect of the latter, however, requires a lower temperature (15°C) than the former (20°C). While this temperature dependency cannot be fully understood at present, it is known that in cold-stored gemmules both the cAMP phosphodiesterase and adenylate cyclase display changes in activity which are also temperature dependent and which differ for each enzyme. It thus seems likely that the temperature dependency of cAMP inhibition of germination is related to *in vivo* changes in the relative activities of these

Table 8-23   Inhibition of Germination by an Inhibitor of Phosphodiesterase[a]

	Number of Nuclei in Five Fields[b]	Percentage Binucleate Cells
Cold-stored gemmules 48-h incubation (20°C)	47	64
Control	104	6
0.7 mM Aminophylline	67	36
7.0 mM Aminophylline	37	54

[a]From Simpson and Rodan (1976b).
[b]Counts made on 1.0 μm sections embedded in Epon and stained with toluidine blue at a magnification of 1000×.

enzymes. However, temperature-dependent changes in the rate of diffusion of cAMP across the coat must also be taken into consideration.

The inhibition of germination (cell division) by aminophylline is correlated with its inhibition of cAMP phosphodiesterase and its ability to inhibit the normal reduction in gemmular cAMP content which occurs during the first few hours of incubation (Simpson and Rodan, 1976a,b). Thus, cAMP phosphodiesterase inhibitors keep the cAMP content of gemmules high, and the latter, at least, is known to inhibit thesocyte division. The normal drop in cAMP content appears due in part to a 40% reduction in adenylate cyclase activity following 2 h incubation at 20°C with little change in the phosphodiesterase activity (Table 8-24). Although *in vitro* cyclase activity of cold-stored gemmules increases with temperature, the phosphodiesterase shows its greatest increase at 15°C as compared to 5 and 10°C. It is likely that this heightened activity (in conjunction with the reduced activity of the cyclase) is responsible for the lowering of the cAMP content during the first few hours of incubation. Although not demonstrated, the possible diffusion of cAMP out of the gemmule should also be considered as possibly playing a role in dormancy release as well as changes in the permeability of the thesocyte plasmalemma. The presence of both cyclic GMP and a cGMP phosphodiesterase has been reported in cold-stored gemmules; the cGMP content is only about 10% of the cAMP level (Simpson and Rodan, 1976a) and no further information on it is available.

The involvement of both cyclic nucleotides in gemmule germination has also been investigated using frozen sections and immunofluorescence techniques (Harrison *et al.*, 1979, 1981). Surprisingly, cGMP and cAMP are only demonstrable after 24-h incubation. This interesting result suggests either that both are initially masked and therefore do not react with the antibody or they are unbound and diffuse and thus are not available to do so following freezing, whereas they are both readily identifiable in homogenates following boiling and radioimmunoassay. While it is not possible to reconcile these results without further investigation, they may indicate that an initially unbound pool of the nucleotides (which are iden-

Table 8-24   Changes in cAMP Related Enzymes During Early Germination[a]

	Adenylate Cyclase[b]	cAMP Phosphodiesterase[b]
Cold stored gemmules	0.27 ± 0.01	65.9 ± 0.3
Two-hour incubation at 20°C	0.16 ± 0.001	56.4 ± 3.8

[a]From Simpson and Rodan (1976a).
[b]Means $\pm$ SEM of activity in pmoles/min/mg protein. Substrate concentration for phosphodiesterase, 10 μM (=high-affinity enzyme).

tifiable by radioimmunoassay but are "washed out" by the immunofluorescent technique) becomes bound during later germination. By 24 h of
incubation, both nucleotides are clearly identifiable by immunofluorescence and are localized primarily at the periphery of the gemmule within
newly developing histoblasts (Harrison et al., 1981). The pattern of fluorescent staining is clearly different for each nucleotide; cGMP staining is
primarily particulate, possibly involving lysosome and/or lipid inclusion
membranes and cAMP staining is more diffuse but apparently elevated at
the periphery of the platelets. The appearance of bound nucleotides precedes or coincides with the initiation of histoblast differentiation and thus
signals platelet breakdown and RNA and protein synthesis. Throughout
the remainder of germination both bound nucleotides appear to increase
somewhat and some centrally located archeocytes and binucleate thesocytes display staining. This sequence of appearance, peripheral followed
by central staining, parallels the morphological events.

Platelet Breakdown.   The release of nutrients from platelets during germination is correlated with an abrupt rise in both acid phosphatase and
nonspecific esterase activities at about 24 h of incubation in *Ephydatia
mulleri* gemmules which were hatching by 48 h (Tessenow and Kreutzmann, 1969, 1970; Tessenow, 1968, 1969). Acid phosphatase has been
cytochemically localized in small dense inclusions around the platelets in
archeocytes and also just prior to and following hatching in the large
inclusion of cystencytes (Tessenow, 1968, 1969). However, the latter cell
type does not now appear to be concerned with platelet breakdown as
previously concluded (Pottu-Boumendil, 1975) (see Chap. 3). According
to the latter worker, cystencytes elaborate ground substance. Nevertheless, their appearance at the end of germination still presents a problem
because they have not been observed by others (Höhr, 1977; Berthold,
1969). Simons and Müller (1966) have also identified acid phosphatase
activity, but *within* platelets possibly in their lipid inclusions. The mobilization of platelet nutrients is correlated with a coincident increase in RNA
and protein synthesis and with increases in cyclic nucleotides (Harrison et
al., 1981).

Puromycin.   Puromycin at a concentration of 7 μg/ml has the interesting
effect of inhibiting platelet breakdown, histoblast differentiation, and to
some extent cell division while still permitting the hatching of mononucleate and binucleate cells packed with platelets (Rozenfeld, 1980). While
the effects of this concentration are reversible, higher ones are not and are
progressively more inhibitory. At 10 μg/ml only 17% of the gemmules
hatch and their cells rapidly disintegrate. Apparently, however, at the
lower concentration the micropyle opens normally even though histoblasts do not form. This result establishes that platelet breakdown is not
essential for the supposed cell activity (? enzyme release) which is responsible for the opening of the micropyle. The secretion of spicules by

some of these cells, including binucleate ones, further supports this conclusion and suggests an absence of dependency upon cell division for at least some cytodifferentiative steps (see Fig. 8-30).

Gemmule Hatching

Freshwater Species.   Gemmule hatching initially involves the movement of cells out of the gemmule coat and thus includes contractile events which are poorly documented and investigated (Fig. 8-27). Earlier studies of hatching include those of Brien (1932) and Wintermann (1951). The first cells to appear outside of the coat are histoblasts and according to Höhr (1977) they do so as part of a continuous pinacoderm which also surrounds the internal developing cells within the coat (Fig. 8-27B). According to these new data, histoblasts migrate through the micropyle and are added to the preexisting pinacoderm which progressively forms two layers—a basopinacoderm in contact with a substratum (either the gemmule coat itself or some other surface) and an exopinacoderm which becomes raised above the latter, thus forming a narrow mesohyl between the two. Only after this process has continued for some time (8 h) do archeocytes begin to migrate into the newly formed mesohyl where some of them differentiate into sclerocytes even before any sign of the formation of canals and choanocyte chambers. Early during hatching, some internal thesocytes become tetranucleate for a time while others are still binucleate; later both divide to form mononucleate archeocytes. Within the mesohyl, a stock of histoblasts and archeocytes builds up and the former begin to develop canal spaces. During the initial migration of histoblasts the cells appear aligned under the micropyle. It is unclear whether contraction of the recently described internal pinacoderm inside the coat aids in the movement of cells through the micropyle but this is possible. Histoblasts represent a cell category in hatching gemmules which is functionally comparable to collencytes in *some* other systems (but, see Chap. 3).

Within the mesohyl, choanocyte chambers develop from archeocytes. According to Rozenfeld and Rasmont (1976), each chamber originates from the repeated mitoses of a single archeocyte to give rise to 20 or so cells. In a recent study, Weissenfels (1981) has not observed the origin of each chamber from a single archeocyte but rather reports that choanoblasts derived from archeocytes aggregate together to form the chamber primordium in which they initially develop flagella and then later collars. This primordium then migrates to a developing excurrent canal where, when it makes contact, a few choanoblasts form cone cells which develop into the choanocytic apopyle of the chamber and a single endopinacocyte forms the pinacocytic apopyle (Chap. 6). Once the chamber primordium has formed, some choanocytes enter mitosis thus increasing the cell number of the chamber. The choanoblasts which initially appear are characterized by small anucleolate nuclei and the absence of platelets

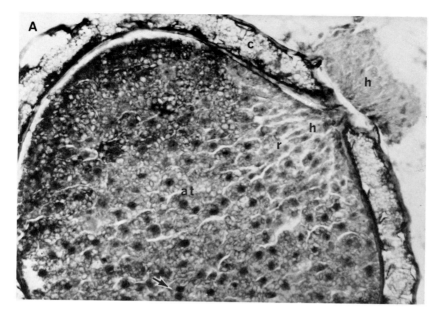

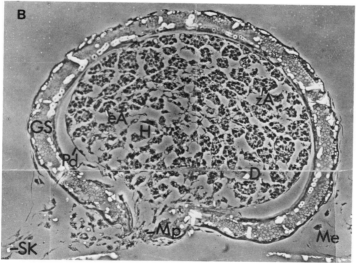

Figure 8-27 Gemmule hatching in *Ephydatia fluviatilis* (light micrographs). **A.** Initial migration of histoblasts (*h*) through and out of the micropyle. Note the gradient of histoblast (*h*), prohistoblast (*r*), and archeocytes–thesocytes (*at*) within the gemmule. *c,* gemmule coat. Some binucleate thesocytes are still present (*arrow*) at this early stage (×230) (Rozenfeld, 1970). **B.** Somewhat later hatching with the development of mesohyl (*ME*) of the new animal and early spicule secretion (*SK*). *H,* histoblast; *eA,* mononucleate archeocyte; *zA,* binucleate thesocyte; *D,* platelet; *GS,* gemmule coat. The cell mass within the gemmule is surrounded by a pinacoderm (*Pd*) which may extend through the micropyle (*Mp*) (phase contrast, semithin section) (×275) (Höhr, 1977) (**A,** courtesy Dr. F. Rozenfeld; **B,** courtesy Dr. D. Höhr.)

(Weissenfels, 1981; Rozenfeld and Rasmont, 1976). The formation of the canals is further discussed in Chapter Six. Spicule secretion (Garrone *et al.,* 1981; Simpson and Vaccaro, 1974) and collagen biosynthesis (Garrone and Pottu, 1973; Pottu-Boumendil, 1975) occur in the mesohyl as discussed in Chapters Four and Five and the basopinacocytes lay down an anchoring layer of collagen in contact with the substratum (Garrone and Rozenfeld, 1981). The origin of ground substance is unclear, since in freshwater species special cells are either few in number or have not been reported (Chap. 3). In *Ephydatia mulleri,* cystencytes may be the origin of such unstructured material, at least in part (Pottu-Boumendil, 1975).

When thesocytes are removed from the gemmule coat and placed in an appropriate medium, the cells not only undergo division (see previous section) but also aggregate together and form a new young organism by about ten days (Schmidt, 1970b). Although the details of the process are described as comparable to those occurring during development in general (Borojevic, 1971), it is clear that the equivalent of hatching in these isolated aggregates can take place in the absence of a specific morphological arrangement of the cells inside in the gemmule coat. In particular, the regional development of histoblasts as described by Rozenfeld (1970) and Höhr (1977) is not a necessary step for the eventual differentiation of the cells.

Marine Species. In *Suberites domuncula,* the smaller division products containing few nutrient inclusions appear to migrate through the micropyle first and establish the initial pinacoderms (Fig. 8-28) (Connes *et al.,* 1978). Collagen fibrils appear abundantly in the newly formed mesohyl and below the basopinacocytes. Choanocytes appear derived from two sources: from the smaller cells within the gemmule which resulted from unequal divisions and from cells derived directly from thesocytes which have lost many of their nutrient inclusions. The newly formed choanocytes contain more highly condensed chromatin, sometimes more abundant endoplasmic reticulum, and more abundant lipid inclusions than adult choanocytes. Archeocytes, which are not always easy to distinguish from thesocytes, migrate into the mesohyl, and gray cells appear there apparently derived directly from thesocytes. Cells resembling spherulous cells, but nucleolated and with much cytoplasmic glycogen, also differentiate in the mesohyl but their origin and function are unclear. The canals system apparently develops through the differentiation of histoblasts.

DNA Synthesis and Hydroxyurea. In *Ephydatia fluviatilis,* following the early peak of thymidine incorporation at about 24 to 36 h of incubation, a second peak occurs at approximately 60 to 72 h, and then following the initiation of hatching, a third peak occurs at about 88 h, and successive peaks about 24 h apart then commence. The formation of choanocytes in the newly hatched animals takes place beginning around 96 h. When incubated in 1.31 mM hydroxyurea, the first two peaks are delayed by 16

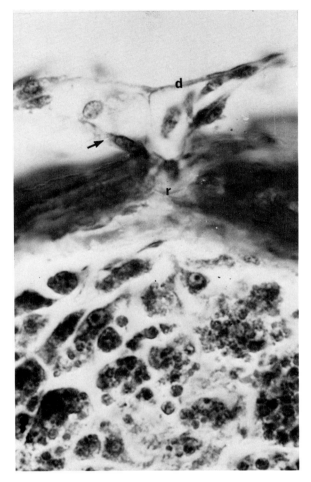

Figure 8-28   Early gemmule hatching in *Suberites domuncula* (light micrograph).
The cells (*arrow*) that migrate through the micropyle (*r*) are similar to freshwater
histoblasts by generally lacking nutrient inclusions. *d,* newly forming pinacoderm.
Many internal cells still contain abundant inclusions (×1,500) (Connes *et al.,*
1978). (Courtesy Dr. R. Connes.)

to 24 h and the third peak is eliminated (Rozenfeld and Rasmont, 1976). In
conjunction, choanocytes fail to form in the young sponge which is also
delayed in its hatching by about two days. However, pinacocytes, archeocytes, and sclerocytes do differentiate (Fig. 8-29). Thus, the 88 h peak in
DNA synthesis appears to be essential for the division of archeocytes that
form choanocytes, whereas the other cell types do not require this particular round of DNA synthesis (and cell division). In the absence of the

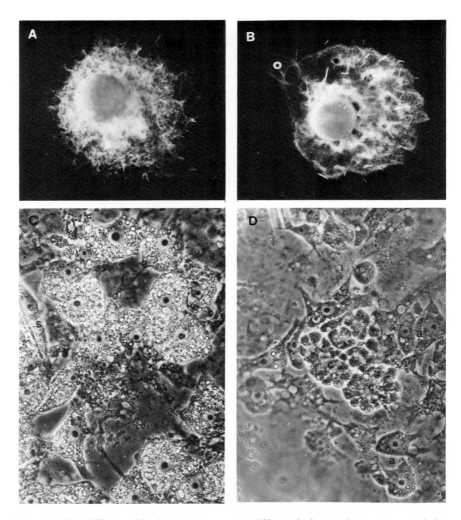

Figure 8-29 Effects of hydroxyurea on cytodifferentiation and morphogenesis in hatching gemmules of *Ephydatia fluviatilis* (light micrographs). This inhibitor stops cell division following hatching and thus prevents the differentiation of choanocytes while permitting pinacoderm formation and spicule secretion. **A.** Hatched gemmule in 100 μg/ml hydroxyurea. The tissue looks "empty" due to the absence of a canal system (×45) (Rozenfeld and Rasmont, 1976). **B.** Control gemmule that has developed a canal system and oscule (*o*) (×45) (Rozenfeld and Rasmont, 1976). **C.** Phase contrast micrograph of the mesohyl of an hydroxyurea-treated gemmule. The mesohyl is filled with archeocytes which have not broken down many of their platelets. While choanocyte chambers are absent, sclerocytes (*s*) differentiate (×720) (Rozenfeld and Rasmont, 1976). **D.** Mesohyl of a control animal showing newly formed choanocyte chambers (*c*) and archeocytes (*a*) which posses few vitelline platelets (phase contrast) (×630) (Rozenfeld and Rasmont, 1976). (All courtesy Dr. F. Rozenfeld.)

development of choanocytes, no canal system develops, which suggests either a dynamic interaction between choanocyte and endopinacocyte differentiation, a possibility that is not clearly evident from observations of normal development (Weissenfels, 1981), or, an inhibition (or disorganization) by hydroxyurea of newly developing canals. The effects of a higher concentration of the substance (3.93 mM) are reversible and when added at 1.31 mM following 96 h of incubation in control medium it was not inhibitory. However, if the latter animals remain in hydroxyurea, the fully formed canal system becomes disorganized thus favoring the view that persistence of the drug results in toxic effects on the endopinacocytes and choanocytes. In a more recent ultrastructural investigation of hydroxyurea effects, however, it was found that some endopinacocytes do differentiate to form the internal epithelium of the dermal membrane but do not form a canal system internally. This also supports the view that developing choanocytes are essential for (and dynamically involved in) the development of the canal system (see also Chap. 6). Further, there appears to be an elevated synthesis of collagen under these conditions (Garrone and Rozenfeld, 1981). Interestingly, sponges treated with hydroxyurea do not display rhythmic contractions of the dermal membrane (see also Chap. 6) establishing the necessity for a functional canal system for such activity. No effects were noted on bundles of microfilaments present in the pinacocytes.

Puromycin. Appropriate concentration of this drug (7 and 5 μg/ml) produces very interesting effects upon gemmule hatching (Rozenfeld, 1980). Both levels result in the secretion of many more spicules than normal. In the lower level, where effects are reversible after washing, pinacoderms develop but not choanocytes or canals as in hydroxyurea. At the higher level, many cells do not divide, but some do migrate out of the coat and form an amorphous clump and they, as well as some left behind, form numerous spicules (Fig. 8-30). This startling result establishes that spicule secretion does not require prior cell division (some *binucleate* cells in puromycin secrete spicules also) nor does it require normal morphogenetic and differentiative processes in other cells. The platelets appear to be completely intact without any signs of breakdown. While requiring further evidence, these very important observations strongly indicate that the differentiation of sclerocytes is normally under intracellular, inhibitory control and that hatching somehow releases this inhibition. This view is in strong opposition to that which considers sclerocyte differentiation as controlled by stimulatory intercellular factors and processes.

Ions and Temperature. The general effect of ions (salinity) on *Haliclona loosanoffi* germination has been previously discussed. In those experiments, the germinative index is actually a measure of the extent of development following hatching as well as a criterion for prior germination. Both high (40‰) and low (20‰) salinities appear to inhibit the develop-

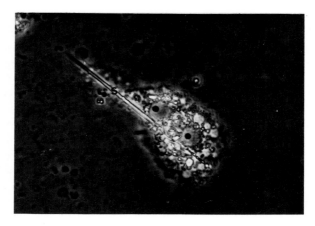

Figure 8-30 Effect of puromycin (7 μg/ml) on sclerocyte differentiation in germinating and hatching gemmules of *Ephydatia mulleri* (phase contrast micrograph, living cell). The drug inhibits mitosis, cytokinesis, platelet breakdown, and the development of pinacoderms, canal system, and mesohyl. Despite this, some binucleate thesocytes migrate (or fall) out of the gemmule coat and differentiate into sclerocytes as shown here. Such a result establishes preprogrammed cytodifferentiation which is not dependent upon morphogenesis. *s,* spicule (×500) (Rozenfeld, 1980). (Courtesy Dr. F. Rozenfeld.)

ment of the hatched sponges (see Table 8-20) as does elevated temperature (30°C) (Table 8-15). The basis of these effects is not known, although in the freshwater species *Spongilla fragilis* the absence of either calcium or magnesium significantly reduces the size of hatched sponges, whereas the absence of silicate, carbonate, or sulfate does not (Strekal and McDiffett, 1974).

Tissue Regression

The natural disappearance of canals and particularly of choanocyte chambers in sponges was recorded in a number of earlier works (see review by Bidder, 1933). This process, which is most often referred to as tissue regression, has been reported more recently in a number of species but has only been studied in detail in a few cases. The process of tissue fragmentation briefly discussed earlier in this chapter has sometimes been considered to represent tissue regression since there can be a dramatic decrease in the surface area covered by the animal, as in *Hymeniacidon perleve* (Stone, 1970a). In this species, fragmentation occurs during the fall and winter (October to April) and is followed by a period of growth and coalescence of the fragments. During fragmentation, the animals display a lower protein content and higher ash content on a dry weight basis

(Stone, 1970b) and they are usually less than 2.0 cm thick (Table 8-25). Such a condition strongly implies, but does not unequivocally demonstrate, a collapse of the canal system. Microscopic analyses are required to establish if, indeed, true tissue regression (in addition to fragmentation) has also occurred. Similarly, Fell and Jacob (1979) refer to overwintering specimens of *Halichondria* sp. as "dormant," suggesting the occurrence of tissue regression, which in *Halichondria bowerbanki* has been reported to involve the loss of choanocyte chambers in the winter but only in some individuals (Hartman, 1958a). Elvin (1976) reports a lowered mesenchymal index—loose arrangement of cells—in *Haliclona permolis* during part of the year (October to July) following a period of maximal spreading. During the former period, the ratio of organic content to spicule weight or total inorganic weight decreases and is the lowest—specifically, protein, glycogen, and lipid contents are minimal (Elvin, 1979). This sequence also suggests tissue regression, although further studies are needed to support this conclusion. It is of interest that in both *Hymeniacidon perleve* and *Haliclona permolis*, organic content is minimal during "regression" since these results can be taken as evidence of cell loss. Van de Vyver and Willenz (1975) have reported an unusual case of tissue regression in *Ephydatia fluviatilis* in which, although gemmules are formed in the autumn, some animals still retain disorganized clumps of tissue in which no canals or choanocytes are present but in which very young oocytes develop. These then undergo oogenesis in the spring, but the fate of the remainder of the regressed tissue is unclear since gemmule hatching is the predominant process which then occurs.

Chen (1976) has reported the disappearance of, or at least vast reduction in, choanocyte chambers and canals in *Halisarca nahatensis* from March to June in New England. During this period, vitellogenesis in oocytes, spermatogenesis, and cleavage are occurring. The loss of canal system components may thus, in this case, be related to the requirements of sexual reproduction, particularly if choanocytes are the origin of spermatogonia (Chap. 7), rather than related to a change in an environmental condition such as temperature. Functional tissue is present throughout

Table 8-25 Seasonal Changes in *Hymeniacidon perleve*[a]

	1966										1967												1968		
	M	A	M	J	J	A	S	O	N	D	J	F	M	A	M	J	J	A	S	O	N	D	J	F	M
Growth		+	+	+	+	+								+	+	+	+	+							
Regression	+	+						+	+	+	+	+				+				+	+	+	+	+	+
Thickness generally more than 2.0 cm			+	+	+	+							+	+	+	+	+								
Thickness generally less than 2.0 cm	+	+	+						+	+	+	+				+				+	+	+	+	+	+

[a]From Stone (1970a). No data for March 1967.

the remainder of the year in this species, indicating an ability of the adult tissue to redevelop the lost structures and cells. In *Halisarca dujardini,* also, functional components of the canal system are reduced or locally absent during the period of spermatogenesis (November to February) (Chen, 1976). In *Microciona prolifera,* tissue regression occurs in the autumn and is accompanied by the loss of canals, choanocytes, oscules, and probably endopinacocytes (Fig. 8-31) (Simpson, 1968b). In this study, it was observed that at the onset of regression the tissue was highly compact (high cell density due to the collapse of the canal system) and

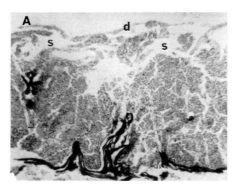

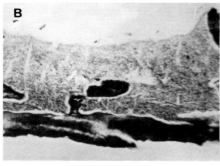

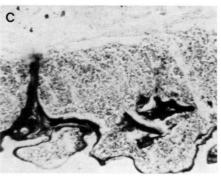

Figure 8-31   Tissue regression in *Microciona prolifera* (light micrographs). Regression occurs from late autumn through late winter. Dark staining material is spongin. **A.** Fully functional tissue in May. Note canal spaces (*s*) and dermal membrane (*d*) (×90) (Simpson, 1968b). **B.** Condensed tissue lacking canals in November (× 90) (Simpson, 1968b). **C.** Loose, "granular" tissue in March which lacks functional components (×90) (Simpson, 1968b).

later it became "loose" (low cell density). Consequently, some caution is required in interpreting loose versus compact tissue relative to tissue regression.

Diaz (1979a) has investigated tissue regression in *Suberites massa* on an ultrastructural level. In this species, variations in salinity in the natural habitat are not correlated with regression but reduced temperature and sexual reproduction are. Regression was observed in a population in the field during May and June directly following the reproductive period and in November and January when water temperature was near or at its minimum (5–10°C). Animals that were cold treated (−2 to 1°C) in the laboratory could be induced to commence regression; removal of oxygen from the water appeared to act as a strong stimulus. During regression, the ectosome comes to contain many fewer cells and the exopinacoderm is lost and replaced by a bare layer of collagen. In the endosome, choanocytes and endopinacocytes progressively disappear while archeocytes increase in number (Fig. 8-32). During this process, canal spaces become lined by collagen (Figs. 8-33A,B), some of which is secreted by endopinacocytes. Some choanocytes (Fig. 8-33C) and endopinacocytes appear to be transformed into archeocytes which in some instances come to fill the canal spaces. The collencytes (? = myocytes) that surround the larger canals degenerate and some endopinacocytes may be eliminated from the animals via excurrent canals. The cords of cells in the mesohyl normally present become dispersed and the tissue comes to contain, in decreasing abundance, archeocytes, collencytes, gray cells, and spherulous cells; the latter however, seem to be more abundant than in normal tissue. Such regressed tissue was found capable of reforming the whole canal system.

Tissue regression appears to be an alternative process to gemmule formation in response to lowered temperature and possibly other factors and may also be a transitory phenomenon set in motion by the widespread changes that ensue in the mesohyl during gametogenesis and larval development. In *Spongilla lacustris,* postlarval aggregates develop in areas of the mesohyl that appear to have previously contained developing larvae. These aggregates, which are relatively large, do not contain canal system elements (Simpson and Gilbert, 1973). In *Suberites massa* also, a phase of widespread phagocytosis takes place following sexual reproduction and leads to global reorganization of the tissue (Diaz, 1979a).

A Special Case of Tissue Regression: Reduction Bodies

Reduction bodies differ from tissue regression in that they are experimentally induced and the resultant cell mass occurs as spherical, compact groups of cells attached to the skeleton. In the case of *Spongilla discoides* and *Corvomeyenia carolinensis,* placement of adult animals into tap water leads rapidly to their formation (Penney, 1933; Harrison *et al.,* 1975). The formation of reduction bodies has also been reported in *Sycandra* (Maas, 1910), *Clathrina cerebrum* (Urban, 1910), *Sycon raphanus* (Tu-

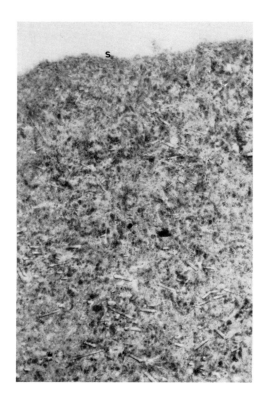

Figure 8-32 Fully regressed tissue of *Suberites massa*. Choanocyte chambers, canals, and the ectosome have been lost, and the tissue is relatively homogeneous. *s*, surface of the animal (light micrograph) (×100) (Diaz, 1979a). (Courtesy Dr. J-P. Diaz.)

zet and Paris, 1963b), *Sycon ciliatum* (Jones, 1971), *Spongilla lacustris* and *Ephydatia fluviatilis* (Müller, 1911a; Harrison and Davis, 1982), and *Leucosolenia botryoides* (Jones, 1956). Maas (1910), Müller (1911a), and Harrison *et al.* (1975) have reported the absence of choanocytes in reduction bodies due to phagocytosis by archeocytes, whereas Penney (1933), Urban (1910), and Jones (1971) find that choanocytes are maintained. In the case of *Spongilla discoides,* they are present but lack flagella and collars. In all cases, the reduction body is covered by an exopinacoderm with the possible exception of *Leucosolenia* (Jones, 1956); the latter report, however, requires further study. Fauré-Frémiet (1932b) induced reduction body formation in *Ficulina ficus* with X-irradiation which initially caused the death of choanocytes followed by the loss of canals. According to this study the loss of choanocytes was the primary stimulus. The cellular nature of the reduction body was not investigated.

In *Spongilla discoides,* Penney (1933) found that the internal cells

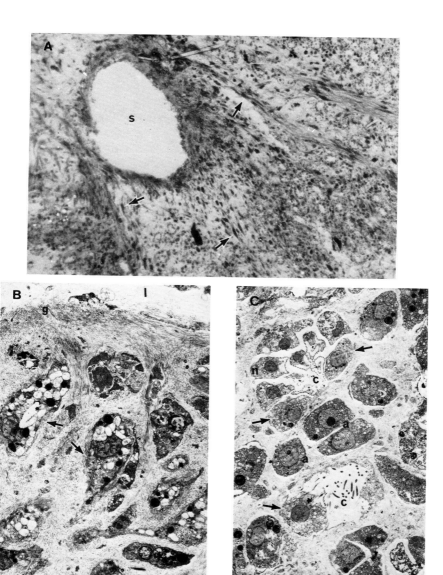

Figure 8-33 Aspects of the development of tissue regression in *Suberites massa*. **A.** A canal space (*s*) is undergoing regression and is no longer limited by endopinacocytes; note the roughened appearance of the border. Collencytes (*arrows*) that previously formed a stratified layer around the canal are migrating into the mesohyl (light micrograph) (×115) (Diaz, 1979a). **B.** The edge of a regressing canal like that in A. above. The lumen (*l*) is bound by collagen (*g*) and not endopinacocytes; collencytes (*arrows*) are perpendicular to it rather than parallel as in nonregressed tissue (TEM) (×2,475) (Diaz, 1979a). **C.** Proposed transformation of choanocytes into archeocytes (*arrows*) in regressing tissue. Note that the marked cells possess larger nuclei and cell size than nontransforming choanocytes (*n*). *c*, choanocyte chambers; *a*, archeocytes (TEM) (×1,665) (Diaz, 1979a). (All courtesy Dr. P-J. Diaz.)

present are the same as those in the functional animal but that canals and choanocyte chambers (but not choanocytes) are absent. The cells that are present include pinacocytes, archeocytes, choanocytes, collencytes, fiber cells, granular cells, and microsclerocytes. The development of a functional animal then involves primarily and possibly totally, morphogenesis rather than cell differentiation also. The one possible differentiative process is the formation of new endopinacocytes, which according to Penney may be derived from either archeocytes or granular cells, whereas exopinacocytes were reported to develop from the pinacocytes surrounding the reduction body. In view of the absence of observations of mitoses in pinacocytes (Chap. 2) and other results with the reaggregation of dissociated cells (Chap. 9), the latter conclusion requires careful reevaluation. In *Clathrina cerebrum,* Urban (1910) described a situation similar to that in *Spongilla discoides* in which the reduction body contains covering pinacocytes, choanocytes, and archeocytes, and in which subsequent development appears to be morphogenetic.

In distinction to the above type of development of reduction bodies, Maas (1910) and Müller (1911a) have described differentiative development. Müller found archeocytes, "dermal cells," and covering pinacocytes in them, and during their development, some archeocytes differentiate into choanocytes while the "dermal cells" form the pinacoderms. In *Sycandra,* the reduction body contains only one cell type, granular cells (? archeocytes) covered by pinacocytes. During later development, the former differentiate into choanocytes (Maas, 1910). This appears also to be the case in tap water-stimulated reduction bodies of *Ephydatia mulleri* (Schmidt, unpubl.) (Fig. 8-34). In them, there is at least a predominance of archeocytes with apparently few choanocytes. These bodies were similarly found capable of developing into functional sponges when placed in control medium. In that investigation, it was shown that the active agent for stimulating the formation of reduction bodies when diluted with distilled water failed to stimulate them; further dilution, however, then resulted in stimulation (Table 8-26). The data suggest that the active agent is

Table 8-26   Effect of Dilution of Tap Water on the Stimulation of Reduction Body Formation in *Ephydatia mulleri*[a]

Medium[b]	Time for Formation of Reduction Bodies
Tap water	18 days
Tap water diluted 2×	Partial formation after 24 days
Tap water diluted 4×	None after 24 days
Tap water diluted 10×	Partial formation after 24 days
Distilled water	14 days

[a]Data from Schmidt (unpubl.). Sponges were hatched from gemmules.
[b]Diluent for the tap water was distilled water.

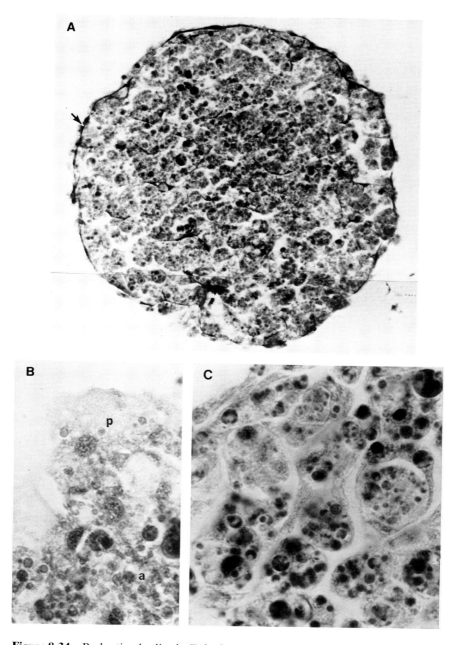

Figure 8-34 Reduction bodies in *Ephydatia mulleri* stimulated by hatching gemmules in tap water (light micrographs). **A.** Section through a reduction body showing the external pinacoderm and associated with it, a thin fibrous layer (*arrow*). Internally are archeocytes filled with phagosomes (×315) (Schmidt, unpubl.). **B.** Pinacocyte (*p*) covering the surface of a reduction body. *a,* internal archeocytes (×1,440) (Schmidt, unpubl.). **C.** Internal archeocytes filled with phagosomes (×1,440) (Schmidt, unpubl.). (All courtesy Dr. I. Schmidt.)

an ion but that other ions in tap water are essential for normal development, and when they are diluted, reduction bodies result. The ratio of sponge tissue to medium directly affects the process of reduction body formation: the greater the number of sponges per unit volume of medium, the more rapidly reduction bodies formed (Schmidt, unpubl.).

Thus, reduction bodies can be quite differently constituted in different species with two types possible: those that contain choanocytes and those that do not. Other differences appear related to the types of special cells present in the adult. The first type is similar to reaggregation masses (Chap. 9) and the latter to tissue regression. The presence or absence of choanocytes may be related to the initiation of phagocytic activity of archeocytes (Harrison *et al.*, 1975). Harrison and Davis (1982) have found that in the very early stages of reduction body formation two processes predominate: phagocytosis of choanocytes and increased collagen biosynthesis and matrix elaboration. An interesting question emerges as to why cell aggregates form isolated masses during reduction body formation but not during the process of tissue regression. Based upon the similarity between reduction bodies and reaggregation masses formed from dissociated cells, it is tempting to conjecture that an aggregation factor (Chap. 9) is involved in the formation of the former but not in the formation of regressed tissue. In species undergoing tissue regression, one would expect to find a masking of such a factor and/or its receptors or possibly its degradation. The eventual "loose" tissue construction in regressed tissue could then be a result of one or both of these.

Of further interest in this regard are the conditions which stimulate reduction body formation in calcareous species (Fig. 8-35). Jones (1956, 1971) and Maas (1910) have both shown that calcium- and/or carbonate-deficient media stimulate their formation. Under such conditions, spicule corrosion (dissolution) also occurs, and according to Jones (1971), its intensity is directly correlated with the intensity of reduction body formation which he refers to as "involution"; in that paper a very useful review of the earlier work of Maas is presented. It is surprising that no consideration has been given to a *direct* role of calcium in reduction body formation. Calcium deficiency, in addition to causing spicule dissolution, will directly affect the binding and availability of calcium to the cells in general. Considering that aggregation factor requires this divalent cation in order to support *in vitro* cell adhesion (Chap. 9), it would be most productive to similarly investigate its possible role *in vivo* relative to reduction body formation. Calcium-deficient media may well cause a translocation of bound calcium leading to cell motility and regrouping. Indeed, in the calcium-deficient experiments of Jones (1971), older animals with more spicules displayed a much more orderly process in reduction body formation, while in young ones with few spicules, the resulting cell mass comes to be covered by pinacocytes that are abnormally rounded up thus permitting some internal cells to "burst" out of the

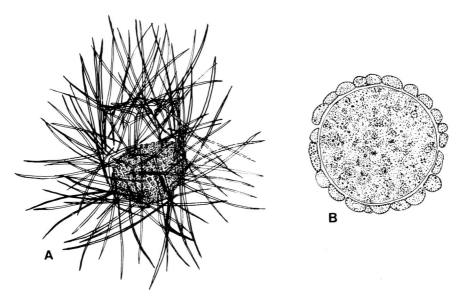

Figure 8-35 Reduction in *Sycon ciliatum*. **A**. Reduction body formation induced in young, newly metamorphosed individuals by low calcium concentrations (5 × 10^{-4} to 5 × 10^{-3} M). The tissue has rounded up within the spicular framework (×225) (Jones, 1971). **B**. Reduction body induced in a young animal by low bicarbonate concentration (5 × 10^{-4} M). The pinacocytes are rounded up at the surface of the choanocytes, and the former may, on occasion, separate permitting the inner cell mass to escape (×455) (Jones, 1971). (Copyright Cambridge University Press.) (Courtesy Dr. W. C. Jones.)

aggregate. This difference may well be related to the greater availability of calcium through spicule dissolution in the older animals.

Some reduction bodies appear strikingly similar to gemmules in that they apparently contain internally only a single cell type (Maas, 1910). In this regard, their function can be viewed as an alternative means of survival and dormancy in which the highly organized morphogenesis of a surrounding collagenous coat is lacking. The possible role of cyclic nucleotides in reduction body formation now presents an interesting new area of investigation especially in light of the observation that addition of 10^{-3} M cyclic AMP to the medium in which newly developing sponges are growing results, within six days, in an irreversible disorganization of the canal system (Rasmont, 1974).

CHAPTER NINE

Growth, Regeneration, Cell Recognition, Perspective on Cell Differentiation

The subject of sponge development is especially complex due to the multiplicity of systems capable of establishing a functional animal. The following, naturally occurring processes are known to lead to the development of a animal possessing a functional canal system: larval metamorphosis, the differentiation of regressed tissue, budding, and the hatching of gemmules. These processes result in the formation of a new (but morphologically immature), functional animal and have been treated in earlier chapters (Chaps. 7, 8). In addition to them, four aspects of growth can be recognized; one of which (initiative growth) can lead to the establishment of a number of additional canal system units in the same animal and consequently to what has been classically referred to as colonialism (Hartman and Reiswig, 1973; Simpson, 1973). Finally, studies of experimental regeneration, encompassing questions of cell recognition, can be separately treated and involve the manipulation of adult tissue including the reaggregation of dissociated cells, explantation (cuttings), transplantation (grafting) of tissue, parabiosis and tissue ablation.

Growth

Four different aspects of growth in sponges can be individually considered: (1) initial formation of new functional areas of an animal including the development of new choanocyte chambers, mesohyl, pinacoderms, ostia, and oscules (initiative growth); (2) maturation of newly formed, functional tissue involving primarily an increase in skeletal structures and in the complexity of the canal system (maturational growth); (3) remodeling of mature tissue; and (4) increase in size or volume (growth in general). Growth in size, of necessity, involves to some extent either maturational and/or initiative growth but deals with the results of these in terms of biomass.

In comparison to experimental regeneration and other forms of development, only meager data are available which relate to growth. However, as indicated in earlier chapters and in following sections, developmental processes that have been elucidated during experimental regeneration, larval metamorphosis, gemmule hatching, and budding, are basically similar to those occurring during growth; thus, the paucity of data may only be apparent and not real. The following discussion of growth focuses considerable attention on neglected problems, since specific data are, in many cases, not available or are incomplete.

Initiative Growth

Initiative growth, the formation in otherwise mature animals, of new areas of the mesohyl including new portions of the canal system, is almost totally uninvestigated. That it occurs in many species is well documented from morphological studies in which a number of oscular units are formed by the same individual. Since the metamorphosis of larvae leads to the initial formation of a single oscular unit in the young sponge (Chap. 7), it is clear that in the vast majority of species much initiative growth occurs routinely. In fully developed animals such as *Spongilla lacustris* and in *Microciona prolifera* and *Haliclona permolis,* regions of new growth, which are the beginnings of initiative growth, are characterized by a high density of mesohyl cells, high mitotic activity, the presence of few or no choanocyte chambers and canals, and the absence of a fully developed skeleton (Brien, 1976; Simpson, 1968b; Elvin, 1976). These observations establish that initiative growth begins through the migration and accumulation of mesohyl cells in specific regions of the animal and that at least some cytodifferentiation (choanocyte and pinacocyte formation) and most morphogenetic processes (elaboration of canals and the skeleton) occur following this initial migratory phase. The early stages of initiative growth thus appear not to include a simultaneous maturational element. The new growth area has been referred to by Brien (1975, 1976) as the "marginal membrane," which may occur at the surface of the animal or lateral to it, attached to the substratum. The marginal membrane appears completely comparable to the outgrowth region of explants which is described later.

Within the marginal membrane of *Ephydatia fluviatilis* are archeocytes and collencytes that have migrated there from the adjoining mesohyl and that may undergo limited mitoses (Brien, 1976); in this newly developing tissue, sclerocytes and special cells then appear. According to Brien (1976), when the canal system makes its appearance, archeocytes form the new choanocytes (see Chap. 6). The new canals also arise *de novo* but some of them become connected to preexisting canals in the adjoining mature tissue. In *Spongilla lacustris,* at the tips of the branches, areas comparable to the marginal membrane in *E. fluviatilis* develop but also contain prominent tracts of archeocytes which are joined by collencytes and other cells (Brien, 1976). These tracts are primordia of the newly developing skeleton (see next section) and the cells that constitute them are initially derived through migration from the mature tissue. In the mesohyl around the tracts, choanocyte chambers and canals appear. Thus, in these two sponges, the new growth area initially contains the same types of mesohyl cells present in the adult, and some of them differentiate into sclerocytes, spongocytes, choanocytes, and pinacocytes, *de novo*. Initially there appears to be no physical continuity of the old endopinacoderm and the newly forming one, but this question requires further reevaluation. There is, however, complete continuity of the old and new exopinacoderm, but new exopinacocytes are derived from mesohyl cells, not through mitoses of preexisting pinacocytes. Initiative growth merges imperceptibly with maturational growth, and it is therefore not possible to precisely define a point in development that separates them.

The growth of oscular tubes of the asconid, *Leucosolenia,* involves the addition of new choanocytes just below the oscular rim; the new cells are derived by mitoses of preexisting choanocytes (Jones, 1964a, 1965); the origin of new pinacocytes is unclear. This growth pattern falls somewhere between initiative and maturational growth since aspects of both are involved. Further, this narrow growth area can undergo rapid changes in the arrangement of choanocytes, pores, and spicules, suggesting that the events may also be considered as a form of remodeling (see later). Finally, some of the observed changes are due to contractility and thus appear physiological in nature. Consequently, in asconoid and *possibly* syconoid calcareous species, there is no known clear distinction between initiative growth, maturational growth, remodeling, and physiological processes. Although such processes can be distinguished separately in leuconoid species, all of them are, in reality, part of a continuum of whole animal function as clearly signaled in *Leucosolenia*.

Connes (1964) has described "budding" in a calcareous sponge, *Sycon raphanus,* which is technically initiative growth. "Buds" develop at the base of the oscular tube and form a new miniature oscular tube which remains attached to the parent. The bud develops asconoid structure initially but the new atrium is partitioned off from the parent (Fig. 9-1). The development of these buds is described as involving a migration of choanocytes, pinacocytes, lophocytes, and collencytes; the latter two cell types may be identical, differing only in their level of collagen biosynthesis, and they apparently degenerate after forming fibrous deposits in the mesohyl. The new asconoid unit then develops syconoid structure through folding of the choanocyte layer, details of which are lacking. Thus, according to Connes (1964), initiative growth in this calcareous species differs fundamentally from that in demosponges in that in the former, fully cytodifferentiated cells migrate into the new growth region. Additional investigations are clearly called for in order to further substantiate this difference.

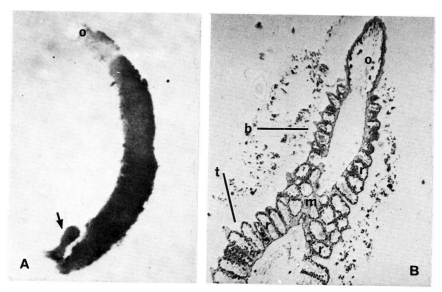

Figure 9-1 "Budding" in *Sycon* sp. The buds produced by this species remain attached to the parent and thus represent a type of somatic growth rather than a means of reproduction and dispersal (light micrographs). **A.** Newly developed bud (*arrow*) which was formed basally by the parent. *o,* oscule of parent (×3.5) (Connes, 1964). **B.** Histological section through the bud (*b*) and the parental tissue (*t*). Note that the atrial cavitites are effectively partitioned by the mesohyl (*m*) but that the mesohyl is continuous. *o,* oscule of the bud; *r,* choanocyte chambers of bud and parent (×100) (Connes, 1964). (Both courtesy Dr. R. Connes.)

Maturational Growth

Brien (1973, pp. 285–288) appears to be the first to emphasize the importance of maturational growth as a set of distinct morphogenetic processes leading to the formation of the adult. Such a view draws attention to processes some of which may potentially be specific to maturational growth. The result of development and of initiative growth is the formation of a juvenile sponge in which, however, the morphology differs significantly in a number of respects from that of adult animals. The differences are amply documented from studies of juvenile sponges derived from larval metamorphosis, gemmule hatching, and the development of reaggregation bodies in which the structure of the adult animal has also been elucidated. Studies of the development of the juvenile stage into adult tissue in the same species are rare, and few investigations have been reported which specifically set out to elucidate these processes. In general, the following structures and structural patterns undergo change dur-

ing maturational growth; (1) the pattern of the canal system and choanocyte chambers; (2) the degree of development of the cortex or ectosome,
when one is present; (3) the quantity and arrangement of collagen fibrils
and spongin fibers; (4) the appearance and localization of spicules and
spicule types. An outstanding reason for the lack of specific data is the
usual difficulty encountered in rearing newly formed sponges to an adult
stage, a problem not peculiar to the Porifera.

The following are some examples of maturational growth processes. In
fully metamorphosed larvae of *Microciona prolifera,* the skeleton is only
rudimentary; the quantity of spongin present is small and there are no
reticulating fibers containing spicules (Simpson, 1968b). In comparison,
fully developed adult tissue contains a substantial quantity of spongin in
the form of large fibers with numerous spicules encased within them
(compare Figs. 1-14 and 7-25) (Simpson, 1968a). This has also been reported in studies of juvenile (metamorphosed larvae) and adult tissue of
Haliclona (=Reniera) elegans (Tuzet, 1932; Garrone and Pottu, 1973),
and similar differences obviously exist in other species in which there are
well-developed spongin fibers and matrix materials in the adult (Garrone,
1978; Cowden, 1970; Cowden and Harrison, 1976). In *Ephydatia fluviatilis,* the newly metamorphosed sponge does not contain developed spicule
tracts (Brien and Meewis, 1938), whereas the adult does (Penney and
Racek, 1968). A similar situation has been reported in *Spongilla lacustris*
by Evans (1899), Brien (1976), and Herlant-Meewis (1948a), and in *Es-
perella fibrexilis* by Wilson (1894). The hatching of gemmules of the freshwater sponges *Spongilla lacustris, S. fragilis, Ephydatia fluviatilis,* and
E. mulleri results in juvenile animals, which similarly lack fully developed
skeletal systems (Wintermann, 1951; Garrone and Pottu, 1973; Pottu-
Boumendil, 1975; Brien, 1932). In ramose individuals of *Spongilla lacustris,* Brien (1975, 1976) has described the alignment of mesohyl cells into
tracts in the marginal membrane occurring at the tips of branches. These
tracts contain archeocytes, collencytes, and other cells initially. Sclerocytes develop within the tracts and secrete spicules which become aligned
tip to tip and side to side in ones, twos, and threes. The positioning of the
spicules is apparently due to the movement of the sclerocytes but may
also involve other cells. Spongin is then secreted around these spicules by
spongocytes, mostly at the spicule tips. The cells that constitute the tracts
migrate from the older tissues, and according to Brien (1975) they differentiate *de novo.* Some mitoses also occur in the surrounding mesohyl. In
Haliclona elegans, Garrone and Pottu (1973) have shown that following
larval metamorphosis, spongocytes aggregate preferentially at points
where two or more spicule tips intersect. In *Axinella polypoides,* the
branch tips lack the central, spiculated, spongin network and contain
instead tracts of spindle-shaped cells (?sclerocytes) along with numerous
spherulous cells (Bretting *et al.,* 1983). The release of lectins from the
latter cells is possibly directly involved in spongin secretion within these

tracts during maturational growth. It is possible that the ability to form vertical tracts of cells, as in *Spongilla lacustris* and *Axinella polypoides,* is related to the ability of an animal to develop upright branches, since similar structures were not found during maturational growth of the flat, encrusting species, *Ephydatia fluviatilis* (Brien, 1975, 1976).

Although few really detailed studies are available, it appears, in general, that juvenile animals have a canal system that differs substantially from that of the adult. In *Sycon raphanus,* the young sponge formed from larval metamorphosis is referred to as an olynthus which possesses asconoid structure (Chap. 7), whereas the adult is syconoid (Tuzet, 1973a). The initial pattern of choanocytes and canals in many postlarval demosponges also clearly differs from that of the adult (Lévi, 1956). For example, in *Oscarella lobularis,* the newly metamorphosed larva, referred to as a rhagon, has asconoid canal structure (Brien, 1973) and further maturational growth results in syconoid structure which then develops into the adult leuconoid system (Lévi and Porte, 1962). In *Halisarca,* the pattern of choanocytes and the canal system undergo considerable and significant change during later maturational growth (Lévi, 1956). While specific, detailed studies are not available, this also seems to be the case in gemmule-hatched, juvenile sponges and in young sponges formed from the reconstitution of reaggregated cells.

Most free-swimming larvae of spicule-bearing species themselves contain spicules (Lévi, 1956; Bergquist and Sinclair, 1968; Brien, 1973) and in some cases not all *adult* spicule types are present (Bergquist and Sinclair, 1968). Missing types are secreted during and following metamorphosis, but critical studies of the timing of their secretion and localization are wanting. The cortex (Chap. 3) is similarly a structure characteristic of adult tissue which undergoes development during maturational growth. Unfortunately, maturational growth is poorly known among tetractinellids where cortical sturcture is sometimes very highly developed. Despite this, it can be inferred from studies of other groups that juvenile sponges will possess little, if any, of the highly specialized, adult cortical features which will be laid down during maturational growth.

Developmental Processes in Maturational Growth. Maturational growth, as defined here, involves secondary processes in morphogenesis and cell differentiation, since functional structures (pinacocytes, choanocytes, canals, mesohyl, mesohyl cells) are already present. Among these secondary processes, one can recognize (1) the rearrangement of preexisting cells, (2) the continuing elaboration of ground substance and skeletal materials, and (3) the formation of new cells. The specific cellular activities underlying them include cell movements, cell division, cell differentiation, and secretion; hypothetically, two cellular mechanisms for maturational growth can be envisioned: chemotaxis (sometimes leading to cell grouping) and induction. The only

relevant data deal with the observations of most workers that choanocytes and archeocytes are able to undergo mitoses (see, for example,
Brien, 1976). There have been no reports during maturational growth of
localized mitotic activity of the type occurring in self-renewing tissues of
other organisms; consequently, cell migration or cell migration followed
by sporadic mitoses are the only means of cell addition to a specific region
of mesohyl (Brien, 1976). Chemotaxis possibly involving the silica of
spicules can be considered to lie at the basis of the formation of groups of
spongocytes, which initiate secretion of large spongin fibers (Garrone *et
al.*, 1981) as in the early maturation of postlarval and gemmule-hatched
sponges (Garrone and Pottu, 1973). In bath sponges, which do not secrete
spicules, the involvement of silica is precluded as a stimulus for the aggregation of spongocytes. Sclerocytes also become concentrated in tracts by
an unknown mechanism during the maturation of the skeleton in
Spongilla lacustris (Brien, 1976). Inductive events during maturational
growth have not been documented, although it is possible that the silica in
newly developing spicules may also directly induce collagen secretion by
surrounding spongocytes, since the latter cells secrete this matrix material only on their surfaces which are in contact with the developing spicule. Such a specific inductive sequence is, however, not conceivable in
the case of lophocytes which deposit collagen fibrils throughout the mesohyl (Chap. 5). This indicates a basic difference between spongin microfi-
bril and collagen fibril secretion. In many adult demosponges and hexactinellids, certain spicule types are localized, occurring only in specific
areas of the tissue (Hartman, 1981). In these animals, maturational growth
may involve either the migration (chemotaxis) of megasclerocytes and
microsclerocytes to these areas or the differentiation (induction) of precursor cells already in place; Brien (1975) considers the former as more
likely. The early maturation of the skeleton of *Ephydatia fluviatilis* involves an exceedingly complex series of events including spicule secretion and release by the sclerocyte, spongocyte movement to spicule surfaces, spongin secretion, and the walling off of the spicule by spongocytes
and pinacocytes (Chap. 4). There is thus a high degree of coordinated
activity by sclerocytes, spongocytes. and pinacocytes. In *E. mulleri,* maturational growth also entails the activity of lophocytes which synthesize
and release collagen fibrils as they move through the mesohyl; the mechanism whereby their movement is directed and their level of collagen biosynthesis controlled is unknown (Pottu-Boumendil, 1975). Other maturational processes that have received no attention include the development
of myocyte layers in the oscular rim of some species; the nature and
cellular bases of the changes in topography of the canal system; the maturation of the basal attachment region of adult animals; the mechanism of
development of nonspicular calcareous deposits in the pharetronids,
sclerosponges and sphinctozoids; the cementing of calcitic spicules in the
pharetronids; the fusion or articulation of siliceous spicules in hexactinel-

lids and lithistids; the patterning of spongin fiber networks in demosponges. Some of these aspects of skeletal maturation are discussed further in Chapter Four. The *specific* origin of cell types during maturational growth is not completely clear, although the cytodifferentiation of archeocytes into spongocytes, lophocytes, and megasclerocytes is clearly indicated. The origin of special cells generally remains unclear as in most other types of development, although Bretting *et al.* (1983) have presented data that strongly support the view that spherulous cells in *Axinella* are derived directly from archeocytes during growth.

Remodeling

Diaz (1979a) has described in detail the spontaneous disorganization and reorganization of the tissues in *Suberites massa*. Disorganized areas occur frequently at the base of irregular, lobulate, finger-like projections of the sponge surface and also within the center of the sponge, particularly in areas where excurrent canals are surrounded by layers of collencytes (a condition referred to as multistratified). The process of disorganization is highly complex and results in areas of tissue in which there are exceedingly few cells and no choanocyte chambers (Fig. 9-2A) (Table 9-1). During disorganization, choanocytes decrease in number by (1) degeneration (Fig. 9-2C), or (2) transformation into archeocytes, or (3) development of an endopinacocytic morphology (highly flattened) and formation of spaces in the mesohyl (Figs. 9-3A,B). Some chambers initially merge with each other (Fig. 9-2B) and with excurrent canals. Multistratified canal spaces are converted to simple endopinacocytic-lined spaces by the migration of collencytes into the mesohyl (Fig. 9-3C) in tracts where they develop typical lophocyte features. Archeocytes phagocytize choanocytes and other cells and they thus develop numerous phagosomes which are strikingly similar to the nutrient reserves in the gemmular thesocytes of *Suberites domuncula* (Chap. 8). Gray cells increase in number in areas undergoing disorganization, and cells with features intermediate between them and archeocytes are frequently seen suggesting that the latter are their origin (Fig. 9-3D). Toward the end of disorganization, most cells are localized in tracts or aggregates which predominantly contain archeocytes but also gray cells and fewer spherulous cells. Some aggregates are elongate and their archeocytes and gray cells develop trailing bundles of collagen fibrils typical of lophocytes. There is thus good evidence in this species that archeocytes as well as collencytes can take on lophocyte morphology. Eventually, the cell aggregates and tracts are displaced into adjoining areas of the mesohyl and the disorganized area is almost devoid of cells except for a few collencytes and archeocytes and more rarely gray cells and spherulous cells. When disorganization of the ectosome occurs, exopinacocytes are lost and the usual parallel layers of collencytes below them are scarce or absent, leaving collagen fibrils in contact with the

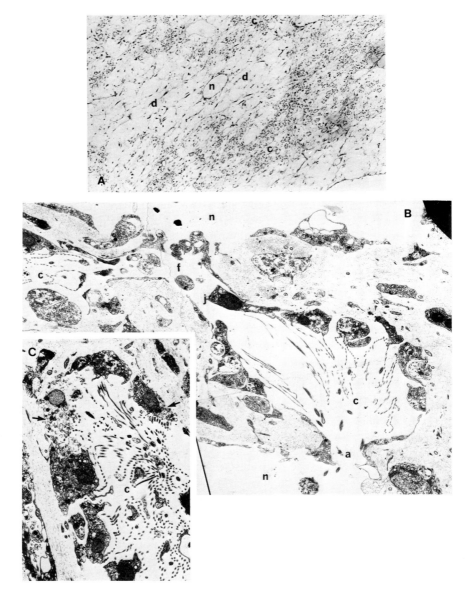

Figure 9-2   Aspects of tissue disorganization in *Suberites massa*. **A**. A disorganized area of the tissue (*d*) lacking choanocyte chambers and surrounded by fully developed and functional tissue containing choanocyte chambers (*c*). *n*, canal (light micrograph) (×76) (Diaz, 1979a). **B**. Confluence (*f*) of two choanocyte chambers (*c*) and canals (*n*). Note the unusual, elongate shape of the choanocyte at the junction of the two chambers (*j*). *a*, apopyle (TEM) (×2,830) (Diaz, 1979a). **C**. Degenerating choanocytes (*arrows*) in a region undergoing disorganization. *c*, choanocyte chamber (TEM) (×3,315) (Diaz, 1979a). (All courtesy Dr. J-P. Diaz.)

Table 9-1 Changes in Cell Populations During Disorganization in
Suberites massa[a]

	Organized Tissue	Early Disorganization	Later Disorganization	Complete Disorganization
Total number of cells[b]	330	250	69	12
Number of choanocyte chambers[b]	18	14	5	0
Number of choanocytes in each chamber[b]	17	14	10	—
Number of archeocytes[b]	19	41	9	5
Number of other mesohyl cells[b]	20	45	10	12

[a]Data taken from Diaz (1979a).
[b]Mean number per 10 mm^2 sections of tissue. Areas of tissue containing ectosome, pluristratified canals, skeletal tracts, or cell cords were not employed in the counts.

environment. This layer may even partially become detached from the surface.

In this same species, areas of the animal, primarily at the tips and surface of lobulate processes, undergo what Diaz (1979a) has referred to as reorganization but which appears to be essentially comparable to initiative growth except that the mesohyl ground substance and skeleton are already in place (Fig. 9-4). Reorganization occurs in two stages which are similar, if not identical, to initiative growth: (1) choanocyte chambers appear and at about the same time new endopinacocyte-lined canal spaces develop, and (2) connections to the canal system are formed and water pumping begins. Frequently cords of cells from adjoining, disorganized regions course toward the reorganizing area. Cell aggregates appear in the area undergoing reorganization and are presumably derived from the cell cords. Archeocytes form choanoblasts (Fig. 9-4B) through mitoses and then lose their nucleoli and develop flagella, collars, and periflagellar sleeves typical of this species (Chap. 2). Archeocytes are also the origin of new endopinacocytes which develop monostratified canal spaces (Fig. 9-4C). The aggregates of cells progressively disappear and the new canals become multistratified through collencyte migration to, and flattening around, them. Frequently, collencytes surround cell aggregates; the latter then disintegrate leaving a lacunal (canal) space. In reorganizing areas the

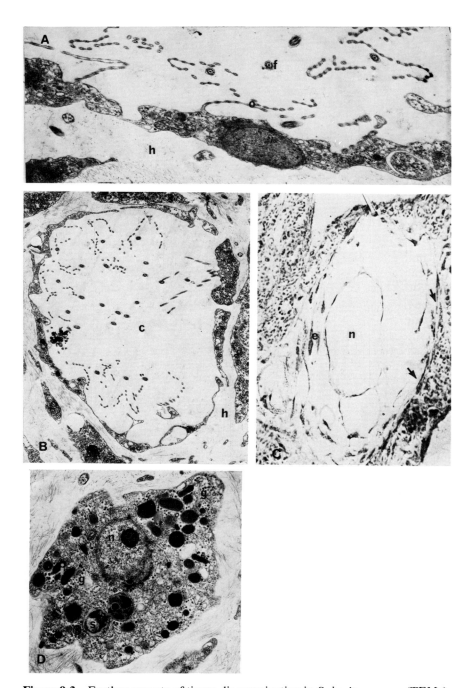

Figure 9-3 Further aspects of tissue disorganization in *Suberites massa* (TEMs). **A, B**. Early transformation of choanocytes into an endopinacocyte morphology. Note the highly flattened shape of the cells but their retention of collars (*o*) and flagella (*f*). In B., all of the choanocytes of the chamber (*c*) are flattening and assuming a pinacocyte morphology. *h,* mesohyl (A: ×8,305; B: ×3,735) (Diaz,

ectosome comes to be covered by an exopinacoderm under which a few parallel layers of collencytes occur. The exopinacocytes are later lost leaving collagen fibrils at the surface, a typical configuration found in this species.

The processes of disorganization and reorganization probably lie at the basis of, respectively, remodeling of the canal system and growth. *Suberites massa* does not possess any well-defined growth regions, although the fact that reorganization occurs at the tips of upright lobules is indicative of them. Growth in this animal thus appears to take place through the complementary processes of disorganization and reorganization with the latter more dominant then the former in actively growing animals. Remodeling of the canal system which occurs during reorganization does not, however, appear to be a unique process specific to *Suberites massa*. Hartman and Reiswig (1973) have found clear examples of the obliteration of oscules in a number of demosponges where old oscules become "filled in." Such remodeling of the canal system in an otherwise mature, adult indicates a fluidity of structure, and these workers visualize such changes as being related to maximizing the efficiency of water flow in the canal system further suggesting that some type of aging occurs in the functional parts of the system. No specific information is available dealing with changes in cellular arrangement and skeletal pattern during the latter type of remodeling but these may be comparable and certainly as complex as events in *Suberites massa*.

Fauré-Frémiet (1932b) has clearly documented, in the marine demosponge *Ficulina ficus,* the spontaneous remodeling of the canals in juvenile animals, and Wintermann (1951) also observed canal obliteration and subsequent formation of new canals and oscules in young freshwater sponges. In this context, Ankel (1965) has emphasized the necessity for a water-tight system in order for water pumping efficiency to be high. Possibly aging or degeneration of choanocytes and/or canal junctions stimulate remodeling and the reestablishment of a water-tight system. Ankel and Wintermann-Kilian (1952) and Wintermann-Kilian and Ankel (1954) have further demonstrated the essentiality of the maintenance of both the prosendopinacoderm and the apendopinacoderm for normal canal functioning suggesting that it is not possible for the organism to interchange these epithelia relative to water pumping. Namely, incurrent canals cannot become excurrent canals and vice versa. Consequently, disturbances in the

---

1979a). **C.** Relocation of collencytes around a canal (*n*). The collencytes (*e*) which originally formed a stratified layer immediately around the canal have moved outward and some of them have taken up new positions (*arrow*) at some distance from the canal (×205) (Diaz, 1979a). **D.** Transformation of an archeocyte into a gray cell. The intermediate stage possesses gray cell features—dense inclusions (*i*) and glycogen (*g*)—and archeocyte features—nucleolate nucleus (*n*) and phagosomes (*s*) (×7,445) (Diaz, 1979a). (All courtesy Dr. J-P. Diaz.)

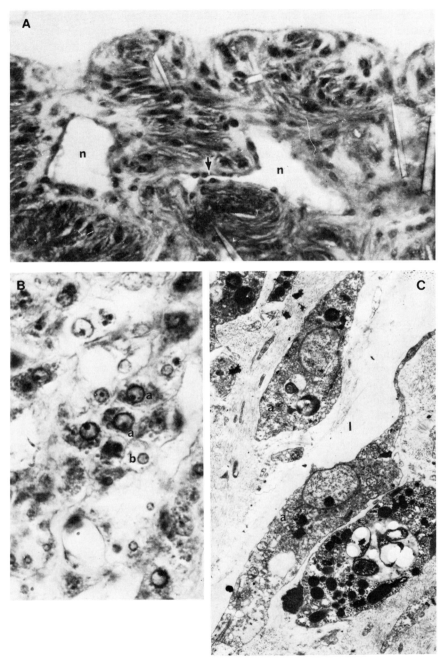

Figure 9-4   Aspects of tissue reorganization in *Suberites massa*. **A**. Early formation and fusion (*arrow*) of canal spaces (*n*). (light micrograph) (×495) (Diaz, 1979a). **B**. Differentiation of choanoblasts (*b*) from archeocytes during reorganization. *a,* archeocytes (light micrograph) (×900) (Diaz, 1979a). **C**. Canal formation.

prosendopinacoderm cannot be compensated for by the apendopinacoderm or the reverse; therefore, if leakage in one of them occurs it must be promptly repaired. Such local "damage" without efficient repair may also lead to the eventual necessity for remodeling.

Remodeling of the canal system has also been reported following sexual reproduction. In species of *Halisarca,* large areas of the mesohyl are occupied by gametes, embryos, and larvae, and the canal system is highly reduced, even degenerate (Chen, 1976). Following the reproductive period, new canals and chambers arise throughout these areas. In some cases, the degeneration of functional structures during sexual reproduction is so vast that remodeling is apparently not possible and the animals die (Lévi, 1956); similarly, this may be the reason why *Tetilla serica* dies after gamete release (Watanabe, 1978a). Although unsubstantiated, the widespread mortality of certain populations of *Clathrina coriacea* and *C. blanca* following the reproductive period (Johnson, 1979b) may similarly be related to a failure in remodeling the canals. In *Suberites massa,* remodeling also occurs annually during a two to three week period following sexual reproduction (Diaz, 1979a). In this instance, ultrastructural analyses have shown explosive phagocytosis of cells by archeocytes and then reconstruction of new canal systems within a mesohyl filled with archeocytes which themselves are packed with nutrients. Finally, the spherical aggregates of cells (postlarval aggregates) appearing after larval release may represent a similar stage in remodeling in *Spongilla lacustris* (Simpson and Gilbert, 1973).

Remodeling thus appears to be related to (1) maximizing canal system efficiency, (2) reestablishing canals and water pumping following sexual reproduction, and (3) producing new growth. Of more than passing interest is the possibility that sexual reproduction acts as a stimulus for renewed development and growth due to the triggering of remodeling processes. Other experimentally induced perturbations similarly lead to extensive developmental activity and are discussed in later sections of this chapter.

Growth as an Increase in Size or Volume

Initiative and possibly also maturational growth lead to an increase in the size of animals. Although appropriate studies of the corresponding increase in organic content are rare, these size increases can be assumed to be due, at least in part, to the net synthesis of organic components. Some increase in size may also be due to the expansion of the canal system with associated maturational growth, which possibly does *not* involve a net increase in organic content but rather an increase in volume. Most studies of growth have, however, not distinguished between these possibilities

---

Archeocytes (*a*) are forming an initial boundary around a lacuna (*l*) and one of them is elongating and flattening (TEM) (×5,445) (Diaz, 1979a). (All courtesy Dr. J-P. Diaz.)

for technical reasons and have emphasized simple measurements of increase in surface area occupied by encrusting sponges, or the increase in diameter and/or height of upright animals, or volume increases.

In long-term studies of growth of the commercial sponge *Hippospongia lachne,* Storr (1964) has measured the diameter of marked sponges over a four year period. Increases in size are proportionally higher in younger sponges: in the second year, the diameters increased ×3.2; in the third year, ×2.0; in the fourth year, ×1.6. However, there were wide fluctuations in growth rates in different habitats ranging from average diameter increases of ×1.8 per year to ×2.94 per year. When growth rates were plotted, they indicated a cessation of growth at about 12 inches in diameter, which correlated well with field observations in which sponges of this size showed tissue death and destruction centrally, producing doughnut-shaped animals. In *Haliclona loosanoffi,* Hartman (1958a) found average volume increases in actively growing summer sponges of ×1.1 to 9.0, although some individual animals actually decreased in volume fivefold. Elvin (1976), using measurements of the surface area occupied by the encrusting, intertidal species, *Haliclona permolis,* found growth rates of 1 mm²/day/cm² of sponge occuring during the summer and fall months. In the winter, 1.5% of the individual sponges died per day, and in the spring this figure dropped to 0.86%. During the period of growth in 1971 (July to October) the density of cells in the mesohyl is highest as is the organic content as related to either spicule weight or inorganic weight. Also during this period, RNA and lipid are close to maximal while glycogen is minimal based upon sponge volume (Elvin, 1976, 1979). Estimates of protein requirements (as μg/mm³/day) for growth as compared to sexual reproduction suggest a much greater requirement for the former, since more energy is invested in it than in reproduction. In a study of Jamaican demosponges, Reiswig (1973) found large differences in growth rates when comparing different species. In *Mycale* sp., growth rates averaged about 60% increase in volume per year, whereas *Aplysina* (*Verongia*) *gigantea* and *Tethya crypta* had, respectively, less than and approximately 5% growth rates. In *Mycale* sp. and *Tethya crypta,* smaller individuals showed a higher percentage growth rate, and in the former, individuals living in a less crowded environment (sand habitat versus a reef habitat) had growth rates twice as high. Stone (1970a) has carried out a study of the growth of the intertidal demosponge *Hymeniacidon perleve* in England. As determined by measurements of the area occupied by the sponge, growth occurs during the period of June to September (Table 8-25); average growth rates were found similar to those in *Haliclona permolis,* namely, 0.3–0.8 mm²/cm²/day. Protein content is also highest (dry weight basis) during the growth period as in *H. permolis* (Stone, 1970b). Conversely, ash content was lowest, possibly due to lowered spicule density in new growth areas. In *H. permolis* the number of spicules per cubic millimeter of tissue is highest during the growth period while the average volume of each spicule is lowest (Elvin, 1979) as one would expect during initiative growth when the newly developed mesohyl contains many new spicules which are not yet fully formed.

Jones (1965) has found that growth (increase of surface area) in *Leucosolenia variabilis* can be as high as 25% per day but taking distention (and contraction) of the tube into consideration the value *per se* is probably closer to 10% per day. The maximum growth rates occurred just below the oscule; rates at the level of the oscule and near the base of the sponge were considerably lower, indicating a gradient of growth potential.

In cave populations of *Clathrina coriacea* and *C. blanca,* maximal growth (surface area occupied) occurs from about February to May (Table 9-2), while sexual reproduction in both takes place in the spring and summer (Johnson, 1979b). Thus, in these calcareous species, as in *Haliclona permolis,* somatic growth is temporally separated from sexual reproduction (Elvin, 1976). Interestingly, in *Clathrina,* water temperatures are minimal during the period of growth, while for *Haliclona* they are maximal; however, temperature fluctuations in both habitats are only on the order of 3 to 5°C. In *Halichondria* sp., newly established sponges derived from larvae have an average growth rate (length increase) of 1.0 mm/day/sponge (Fell and Lewandrowski, 1981). However, individual growth rates are highly variable; sponges that are less than 30 mm in length grew at 1.0 mm/day/sponge, those which are 30 to 60 mm in length at 1.5 mm/day/sponge, and those that are more than 60 mm in length at 0.3 mm/day/sponge, suggesting that newly established, smaller sponges have a much higher growth rate than older ones as in *Mycale* sp. (Reiswig, 1973).

Table 9-2 Growth of Two Calcareous Species[a]

Month	*Clathrina coriacea* Mean Number of Sponges Per 25 cm^2	Mean Area Covered (mm^2)	*Clathrina blanca* Mean Number of Sponges Per 25 cm^2	Mean Area Covered (mm^2)
Aug	0.8	3.2	2.0	2.4
Sep	—	—	—	—
Oct	—	—	—	—
Nov	11.3	80.6	9.8	24.8
Dec	12.8	75.1	14.8	84.6
Jan	16.7	103.4	15.0	167.1
Feb	21.2	205.0	19.3	282.7
Mar	23.3	233.5	20.3	414.9
Apr	21.3	334.5	19.8	469.0
May	20.8	392.4	16.0	448.1
Jun	19.0	341.4	16.8	310.6
Jul	22.8	155.1	12.8	113.6
Aug	2.8	7.0	4.8	11.6

[a]Data taken from Johnson (1979b) for the years 1974–1975.

In an *in situ* study of Mediterranean demosponges, volume increases of as much as 80% during a fifty week period were observed [*Aplysina (Verongia) aerophoba*] as well as volume decreases of as much as 50% [*Aplysina (Verongia) cavernicola*] (Wilkinson and Vacelet, 1979). Growth rates in some species studied were very strongly affected by light, availability of nutrients, and rates of sedimentation on the sponge surface. For example, in *Aplysina (Verongia) aerophoba,* which contains symbiotic cyanobacteria, growth was about four times greater in light than in dim light and was greater when water currents were more available. In *Aplysina (Verongia) cavernicola,* which lacks symbionts, the absence of light increased growth over the controls by about threefold and protection from sedimentation permitted about 50% more growth. This study suggests that the variability in growth rates recorded from the field may be to some extent a reflection of the variability of environmental factors on a microhabitat level. In all of the species studied by Wilkinson and Vacelet (1979), reduced water currents resulted in reduced growth, although possession of symbiotic cyanobacteria compensated to some extent for reduced currents. Similarly, in an *in situ* experiment with the zoochlorella-containing freshwater sponge, *Spongilla lacustris,* the exclusion of light results in a 20 to 40% lower growth rate but no significant difference in water pumping and feeding (Frost and Williamson, 1980). Using a specially designed growth chamber, Francis *et al.* (1982) have found a positive correlation between calcium concentration and short-term growth of *Ephydatia fluviatilis*.

The variability in growth of sponges under field conditions has been further documented by Dayton (1979) in a long-term, *in situ,* study of the Antarctic species, *Mycale acerata* and *Rosella racovitzae*. Among smaller individuals of the latter, the smallest appear to grow more rapidly although not exclusively. Percentage volume increases during three years ranged from -30 to $+292$ with a mean increase of 99% for 33 sponges. Long-term observations of *Mycale* suggest that on average the animals can grow 2 to 4 cm in diameter per year. However, some individuals show negative growth and others no growth so that there is much variability here also.

Experimental Regeneration

Sponges possess remarkably high regenerative ability which is probably not exceeded by any other metazoan group. Historically, the sponge "fishing" industry has employed small cuttings of adult animals as a means of propagating commercial species; records of such go back at least to the eighteenth-century (Storr, 1964; see also Moore, 1910a,b). Cuttings are able to attach and establish a new, small sponge and can undergo long-term growth (Storr, 1964). As expected, many other types of manipulation of functional tissue lead to regeneration.

Explants

The removal of small pieces of tissue (explants) from an adult sponge and the application of them to appropriate substrata results in their attachment and the production of an outgrowth region (Fig. 9-5) (Simpson, 1963, 1968a). A similar technique, described by Harrison (1974b), involves the attachment of small, whole sponges onto glass slides and then studying the outgrowth region which they produce as they grow onto the slide. These techniques are similar to making cuttings except that the outgrowth region is frequently thin enough to be studied *in vivo* as well as following preparation as whole mounts. The outgrowth region which forms initially is undifferentiated except for the presence of exo- and basopinacoderms. In *Microciona prolifera* these pinacocytes have typical archeocyte features and it is likely that they are formed by them (Simpson, 1963, 1968a). In the mesohyl of the undifferentiated area are archeocytes, gray cells, globoferous cells, and rhabdiferous cells. Magasclerocytes with archeocyte features form spicules (megascleres) as the region undergoes differentiation. Newly formed choanocyte chambers appear but the origin of chaonocytes is not clear; since, however, migrating choanocytes have not been detected these newly differentiated cells may develop from mesohyl cells (archeocytes). Two types of microscleres (chelas, toxas) also develop in the undifferentiated area; chelas are possibly formed by exopinacocytes and/or endopinacocytes and toxas appear within an apparently extracellular material (Chap. 4). Collagen is secreted by spongocytes

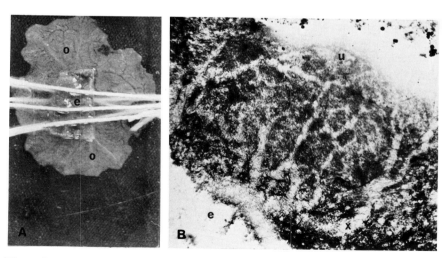

Figure 9-5 Growth of an explant of *Microciona prolifera* (light micrographs). **A.** The adult explant (*e*) has formed an extensive outgrowth region (*o*) on the glass substratum. White lines are nylon thread used for initially attaching the explant (×1.8) (Simpson, 1963). **B.** Whole mount of part of the outgrowth region. *x*, excurrent canal; *u*, undifferentiated marginal zone; *e*, area from which original explant was removed (×23) (Simpson, 1963).

around megascleres. There is no pattern of mitotic activity in adult (i.e., explant) pinacocytes or choanocytes which could account for the origin of these cell types in the outgrowth region through continuity with the corresponding adult epithelia. In a closely related species, *Microciona spinosa,* a similar sequence has been reported and in three other demosponge species, *Thalysias juniperina* and *T. schoenus* and *Tedania ignis,* pinacocytes in the outgrowth region also possess archeocyte features and are probably formed by them (Simpson, 1968a). Furthermore, in the latter species, cells with archeocyte features secrete megascleres and spongin; microscleres are secreted by different cells as discussed in Chapter Four. The formation of choanocyte chambers may involve mesohyl cell transformation as in *Microciona.*

In the freshwater species *Corvomeyenia carolinensis,* Harrison (1974b) has cytochemically characterized the cells in the outgrowth region and has concluded that archeocytes are similar to unspecialized stem cells in other organisms. The basopinacocytes display relatively unspecialized features in comparison to exopinacocytes, in particular they possess a nucleolus, cytoplasmic RNA, and retain the ability to migrate, indicating little differentiation beyond archeocytes from which they are apparently derived. Megasclerocytes in this sponge possess typical archeocyte features and doubtless originate from them (Harrison, 1974b). Although mitotic activity was observed in choanocytes, their origin in the outgrowth region was not established. The development of the outgrowth of explants appears to be completely comparable to naturally occurring initiative growth (see previous section) and the *overall* sequence of development in both cases is strongly reminiscent of gemmule hatching (Chap. 8) in that in all three instances the following processes occur: cell migration with the formation of exopinacoderm and basopinacoderm, continued cell migration and limited mitoses of some migrated cells, limited spicule secretion, formation of isolated choanocyte chambers, formation of canals.

Transection of Whole Animals

In the calcareous sponge *Sycon raphanus,* Tuzet and Paris (1963b) have preformed a number of interesting regeneration experiments. When an individual oscular tube is cut in half transversely, both the upper and lower portion regenerate complete, smaller animals with the former developing a new basopinacoderm for attachment and the latter forming a new oscular opening. The polarity, oscular pole versus basal pole, of the regenerates is the same as that of the original animal. When two transverse cuts are made, three new sponges result each with the polarity of the original and when a longitudinal cut is made part way down the tube, two oscules develop. These results suggest that the original oscule exerts an inhibitory influence over the rest of the tissue preventing the formation of additional oscules unless the tissue is separated. Korotkova (1963, 1970) has confirmed the results of these studies and has further discovered in a multioscular species, *Sycon lingua*, that a potential for the experimental development of multioscular regenerates exists, which suggests that the excised pieces may lose their polarity.

In *Tethya lyncurium*, a spherical demosponge species with a well-developed cortex, Connes (1966a) has cut whole animals into halves, quarters, eighths, and sixteenths. Halves and quarters undergo contraction and round up in such a manner that the original cortex comes to surround the medulla. Each piece then forms thin filaments that attach to the substratum. Many of these filaments eventually develop into buds (Chap. 8). Cutting thus not only results in restoration of a functional animal but also stimulates budding. One-eighth pieces of *Tethya* apparently develop some new exopinacocytes since the old cortex does not completely surround the medulla. In this case the cortex becomes indistinguishable from the medulla and attachment and budding do no always occur; one-sixteenth pieces degenerate. When pieces of the cortex are cut out, they form doughnut-shaped structures by curling and then attach but do not form a definitive canal system, although some choanocytes do differentiate from archeocytes. Excised pieces of the medulla undergo degeneration and appear poorly adapted to exposure to the environment; the medulla in this species is considered to depend upon the cortex for its stability (Connes, 1966a). This dependency could be due to a specialization of the cortex for osmotic and ionic regulation although no data are available relating to this possibility. During the regeneration of the cortex (Connes, 1966b) layers of lophocytes are found at the surface and secrete collagen, forming a superficial fibrous layer. Below this layer are archeocytes and cellules spheruleuses; many of the latter form an alveolar-like tissue due to the fact that their cytoplasmic inclusions are empty, leaving a network of vacuoles, an observation similar to that made by Thiney (1972) on regenerates of *Hippospongia communis* (see following). The origin of new exopinacocytes is not clear. The regeneration experiments with *Tethya* indicate that adult tissue is capable of developing new exopinacocytes, basopinacocytes, and possibly choanocytes. In no case is there a suggestion that preformed cells of these types give rise to them.

Tissue Ablation

When part of the surface of *Ircinia strobilina* is cut away the underlying tissue contracts within 24 h and a new exopinacoderm is formed by 72 h (Storr, 1976). Repeated surface cuttings result in the same rate of regeneration indicating the presence of a stock of cells (archeocytes) which are able to differentiate into pinacocytes. In a pioneering study, Wilson (1910) observed the formation of a new exopinacoderm following cutting the surface of *Stylotella heliophila*. He appears to have been the first to document the origin of new pinacocytes directly from mesohyl cells rather than from preexisting pinacocytes during regeneration. In his experiments, regeneration was very rapid, being substantially complete within one to two days. In hatched gemmules of the freshwater species, *Spongilla lacustris,* Brønsted (1953) has found that the newly hatched sponge when removed from its substratum and then attached to a new one regenerates a new basopinacoderm—the younger the sponge the greater its ability to repeatedly regenerate the basal epithelium (Table 9-3). The percentage of nucleolated basopinacocytes increases with the number of repetitive regenerations indicating that a stock of histoblasts is depleted and replaced by archeocytes. An unexplained result of this work is the observation that the nuclear size of basopinacocytes decreases with repeated regeneration as does cell size. Possibly some of the division products of archeocytes destined to become choanocytes are diverted to forming basopinacocytes (Chap. 8). In contrast, Harrison (1972a) has found that when circular wounds (~60 μm) are produced in explants of *Corvomeyenia carolinensis,* the remaining basopinacocytes produce cell extensions and bridges and fill in the basopinacoderm, suggesting that when the amount of tissue removed is small, existing pinacocytes can fill in the gap more rapidly than new ones can form. Jackson and Palumbi (1979) have followed regeneration *in situ* in a number of unidentified, coral reef, Jamaican demosponges in which 4 mm plugs of tissue were removed from the animals. The rate of complete regeneration (=infilling) during thirty days was highly variable ranging from 1 to 3 days up to 21 to 30 days in different species. These rates are among some of the most rapid known in animal systems. In distinction to these observations, Fauŕe-Frémiet (1932b) found that when areas of thin, newly developed sponges (*Ficulina ficus*) are mechanically removed, no regeneration occurs; only the cut edges heal and the excurrent canals eventually are remodeled. It is probably the case in these juvenile animals that there are insufficient numbers of cells for regeneration since maturational growth is progressing in them, thus involving many of the archeocytes. In this same context, Diaz (1977) has found that repetitive sampling of the same individuals of *Suberites massa* eventually results in tissue disorganization and degeneration. One can assume in this case too that there is a depletion of mesohyl cells

Table 9-3 Regeneration of the Basopinacoderm in Hatched Gemmules of *Spongilla lacustris*[a]

Age of Hatched Sponge When Initially Removed from Substratum	Mean Number of New Basopinacoderms Formed Per Sponge
Few Hours	6
2 Days	3
4 Days	0.5

[a]Taken from Brønsted (1953).

necessary for regeneration. Indeed, during degeneration, choanocytes and pinacocytes are reported to transform into archeocytes and there is widespread phagocytosis of spherulous cells, gray cells and collencytes. The resulting imbalance in cell types interestingly leads transitorily to the development of abnormally large archeocytes and oocyte-like cells (Fig. 9-6).

In *Leucosolenia complicata,* the removal of small pieces of tissue along the upright oscular tubes or the cauterization of small areas leads to the formation of a regeneration membrane consisting of exopinacocytes. Sclerocytes then migrate into the region and choanocytes spread from the edge inward to reconstitute the choanoderm. There is disagreement as to the origin of new choanocytes; Korotkova (1970) concludes they form through the migration of preexisting choanocytes, while Tuzet and Paris (1963b) conclude that they are derived from "amoebocytes." In both of these sets of experiments the lineage of new cells is not completely clear and requires further investigation. Jones (1964a), however, considers that during normal growth in this species new choanocytes are derived through the multiplication of preexisting ones.

In *Halichondria panicea,* the destruction of oscules results in either a slow regeneration of the oscule in the same area, or a healing over of the old oscule and the development of new ones close to the original (Korotkova, 1970). The latter result indicates that the presence of oscules suppresses the development of additional oscules in adjacent areas, and thus reinforces the conclusion arrived at by Tuzet and Paris (1963b).

Korotkova and Tonkin (1968) have investigated regeneration following exposure to carcinogens in *Leucosolenia variabilis* and *complicata* and in *Sycon raphanus.* In the former two species, these drugs (orthotolidine, 3,3-dichlorbenzidine and benzpyrene) cause the eventual production of outgrowths of tissue ("buds") from the surface. In *L. complicata* after exposure to orthotolidine, choanocytes lose their flagella and collars, many break away from the choanoderm, and the remainder become less organized. With 24 h large patches of the choanoderm lack choanocytes and among the remaining cells mitotic activity has increased from control levels of 8–9 cells/100 cells to 21–23 cells/100 cells. After four days, the choanoderm is reconstituted and lateral buds containing choanocytes have developed. The regeneration of new choanocytes in these experiments is due to the activity of preexisting ones, an observation that has been made only in calcareous species. The structure of *Leucosolenia* (asconoid) is such that the regeneration of choanocytes may follow a different path than in leuconoid species; in the latter there is no continuous layer of choanocytes as in the former.

In the commercial bath sponge, *Hippospongia communis,* Thiney (1972) has preformed regeneration experiments on the oscular rim by cutting out small segments of the structure and then following the remaining tissue. The oscular rim is covered externally by exopinacocytes and

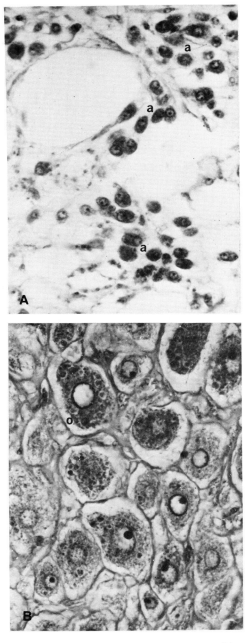

Figure 9-6 Tissue response to mechanical trauma (repetitive removal of tissue samples) in *Suberites massa* (light micrographs). **A.** There is a dramatic increase in archeocyte (*a*) numbers in regions of the tissue adjoining those where tissue had been removed (×475) (Diaz, 1977). **B.** In some adjoining areas, oocyte-like cells (*o*) are stimulated to form and produce an ovary-like region in the tissue (×475) (Diaz, 1977). (Both courtesy Dr. J-P. Diaz.)

internally by endopinacocytes; within the thin mesohyl layer are numerous aligned myocytes forming a sphincter as well as archeocytes, cellules spheruleuses, and collagen fibrils. The myocytes possess both microtubules and microfilaments and stain positively for cholinesterase. After cutting, three stages can be recognized: (1) disorganization of the tissue, (2) healing, and (3) reorganization. During these stages the cellules spheruleuses undergo loss of their inclusions, followed by the development of an intracytoplasmic network, which apparently represents remnants of the membranes which previously surrounded the inclusions. The inclusions are then reformed. This sequence establishes that the contents of the inclusions are released and possibly utilized for ground substance elaboration or some other required function, as in other species (see Chap. 3).

After cutting, during disorganization, pinacocytes, archeocytes, and myocytes retain and/or develop strikingly similar features including microfilaments, phagosomes, nucleoli, rough endoplasmic reticulum, Golgi membranes, and an external coating on their surfaces. Archeocytes and old exopinacocytes adjacent to the cut apparently form new exopinacocytes. During healing, many cells are present in a compact mass below the developing exopinacoderm; among them are archeocytes, myocytes, and polyblasts; the latter may be division products. During reorganization, myocytes become aligned and collagen fibrils are secreted. The precise lineage of the cells during reorganization is not clear and presents a difficult problem for future investigations.

Boury-Esnault (1976b) has followed the early stages of regeneration in *Polymastia mamilaris* following the removal of incurrent papilae (described in Chap. 6). When papillae are cut off at the level of the sponge, surface regeneration always occurs, whereas if the underlying mesohyl is also simultaneously removed no regeneration takes place demonstrating that the regenerating tissue is derived through cell migration from the underlying choanosome (Figs. 9-7A–C). Within 6 to 12 h the cut surface becomes occluded and covered by new exopinacocytes (Fig. 9-8A) except for the cut ends of the vertical spicule tracts; the new pinacocytes possess typical archeocyte features and are considered derived from them. By 24 h three zones can be recognized: exopinacoderm; under this, cell fragments and many collagen fibrils (Fig. 9-7D); and most internally archeocytes charged with phagosomes (Fig. 9-8B) and gray cells with exceptionally abundant glycogen. Gray cells, with their abundant stores of glycogen, are considered as the primary source of energy for development in this (Boury-Esnault, 1976b) and other species (Boury-Esnault, 1977; Boury-Esnault and Doumenc, 1979), although not all have been reported to possess them (Chap. 3). After about three days a blastema has formed due to the upward migration of cells along the spicule tracts (Fig. 9-8C) and their lateral movement toward the edge of the centrally exposed incurrent canal. Within the blastema is a more superficial region of arche-

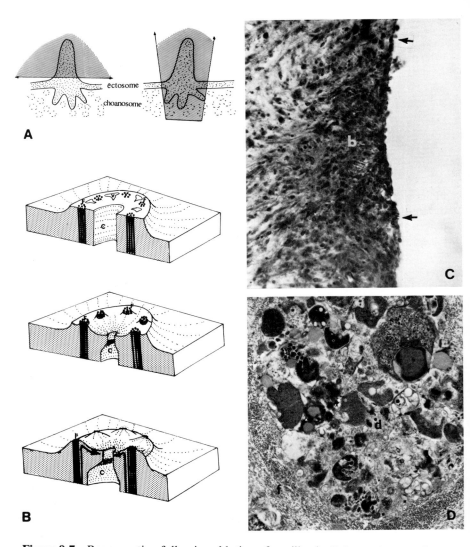

Figure 9-7 Regeneration following ablation of papillae in *Polymastia mamillaris*. **A**. Method of tissue removal. On the left, the papilla only was removed flush with the surface (*hatched area*). On the right, both papilla and underlying mesohyl were removed. In the former, regeneration takes place and in the latter it does not (Boury-Esnault, 1976b). **B**. Drawing of stages in regeneration. Above: initial papilla removal exposing bundles of spicules (*F*), the central incurrent canal (*C*), and the vestibules (*v*). Middle: the vestibules have been covered over and the central incurrent canal (*C*) is significantly reduced in diameter. Lower: arrows indicate direction of cell migration. The ends of the spicule bundles (*F*) are now covered by tissue (Boury-Esnault, 1976b). **C**. Regenerating tissue 12 h after papilla ablation. A regeneration blastema (*b*) has developed and the surface is becoming covered by cells (*arrow*) which will form exopinacocytes (light micrograph) (×610) (Boury-Esnault, 1976b). **D**. An area at the base of the blastema showing cell debris (*d*) and abundant collagen fibrils (*f*) (TEM) (×13,300) (Boury-Esnault, 1976b). (All courtesy Dr. N. Boury-Esnault.)

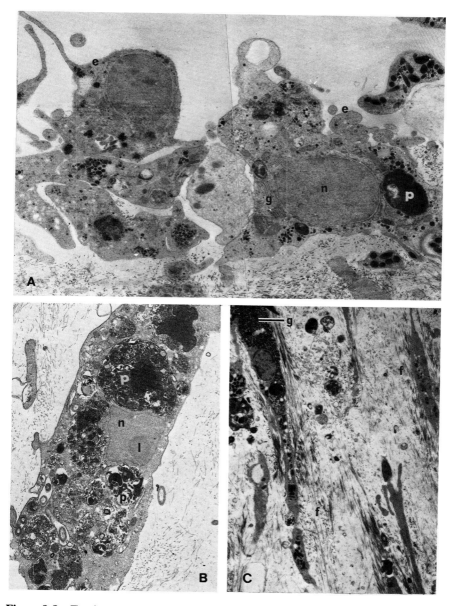

Figure 9-8 Further aspects of regeneration in *Polymastia mamillaris* (TEMs). **A.** Formation of new exopinacocytes (*e*) at the surface of the blastema. The presence in them of phagosomes (*p*) indicates their archeocyte origin. *g*, Golgi; *n*, nucleus (×7,500) (Boury-Esnault, 1976b). **B.** In the zone of the forming blastema, archeocytes are charged with phagosomes (*p*). *n*, nucleus; *l*, nucleolus (×4,140) (Boury-Esnault, 1976b). **C.** By 48 h after ablation, cell migration along the spicule bundles is a prominent process and is signaled by the parallel orientation of the collagen fibrils (*f*). *g*, abundant glycogen in a migrating cell (×3,600) (Boury-Esnault, 1976b). (All courtesy Dr. N. Boury-Esnault.)

ocytes and gray cells and more internally there are in addition sclero-cytes, spherulous cells and cellules à batonnets. All of the blastema cells take on similar features and contain nucleoli, endoplasmic reticulum, Golgi membranes, mitochondria, glycogen, and some phagosomes in a manner completely comparable to that described previously in *Hippo-spongia* regeneration (Thiney, 1972). The spherulous cells thus appear derived from archeocytes and the volume of their inclusions relative to the cytoplasmic volume is much less than in older cells which also do not possess nucleoli. This is one of only a few instances in which the origin of a special cell type is indicated. Later, from about three days onward, spicules are carried into the blastema by the widespread movement of the surrounding cells and, with some exceptions, larger spicules are added to the preexisting spicular tracts, medium sized ones come to lie parallel to the exopinacoderm just below it, and the smallest ones are "placed" perpendicular to the surface of the newly developing papilla. The means by which such a precise placement of these structures occurs is not known but one is reminded of a similar set of events which has been described during initiative growth in *Spongilla lacustris* (Brien, 1976) and gemmule coat formation in freshwater species (Chap. 8).

Tissue Recognition

Three substantially different techniques have been employed to experi-mentally investigate tissue compatability: (1) the growth of whole animals on a solid substratum toward one another producing a region of contact (coalescence–noncoalescence), (2) the tying together of the intact sur-faces of two or more animals producing an artificial contact zone (parabio-sis), and (3) the transplantation of pieces of tissue from one animal into the tissue of a second (grafts). It cannot be emphasized too strongly that, given the present state of our knowledge, these three techniques may not be completely comparable to each other and therefore results from them are not necessarily reconcilable. Despite this, some recent investigations to be discussed have indicated the interesting possibility that some types of tissue incompatibility may have a common basis which resides in the production of soluble factors that may be strain or species specific.

Coalescence and Noncoalescence. Following the initial observations of Rasmont (1956) and Kilian (1964), Van de Vyver (1970) demonstrated that some individuals of *Ephydatia fluviatilis* form a noncoalescing front when they grow toward each other while others completely coalesce (Fig. 9-9). Based upon this, she has been able to recognize eight different strains; sponges of the same strain coalesce and those of differing strains do not. Even newly developing animals (from gemmule hatching) display this difference, which thus is not age dependent and larvae from one strain do not fuse with those from another but do so with those of the same strain. In coalescing sponges, when this occurs before the excurrent canals are

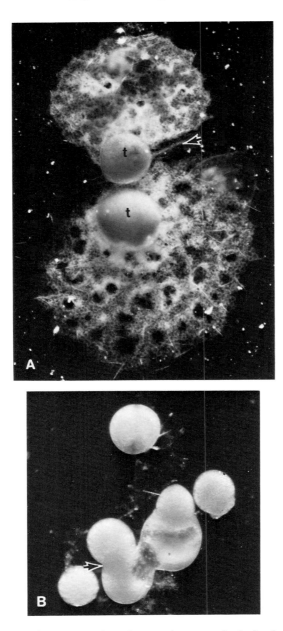

Figure 9-9 Noncoalescence and coalesence in gemmule-derived animals and in metamorphosing larvae (light micrographs). **A**. Noncoalescence (*arrow*) of newly hatched animals from different strains of *Ephydatia fluviatilis*. *t*, gemmule coat (×40) (Van de Vyver, 1970). **B**. Fusion (*arrow*) of larvae derived from animals of the same strain of *Ephydatia fluviatilis*. Those derived from differing strains do not fuse (×30) (Van de Vyver, 1970). (Both courtesy Prof. G. Van de Vyver.)

formed, the latter develop in common in both animals while if coalescence takes place after excurrent canals are formed in each they are separately developed and are not shared in common (Weissenfels and Striegler, 1979). In both cases, however, the incurrent canals and mesohyl are intermingled suggesting a more pronounced plasticity of the incurrent canals than of the excurrent ones, at least in young animals. *In habitat* observations of the noncoalescence of individuals of the same species growing adjacent to each other on the same substratum have also been reported in *Crambe crambe* (Van de Vyver, 1970), *Hymeniacidon perleve* (Fig. 9-10A) (Curtis, 1979b), *Halichondria panicea, Pachymatisma john-*

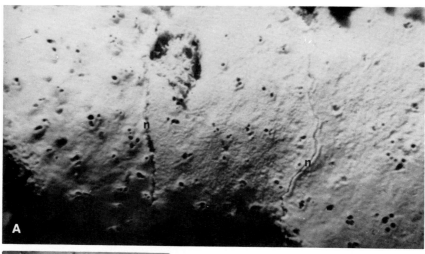

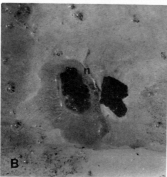

Figure 9-10   Noncoalescence among adult and explant-grown individuals (light micrographs). **A**. Noncoalescence (*n*) among three individuals of *Hymeniacidon* sp. (underwater photograph) (×0.68) (Curtis, 1979b). **B**. Noncoalescence (*n*) of the outgrowth regions of explants derived from noncoalescing adults demonstrating an absence of age dependency on the phenomenon (×0.9) (Unpubl. micrograph, author). (**A**, courtesy Prof. A. G. S. Curtis.)

stonii, and *Plocamionida* sp. (Curtis, 1979a), *Microciona prolifera* (Simpson, 1973), and *Cliona celata* (Fig. 9-11) (Bromley and Tendal, 1973). In *M. prolifera* the newly formed outgrowths from explants are noncoalescent when they are derived from noncoalescent animals (Fig. 9-10B) but coalesce when the explants come from the same sponge. In a scanning electron microscopic study of noncoalescence between young sponges of different strains of *E. fluviatilis,* Van de Vyver and De Vos (1979) have shown that initially the exopinacoderms and basopinacoderms make contact and then secrete a thin fibrous "pad" of material, which is probably collagenous, between them (Fig. 9-12). This pad is continuous with the basal layer of collagen fibrils secreted by the basopinacocytes, and there is some suggestion that its secretion begins as soon as the pinacoderms touch. The two sponges thus use each other's pinacoderm as a substratum (Van de Vyver and De Vos, 1979); no cells cross the barrier and there is no damage to either sponge. If, following the noncoalescence of two sponge strains, a third younger sponge belonging to one of the two original strains comes into contact with the older sponge of the different strain, the timing and sequence of noncoalescence are the same establishing that no memory (potentiation) of the rejection process has occurred (Van de Vyver, 1980).

Curtis and Van de Vyver (1971) have found that soluble factors released from the cells of different strains of *E. fluviatilis* tend to decrease cell adhesiveness while stimulating to some extent the adhesiveness of cells

Figure 9-11   A unique example of noncoalescence between two individuals of the burrowing species, *Cliona celata.* X-radiograph of the bivalve shell excavated by the sponges. At the region of contact, there is a clear noncoalescence pattern of the tunnels being etched (*arrows*) (×1.0) (Bromley and Tendal, 1973). (Copyright 1973, The Zoological Society of London.) (Courtesy Dr. O. S. Tendal.)

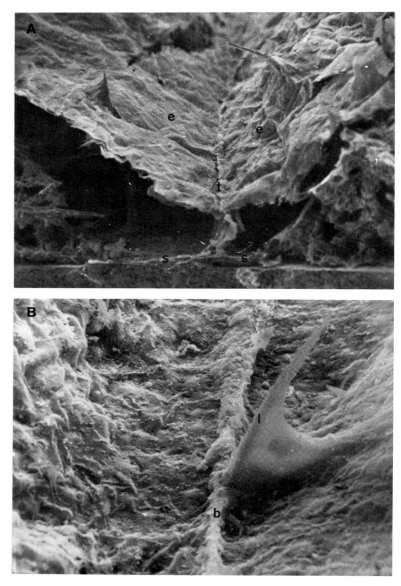

Figure 9-12 Details of noncoalescence between young individuals from different strains of *Ephydatia fluviatilis* (SEMs). **A**. Initial contact (*t*) between the animals in which the pinacoderms become apposed. *e*, exopinacoderms; *s*, basal spongin (×60) (Van de Vyver and De Vos, 1979). **B**. Later, as the tissues pull away, a barrier of collagen (*b*), which was laid down during contact, is obvious. No cells cross the barrier. *l*, spicule enrobed in spongin (×60) (Van de Vyver and De Vos, 1979). (Courtesy Prof. G. Van de Vyver.)

from the same strain (see Reaggregation and Reconstitution of Dissociated Cells). That such factors may play a role in coalescence–noncoalescence is further suggested by similar results with different strains of *Hymeniacidon perleve* (Curtis, 1979b). A unique case of noncoalescence in *Cliona celata* has been documented by x-radiography of a bivalve shell which was burrowed into by two animals. At the zone of contact the excavation tunnels are very narrow and numerous suggesting an avoidance reaction (Bromely and Tendal, 1973) (Fig. 9-11).

Under field conditions, individuals of different *species* are often observed in contact but not coalescing (Sara and Vacelet, 1973; Jackson, 1977). Such an association is that of *Hymeniacidon perleve* and *Amphilectus fucorum* in which apparently no necrosis occurs adjacent to the contact area despite very close physical contact (Evans and Curtis, 1979). Hildemann and Linthicum (1981) report on numerous, similar cases of interspecific noncoalescence in the Palau Islands which apparently do not involve necrosis and they suggest that mucous secretion or the formation of interfacial barriers as in *E. fluviatilis* produce these noncytotoxic, stable associations. The absence of a cytotoxic response is possibly due to the direct involvement of the basopinacoderms, as discussed in *Ephydatia,* which are capable of collagen (and possibly matrix) biosynthesis (Chap. 5). It is well to keep this in mind when considering the results of allogenic parabiotic and grafting experiments in which the areas of tissue contact are, respectively, the exopinacoderm and mesohyl. While the results of the latter experiments are of much interest and potential importance for an understanding of the basis of "recognition of self" in sponges they are clearly far removed from normal *in habitat* interactions and thus may be of more importance in the context of tissue survival *per se* rather than in the context of a rejection response.

Parabiosis. A number of recent studies have employed the technique of tying the exopinacoderms (portions of branches) of different sponges together and following them in order to determine if there is histocompatability (coalescence) between them. When isoparabionts (branches from the same sponge) are prepared in *Polymastia* (Van de Vyver and Barbieux, 1983), *Callyspongia diffusa* (Hildemann et al., 1979), *Axinella* (Van de Vyver, 1980; Buscema and Van de Vyver, 1983a,b,c), *Xestospongia exigua* (Hildemann and Linthicum, 1981), and *Toxadocia violacea* (Bigger et al., 1983) they always coalesce within a short time (1–2 days). Such branch coalescence is also seen within single animals in the field (Hildemann and Linthicum, 1981; Hildemann et al., 1980). The process of isoparabiotic coalescence has only been studied microscopically in one case, *Axinella polypoides,* and presents a number of interesting questions (Van de Vyver, 1980). Under these conditions, the exopinacoderms are brought into contact, and although no clear data are available, these cells must either become mobilized or destroyed in order for the underlying ectosomal mesohyl of each to become continuous as occurs within about 2 to 3 days. Much later (30 days), after ectosomal coalescence, the ectosomes of both parabionts disappear in the region of fusion and are replaced by choanosomal tissue (Van de Vyver, 1980). The processes occurring during initial interaction of the exopinacoderms are intriguing, since extensive remodeling, possibly similar to the disorganization–reorganization processes in *Suberites* (Diaz, 1979a), must take place.

When alloparabionts (branches from different sponges of the same species) are tied together, there can be tissue necrosis at the region of contact in both branches (Fig. 9-13B) (Hildemann *et al.*, 1979; Van de Vyver, 1980). Prior to necrosis in *Callyspongia diffusa*, tissue bridges form between the parabionts and then disappear and a substantial region of tissue is destroyed in both (0.5 to 4.0-mm strips in each branch); then, a new exopinacoderm forms at the limits of the necrosis in each branch (Hildemann *et al.*, 1980). The time for necrosis to occur and its extent are not influenced by the size of the branches but are inherent features of each individual with some showing shorter reaction times and/or more intense reactions. The time for necrosis to occur in first set alloparabionts is substantially shorter at higher temperatures (Johnston *et al.*, 1981), an observation which may be of much significance relative to the results reported for *Xestospongia exigua* (Hildemann and Linthicum, 1981). In *C. diffusa*, in order for necrosis to occur the sponges must be in direct contact since when separated by filters, no rejection response is forthcoming and the time for necrosis to occur is not shortened by first placing the sponges in contact with an intervening filter prior to joining them together directly without a filter barrier (Bigger *et al.*, 1981). Thus, both the initial phase of the rejection (=sensitization) and the definitive phase (=cytotoxicity) require direct contact. In *Axinella polypoides*, again, only at the contact region of alloparabionts does a necrotic "pad" of cells form within 48 h (Fig. 9-13A); these cells are then sloughed off and the adjoining tissue in each sponge becomes necrotic by about five days. Later, a new ectosome begins to form at the limits of the necrotic regions in both sponges; lower temperatures result in a much slower response which initially can be mistaken for coalescence (Van de Vyver, 1980). In both of these species, incompatability between different sponges is absolute—in all cases rejection occurs and no intraspecific strains as in *Ephydatia* or *Hymeniacidon* are evident. In *C. diffusa* this has been found to be the case in 960 different sponges, each one of which can thus be considered to be a separate "strain."

In *Callyspongia diffusa* (Hildemann *et al.*, 1979, 1980; Bigger *et al.*, 1981), *Xestospongia exigua* (Hildemann and Linthicum, 1981), and *Toxadocia violacea* (Bigger *et al.*, 1983) the reaction time for necrosis in alloparabionts is significantly decreased when one or both sponges are sensitized by a previous (first set) alloparabiosis. The shortened reaction

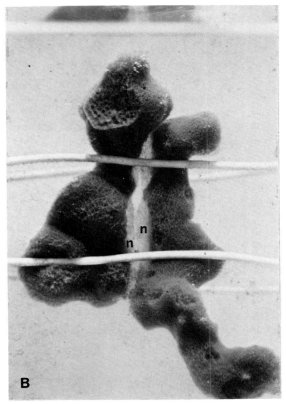

Figure 9-13 Results of parabiotic experiments. **A**. Production of a "pad" of necrotic tissue (*arrow*) between pieces of branches from two individuals of *Axinella polypoides* which were tied together for a number of days (light micrograph) (×1.0) (Van de Vyver, 1980). **B**. Tissue necrosis (*n*) in regions of apposition between pieces of branches from two individuals of *Callyspongia diffusa* (light micrograph) (×0.8) (Hildemann *et al.*, 1979.) (Copyright 1979 by the American Association for the Advancement of Science). (**A**, courtesy Prof. G. Van de Vyver; **B**, courtesy Prof. W. H. Hildemann.)

time is nonspecific in that the previously sensitized sponge reacts faster to any other sponge not simply to the sponge with which it was initially sensitized; this heightened sensitivity persists for 2 to 3 weeks (Table 9-4). In complete disagreement with these results are those of Van de Vyver (1980) in which no such acceleration of necrosis occurs in second set alloparabionts of *Axinella polypoides*. The latter results thus bring into question the concept of an "alloimmune memory" in sponges which has been put forth by Hildemann *et al.* (1979, 1980). This sharp disagreement may be related to the difference in techniques employed since in *Axinella* the first set alloparabionts were left undisturbed and a third branch was tied against one of the two original ones, while in *Callyspongia* and *Xestospongia* the first set branches were separated and either rejoined at new contact points to each other or to a branch from a different sponge (third party). Thus, in the latter studies, the tissue at the surface of the necroses was fully exposed to the environment (water currents, microorganisms, light, etc.), probably during a period when remodeling was incomplete. In the former, on the other hand, the regenerating surfaces were maintained in their original "sheltered" positions. Such exposure as in the first case may intensify phagocytic activity and cell migration as in regeneration and remodeling in general, and consequently the shortened reaction time may be related to a heightened fluidity of structure rather than to specific alloimmune memory. Considerably more detailed, and in particular combined microscopic and biochemical, studies are required in order to elucidate the basis of recognition of nonself in parabiotic experiments as well as in all types of experimental settings, including grafting which will be discussed presently. In addition to phagocytosis as a possible basis for cytotoxicity in alloparabionts, Hildemann *et al.* (1980) suggest that toxins may be involved as well as other soluble factors, which are also known to

Table 9-4   Parabiosis in Two Subtropical Demosponges[a]

	Median Reaction Times (days) for Necrosis		
	First Sets[b]	Second Sets[c]	Third Party[d]
Callyspongia diffusa[e]	9.1	4.8	6.2
Xestospongia exigua	8.2	3.2	4.2

[a]Data taken from Hildemann *et al.* (1979) and Hildemann and Linthicum (1981).
[b]Initial parabiosis between branches of two different sponges.
[c]Following initial parabiosis the same two sponges were rejoined in different areas.
[d]Following initial parabiosis, one of the parabionts was joined to a completely different sponge which had not previously been treated experimentally.
[e]Median reaction times listed are the average median times for a large number of different experiments.

modulate cell adhesion in reaggregating cells (see later section). There have, however, been no direct demonstrations that soluble factors are involved in necrosis *per se*.

As this volume is going to press, the complexities of parabiont allograft rejection are just beginning to be appreciated. In alloparabionts of *Polymastia robusta,* archeocytes and collencytes from both partners become aligned in the contact zone and secrete collagen which firmly holds the parabionts together, whereas in *Polymastia mamillaris* no cell alignment or collagen secretion occur; rather, there is cell migration and remodeling in each parabiont without adherence (Van de Vyver and Barbieux, 1983). In alloparabionts of *Axinella polypoides* studied with light, scanning, and transmission electron microscopy, after three days the contact zone is characterized by archeocyte activity leading to a zone of necrosis; archeocytes in this species appear to display both cytotoxic and phagocytic activities (Buscema, 1982; Buscema and Van de Vyver, 1983a). In alloparabionts of *Axinella damicornis,* collencytes become aligned on each side of the contact zone and a collagen barrier (as in *Polymastia robusta*) develops which does *not,* however, join the parabionts (Buscema and Van de Vyver, 1983b). In alloparabionts of *Axinella verrucosa,* three different reactions are possible: acceptance, nonfusion, or chronic rejection (Buscema and Van de Vyver, 1983c). Nonfusion does not involve any discernible reaction between the parabionts and chronic rejection is similar to that in *A. damicornis* except that the parabionts are firmly attached to each other by the collagen barrier (Buscema, 1982; Buscema and Van de Vyver, 1983b,c). These new data make it progressively more difficult to consider all sponge alloparabiont reactions as due to a similar "immune" system. Buscema and Van de Vyver (personal communication) consider that sponges manifest three rejection responses: phagocytosis, cytotoxicity, and encapsulation. Of these, cytotoxicity is recently discovered; the remaining two have been known for some time (see later, Reactions to Foreign Materials).

Grafts.   Mergner (1970) has carried out a series of highly unusual grafting experiments in *Ephydatia fluviatilis* in which small patches of the oscular chimney are cut out and placed against the exopinacoderm. Such pieces of tissue, which contain both exopinacoderm and apendopinacoderm, roll up and form a double epithelial lined "ball" with the exopinacocytes facing outward and the apendopinacocytes lining the internal cavity. Balls from the same sponge are able to fuse together to form larger balls but each pinacocyte layer retains its original orientation, thus demonstrating a basic difference between them and the ability of the cells to recognize like tissue. Oscular chimney balls will also freely fuse with and become an integral part of the wall of intact oscular chimneys again with the two types of pinacocytes forming contacts only with like tissue. These balls, that is the covering exopinacocytes, fail to fuse with the mesohyl surface of the basopinacoderm establishing a fundamental difference in these epithelia or at least such a difference in their surfaces (external facing versus mesohyl facing). Similarly, balls formed from the dermal membrane overlying the incurrent canal spaces fuse with each other. Balls from the oscular chimney will fuse with the dermal membrane overlying the incurrent canals in such a way that their exopinacocytes become part of the exopinacoderm of the host and the remaining internal sphere of apendopinacocytes is moved into the mesohyl where it eventually fuses with the apendopinacoderm of an excurrent canal but not with the proendopinacoderm of incurrent canals. The apendopinacocytic ball, now fused with an excurrent canal, expands upward, possibly due pressure in the canal, and forms a new oscule by pushing the overlying exopinacoderm outward. During this complex and poorly understood process the prosendopinacoderm may form new contacts with itself in the region lateral to the presumptive new oscule. Even when the oscular balls do not maintain a lasting fusion with the exopinacoderm, the underlying apendopinacoderm is induced to grow upward and form a new oscule in the area previously occupied by a ball, which has fallen away. This appears to be the only demonstrated case of classical induction in sponges and it possibly involves a diffusable substance. The induction of new oscules in this manner was shown to be species specific; oscular balls of other species (*Spongilla lacustris*), although they may sink into the mesohyl, actively move and/or are pushed back out again through the dermal membrane or move to and are expelled in the excurrent canals and then to the outside; in neither case are new oscules formed. Rejection of these xenografts takes much longer at lower temperatures and does not involve obvious necrosis. The results suggest that the first steps involve fusion of the exopinacocytes of the two sponges.

In more classical grafting experiments, tissue grafts have been placed in hollowed out areas of a host animal such that the mesohyl of both graft and host tissue are brought into contact. In *Tethya lyncurium,* such allografts are eventually rejected (Paris, 1961). Initial contact results in the accumulation of polyblasts and spicules, both of which are involved in initially holding the graft in place; however, this zone of contact is eventually broken and the graft is rejected. In distinction, allografts of *Suberites* are readily incorporated into the host with polyblasts, apparently derived from the host, accumulating at the graft–host interface and acting as an adhesive surface. However, a point of similarity is found in comparing *Tethya* and *Suberites* allografts: the initial contact induces the formation of collagen as well as polyblast accumulation although in *Tethya* allografts the host tissue acts as a substratum for the graft which develops a surrounding pinacoderm and, by the time it breaks away, contains normal functional tissue (Paris, 1961).

Xenografts involving *Suberites* as host and *Tethya* as donor develop contacts in three stages: (1) a pseudostratified epithelial layer of polyblasts from both host and graft forms in the contact area. In the cortex of the graft there is a marked secretion of collagen and a dispersion of microscleres (spherasters); (2) a partial union of contact areas occurs through cell elongation of *Suberites* cells, thus forming bridges; *Tethya* cells then appear to secrete a mucoid ground substance material; (3) there is a dispersal of the polyblasts which formed the pseudostratified layer and the contact area comes to contain a mixture of cells of both species. This final stage is characterized by a lack of specificity which Paris (1961) attributes to the totipotent nature of the polyblasts which permits the fusion of graft and host tissue.

Moscona (1968) has also found that allografts of *Microciona* (apparently *prolifera*) and *Haliclona* (probably *oculata*) fuse and are maintained while xenografts are rejected, sometimes within 6 h of grafting. Warburton (1958c) reports a comparable situation in *Cliona celata* and *C. lobata*. Hildemann *et al.* (1980) consider that the relatively low temperature regimes in these studies accounts for the allograft acceptances. However, in an *in situ* grafting experiment in cold water (Great Britain) some of the allografts of *Hymeniacidon perleve* become necrotic (Curtis, 1979b) so that temperature alone does not appear to be the only contributing factor. In the latter investigation, Curtis (1979b) was able to demonstrate, based upon the results of allografts, that *H. perleve* possess strains as in *Ephydatia*. In allografts (cut branch tip apposed to cut branch tip) of tropical species that were studied at significantly higher temperatures (25–30°C), necrosis was always observed and no strains were evident, each individual animal representing its own strain (Hildemann *et al.*, 1979, 1980; Bigger *et al.*, 1981). Further, although few quantitative data are available, these allografts are reported to behave in the same way as alloparabionts (see previous section). The significant question is whether lower temperature suppresses the mechanism(s) of recognition of self (at least in some species) or whether higher temperature accelerates otherwise unrelated cell activities (phagocytosis, metabolic pathways) which result in necrosis. There is little question that temperature affects the rate of alloparabiotic reactions (Van de Vyver, 1980; Hildemann *et al.*, 1980; Johnston *et al.*, 1981), but the question still remains whether necrosis is indeed an immune process in sponges. Further, if grafting is truly equivalent to parabiosis then allografts should sensitize in the same fashion as alloparabiosis. Evans *et al.* (1980) have recently carried out such allografting in *Hymeniacidon* and do indeed find that second-set allografts are rejected in a shorter time than first sets—that is when rejection occurs initially in the latter. However, third-party allografts were rejected at the same rate as first sets. Such results, using grafting (rather than parabionts) substantially increases the validity of the concept of a rejection "memory." In this study histological examination revealed necrosis (either of host or graft) as an initial response followed by the formation of new pinacoderms. Interestingly, within 24 h of grafting a temporary fusion of the tissues occurred as in parabiosis. The same problems, previously discussed relative to parabionts, are inherent in grafting experiments— namely, the unknown relationships of remodeling processes and of new pinacoderm formation relative to grafting responses. Finally, Curtis (1979b) has attempted to establish that noncoalescence, graft rejection, and the production of factors inhibitory to cell aggregation are all positively correlated suggesting that all three phenomena may have a common basis. The situation with factors that are inhibitory for cell aggregation is complicated by the finding that there are also factors that promote cell aggregation (Evans and Curtis, 1979). Grafts of *Geodia rovinjensis* are rejected by *Geodia cydonium* causing necrosis in the latter (Müller, 1982). A factor (glycoprotein) is produced by *G. rovinjensis* grafts which when injected into *G. cydonium* causes necrosis. This factor is also an inhibitor of cell aggregation, and Müller (1982) considers that it as well as other active components that are involved in *in vitro* cell aggregation are also *the* active substances in graft rejection and graft acceptance. Given the present state of knowledge, the excitement of these correlations has to be modulated with some caution since we do not even know the precise cell activities involved in graft rejection (necrosis) or for that matter in isograft acceptance. There are also compelling reasons for such caution in the results of studies of cell aggregation, which likewise present many more questions than solutions and which will be discussed after generally considering data that deal with the processes of rejection of foreign materials.

Reactions to Foreign Materials. As is the case with other forms of tissue recognition, there is relatively little understanding of the basis of tissue responses to distantly related organisms such as commensals and epizoans and to experimentally introduced organisms and materials. Some major aspects of this subject rightfully belong within the field of ecology, ecological relationships, and physiological ecology and thus only a limited discussion is presented here; an excellent ecologically based review is to be found in Sara and Vacelet (1973).

In *Suberites domuncula,* the presence of commensal amphipods and copepods within the tissue is associated with supernumery spicules and polyblasts at the interface between the sponge and commensal (Tuzet and Paris, 1964). In excised pieces of the ectosome of *Tethya lyncurium* the growth of bacteria or other unicells evokes a similar response in which layers of microscleres (asters) form a kind of surface barrier within the sponge tissue; below them archeocytes accumulate and apparently play a role in phagocytosis. Sometimes the tissue bordering the area of "infection" proliferates and cuts off a lacuna in which the unicells are trapped (Connes, 1968). Localized proliferation at the cut surfaces of the mesohyl in this species also results in a great increase in the numbers of microscleres. On the other hand, the presence of amphipods within cavities in the tissue results in the formation of a cortical-like layer of tissue at the periphery of the cavity. The limiting tissue is three-layered possessing an outer, thin collagen-like cuticle without an exopinacoderm, a middle layer of highly vacuolated, and possibly degenerating polyblasts and archeocytes with random orientation, and an internal, fibrous layer with tracts of lophocytes and archeocytes at approximately 90° to the cuticle thus forming "rays"; canals and choanocyte chambers are absent throughout this specialized contact region (Connes, 1968). Thus, in *Suberites domuncula*, two types of responses to foreign materials can be recognized: one involves a high level of spiculogenesis and the second fibrogenesis.

In *Terpios zeteki*, Cheng *et al.* (1968b) have introduced a number of foreign materials into the tissue. Human erythrocytes elicit primarily a phagocytic response of archeocytes which ingest and eliminate them although some archeocytes tend to encapsulate the implanted cells. Implanted trematode rediae and cecariae evoke an encapsulation response with collencytes and archeocytes surrounding them but by 48 h the foreign material becomes decomposed and the capsule is disorganized, although the implanted material remains within a cavity. Implanted gastropod muscles also resulted in archeocytes and collencytes collecting at the implant surface but without encapsulation. Interestingly, controls (incisions without implantation of foreign material) also displayed cell aggregation at the cut surfaces suggesting that direct contact of the mesohyl with the environment may result in a kind of response to foreign material. Such a finding has a direct bearing on the results of grafting and parabiotic experiments.

The exopinacoderm of at least some sponges is remarkably clear of epizoic organisms as, for example, in *Spongilla lacustris* (Frost, 1976b) (Table 9-5). A substantial proportion of the small amount of attached

Table 9-5 Attached Materials on the Surface of *Spongilla lacustris*[a]

	September 5	October 3	October 10
	Percentage of surface with attached material[b]		
Spongilla lacustris	14.8	21.2	44.3
Macrophytic plants in the same habitat	100.0	100.0	100.0
	Percentage of attached material associated with surface spicules[b]		
Spongilla lacustris	59.2	47.6	40.9
	Number[b] of attached algal filaments per 0.04 mm^2		
Spongilla lacustris	No data	0.36	0.48
Macrophytic plants in the same habitat	No data	10.7	5.5

[a]Data taken from Frost (1976b).
[b]Mean.

material present is associated with surface spicules implying an efficient cellular mechanism for inhibiting settling. An increasingly large number of recent biochemical studies have identified antimicrobial substances in marine demosponges and these possibly play some role in inhibiting surface settlement (McIntyre *et al.*, 1979; Fusetani *et al.*, 1981; Sullivan and Faulkner, 1982; Frincke and Faulkner, 1982). Extensive field studies of marine species establishes that the primary epizoic species are other sponges (Jackson, 1977). This observation is most interesting since it suggests a degree of contact compatability between sponges that may have as its basis the use of exposed portions of the skeleton which act as a substratum for the epizoic sponge. Thus, exposed spicules and spongin apparently do not stimulate a necrotic response but rather act as an attachment surface.

Vacelet and Gallissian (1978) have reported the presence of giant cells in *Aplysina* (*Verongia*) *cavernicola* (see Fig. 3-1D) in response to what seems to have been an intracellular and intranuclear virus infection. The affected area of the sponge was also devoid of choanocytes. In comparison, species containing algal or bacterial symbionts (Chap. 3) have obviously developed a special recognition system which is tolerant of the symbiont. However, these tolerances appear variable since in *Spongilla lacustris* little, if any, intracellular digestion of the symbiotic zoochlorelle is manifest (Williamson, 1979), while in marine species that possess bacterial symbionts, intracellular digestion of some of them is frequent and is probably involved in maintaining an equilibrium in the number of bacterial cells present at any given time (Vacelet, 1979c). Whether this difference resides in the different nature of the symbionts or in the host's recognition system is not known.

Connes *et al.* (1971b) have described a number of tissue reactions to commensal and parasitic organisms. The oscules of *Cacospongia scalaris* are sometimes occupied by the barnacle *Acasta spongites*. The tissue at the oscular rim can grow down onto the barnacle and eventually kill it. Such tissue surrounding the barnacle skeleton contains many thick spongin fibers and a thin layer of spongin occurs also on the atrial wall. Similarly the tunnels that surround commensal polychaetes within the tissue of *Geodia cydonium* are limited by a fibrous layer in which frequently many microscleres are secreted thus forming an armoured barrier between the sponge and commensal; a similar fibrous layer is laid down by *Ircinia fasiculata* when it is in contact with the barnacle, *Balanus perforatus*. And, in *Suberites carnosus typicus,* the canal diverticulae that are occupied by commensal amphipods have walls that are strengthened by collagen fibers and layers of lophocytes and collencytes. Sciscioli (1966) has observed the growth of epiphytic algae on *Stelleta grubii;* the algal rhizoids may penetrate the sponge tissue which forms a fibrous layer around them.

Reaggregation and Reconstitution of
Dissociated Cells

The reaggregation and subsequent development of reaggregation masses following the dissociation of sponge cells have attracted considerably more attention than other types of experimental regeneration and there is now a large literature dealing with these phenomena (see, for example, Turner, 1978; Müller, 1982). Sponges were the first metazoans in which the reconstitution of dissociated cells was demonstrated (Wilson, 1907). Regardless of the method of dissociation (placing into suspension single, unattached cells), either chemical or mechanical, the general features of this type of development include (1) dissociation of these cells and their suspension in seawater, pond water, or an artificial medium; (2) settlement of the dissociated cells onto a surface; (3) movement and coalescence of cells to form reaggregation masses; (4) development of the reaggregation masses to form a functional sponge. In more recent studies dealing with the mechanism of cell adhesion, dissociated cells are placed on a gyratory shaker or roller tube and the formation of aggregates takes place in suspension (Humphreys, 1963; Müller and Zahn, 1973). In these studies, further development is generally not followed and it is not known if the events occurring during rotation-mediated cell adhesion are comparable to those occurring in stationary cultures. This should always be kept in mind when comparing the results of different studies. The preparative techniques for dissociating cells also varies considerably from one study to another, thus further greatly complicating a synthesis of available data.

Studies of Cell Adhesion. A number of recent reviews of this subject have appeared and can be consulted for further details and references (Kuhns *et al.*, 1973, 1974; Burger, 1977; Burger *et al.*, 1978; Burkart *et al.*, 1979; Van de Vyver, 1979; Turner, 1978; Müller, 1982). In particular, the reviews by Turner (1978) and Müller (1982) are relatively detailed and complete although the emphasis on certain data and their interpretation are significantly different and to some extent conflicting.

Humphreys (1963) and Moscona (1963) demonstrated the essentiality of three components for the formation of aggregates in suspension (=cell adhesion) in *Microciona prolifera:* (1) the cell surface, (2) calcium, and (3) an aggregation factor (AF) which has been purified and subsequently identified as a proteoglycan in *Microciona parthena* (Henkart *et al.*, 1973) (Table 9-6). AF can be obtained by pretreating adult tissue with calcium and magnesium-free seawater (CMFSW), dissociating the cells in CMFSW, maintaining them in suspension at low temperature for a number of hours, and then recovering the supernatant. The factor present in the supernatant requires calcium (1.8 mM) for its stabilization. At 5°C, dissociated cells in CMFSW require both calcium (or magnesium) and AF in order to form aggregates (Fig. 9-14). The role of magnesium is not

Table 9-6 Composition of Aggregation Factor from *Microciona parthena*[b]

Constituent	Percentage of Dry Weight (minus ash)
Protein	47.1
Neutral hexose	26.0
Uronic acid, sodium salt	10.4
Galactosamine	5.8
Glucosamine	5.5
Methyl pentose	1.2
Sulfur	1.5
Phosphate	0.3
Sialic acid	0.1

Amino Acids	Molecules/10^5 g of Protein
Lysine	9.2
Histidine	4.8
Arginine	35.1
Cysteine	25.5
Aspartic acid	147
Threonine	77.7
Serine	56.7
Glutamic acid	125
Proline	57.5
Glycine	85.6
Alanine	61.9
Valine	94.9
Methionine	11.0
Isoleucine	64.2
Leucine	78.8
Tyrosine	21.8
Phenylalanine	57.8

[a]Data taken from Henkart *et al.* (1973).

completely clear since chemically dissociated cells at 25°C when shaken in magnesium only form aggregates which are one-half the size of those formed in calcium only. In a classical study, Galtsoff (1925a) also found differences between calcium and magnesium in mechanically dissociated cells reaggregating on a solid surface; in the latter system magnesium is possibly needed for cell migration (movement) and both calcium and magnesium are apparently required for cell adhesion. On the other hand, with chemically dissociated cells at 5°C to which AF was added, either magnesium or calcium was sufficient to produce aggregates (Humphreys, 1963).

Strontium was found ineffective as a substitute under any conditions, although it permits small, loose aggregates to form at 25°C.

The aggregation factor from *Microciona parthena* is a unique proteoglycan containing 47% protein which, *in vitro,* forms a gel at high calcium concentrations (20 mM); it is denatured by heat and EDTA (Henkart *et al.*, 1973). More recently, the effect of heat and EDTA on *M. prolifera* AF have been shown to effect only AF–AF interactions and not AF–cell interactions (Jumblatt *et al.*, 1980). The factor has an estimated molecular weight of 2×10^7 daltons and in electron micrographs has a sunburst shape with a diameter of at least 1600 Å (Fig. 9-15). Of possible physiological interest is the observation that in the absence of calcium, the factor dissociates into smaller glycoprotein subunits of about 2×10^5 daltons (Cauldwell *et al.*, 1973). Previous chemical data on the factor of *Microciona prolifera* (Margoliash *et al.*, 1965) differ significantly from those of Cauldwell *et al.* (1973) for *M. parthena;* the disagreement, however, is apparently due to differences in the method of purification (Henkart *et al.*, 1973). Gasic and Galanti (1966) have shown that the protein portion of AF includes disulfide groups essential to its integrity and activity and Turner and Burger (1973) conclude that the protein portion of the factor acts as a carrier for critical carbohydrate groups.

Quantitative studies of the binding of highly purified, labeled, *Microciona prolifera* AF to cells establishes its species specificity in a very clear fashion (Table 9-7) (Jumblatt *et al.*, 1980). Based upon these binding data, it was calculated that *in vivo* each cell has on average some 28,000 molecules of AF associated with it, an immense excess which suggests a function in addition to cell adhesion. AF binding to cells was shown to be calcium independent and the absence of its saturation binding to cells appears due to the ability of AF to crosslink with other AF molecules. Single molecules of AF, under experimental conditions, appear unable to crosslink two cells suggesting the necessity of at least two molecules per binding point and the essentiality of calcium for such intercellular binding (Fig. 9-16). Further, differences in the effects of EDTA, periodate, and heat on AF suggest that AF–cell and AF–AF interactions involve different parts of the molecule and that much AF *in vivo* is bound to other AF molecules rather than to cell surfaces despite the demonstration that it is bound to cell surfaces in dissociated cells (Kuhns *et al.*, 1980). According to the precise binding studies of Jumblatt *et al.* (1980), cell aggregation occurs in two steps: (1) calcium-independent binding of AF to cell surfaces, and (2) calcium-dependent crosslinking of AF from one cell to another. The exciting question of the relationship of this two-step process to cell recognition as distinct from cell adhesion awaits elucidation. While similar precise binding studies have yet to be accomplished it appears, based upon aggregation assays, that all of the cell types in *Microciona prolifera* respond to AF. Semipure suspensions of archeocytes, gray cells and choanocytes each respond to AF with no apparent quantitative

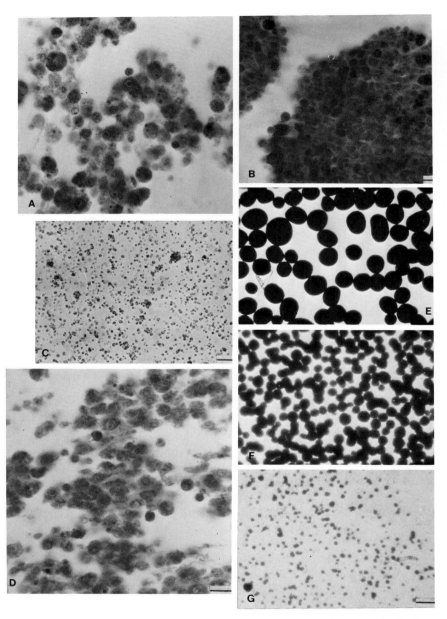

Figure 9-14 Demonstration of essentiality of aggregation factor and divalent cations (Ca^{2+}) for cell adhesion in rotation-mediated aggregation of *Microciona prolifera* cells (light micrographs). **A**, **B**. Reaggregation of chemically dissociated cells at 22°C. A. At 15 min. B. At 3 h. Scale bar: 10 μm (both, ×565) (Humphreys, 1963). **C**. Chemically dissociated cells after 24 h of rotation at 5°C without addition of aggregation factor. Note only very small clumps and single cells are present. Scale bar: 50 μm (×110) (Humphreys, 1963). **D**. The same as in C., but with aggregation factor added. Note the identical appearance of the aggregates

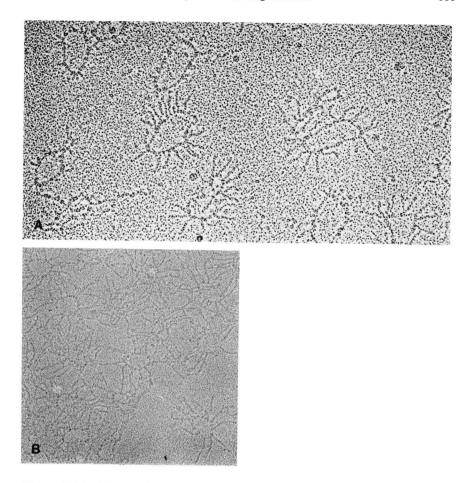

Figure 9-15 Macromolecular configuration of purified aggregation factor from two demosponges (TEMs). **A**. Aggregation factor from *Geodia cydonium* with a central ring and arms (×95,000) (Müller and Zahn, 1973). **B**. Aggregation factor from *Microciona parthena* showing strikingly similar configuration to that in *Geodia*. (×64,315) (Reprinted with permission from Henkart *et al.* (1973). Copyright 1973 American Chemical Society.) (Henkart *et al.*, 1973). (**A**, courtesy Prof. W. E. G. Müller; **B**, courtesy Dr. S. Humphreys.)

with those in A. above. Scale bar: 10 μm (×565) (Humphreys, 1963). **E, F, G**. Chemically dissociated cells plus aggregation factor in the presence of calcium ions (E.), magnesium ions (F.), and strontium ions (G.). Note that magnesium supports aggregation to some extent. Scale bar for E.–G: 200 μm (×36) (Humphreys, 1963). (All courtesy Dr. T. Humphreys.)

Table 9-7   Binding of *Microciona* ^{125}I-Aggregation Factor to Cells[a]

Sponge Cells Tested	Bound AF	
	Molecules/Cell	Molecules/mg Protein $\times$ 10^{-10}
Microciona prolifera		
Live	516	1.28
Fixed	407	1.36
Halichondria panicea		
Live	18	0.11
Fixed	33	0.19
Cliona celata		
Live	28	0.11
Fixed	32	0.12

[a]Data taken from Jumblatt *et al.* (1980). Cells were fixed in glutaraldehyde.

differences, and each of the separate fractions bind equally well to Sepharose beads which carry surface-bound AF (Burger *et al.*, 1978). In this regard, initial results establish that *Microciona* AF supports the adhesion of homospecific, chemically dissociated larval cells further indicating the adult-like nature of the parenchymella larva (Burkart *et al.*, 1979).

Müller and Zahn (1973) have purified the aggregation factor from the tetractinellid sponge, *Geodia cydonium,* and their studies indicate a substantially higher molecular weight for it than reported by Cauldwell *et al.*

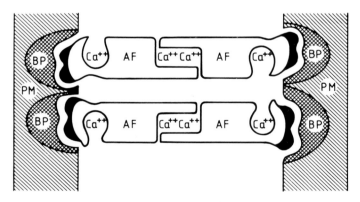

Figure 9-16 Model of aggregation factor (*AF*) and membrane-bound baseplate (*BP*) interaction in the adhesion of sponge cells. *AF* interacts with *BP* at the plasmalemma (*PM*) without the direct involvement or necessity for calcium ions (*Ca^{2+}*). *AF* molecules crosslink between cells, a process requiring Ca^{2+} (Burger *et al.*, 1978). (Copyright Cambridge University Press.) (Courtesy Prof. M. M. Burger.)

(1973) for *Microciona parthena,* namely, 1.5×10^8 daltons. The physical size of *Geodia* AF in electron micrographs is also larger, 2500 Å; its protein content is appreciably higher, 74%, and it contains 10% carbohydrate and 5% lipid (Müller *et al.,* 1976, 1979). However, the shape of the *Geodia* factor in electron micrographs is remarkably similar to that of the *Microciona* factor (see Fig. 9-15) (Müller and Zahn, 1973). These high-molecular-weight *Geodia* particles contain subunits, some of which are functional AFs and others of which possess glycosyltransferase activity (Müller *et al.,* 1979). As clearly found with *Microciona* AF, the *Geodia* AF is also capable of self-aggregation when the calcium concentration is raised. The very significant differences between *Microciona* and *Geodia* AF may be related to the differences in preparative and purification techniques. An AF has also been isolated from *Suberites domuncula,* which is associated with a high-molecular-weight particle, which in electron micrographs has a filamentous shape rather than a sunburst appearance. The molecular weight of the purified AF, not the whole particle, is 54,000, drastically different from that of the AFs of *Geodia* and *Microciona* (Müller *et al.,* 1978a). Possibly this is due to its dissociation during processing from the much heavier particles with which it can be shown to be associated. Chemically, this AF is protein with about 17% carbohydrate content and it is heat sensitive. *Suberites* AF supports rotation-mediated aggregation which is calcium dependent and appears species specific when tested with *Geodia* cells. Van de Vyver (1971) has found that a soluble factor released from *Ephydatia fluviatilis* cells is strain specific for accelerating cell aggregation *in stationary cultures* but that the factor at high concentration slows the timing of attachment of the aggregates and their reconstitution into functional sponges. At the highest concentrations tested, the factor completely inhibits attachment and further development; the latter effect is not strain specific. Thus, this factor appears to have two very different effects, one upon aggregation and the second on attachment. There are few, if any, other studies of the role of AFs on the histogenesis (including attachment) of reaggregates and this is a fertile field for further investigation. AFs from some 20 demosponges have either a circular or rod shape usually with arms when observed ultrastructurally (Müller, 1982).

Moscona (1968) was the first to demonstrate that aggregation factor is involved in forming linkages to and between cells rather than acting indirectly through other metabolic pathways or through stimulation of them. He demonstrated that Formalin-fixed cells of *Microciona prolifera* are stimulated to aggregate by factor and during their aggregation, factor is lost from the medium. Glutaraldehyde-fixed cells are now routinely used in kinetic studies of cell adhesion (Jumblatt *et al.,* 1980).

Unexpectedly, Humphreys (1965) discovered that aggregation takes place in the absence of protein synthesis indicating a storage of the factor, or protein synthesis which is independent of nucleic acids. The former is unlikely in view of the fact that cells will repeatedly (five times) reaggregate in the presence of puromycin or ethionine which inhibit protein synthesis by about 90%. In dissociated cells of *Spongilla carteri,* inhibition of protein synthesis does not affect aggregation despite the finding that protein and RNA syntheses increase significantly during normal, early aggregation (2–6 h) (Kartha and Mookerjee, 1978a). In *Geodia cydonium,* such an increase in protein, RNA, and DNA synthesis also occurs at about 2–3 h and was shown to be AF dependent (Müller *et al.,* 1976). At about 4 h of incubation an AF-dependent increase in DNA synthesis occurs which can be blocked by bleomycin, actinomycin D, and puromycin (Müller *et al.,* 1976). In this system AF is also reported to increase O_2 uptake and cause changes in cyclic nucleotides (see Müller, 1982). It is to be emphasized that these reported events occur well after the initial cell adhesion stage and deal with older aggregates (Müller, 1982). Further, the absence of gyratory shaking and the preparative employment of EDTA and trypsin in these experiments make it difficult to compare the results with those from experiments using the more usual protocol (Humphreys, 1963; Moscona, 1963; Kuhns *et al.,* 1974; Burger *et al.,* 1975). This is especially true in view of the finding by Van de Vyver and Buscema (1976) that trypsin treatment enhances the aggregation of dissociated cells of *Ephydatia fluviatilis.* An understanding of AF-mediated aggregation in the absence of protein synthesis has yet to be achieved and the phenomenon may be of much importance for understanding cell adhesion in general.

A number of studies indicate an essential role for bound sugars in cell adhesion. These sugars are part of either the aggregation factor and/or the cell surface and apparently interact in establishing adhesions. Preparations of *Helix* glusulase can destroy the effectiveness of *Microciona* AF and this is due at least partially to the presence of glucuronidase activity indicating a critical role for glucuronic acid in the activity of AF (Turner *et al.,* 1974); periodate treatment also inactivates the factor (Turner and Burger, 1973), although it does not substantially effect AF–cell binding (Jumblatt *et al.,* 1980). In distinction, *Geodia* AF is not inactivated by beta glucuronidase (Müller, 1982). The use of commercially available lectins has aided in establishing a role for specific sugars in sponge cell adhesions. Although these substances do not agglutinate sponge cells, *Microciona* AF inhibits some lectins from agglutinating specific red blood cells (Kuhns *et al.,* 1973). However, some lectins are also capable of inhibiting *Microciona* cells from reacting with its aggregation factor (Table 9-8). Based upon knowledge of the sugars that inhibit these lectins from agglutinating red blood cells, it has been postulated that *Microciona* AF contains complementary sugars as part of its functional site. Experimental results indeed indicate this; pretreatment of *Microciona* cells with α-methyl mannoside or 3-0-methyl glucose inhibits aggregation in the presence of factor. Both of these sugars are known inhibitors of lectins, which in turn inhibit sponge cell reaggregation. Furthermore, glucuronic

Table 9-8 Lectin Inhibition of Aggregation Factor Stimulated
Cell Aggregation[a]

Lectin	Aggregation Factor Derived From	Aggregation of Dissociated Cells From		
		Microciona	*Haliclona*	*Cliona*
Lentil, green peas, fava beans,[b] jack beans (Con A)[c]	*Microciona*	−		
None	*Microciona*	+		
Lentil	*Haliclona*		+	
Lentil	*Cliona*			+

[a]From Kuhns *et al.* (1973).
[b]Principal sugars with which lectins interact: α-Methyl-D-Mannose, 3-O-Methyl-D-glucose, N-Acetyl-D-glucosamine, D-Glucose, D-Mannose.
[c]Principal sugars with which Con-A interacts: α-Methyl-D-mannose, N-Acetyl-D-glucosamine, D-glucose, D-Mannose.

acid, and to a lesser extent, galacturonic acid inhibit aggregation indicating additional complementary sugars as part of the functional site(s) of the AF molecule (Kuhns *et al.*, 1973; Turner and Burger, 1973). The involvement of glucuronic acid residues in *Microciona* AF has been the most thoroughly studied (Turner *et al.*, 1974). Reincubation of cells with this sugar or pretreatment of AF with glycosidase results in no aggregation. The sugar is ineffective in inhibiting AF–AF interactions and was shown to be a part of the AF molecule which is recognized by the cell surface (Fig. 9-17). Since lectins, which do not interact with glucuronic acid, inhibit aggregation, there are probably other sugar residues in AF and/or on the cell surface which are directly or indirectly involved in cell adhesion in this system. For example, in a freshwater species, α-methyl mannose as well as glucuronic acid interferes with the reestablishment of cell adhesion following pretreatment of the cells with EDTA or periodate thus further supporting a possible role of this sugar in cell aggregation (Kartha and Mookerjee, 1978b). There are two contradictory reports of the effects of the lectin Concanavalin-A on reaggregation. In *Ephydatia fluviatilis,* Con-A stimulates cell adhesion in a CMF medium in which the cells alone do not aggregate (Van de Vyver and Buscema, 1976); whereas in *Spongilla carteri,* Kartha and Mookerjee (1978b) have reported that Con-A inhibits aggregation as it also does in the *Microciona* system. It is difficult to try to reconcile these results at the present time. The failure to find an active role of carbohydrates in cell aggregation in 15 demosponges and two calcareous species was probably due to the severe methods of preparation (MacLennan, 1970); the carbohydrate fractions did nevertheless show complementarity to homologous cell surfaces.

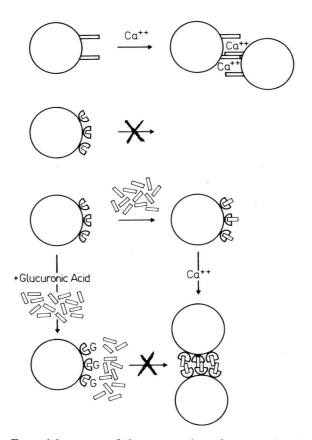

Figure 9-17   Essential aspects of the aggregation of agarose beads (circles) to which aggregation factor (= bars) is covalently bound (top line) or to which baseplate (small grooved half-circles) is covalently bound. **Top line:** aggregation factor bound to beads crosslinks in the presence of calcium ions (Ca^{2+}) forming bead aggregation. **Second line:** beads to which baseplate is bound do not aggregate. **Third line:** beads to which baseplate is bound bind aggregation factor and in the presence of calcium ions (Ca^{2+}) they aggregate (**fourth line, right side**). Addition of glucuronic acid to these baseplate beads inhibits binding to aggregation factor and thus inhibits bead aggregation (**fourth line, left side**). (Burger *et al.,* 1978). (Copyright Cambridge University Press.) (Courtesy Prof. M. M. Burger.)

Weinbaum and Burger (1973) osmotically shocked *Microciona* cells and isolated in the supernatant a 40,000 to 60,000 dalton component (baseplate) which, when incubated with AF, inhibits factor-induced aggregation of chemically dissociated cells. Osmotically shocked cells, which are baseplate depleted, can be stimulated to aggregate when incubated first with baseplate, which apparently self-assembles on the cell surface, and then with AF. The activity of baseplate is destroyed by periodate and heat but is stable in EDTA (Burger, 1977) and it can be inhibited from interacting with aggregation factor by preincubation in glucuronic acid (Weinbaum and Burger, 1973). Both baseplate and aggregation factor can be chemically bound to Sepharose beads and their interactions studied *in vitro* (Turner *et al.*, 1974); furthermore, they can be used as a means of purifying the components (Kuhns *et al.*, 1973). When baseplate is covalently bound to Sepharose beads, the beads aggregate in the presence of AF but not in its absence. This AF-stimulated bead aggregation can be inhibited by glucuronic acid, suggesting that baseplate may interact with this sugar in AF during aggregation (Burger *et al.*, 1978). Much less is known about baseplate because of the difficulty of obtaining and purifying it, although it has now been established that it too is present at the cell surface of dissociated cells (Kuhns *et al.*, 1980). Baseplate (also referred to as aggregation receptor) has been isolated from *Geodia cydonium* cells and shown to contain galactose, glucose, and glucuronic acid as the primary sugars (Vaith *et al.*, 1979a) (Table 9-9). Using enzyme preparations, lectins, and the sugars themselves in aggregation assays, glucuronic acid was shown to be the primary carbohydrate in baseplate which is involved in aggregation (Müller, 1982). These and the results of immunofluorescent studies (Kuhns *et al.*, 1980) lends significant support to the original conclusion that a specific receptor molecule is involved in AF interaction with the cell surface (Burger *et al.*, 1978; Burger, 1977), despite the unexpected and unexplained result that glucuronic acid residues, which are part of *Geodia* baseplate, appear to interact with sites on the *Geodia* AF (Müller, 1982), whereas in the *Microciona* system, glucuronic acid bound to AF interacts with sites on the baseplate (Turner *et al.*, 1974). In a unique study of the low-molecular-weight (42,500) baseplate purified from *Suberites domuncula*, Müller *et al.* (1978b) have been able to attach this

Table 9-9 Carbohydrate Content of *Geodia* Baseplate[a]

Sugar	Percentage	Sugar	Percentage
D-Galactose	19.23	L-Arabinose	0.95
D-Glucose	17.34	L-Rhamnose	0.94
D-Mannose	1.63	N-Acetyl-D-galactosamine	0.55
D-Xylose	1.50	N-Acetyl-D-glucosamine	1.00
L-Fucose	1.43	Hexuronic acid	8.90
		(D-Glucuronic acid)	
Total		53.47%	

[a]Data taken from Vaith *et al.* (1979a). Sugars determined by gas–liquid chromatography. Hexuronic acid determined colorimetrically and identified by paper chromatography.

component to *Geodia* cells, which are baseplate depleted, and then stimulate aggregation of the latter cells with *Suberites* AF which under control conditions has no effect on the aggregation of these cells. Such a result suggests a lack of species specificity of baseplate for cell membranes and its ability to spontaneously insert itself in them. While further conformation of these results is required, they are of much interest in a number of contexts, particularly that of cell recognition.

Reed *et al.* (1976) have found that cytochalasins inhibit aggregation and simultaneously increase the production and/or secretion of a fibrous material on the cell surface. They suggest that its inhibition is possibly due to stimulation of excess aggregation factor production. In a further study, Greenberg *et al.* (1977) have shown that cytochalasins do not affect pseudopod formation or cell motility and they conclude that the inhibition of aggregation is affected directly through adhesion events. A recent report has suggested the possible involvement of fibronection in cell adhesion in *Ephydatia* since a highly purified antibody to it inhibits reaggregation (Robert *et al.*, 1981), although Conrad *et al.* (1982) were unable to demonstrate a role for it in *Geodia* aggregation.

Evans and Bergquist (1974) have observed the formation of membrane bridges between aggregating cells in *Microciona rubens* and *Holoplocamia neozelancium* (Fig. 9-18). They suggest that these bridges may be the first phase of cell adhesions which develop soon after reaggregation has begun. Although Kartha and Mookerjee (1979) also noted similar types of contacts in *Spongilla carteri,* tight junctions are formed initially with some suggestion of occasional formation of desmosome-like contacts.

Müller (1982) has recently presented the view that there are two phases of sponge cell aggregation: (1) an initial, nonspecific phase, which is independent of soluble AF in the medium and leads to the formation of small (60 to 200 μm) "primary aggregates" and (2) a second phase which is species specific, AF dependent, and leads to larger secondary aggregates, which are then capable of reconstituting a functional organism. The basis for primary aggregation is unknown. Further recent studies (see Müller, 1982) of the *Geodia* system have revealed an extremely complex situation in which an antiaggregation receptor has been isolated and found able to convert aggregation-susceptible cells to aggregation-deficient cells. A galactose binding lectin, isolated from crude *Geodia* AF, is able to inhibit the antiaggregation effect of the antiaggregation receptor; the lectin itself does not promote aggregation. Both of these "factors" are viewed as possible control mechanisms for cell adhesion and sorting out. This view coupled with the apparent importance of glucuronylation (by *Geodia* AF) and deglucuronylation (by cell-bound β-glucuronidase) of *Geodia* baseplate now make possible a number of interpretations (Müller, 1982).

Specificity of Aggregation.   There are a variety of opinions and experimental results concerning the species specificity of cell aggregation and of

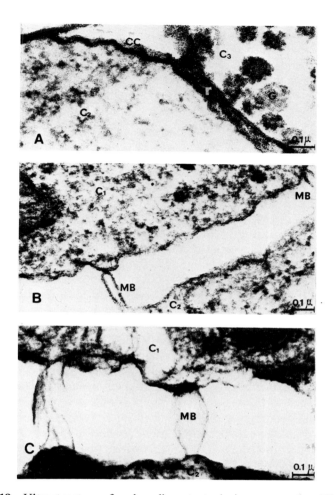

Figure 9-18   Ultrastructure of early cell contacts during aggregation (TEMs). **A.** Cell coats are joined by a dense, ruthenium red staining region (*r*). *G,* glycogen; *CC,* cell coat. *Microciona coccinea* cells (×70,000) (Evans and Bergquist, 1974). **B.** Membrane bridges (*MB*) formed between cells (*C₁, C₂*) of *Holoplocamia neozaelanicum* (×60,000) (Evans and Bergquist, 1974). **C.** Similar types of membrane bridges (*MB*) between cells of *Microciona rubens* (×60,000) (Evans and Bergquist, 1974). (All courtesy Dr. C. W. Evans.)

aggregation factors; these are well reviewed by Turner (1978) and only some of them will be discussed here. McClay (1974) has investigated aggregation factors from five demosponge species and has found that each of them only enhances the aggregation of homologous cells, that is, each factor is species specific. Initially, Spiegel (1955) showed that specific antisera prepared against *Microciona prolifera* cells inhibits *Micro-*

ciona aggregation but not that of *Cliona celata;* while anti-*Cliona* serum inhibits *Cliona* reaggregation but not that of *Microciona*. Later, Moscona (1968) found that *Microciona prolifera* and *Haliclona oculata* aggregation factors are species specific in stimulating aggregation and that antibodies to *Microciona* factor precipitate and inactivate it as well as cause agglutination of *Microciona* cells but not *Haliclona* cells. In contrast, Kuhns *et al.* (1973) report that *Haliclona oculata* AF does stimulate, to some extent, the aggregation of *Microciona* cells, even though antibodies to *Microciona* factor do not enter into a precipitin reaction with *Haliclona* factor and antibodies to the latter do not precipitate *Microciona* AF. MacLennan and Dodd (1967) have observed that *Hymeniacidon perleve* AF promotes the aggregation of other species whose factors are, however, serologically distinct. The precise binding studies of *Microciona* AF (Jumblatt *et al.*, 1980) are very instructive relative to these and other conflicting results in the literature. Although the binding of *Microciona* AF to cells is highly species specific (see Table 9-7), it is not exclusive. Thus, a comparable, low-level but real binding of *Haliclona* AF to *Microciona* cells may lie at the basis of low, but real, rotation-mediated aggregation. Since *Microciona* AF binds at low levels to both *Halichondria* and *Cliona* cells it can be further conjectured that some AFs are able to nonspecifically insert in or interact with the membranes of heterologous cells and thus support aggregation to some extent. In stationary cultures and in assays using mechanically dissociated cells, the situation is much more complex during *early* reaggregation. Interspecific mixtures could result due to nonspecific AF binding as above, or no interspecific mixing could occur due to the presence of inhibitory factors (see following), or limited mixing could occur due to both. In literally all cases in which the *later* stages of interspecific reaggregation have been followed, sorting out occurs. Of much interest are the observations of De Sutter and Van de Vyver (1979a,b): when almost pure choanocytes from two strains of *Ephydatia fluviatilis* are mixed, the cells of each fail to segregate completely and form mosaic aggregates (Fig. 9-19). It is therefore possible that the degree of intermixing reported in other interspecific mixtures is a direct measure of the relative proportion of choanocytes in the aggregate— the higher their proportion, the greater the intermixing; and possibly more intermixing results in slower sorting out which may thus go undetected. As also reported by De Sutter and Van de Vyver (1979a,b) the presence of a small percentage of allogenic (other strain) archeocytes in choanocyte reaggregates, while permitting their attachment, substantially slows any histogenesis (Fig 9-20).

MacLennan (1970) and Turner (1978) have reviewed the literature relative to species-specific aggregation in binary mixtures of cells. Some workers have reported the mixing of cells in aggregates and others have found species specificity (Table 9-10). Humphreys (1970) has been unable to find species-specific aggregation among a large number of marine

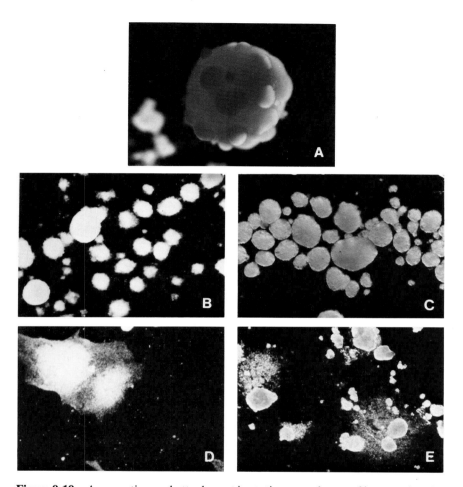

Figure 9-19   Aggregation and attachment in stationary cultures of interstrain mixtures of purified cell types of *Ephydatia fluviatilis* (light micrographs). **A**. Choanocytes from two strains mixed. Note segregation of cell aggregates but the lack of attachment (×60) (DeSutter and Van de Vyver, 1979b). **B**. Limited aggregation and cytolysis (fuzzy surfaces) of purified choanocytes from a single strain (×20) (DeSutter and Van de Vyver, 1979b). **C**. Choanocytes plus 0.5% allogenic archeocytes which tend to stabilize the aggregates (×20) (DeSutter and Van de Vyver, 1979b). **D**. Choanocytes plus 1.0% allogenic archeocytes which permit some attachment (×20) (DeSutter and Van de Vyver, 1979b). **E**. Choanocytes plus 2.0% allogenic archeocytes which considerably increase attachment (×20) (DeSutter and Van de Vyver, 1979b). (All courtesy Prof. G. Van de Vyver.)

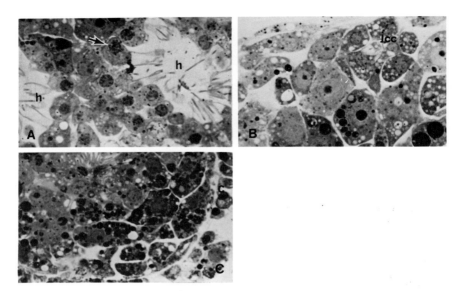

Figure 9-20   Histology of experimental aggregation in *Ephydatia fluviatilis* (light micrographs, semithin sections). **A**. Complete cell suspension (labeled with [³H]thymidine). Autoradiograph shows original choanocytes (with more label, *arrow*) forming new chambers (*h*) (×1,350) (DeSutter and Van de Vyver, 1979b). **B**. Labeled archeocyte fraction at the same time as in A., showing delayed histogenesis and the origin of a new chamber (*icc*) from the weakly labeled archeocytes, (×1,350) (DeSutter and Van de Vyver, 1979b). C. Choanocytes plus 10% allogenic archeocytes showing choanocytes (*c*) segregated at the surface and delayed internal development. Same time for aggregation as in A. and B. (×1,350) (DeSutter and Van de Vyver, 1979b). (All courtesy Prof. G. Van de Vyver and Dr. D. DeSutter.)

sponges, although in some cases sorting out occurred after a period of time. Curtis (1962) has suggested that the mixing of cells from different species or their sorting out depends upon time-dependent processes, such that with proper timing and choice of species, mixing occurs. That is, cell adhesion is not species specific but the timing of events leading to it are. Van de Vyver (1975) has also found the mixing of cells in aggregates of two strains of *Ephydatia fluviatilis* but sorting out eventually does occur in this case also (De Sutter and Van de Vyver, 1979a). The aggregation factors from these strains were found, on the other hand, to stimulate aggregation only of the homologous cells.

   Not only may there be no stimulation of aggregation by heterologous factors but also there can be inhibition. In two marine demosponges, *Crambe crambe* and *Axinella polypoides,* the mixing of cells results in no aggregation. This is due to the presence of inhibitors of aggregation, which can be obtained from the supernatant of the dissociated cells. The

Table 9-10   Nonspecific and Species Specific Aggregation of Dissociated Cells[a]

Taxon	Pairs of Sponges in which Dissociated Cells Form Mixed Aggregates	Pairs of Sponges in which Dissociated Cells Aggregate Species Specifically
Variety		Pairs from four varieties of *Clathrina coriacea*
Species	*Leucosolenia complicata/L. botryoides* Pairs among three species of *Pachychalina*	Pairs among *Haliclona rubens, H. longleyi, H. viridis* *Leucosolenia complicata/Clathrina coriacea*
Genus		
Family	*Halichondria/Hymeniacidon* *Iotrochota/Haliclona*	*Microciona/Lissodendoryx* *Microciona/Petrosia* *Haliclona/Iotrochota* *Halichondria/Hymeniacidon*
Order	*Hymeniacidon/Suberites* *Microciona/Halichondria* *Microciona/Suberites* *Halichondria/Suberites* *Tethya/Hymeniacidon* *Tethya/Haliclona* *Tethya/Petrosia* *Hymeniacidon/Polymastia*	*Microciona/Stylotella* *Microciona/Halichondria* *Microciona/Reniera* *Iotrochota/Halichondria* *Microciona/Cliona* *Halichondria/Suberites* *Microciona/Haliclona* *Halichondria/Reniera* *Tethya/Ircinia* *Hymeniacidon/Suberites*
Class	*Hymeniacidon/Clathrina* *Haliclona/Clathrina* *Tethya/Clathrina*	*Hymeniacidon/Clathrina* *Haliclona/Clathrina* *Tethya/Clathrina*

[a]Taken from MacLennan (1970).

Crambe inhibitor actually causes the lysis of substantial numbers of *Axinella* cells (Van de Vyver, 1975). Furthermore, interstrain mixtures of purified archeocytes, highly enriched choanocytes, and complete cell suspensions may result in the degeneration of the cells of one of the strains (De Sutter and Van de Vyver, 1979a); the phagocytic activity of archeocytes is significantly higher in such interstrain cell mixtures (Fig. 9-21) (Van de Vyver and Buscema, 1977). McClay (1974) has also found an inhibitor of aggregation in the supernatant of *Haliclona viridis* cells which is separable from the aggregation factor. Curtis and Van de Vyver (1971) similarly reported such inhibitors between strains of *E. fluviatilis,* and Curtis (1979a) more recently reports them in noncoalescing individuals of *Hymeniacidon perleve* (Table 9-11). Inhibitory factors are also reported in *Amphilectus fucorum* when tested on *H. perleve* cells (Evans and Curtis, 1979).

Based upon current data, it is reasonable to suggest that although AFs

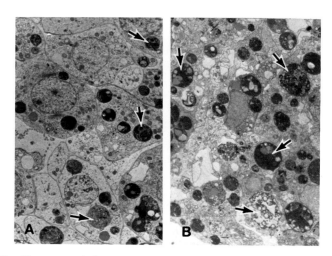

Figure 9-21   Phagocytosis in aggregating cells of *Ephydatia fluviatilis* (TEMs). **A.** Typical level of phagocytosis among cells from the same strain as indicated by phagosome content (*arrows*) of the archeocytes (×2,400) (Van de Vyver and Buscema, 1977). **B.** Marked increased in phagosome content and size (*arrows*) in a mixture of cells from two strains (×2,400) (Van de Vyver and Buscema, 1977). (Courtesy Prof. G. Van de Vyver and Dr. M. Buscema.)

possess species specificity (and even strain specificity) in their stimulation of aggregation and are also serologically distinct that the act of dissociating cells somehow modifies the specificity of the cell surface and/or cell surface–AF complex in such a way that a nonspecific configuration(s) can

Table 9-11   Factors Inhibiting Cell Adhesion in *Hymeniacidon perleve*[a]

Test System	Cell Adhesion (=collision efficiency)
Inhibitory factor tested on homologous cells	15.04 ± 4.17%
Inhibitory factor tested on cells of sponge whose allografts are accepted	15.69 ± 5.03%
Inhibitory factor tested on cells of sponge which is noncoalescing and whose allografts are rejected	0.36 ± 0.63%

[a]Data taken from Curtis (1979a).

result; this in turn can lead to mixed aggregates. This nonspecific configuration appears time dependent and its loss results in the eventual reestablishment of specificity (Humphreys, 1970; Van de Vyver, 1975). The data of McClay (1971) clearly support this proposition. He has observed radioactively labeled cells of one species forming temporary attachments to preformed aggregates of a second species; these initial contacts are then later broken and the labeled cells form discrete aggregates separate from the initial ones. Müller (1982) considers that lectin contamination of AF preparations makes possible the nonspecific aggregation of cells by heterologous AF. Only future investigations of the basis of sponge cell adhesion will shed light on the many outstanding and fundamental questions of cell recognition. In his review, Turner (1978) concludes that the present data are actually insufficient to serve as a basis for generalization. Specifically, he suggests that observations and/or reevaluation of *all* stages of aggregation are required to determine if cell adhesion and species specificity are discrete phenomena. Of some note is his suggestion, based upon the work of John *et al.* (1971) and Leith and Steinberg (1972), that archeocytes may act as essential elements for cell adhesion while species specificity may reside in other cells. No further supporting data for this view have appeared and the data of Burger *et al.* (1978) do not lend credence to it.

Histogenesis of Reaggregates.   In classical studies of sponge cell dissociation, reaggregation, and reconstitution, mechanically dissociated cells are permitted to settle and reaggregate on a glass (or other) substratum. In this type of reaggregation, cells and small aggregates actively move and coalesce to form larger reaggregates (Sara *et al.*, 1974a). Galtsoff (1925a) indicates an essential role for magnesium as well as for calcium in their formation. The initial aggregates that form are, according to Brien (1936) and Van de Vyver (1975), a random mixture of cells in which sorting out of at least one cell type, choanocytes, occurs by 24 h. This internal sorting out implies a recognition system that is based upon cell types. Leith and Steinberg (1972) reported that gray cells of *Microciona prolifera* selectively stain with Nile Blue sulfate and, when followed, tend to become concentrated internally in the aggregation factor-stimulated reaggregates; they thus separate themselves from the more peripherally located choanocytes and archeocytes. These observations further support a view for the sorting out of specific cell types within reaggregation masses, although in later stages gray cells are found peripherally.

Efremova (1970) has investigated cell division and protein synthesis in reaggregating cells of *Ephydatia fluviatilis*. During reaggregation, there is a substantial increase in cell division among archeocytes but none in anucleolate mesohyl cells. Furthermore, archeocytes undergoing division develop a shorter generation time as well as a shorter duration of mitosis. Following dissociation, protein synthesis in archeocytes increases, but by

24 h returns to the previous level, while in collencytes it increases throughout the reaggregation period. These results are compatible with the findings of Müller *et al.* (1976) that AF may stimulate protein synthesis.

In reviewing studies of the development of reaggregation masses, it is clear that in most cases, in both calcareous and demosponge species, reaggregates contain the major cell types of the adult, and the development of a new functional sponge is a "mise en place" of the cellular elements (Huxley, 1911; Brien, 1936; Borojevic and Lévi, 1965; Tuzet and Connes, 1963; Van de Vyver, 1975; Buscema and Van de Vyver, 1979; Connes, 1968). There are no recent data that support other views, and indeed a very recent ultrastructural reinvestigation of *E. fluviatilis* fully supports this conclusion (Buscema and Van de Vyver, 1979) (see below). This conclusion is equally valid for reaggregating cells of the larvae of two demosponges, *Mycale contarenii* and *Adocia elegans* (Borojevic and Lévi, 1964a).

Despite this, in some studies the origin of new pinacocytes is not clear or is disputed (Wilson and Penney, 1930; Borojevic and Lévi, 1965). The question of the origin of these cells still require further reevaluation, since in many studies pinacocytes are either absent in dissociated cells (Borojevic and Lévi, 1965; Wilson and Penney, 1930) or are difficult to identify (Fauré-Frémiet, 1932a; Tuzet and Connes, 1963; Connes, 1968; De Sutter and Van de Vyver, 1977). In an ultrastructural study of reaggregation in *Ophlitaspongia seriata,* Borojevic and Lévi (1964b) found direct evidence that archeocytes form new pinacocytes. This species is cytologically almost identical to *Microciona prolifera* (Simpson, 1963), and their conclusion brings into question the findings of Wilson and Penney (1930) who state that gray cells in the latter species form new pinacocytes. In a study of the behavior of gray cells in *M. atrasanguinea,* Borojevic and Simpson (unpubl. observ.) found that these cells preferentially maintain contact with and spread on other cells rather than migrating onto a glass substratum. They frequently spread on new basopinacocytes and are thus difficult to distinguish from the latter on a light microscope level; they could easily be identified as new pinacocytes. Further, in an ultrastructural investigation of the reaggregation of *M. prolifera,* Bagby (1972) has found that gray cells frequently lie just below the newly formed exopinacoderm and that these exopinacocytes are formed by archeocytes. No evidence was found of adult pinacocyte involvement in the formation of the new pinacoderm. However, in *E. fluviatilis,* the new exopinacoderm, which develops at the surface of the reaggregates, apparently is formed by pinacocytes derived directly from the sponge tissue which as dissociated (Buscema and Van de Vyver, 1979). This clear difference in their origin is ascribed to the fact that the animals used for dissociation in the latter study were very young (gemmule hatched) and consequently their pinacocytes had *not* reached an advanced stage of differentiation, which permits them to take an active part in the histogenesis of the reaggregates (Buscema and Van de Vyver, 1979). Such an interpretation also lends further support to the conclusion that pinacocytes undergo a significant maturation process (Chap. 2). Still further cases of disagreement concerning the origin of new pinacocytes can be found in the literature. Korotkova (1970) claims that in developing reaggregation masses of *Sycon lingua* choanocytes form new pinacocytes. In *Leucosolenia complicata,* choanocytes appear highly plastic, some form pinacocytes while others form amebocytes and the remainder are stable (Korotkova, 1970). In contrast, in *Halichondria panicea,* new exopinacocytes are formed by amebocytes and choanocytes form new chambers (Korotkova, 1970). Agrell (1951) reports that 13% of the dissociated cells of the latter species are pinacocytes, while in *Ephydatia* sp. (adult animals), Ganguly (1960) finds only 1% pinacocytes and indicates that ameboid cells (archeocytes) form new pinacocytes. It is surprising that no study to date has been made of the number of adult pinacocytes, which possibly remain attached to the skeleton following dissociation. This would, at a minimum, help to clarify the question of their presence and percentage in dissociated cells. Korotkova (1970) is of the opinion that the kinds of cellular transformations that occur during reaggregation depend upon the general organization of the adult sponge and thus major differences in cell origins can be observed. No recent supporting data for, or reevaluation of, this view (somatic embyogenesis) are available.

Although other opinions have been expressed (Müller, 1911b), it appears relatively well established that choanocytes in dissociated cells, after withdrawing their collars and flagella, redifferentiate to form new choanocytes despite the fact that there is some phagocytosis of them (Borojevic and Lévi, 1964b, 1965; Tuzet and Connes, 1963; Connes, 1968; Brien, 1936; Van de Vyver, 1975; Buscema and Van de Vyver, 1979). In dissociated cells issuing from young *Ephydatia fluviatilis,* both collars and flagella are maintained on choanocytes (Buscema and Van de Vyver, 1979). Relatively pure suspensions of choanocytes from *Ficulina ficus* and *Hymeniacidon sanguinea* fail to form any other cell type and do not form definitive choanocytes (Borojevic, 1963). Similarly, isolated groups of choanocytes from *Sycon coronatum* do not form other cell types while, however, maintaining their basic morphology (Huxley, 1911, 1921). Almost pure suspensions of dissociated larval flagellated cells of *Mycale contarenii* settle and only form choanocyte chambers which, however, do not survive (Borojevic, 1966).

De Sutter and Buscema (1977), De Sutter and Van de Vyver (1977, 1979b), Van de Vyver and Buscema (1981) and Buscema *et al.* (1980) have followed the formation and development of reaggregates derived from Ficoll gradient-purified archeocytes and almost pure choanocytes (Fig.

9-22). A third, poorly characterized cell fraction probably consists partially of pinacocytes. Of some interest was the finding that cell adhesions occurred spontaneously in all fractions during their preparation (centrifugation). Pure archeocytes reaggregated, attached, and formed fully functional sponges, which, however, contained an excess of spicules (De

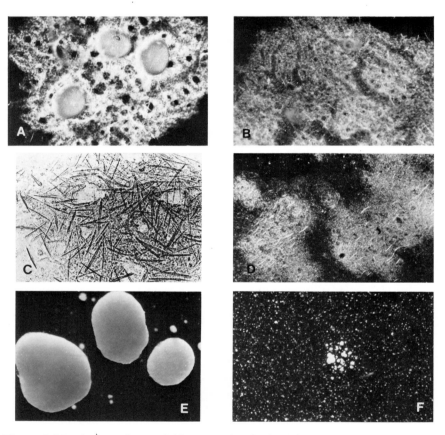

Figure 9-22 Aggregation and histogenesis of Ficoll-fractionated cell types of *Ephydatia fluviatilis* (light micrographs). **A.** Young, control animal derived from the hatching of three gemmules (×27) (DeSutter and Van de Vyver, 1977). **B.** Recombining of all three purified fractions to form a fully functional animal (×27) (DeSutter and Van de Vyver, 1977). **C, D.** Development of a fully functional animal from the highly purified archeocyte fraction alone. Many extra spicules are secreted by these reconstructed animals. C., transmitted light; D., oblique light (×27) (DeSutter and Van de Vyver, 1977). **E.** Reaggregates from a mixture of pure choanocytes and pure pinacocytes. No attachment or further development occurs (×27) (DeSutter and Van de Vyver, 1977). **F.** Absence of both aggregation and attachment of purified pinacocytes (×27) (DeSutter and Van de Vyver, 1977). (All courtesy Prof. G. Van de Vyver and Dr. D. DeSutter.)

Sutter and Van de Vyver, 1977). Based upon discernible ultrastructural differences, archeocytes were directly followed as they differentiated into pinacocytes and choanocytes (Buscema *et al.*, 1980). This is the first absolutely clear demonstration of the pluripotence of *adult* archeocytes, although such a conclusion has been indirectly forthcoming for many years from other studies of experimental regeneration, gemmule hatching, and larval metamorphosis. Reaggregates of enriched choanocytes and other cells (pinacocytes), but lacking archeocytes, do not attach or develop, thus establishing the essentiality of the latter cells for development beyond initial cell adhesion. Using a recently developed, higher-resolution separation technique, De Sutter and Tulp (1981) have separated five fractions of cells from *Ephydatia fluviatilis* and have studied their potential for development into a functional sponge. The fractions consisted of (1) two peaks of mixed choanocytes and pinacocytes, (2) one peak of archeocytes, (3) one peak of archeocytes and sclerocytes, and (4) archeocytes with many undigested platelets. The functional sponges formed by (3) above contain an excess of spicules due to the higher sclerocyte content. Other fractions behaved as in previous experiments (De Sutter and Van de Vyver, 1977, 1979b): reaggregation but no functional tissue from (1), functional tissue from (2), and smaller functional sponges from (4). This new method now makes available a source of enriched sclerocytes. In all of the above studies, it was found that an enrichment of one cell type—i.e., choanocytes, or archeocytes, or sclerocytes—leads to morphogenetic differences; enriched pinacocytes lead to excess canal and dermal membrane development. Thus, although archeocytes retain their capacity to reform a whole organism, subtle changes in cell proportions result in recognizeable morphogenetic changes. Such a result reenforces the view that there is a cell-type equilibrium in sponges which is normally subject to strict control mechanisms (Van de Vyver and Buscema, 1981).

In *Sycon vigilans,* aggregates that are not fully covered by a pinacoderm fail to attach and develop, although some spicule secretion occurs within them (Sara *et al.*, 1974b). In developing aggregates, sometimes multiple oscules form, although the developmental sequence appears completely comparable to larval metamorphosis in which only single oscules form. Possibly an imbalance in cell-type proportions causes the former.

Lévi (1960) has described the elaboration of spongin by spongocytes in older developing reaggregation masses of *Ophlitaspongia seriata.* During the development of reaggregates, the canal system forms through the development of lacunae, which come to be lined by endopinacocytes and which eventually communicate with choanocyte chambers which are formed early in development (Brien, 1936). Subdermal cavities (incurrent vestibules) are also initiated as lacunae just below the exopinacoderm, in some cases prior to the attachment of the reaggregate (see Chap. 6).

Buscema and Van de Vyver (1979) have conducted a thorough ultrastructural reinvestigation of the histogenesis of stationary reaggregates of *Ephydatia fluviatilis* (Fig. 9-23). The mechanically dissociated cells contain archeocytes, choanocytes, and a third, poorly characterized cell type, which is probably pinacocytes but is referred to by these workers as *collencytes*. After 1 h of reaggregation, the surface of the reaggregates is covered by archeocytes, choanocytes with collars and flagella directed outward, and collencytes; by 2 h, many pinacocytes sometimes in two or three layers, form the surface layer, and by 6 h the whole surface is pinacocyte covered and spaces appear below the newly formed exopinacoderm. The new pinacoderm thus appears to be formed directly from adult pinacocytes (=collencytes). Somewhat irregularly shaped and small choanocyte chambers form by 2 h through the movement and grouping together of choanocytes, some of whose flagella and collars are not directed toward the future lumen of the chamber. By 6 h, almost all choanocytes are grouped into definitive chambers. As is the case in the hatching of gemmules (Chap. 8), choanocyte chambers appear prior to their attachment to the canal system; many choanocyte–choanocyte contacts resemble desmosomes. By 1 h, archeocytes are dispersed throughout the aggregate, and by 2 h they contain phagosomes as a result of the phagocytosis of cellular debris and sometimes of whole, apparently healthy choanocytes. In older aggregates, some archeocytes are packed with phagosomes in various stages of digestion. The significance of this phagocytic activity directed toward healthy choanocytes is not known but may have something to do with the necessity of establishing a specific equilibrium in the proportion of cell types in the newly forming animal (Buscema and Van de Vyver, 1979).

Reaggregation of a Hexactinellid. A single study of reaggregation in a hexactinellid (*Rhabdocalyptus dawsoni*) is available (Pavans de Ceccatty, 1982). Mechanical dissociation in sea water resulted in various sized fragments of the syncytial trabeculum, dermal membrane (Chap. 2), and collar body reticula, as well as isolated, discrete archeocytes. Little or no cell movement occurred after settlement, and water currents produced by the movement of collar body flagella resulted in various sized aggregates, which then fused together. No mitoses or nuclear divisions were observed. The reaggregation bodies so formed consist of giant syncytia in which archeocytes and collar bodies are internalized. The syncytia phagocytize debris, while archeocytes appear only minimally involved in phagocytosis in strong distinction to demosponge reaggregation. The collar bodies eventually degenerate, but both they and archeocytes form plugged junctions with the syncytia. These junctions are dense plugs which are elaborated close to the Golgi and which, with microvesicles and larger vesicles, migrate to and partition junctional regions between the archeocytes and the syncytium, between the choanoblasts and the syncytium, and between so-called syncytial compartments (Pavans de Ceccatty

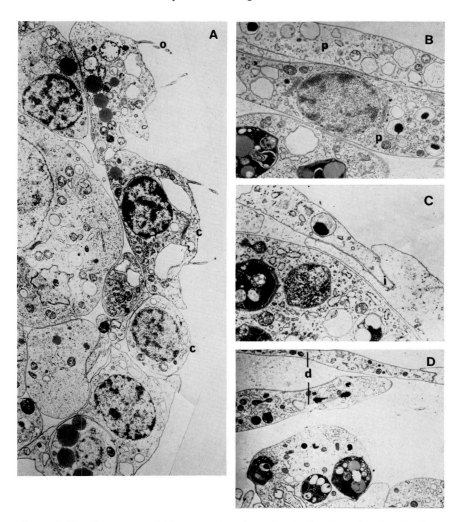

Figure 9-23 Sequence of histogenesis of mechanically dissociated cells from young animals of *Ephydatia fluviatilis* of the same strain (=normal histogenesis) (TEMs). **A.** One hour following dissociation. The aggregates can be partially covered by choanocytes (*c*) at the surface while still retaining their collars (*o*). (×4,500) (Buscema and Van de Vyver, 1979). **B.** After 2 h, the aggregates are covered by pinacocytes (*p*) here seen in two layers (×4,500) (Buscema and Van de Vyver, 1979). **C.** After 6 h, the exopinacocytes form typical interdigitations (*i*) at the surface (×6,300) (Buscema and Van de Vyver, 1979). **D.** In some aggregates at 6 h, the dermal membrane (*d*) is forming (×4,500) (Buscema and Van de Vyver, 1979). The involvement of pinacocytes in these reaggregates appears related to the youth of the animals employed for dissociation and is not an attribute of adult cell reaggregates (see text). (All courtesy Prof. G. Van de Vyver and Dr. M. Buscema.)

and Mackie, 1982). These plugs are discontinuous, containing pores of various sizes. The reaggregation bodies finally become more compact and slowly degenerate. The absence of a siliceous skeleton is considered as a possible reason for their loss of viability (Pavans de Ceccatty, 1982). Thus, the syncytial nature of hexactinellids presents a completely different set of problems and questions relative to their "reaggregation." Those dealing with cell adhesion involve cell–cell, cell–syncytium, and syncytium–syncytium interactions and will be difficult to address.

Sponge Lectins.   Although a specific role for sponge lectins in cell adhesion and reaggregation has not been established, a brief discussion of them here seems appropriate since they may very well be involved in cell–cell interactions (Müller, 1982) and/or reactions to foreign materials *in vivo*. Gold *et al.* (1974) partially characterized a low-molecular-weight protein (15–18,000) from *Axinella* sp., which agglutinates human red cells and is inhibited in its agglutination by D-galactose and other D-galactose containing saccharides (lacto-N-tetrose-β-1,3; lactose; melibiose). Interestingly, this sponge lectin binds both calcium and iron and contains a high carboxylic acid content. It also agglutinates other types of mammalian cells and it was suggested that it may act *in vivo* as a type of AF (Gold *et al.*, 1974), although this now seems unlikely. The *Axinella* lectin prepared by MacLennan (1974) had a higher molecular weight (32,000), but this may be due to differences in preparative techniques, since Bretting (1979) has now shown that there are at least two galactose-specific *Axinella* lectins that can be purified. MacLennan (1974) (see his review of the earlier data) found that *Axinella* lectins also agglutinate sponge cells, those of *Hymeniacidon, Halichondria, Leucosolenia,* but *not* of *Axinella,* and thus may be specifically involved in self-recognition phenomena (see MacLennan, 1974). Bretting and Konigsmann (1979) established that *Axinella polypoides* lectins are stored within the inclusions of spherulous cells and thus do not appear to be involved in cell–cell interactions. They originally suggested that the lectins may function in stabilizing symbionts or as a defense mechanism. More recently, Bretting *et al.* (1983) have studied the tissue distribution of the two *Axinella* lectins (I and II) using immunohistochemical techniques. Lectin I is present predominantly in the vesicles of spherulous cells in which the vesicle size is small and the contents are dense; lectin II is primarily found in the larger-sized vesicles present in the other morphological variants of spherulous cells. Smaller amounts of the other lectin are found intermixed in both cases. The cells with smaller vesicles are apparently transformed into those with larger ones along with a change from lectin I to lectin II. Antibodies to these lectins react with the spongin fibers, and it was concluded, based upon this and the distribution of the spherulous cells in areas of growth, that these lectins are directly involved in spongin biosynthesis. Interestingly, the release of the inclusion contents of these cells *in vivo* had previously been related to matrix elaboration (Donadey and Vacelet, 1977); such release occurs during development in some species (see Tissue Ablation and in Chap. 8, Budding). Additional *Axinella* lectins (III and IV) have been identified (Bretting *et al.*, 1978; Bretting, 1979), and lectins have also been isolated and characterized from *Aaptos paillata* and *Geodia cydonium* (Bretting, 1979). In the latter case, it has been clearly established that the lectin is *not* an aggregation factor (Vaith *et al.*, 1979b), although it is a potent mitogenic substance for some types of mammalian cells (Bretting *et al.*, 1981a) and furthermore it agglutinates heterologous sponge cells from six other sponge species, reduces cell viability, and inhibits synthetic activities (Müller *et al.*, 1980). In a survey of eighteen sponge families (Table 9-12), more than twenty species were found to contain red blood cell agglutinating factors (lectins), but not all species within a single genus (*Axinella*) contain them (Bretting *et al.*, 1981b). If this sampling is indicative, then some 50% or more of sponge species can be expected to be lectin producers. The pressing issue is that of the role of these substances, which may or may not be related to their lectin nature. The most optimistic view is that they are indeed involved with *in vivo* recognition phenomena, but this has yet to be clearly demonstrated, although Müller (1982) considers that native lectins play a central role in sponge cell adhesions and sorting out phenomena during reaggregation.

Müller *et al.* (1981) have also isolated a lectin from *Halichondria panicea* which, *in vitro*, permits the growth of symbiotic bacteria isolated from the sponge. This lectin had no effect on the *in vitro* growth of symbiotic bacteria from other sponge species, and other heterologous lectins did not support the growth of *H. panicea* symbiotic bacteria. The substance is considered to have binding sites for both *H. panicea* cells and for the bacterial cells and to function as a mediator of symbiosis.

Perspective on Cell Differentiation

There are two schools of thought concerning cytodifferentiation. One of them, formalized by Borojevic (1966), maintains that archeocytes are the origin of new pinacocytes and choanocytes during development and that the latter epithelial cells are terminally differentiated. In species that possess collencytes, they are considered as a stable intermediate stage between archeocytes and pinacocytes (Fig. 9-24). There is good evidence to support this view from experimental embryological studies (Borojevic, 1966), from the reconstitution of young sponges from purified archeocytes (De Sutter and Van de Vyver, 1977), and from the formation and hatching of gemmules (Chap. 8). The other view, which has less supporting data, contends that choanocytes are able to develop into polyblasts (Fig. 9-25) which are then able to function as archeocytes (Connes *et al.*, 1974b). There is no disagreement in these views relative to the totipotence of the

Table 9-12   Effects of Crude Saline Extracts on Erythrocytes[a]

Hemagglutination of Erythrocytes[b] by Extracts Derived From:	Lysis of Erythrocytes[b] by Extracts Derived From:	No Effect of Extracts Derived From:
DEMOSPONGIAE		
	Homoscleromorpha	
Oscarella lobularis		
	Tetratinomorpha	
Chondrilla nucula	*Erylus deficiens*	*Cliona celata*
Chondrosia reniformis	*Tethya aurantium*	*Axinella flustra*
Geodia cydonium		*Axinella verrucosa*
Aaptos aaptos		*Axinella damicornis*
Suberites massa		
Cliona viridis		
Axinella polypoides		
Axinella dissimilis		
Acanthella acuta		
	Ceractinomorpha	
Dictyonella incisa	*Anchinoe paupertas*	*Agelas oroides*
Reniera fulva	*Ircinia oros*	*Haliclona mediterranea*
Petrosia ficiformis	*Petrosia ficiformis*	*Ircinia variabilis*
Aplysina (Verongia) cavernicola	*Spongia nitens*	
Aplysina (Verongia) aerophoba		
Dysidea fragilis		
Spongia officinalis		
Spongia nitens		
Cacospongia scalaris		
Ircinia muscarum		
Hippospongia communis		
CALCAREA		
		Clathrina cerebrum

[a]Data taken from Bretting *et al.* (1981b).
[b]Effect upon human and/or rabbit and/or pigeon erythrocytes.

archeocyte state, but there is sharp conflict concerning the differentiative potential of choanocytes. Borojevic (1966) and others maintain that choanocytes are terminally differentiated, while Connes *et al.* (1974b) consider that they can act as a stock of archeocytes, are able to form gametes (Diaz *et al.*, 1973, 1975; Diaz, 1979a; Sara, 1974), and can develop into polyblasts which can form gemmules (Connes, 1977). Further, choanocytes are able, under certain conditions, to develop typical pinacocyte features

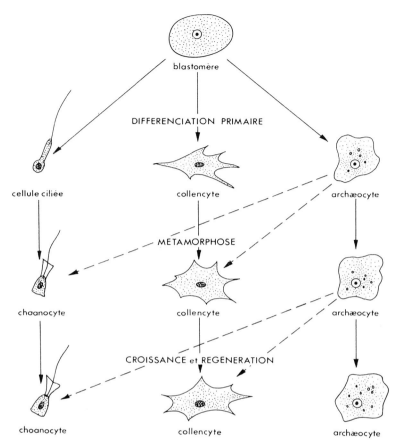

Figure 9-24 Scheme depicting the level of differentiation of the three primary types of cells. Blastomeres give rise to flagellated cells (cellule cilliée), collencytes, and archeocytes. During larval metamorphosis, the former develop into choanocytes while collencytes form pinacocytes and archeocytes are retained in the mesohyl. Experimentally, larval archeocytes can form the other two types as is the case during growth and regeneration. This view does not take into account all of the pertinent data, but is widely accepted particularly as concerns the totipotence of archeocytes (Borojevic, 1966). (Courtesy Dr. R. Borojevic.)

(Diaz, 1979a). Based on this view, the activity of choanocytes, namely, their level of mitoses, establishes cell type equilibria which, depending upon cell numbers, can lead to (1) maintenance of functional tissue, (2) reproduction, or (3) growth and remodeling. It must be admitted that the idea of choanocytes acting as a proliferative tissue which gives rise to mesohyl cells is most appealing, and the more recent data (Diaz, 1979a) are now sufficiently provocative that serious consideration must be given to it. Further, Diaz (1977) concludes that tissue trauma is able to stimulate

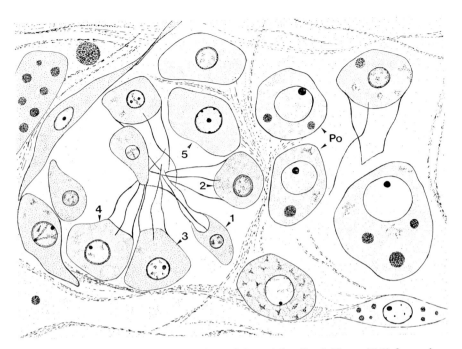

Figure 9-25   Schematic representation of the origin of polyblasts (*PO*) from choanocytes. Successive stages (1 to 5) in polyblast differentiation are pictured. The view that choanocytes are a self-renewing tissue which can, depending upon the equilibrium in cell numbers, give rise to archeocyte-type mesohyl cells presently has some supporting data but requires further verification. Such a view, however, holds much inherent interest developmentally (Connes *et al.*, 1974b). (Courtesy Dr. R. Connes.)

choanocytes and pinacocytes to develop into archeocytes (Fig. 9-26), suggesting a significant ability for these cells to modulate their differentiative states. The occurrence of flagellated endopinacocytes (Chap. 2) also leads credence to this perspective. Such trauma can also stimulate myocytes, as well, to develop archeocyte features (Thiney, 1972). Among calcareous sponges, the general absence of archeocytes in some species seems to be compensated for by the ability of pinacocytes to form sclerocytes.

There is little evidence to suggest that special cells can revert to an archeocyte condition with the possible exception of gray cells which in at least one instance can be interpreted to approach lophocyte morphology (Garrone, 1974) and thus possibly also function as archeocytes (Diaz, 1979a; Connes *et al.*, 1972). With this exception, then, those special cells which have been well-studied clearly appear terminally differentiated, but not static.

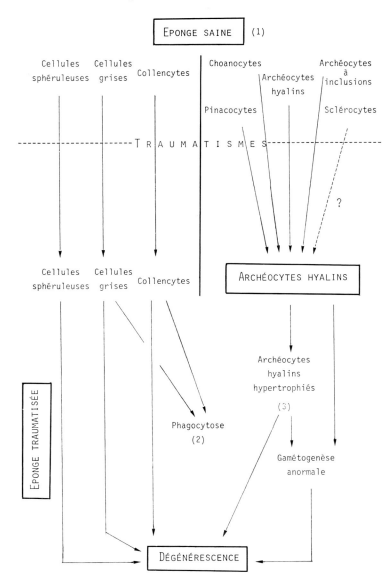

Figure 9-26 Summary of changes in the cell types of *Suberites massa* induced by trauma (repetitive tissue removal). There is reasonably good evidence for these transformations which, however, eventually result in cell degeneration. (*1*) Cell types in normal tissue; (*2*) phagocytosis of some cell types by archeocytes; and (*3*) formation of oocyte-like cells (gamétogenèse anormale) (Diaz, 1977). (Courtesy Dr. J-P. Diaz.)

Regardless of whether choanocytes are considered to play a central role in the formation of mesohyl cells, the differentiation of archeocytes into sclerocytes, pinacocytes, lophocytes, spongocytes, spherulous cells, and choanocytes has been documented in a number of instances and suggests that subtle inductive phenomena lie at the basis of these transformations. An alternate view, for which there is little evidence, is that archeocytes while morphologically homogeneous are functionally heterogeneous, namely, that there are a number of types of archeocytes and each type is predetermined. It is difficult to visualize how gemmules are formed if this is the case and, in any event, some archeocytes would have to maintain or develop totipotence in order to form the definitive thesocytes. The direct development into sclerocytes of undivided thesocytes treated with puromycin (Rozenfeld, 1980) appears to support a view of predetermination, although other interpretations are possible. It is well to keep in mind, as emphasized by Pavans de Ceccatty (1979), that sponge cell types appear less dependent upon their lineage than on their location.

Borojevic (1971) has described common features of morphogenesis in larvae, reduction bodies, gemmules, and reaggregation bodies. He considers each of these stages as "reorganization spherules," which are characterized by reduced surface area and a tendency for the cells to move inward into the spherule; attachment of the spherule is required before morphogenesis and development commence. After attachment, a new force arises—that of expansion due to the movement of cells outward. Ensuing development and shape changes are then influenced by cell movements outward as well as by continuing cell movements inward, resulting in periodic expansion and retraction of the attached spherule. The resulting lines of force (stretch) thus create a milieu in which cytodifferentiation and morphogenesis are induced. Overlying and intermingled with such states of stretch are the contraction of the pinacoderms and the independent movements of cells through the mesohyl (Pottu-Boumendil and Pavans de Ceccatty, 1976). Lines of force, contractions, and cell movements are, in turn, influenced by the density of the matrix and its specific chemistry (Garrone, 1978), while specific interactions at the cell surface may provide a means of fine tuning for directing or stabilizing cell activities and differentiation (Pavans de Ceccatty, 1979).

References

Afzelius, B. A. 1961. Flimmer-flagellum of the sponge. Nature (London), *191*: 1318–1319.

Agrell, I. 1951. Observations on cell differentiation in sponges. Arkiv. Zool., 2(4): 519–523.

Agrell, I. 1952. Enzymes and cell differentiation in sponges. Arkiv. Zool., 3(23): 325–330.

Aisenstadt, T. B., and Korotkova, G. P. 1976. A study of oogenesis in the marine sponge *Halisarca dujardini*. II. Phagocytic activity of the oocytes and vitellogenesis. Tsitologiya, *18*: 818–823 (in Russian).

Ankel, W. E. 1949. Über fragen der formbildung und der zelldetermination bei susswasserschwämmen. Verh. Zool. Ges. (for the year 1948): 58–66.

Ankel, W. E. 1965. Der susswasserschwämm *Ephydatia fluviatilis* (Einleitende Worte zur Vorführung des Films). Zool. Anz., *28* (Suppl.): 426–444.

Ankel, W. E., and Wintermann-Kilian, G. 1952. Über den nachweis von morphologischen und funktionellen differenzierungen bei den epithelzellen der spongillidae. Verh. Zool. Ges. (for the year 1951): 248–255.

Annandale, N. 1907. Notes on freshwater sponges. VI. The midday siesta of *Spongilla* in the tropics. Rec. Ind. Mus., *1*: 387–392.

Annandale, N. 1915. Fauna of the Chilka Lake sponges. Mem. Ind. Mus., 5: 23–54.

Arndt, W. 1930. Schwämme. In: Tabulae Biologicae, Suppl. II. W. Junk, Berlin, pp. 39–120.

Ayling, A. L. 1980. Patterns of sexuality, asexual reproduction and recruitment in some subtidal marine Demospongiae. Biol. Bull., *158*: 271–282.

Azam, F., and Volcani, B. E. 1981. Germanium-silicon interactions in biological systems. In: T. L. Simpson and B. E. Volcani (eds.). Silicon and Siliceous Structures in Biological Systems. Springer-Verlag, New York, pp. 43–67.

Bagby, R. M. 1966. The fine structure of myocytes in the sponges *Microciona prolifera* (Ellis and Solander) and *Tedania ignis* (Duchassaing and Michelotti). J. Morph., *118*: 167–182.

Bagby, R. M. 1970. The fine structure of pinacocytes in the marine sponge *Microciona prolifera* (Ellis and Solander). Zeit. Zellforsch., *105*: 579–594.

Bagby, R. M. 1972. Formation and differentiation of the upper pinacoderm in reaggregation masses of the sponge *Microciona prolifera* (Ellis and Solander). J. Exp. Zool., *180*: 217–244.

Benfey, T. J. and Reiswig, H. M. 1982. Temperature, pH, and photoperiod effects upon gemmule hatching in the freshwater sponge *Ephydatia mülleri* (Porifera, Spongillidae). J. Exp. Zool., *221*: 13–21.

Bergmann, W. 1949. Comparative biochemical studies on the lipids of marine invertebrates, with special reference to the sterols. J. Mar. Res. (Sears Found.), 8: 137–176.

Bergmann, W. 1962. Sterols: Their structure and distribution. In: M. Florkin and H. S. Mason (eds.). Comparative Biochemistry. Academic Press, New York, *III*:103–162.

Bergquist, P. R. 1965. The sponges of Micronesia. Part I. The Palau Archipelago. Pac. Sci., *19*: 123–174.

Bergquist, P. R. 1968. The marine fauna of New Zealand. Porifera, Demospongiae. Part I. (Tetractinomorpha and Lithistida). N. Zeal. Dep. Sci. Ind. Res. Bull., *188*: 1–106.

Bergquist, P. R. 1978. Sponges. Univ. Calif. Press, Los Angeles, pp. 1–268.

Bergquist, P. R. 1979. Sponge chemistry—A review. In: C. Lévi and N. Boury-Esnault (eds.). Biologie des Spongiaires. Colloq. Internat. C.N.R.S. Paris, *291*: 383–392.

Bergquist, P. R., and Green, C. R. 1977a. A method for preserving larva substrate relationships during preparation for electron microscopy. Biol. Cell., *28*: 85–86.

Bergquist, P. R., and Green, C. R. 1977b. An ultrastructural study of settlement and metamorphosis in sponge larvae. Cah. Biol. Mar., *18*: 289–302.

Bergquist, P. R., and Hartman, W. D. 1969. Free amino acid patterns and the classification of the Demospongiae. Mar. Biol., *3*: 247–268.

Bergquist, P. R., and Hogg, J. 1969. Free amino acid patterns in demospongiae: A biochemical approach to sponge classification. Cah. Biol. Mar., *10*: 205–220.

Bergquist, P. R., and Sinclair, M. 1968. The morphology and behavior of larvae of some intertidal sponges. N. Zeal. J. Mar. Fresh. Res., *2*: 426–437.

Bergquist, P. R., and Sinclair, M. E. 1973. Seasonal variation in settlement and spiculation of sponge larvae. Mar. Biol., *20*: 35–44.

Bergquist, P. R., Sinclair, M. E., and Hogg, J. J. 1970. Adaptation to intertidal existence: Reproductive cycles and larval behavior in Demospongiae. In: W. G. Fry (ed.). The Biology of the Porifera. Academic Press, London. Sym. Zool. Soc. Lond., *25*: 274–271.

Bergquist, P. R., Sinclair, M. E., Green, C. R., and Silyn-Roberts, H. 1979. Comparative morphology and behavior of larvae of Demospongiae. In: C. Lévi and N. Boury-Esnault (eds.). Biologie des Spongiaires. Colloq. Internat. C.N.R.S. Paris, *291*: 103–111.

Berthold, G. 1969. Untersuchungen über de histoblastendifferenzierung in der gemmula von *Ephydatia fluviatilis*. Zeit. Wiss. Mikrosk., *69*: 227–243.

Bertrand, J. C., and Vacelet, J. 1971. L'association entre éponges cornées et bacteries. C.R. Acad. Sci. Paris, *273*: 638–641.

Bidder, G. P. 1892. Note on excretion in sponges. Proc. Roy. Soc. Lond., *51*: 474–485.

Bidder, G. P. 1898. The skeleton and classification of calcareous sponges. Proc. Roy. Soc. Lond., *64*: 61–76.

Bidder, G. P. 1923. The relation of the form of a sponge to its currents. Quart. J. Micros. Sci., *67*: 293–325.

Bidder, G. P. 1933. Sponges without collared cells. Nature (London), *132*: 441.

Bigger, C. H., Hildemann, W. H., Jokiel, P. L., and Johnston, I. S. 1981. Afferent sensitization and efferent cytotoxicity in allogenic tissue responses of the marine sponge *Callyspongia diffusa*. Transplant., *31*: 461–464.

Bigger, C., Jokiel, P. L. and Hildemann, W. H. 1983. Cytotoxic transplantation immunity in the sponge *Toxadocia violacea*. Transplant., *35*: 239–243.

Borojevic, R. 1963. Essai de reconstitution du choanoderm à partir d'une suspension choanocytaire d'éponge acalcaire. C.R. Acad. Sci., Paris, *257*: 961–962.

Borojevic, R. 1966. Étude experimentale de la différenciation des cellules de l'éponge au cours de son développement. Devel. Biol., *14*: 130–153.

Borojevic, R. 1967. La ponte et le developpement de *Polymastia robusta* (Demosponges). Cah. Biol. Mar., *8*: 1–6.

Borojevic, R. 1968. Éponges calcaires des côtes de France. IV. Le genre *Ascaltis* Haeckel emend. Arch. Zool Exp. Gén., *109*: 193–210.

Borojevic, R. 1969. Étude du développement et la différenciation cellulaire d'éponges calcaires calcinéennes (genres *Clathrina* et *Ascandra*). Ann. Embry. Morph., *2*: 15–36.

Borojevic, R. 1970. Differenciation cellulaire dans l'embryogénèse et la morphogenèse chez les spongiaires. In: W. G. Fry (ed.). The Biology of the Porifera. Academic Press, London. Sym. Zool. Soc. Lond., *25*: 467–490.

Borojevic, R. 1971. Le comportement des cellules d'éponge lors de processus morphogénétique. Ann. Biol., *10*: 533–545.

Borojevic, R., and Lévi, C. 1964a. Métamorphose artificielle de larves d'éponge, après dissociation et réaggregation des cellules larvaires. C.R. Acad. Sci., Paris, *259*: 4364–4366.

Borojevic, R., and Lévi, C. 1964b. Étude au microscope electronique des cellules de l'éponge *Ophlitaspongia seriata* (Grant) au cours de la réorganisation après dissociation. Zeit. Zellforsch., *64*: 708–725.

Borojevic, R., and Lévi, C. 1965. Morphogenese experimentale d'une éponge à partir des cellules de la larve nageante dissociée. Zeit. Zellforsch., *68*: 57–69.

Borojevic, R., and Lévi, P. 1967. Le basopinacoderme de l'éponge *Mycale contarenii* (Martens). Technique d'étude des fibres extracellulaires basales. J. Micros., *6*: 857–862.

Borojevic, R., Fry, W. G., Jones, W. C., Lévi, C., Rasmont, R., Sara, M., and Vacelet, J. 1967. Mise au point actuelle de la terminologie des éponges. Bull. Mus. Nat. Hist. Natur. (Paris), *39*: 1224–1235.

Boury-Esnault, N. 1970. Un phénomène de bourgeonnement externe chez l'eponge *Axinella damicornis* (Esper.). Cah. Biol. Mar., *11*: 491–496.

Boury-Esnault, N. 1972. Une structure inhalante remarquable des spongiaires: le crible. Étude morphologique and cytologique. Arch. Zool. Exp. Gén., *113*: 7–23.

Boury-Esnault, N. 1973. L'exopinacoderme des spongiaires. Bull. Mus. Nat. Hist. Natur. (Paris), 3rd Ser., No. 178 (Zool. *117*): 1193–1206.

Boury-Esnault, N. 1974. Structure et ultrastructure des papilles d'éponges du genre *Polymastia* Bowerbank. Arch. Zool. Exp. Gén., *115*: 141–165.

Boury-Esnault, N. 1976a. Ultrastructure de la larve parenchymella d'*Hamigera hamigera* (Schmidt) (Demosponge, Poecilosclerida). Cah. Biol. Mar., *27*: 9–20.

Boury-Esnault, N. 1976b. Morphogenèse expérimentale des papilles inhalantes de l'éponge *Polymastia mamillaris* (Muller). Arch. Zool. Exp. Gén., *117*: 181–196.

Boury-Esnault, N. 1977. A cell type in sponges involved in the metabolism of glycogen. The gray cells. Cell Tiss. Res., *175*: 523–539.

Boury-Esnault, N., and Doumenc, D. A. 1979. Glycogen storage and transfer in primitive invertebrates: Demospongea and Actinaris. In: C. Lévi and N. Boury-Esnault (eds.). Biologie des Spongiaires. Colloq. Internat. C.N.R.S., Paris, *291*: 181–192.

Boury-Esnault, N., De Vos, L., Donadey, C., and Vacelet, J. *in press*. Comparative study of the choanosome of Porifera. I. The Homoscleromorpha. J. Morph.

Bowerbank, J. S. 1862. On the anatomy and physiology of the Spongiadae. Phil. Trans. Roy. Soc., Lond., *152*:747–836; 1087–1135.

Brauer, E. B. 1975. Osmoregulation in the freshwater sponge, *Spongilla lacustris*. J. Exp. Zool., *192*: 181–192.

Bretting, H. 1979. Purification and characterization of sponge lectins and a study of their immunochemical and biological activities. In: C. Lévi and N. Boury-Esnault (eds.). Biologie des spongiaires. Colloq. Internat. C.N.R.S., Paris, *291*: 247–255.

Bretting, H., and Konigsmann, K. 1979. Investigations on the lectin producing cells in the sponge *Axinella polypoides*. Cell Tiss. Res., *201*: 487–497.

Bretting, H., Dalthoff, H., and Fehr, S. 1978. Studies on the relationship between lectins from *Axinella polypoides* agglutinating bacteria and human erythocytes. J. Invert. Pathol., *32*: 151–157.

Bretting, H., Phillips, S. G., Klumpart, H. J., and Kabat, E. A. 1981a. A mitogenic lactose-binding lectin from the sponge *Geodia cydonium*. J. Immunol., *127*: 1652–1658.

Bretting, H., Donadey, C., Vacelet, J., and Jacobs, G. 1981b. Investigations on the occurence of lectins in marine sponges with special regard to some species of the family axinellidae. Comp. Biochem. Physiol., *70B*: 69–76.

Bretting, H., Jacobs, G., Donadey, C., and Vacelet, C. 1983. Immunohistochemical studies on the distribution and the function of the D-galactose-specific lectins in the sponge *Axinella polypoides* (Schmidt). Cell Tiss. Res., *229*: 551–571.

Brien, P. 1932. Contribution a l'étude de la régéneration naturelle chez les spongillidae. *Spongilla lacustris* (L.), *Ephydatia fluviatilis* (L.) Arch. Zool. Exp. Gén., *74*: 461–506.

Brien, P. 1936. La réorganisation de l'éponge après dissociation par filtration et phénomènes d'involution chez *Ephydatia fluviatilis*. Arch. Biol., *48*: 185–268.

Brien, P. 1943. La formation des orifices inhalants chez les spongillidae (*Spongilla lacustris* L.-*Ephydatia fluviatilis* L.). Bull Mus. Roy. Hist. Nat. Belg., *19*: 1–16.

Brien, P. 1967a. Les éponges. Leur nature matazoaire, leur gastrulation, leur état colonial. Ann. Soc. Roy. Zool. Belg., *97*: 197–235.

Brien, P. 1967b. Une nouveau mode de statoblastogénèse chez une éponge d'eau douce africaine: *Potamolepsis stendelli* (Jaffé). Bull Acad. Roy. Belg., 5th Ser., *53*: 552–572.

Brien, P. 1967c. Formation des statoblastes dans le genre *Potamolepis P. symoensi* (Brien), *P. pechuelli* (Marshall), *P. schoutedeni* (Burton). Bull. Acad. Roy. Belg., 5th Ser., *53*: 573–591.

Brien, P. 1970. Les potamopepides africaines nouvelles du Luapula et du lac Moero. In: W. G. Fry (ed.). The Biology of the Porifera. Academic Press, London. Sym. Zool. Soc. Lond., *25*: 163–187.

Brien, P. 1973. Les Demosponges. In: P-P. Grassé (ed). Traité de Zoologie, Vol. III, Fasc. 1, Mason Cie, Paris, pp. 133–461.

Brien, P. 1975. La croissance de l'éponge étudiée chez *Ephydatia fluviatilis* Lin. et *Spongilla lacustris* Lam. C.R. Acad. Sci. Paris, *280*: 1599–1602.

Brien, P. 1976. La croissance des spongillidae. Formation des choanocytes et des spicules. Bull. Biol. France Belg., *110*: 211–252.

Brien, P., and Govaert-Mallebranche, D. 1958. A propos de deux éponges du Tanganika. Acad. Roy. Sci. Colon., 8th Ser., *8*: 1–43.

Brien, P., and Meewis, H. 1938. Contribution a l'étude de l'embryogénèse des spongillidae. Arch. Biol., *49*: 177–250.

Brill, B. 1973. Untersuchungen zur ultrastruktur des choanocyte von *Ephydatia fluviatilis* L. Zeit. Zellforsch., *144*: 231–245.

Bromley, R. G., and Tendal, O. S. 1973. Example of substrate competition and phobotropism between two clionid sponges. J. Zool. Lond., *169*: 151–155.

Brønsted, H. V. 1931. On the development of the acanthostrongyle in *Halicnemia verticillata* (Bow.). Vidensk. Medd. Dansk Naturhist. Foren., *90*: 9–12.

Brønsted, H. V. 1936. Entwicklungsphysiologische studien über *Spongilla lacustris*. Acta. Zool., *17*: 75–172.

Brønsted, H. V. 1953. The ability to differentiate and the size of regenerated cells after repeated regeneration in *Spongilla lacustris*. Quart. J. Micros. Sci., *94*: 177–184.

Brønsted, H. V. 1962. Entwicklungsphysiologie der poriferen. Fortsch. Zool., *14*: 115–129.

Brønsted, A., and Brønsted, H. V. 1953. The effect of symbiotic zoochlorellae on the germination rate of gemmules of *Spongilla lacustris* (L.). Vidensk. Medd. Dansk. Naturhist. Foren., *115*: 133–145.

Brønsted, H. V., and Carlsen, F. E. 1951. A cortical cytoskeleton in expanded epithelium cells of sponge gemmules. Exp. Cell Res., *2*: 90–96.

Brønsted, H. V., and Løvtrup, E. 1953. The respiration of sponge gemmules without and with symbiotic unicellular algae. Vidensk. Medd. Dansk. Naturhist. Foren., *115*: 145–157.

Buchecker, R., Eugster, C. H., and Litchfield, C. 1977. Carotinoide aus marinen schwämmen (Porifera). Isolierung und struktur von sieben hauptcarotinoiden aus *Agelas schmidtii*. Hel. Chim. Acta, *60*: 2780–2788.

Burger, M. M. 1977. Mechanisms of cell-cell recognition: Some comparisons between lower organisms and vertebrates. In: M. Karkinen-Jaaskelainen and L. Saxen (eds.). Cell Interactions in Differentiation. Academic Press, London, pp. 357–376.

Burger, M. M., and Jumblatt, J. 1977. Membrane involvement in cell-cell interactions: A two component system for cellular recognition that does not require live cells. In: J. W. Lash and M. M. Burger (eds.). Cell and Tissue Interactions. Raven, New York, pp. 155–172.

Burger, M. M., Turner, R. S., Kuhns, W. J., and Weinbaum, G. A. 1975. A possible model for cell-cell recognition via surface macromolecules. Phil. Trans. Roy Soc. Lond., B, *271*: 379–393.

Burger, M. M., Burkart, W., Weinbaum, G., and Jumblatt, J. 1978. Cell-cell recognition: molecular aspects. Recognition and its relation to morphogenetic processes in general. Sym. Soc. Exp. Biol., No. *32*: 1–23.

Burkart, W., Simpson, T. L., and Burger, M. M. 1978. Cell surface properties of larval and adult cell types in the marine sponge *Microciona prolifera*. Biol. Bull., *155*: 430.

Burkart, W., Jumblatt, J., Simpson, T. L., and Burger, M. M. 1979. Macromolecules which mediate cell-cell recognition in *Microciona prolifera* In: C. Lévi and N. Boury-Esnault (eds.). Biologie des Spongiaires. Colloq. Internat. C.N.R.S. Paris, *291*: 239–246.

Burton, M. 1931. The interpretation of the embryonic and post-larval characters of certain tetraxonid sponges. With observations on post-larval growth stages in some species. Proc. Zool. Soc. Lond., (1931–1932): 511–525.

Burton, M. 1949a. Non-sexual reproduction in sponges, with special reference to a collection of young *Geodia*. Proc. Linn. Soc. Lond., *160*: 163–178.

Burton, M. 1949b. Observations on littoral sponges, including the supposed swarming of larvae, movement and coalescence in mature individuals, longevity and death. Proc. Zool Soc. Lond., *118*: 893–915.

Burton, M. 1963. A revision of the calcareous sponges. Wm. Clones and Sons Ltd., London, pp. 1–693.

Buscema, M. 1982. Diversité des manifestations de la reconnaissance de soi et du non-soi chez les spongiaires. Thèse. Université Libre de Bruxelles. 164 pp. Figures in a separate volume.

Buscema, M., and Van de Vyver, G. 1979. Étude ultrastructurale de l'aggrégation des cellules dissociées de l'éponge *Ephydatia fluviatilis*. In: C. Lévi and N. Boury-Esnault (eds.). Biologie des Spongiaires. Colloq. Internat. C.N.R.S., Paris, *291*: 225–231.

Buscema, M. and Van de Vyver, G. 1983a. Cellular aspects of alloimmune reactions in sponges of the genus *Axinella*.I. *Axinella polypoides*, J. Exp. Zool., *228*: in press.

Buscema, M. and Van de Vyver, G. 1983b. Cellular aspects of alloimmune reactions in sponges of the genus *Axinella*. II. *Axinella verrucosa* and *Axinella damicornis*. J. Exp. Zool., *228*: in press.

Buscema, M. and Van de Vyver, G. 1983c. Variability of allograff rejection processes in *Axinella verrucosa*. Develop. Comp. Immunol., 7: 405–408.

Buscema, M., DeSutter, D., and Van de Vyver, G. 1980. Ultrastructural study of differentiation processes during aggregation of purified sponge archeocytes. Wilhelm Roux's Arch., *188*: 45–53.

Butschli, O. 1901. Einige beobachtungen über kiesel- und kalknadeln von Spongien. Zeit. Wiss. Zool., 69:235–286.

Carrière, D., Connes, R., and Paris, J. 1974. Ultrastructure et nature chimique de la coque et du vitellus gemmulaires chez l'éponge marine: *Suberites domuncula* (Olivi) Nardo. C.R. Acad. Sci., Paris, *278*: 1577–1580.

Castro, P. 1979. Studies on the symbiosis between a filamentous microorganism and *Hymenamphiastra cyanocrypta*, a sponge from California. In: C. Lévi and N. Boury-Esnault (eds.). Biologie des Spongiaires. Colloq. Internat. C.N.R.S., Paris, *291*: 365–371.

Castro-Rodriguez, G. 1930. De la symbiose entre la *Spongilla lacustris* et les zoochlorelles. Contribution a l'étude de la nutrition des spongiaires. Remarques sur la fecondation des spongiaires. Ann. Soc. Roy. Zool. Belg., *61*: 111–122.

Cauldwell, C. B., Henkart, P. and Humphreys, T. 1973. Physical properties of sponge aggregation factor. A unique proteoglycan complex. Biochemistry, *12*: 3051–3055.

Chen, W-T. 1976. Reproduction and speciation in *Halisarca*. In: F. W. Harrison and R. R. Cowden (eds.). Aspects of Sponge Biology. Academic Press, New York, pp. 113–139.

Cheng, T. C., Yee, H. W. F., and Rifkin, E. 1968a. The cell types occurring in the mesoglea of *Terpios zeteki* (de Laubenfels) (Porifera: Demospongiae). Pac. Sci., *23*: 395–401.

Cheng, T. C., Yee, H. W. F., Rifkin, E. and Kramer, M. 1968b. Cellular reactions in *Terpios zeteki* to implanted heterologous biological materials. J. Invert. Pathol., *12*: 29–35.

Claus, G., Madri, P., and Kunen, S. 1967. Removal of microbial pollutants from waste effluents by the redbeard sponge. Nature (London), *216*: 712–714.

Cobb, W. R. 1969. Penetration of calcium carbonate substrates by the boring sponge, *Cliona*. Amer. Zool., *9*: 783–790.

Cobb, W. R. 1975. Fine structural features of destruction of calcareous substrata by the burrowing sponge *Cliona celata*. Trans. Amer. Micros. Soc., *94*: 197–202.

Colussi, A. 1958. Sulla degenerazione di ovociti in *Sycon raphanus* (O. Schmidt) (Calcispongiae). Ann. Ist. Mus. Zool. Univ. Napoli, *10*: 1–7.

Connes, R. 1964. Contribution a l'étude de la proliferation par voie asexuée chez le *Sycon*. Bull. Soc. Zool. France, *89*: 188–195.

Connes, R. 1966a. Aspects morphologiques de la régéneration de *Tethya lyncurium* Lamarck. Bull Soc. Zool. France, *91*: 43–53.

Connes, R. 1966b. Contribution a l'étude histologique des premires stades d'embryogenèse somatique chez *Tethya lyncurium* Lamarck. Bull. Soc. Zool. France, *91*: 639–645.

Connes, R. 1967. Structure et développement des bourgeons chez l'éponge siliceuse *Tethya lyncurium* Lamarck. Arch. Zool. Exp. Gén., *108*: 157–195.

Connes, R. 1968. Étude histologique, cytologique et expérimentale de la régénération et de la reproduction asexuée chez *Tethya lyncurium* Lamarck (=*T. aurantium* Pallas) (Demosponges). Thèse. Univ. Montpellier, pp. 1–193.

Connes, R. 1975. Mode de formation de certains systèmes membranaires au niveau des plaquettes vitellines de thésocytes d'une Démosponge marine: *Suberites domuncula* (Olivi) Nardo. C.R. Acad. Sci., Paris, *281*: 1851–1854.

Connes, R. 1977. Contribution a l'étude de la gemmulogenèse chez la démosponge marine *Suberites domuncula* (Olivi) Nardo. Arch. Zool Exp. Gén., *118*: 391–407.

Connes, R., and Artiges, J-M. 1980. Nature chimique structure et biosynthese de l'enveloppe gemmulaire chez une demosponge marine. Arch. Zool. Exp. Gén., *121*: 213–225.

Connes, R., Diaz, J-P., and Paris, J. 1971a. Choanocytes et cellule centrale chez la demosponge *Suberites massa* Nardo. C.R. Acad. Sci., Paris, *273*: 1590–1593.

Connes, R., Paris, J., and Sube, J. 1971b. Reactions tissulaire de quelques démosponges vis-à-vis de leurs commensaux et parasites. Naturliste Can., *98*: 923–935.

Connes, R., Diaz, J-P., and Paris, J. 1972. Variations saisonnières des populations cellulaires de l'éponge *Suberites massa* Nardo. I. Étude histologique et cytologique. Bull. Mus. Nat. Hist. Natur. (Paris), 3rd Ser., No. 84 (Zoologie 63): 1013–1038.

Connes, R., Diaz, J-P., Negre, G., and Paris, J. 1974a. Étude morphologique cytologique et sérologique de deux formes de *Suberites massa* de l'etang de Thau. Vie et Milieux, *24*: 213–224.

Connes, R., Paris, J., and Artiges, J. M. 1974b. L'origine des cellules blastogenetiques chez *Suberites domuncula* Nardo. L'équilibre choanocytes-archeocytes chez les spongiaires. Ann. Sci. Natur. Zool., Paris, *16*: 111–118.

Connes, R., Carrière, D., and Paris, J. 1978. Étude du developpement des gemmules chez la demosponge marine *Suberites domuncula* (Olivi) Nardo. Ann. Sci. Natur. Zool. Paris, *20*: 357–387.

Conrad, J., Diehl-Seifert, B., Zahn, R. K., Uhlenbruck, G., Zimmermann, E., and Müller, W. E. G. 1982. Fibronectin is apparently not involved in species-specific reaggregation of cells from the marine sponge *Geodia cydonium*. J. Cell. Biochem., *19*: 395–404.

Cotte, J. 1902. Comment les choanocytes de *Syncandra raphanus* absorbent-ils les particules aliments. C.R. Soc. Biol. Paris, *54*: 1315–1317.

Cotte, J. 1904. Des phenomenes de la nutrition chez les spongiaires. C.R. Assoc. Fr. Av. Sci., *32*: 776–780.

Cowden, R. R. 1970. Connective tissue in six marine sponges: A histological and histochemical study. Zeit. Mikrosk.-Anat. Forsch., *82*: 557–569.

Cowden, R. R., and Harrison, F. W. 1976. Cytochemical studies of connective tissue in sponges. In: F. W. Harrison and R. R. Cowden (eds.). Aspects of Sponge Biology. Academic Press, New York, pp. 69–82.

Cuif, J-P., Debrenne, F., Lafuste, J. G., and Vacelet, J. 1979. Comparison de la microstructure du squelette carbonate non spiculaire d'éponges actuelles et fossiles. In: C. Lévi and N. Boury-Esnault (eds.). Biologie des Spongiaires. Colloq. Internat. C.N.R.S., Paris, *291*: 459–465.

Curtis, A. S. G. 1962. Pattern and mechanism in the reaggregation of sponges. Nature (London), *196*: 245–248.

Curtis, A. S. G. 1970. Problems and some solutions in the study of cellular aggregation. In: W. G. Fry (ed.). The Biology of the Porifera. Academic Press, London, Sym. Zool. Soc. Lond., *25*: 335–352.

Curtis, A. S. G. 1979a. Recognition by sponge cells. In: C. Lévi and N. Boury-Esnault (eds.). Biologie des Spongiaires. Colloq. Internat. C.N.R.S., Paris, *291*: 205–209.

Curtis, A. S. G. 1979b. Individuality and graft rejection in sponges or a cellular basis for individuality in sponges. In: G. Larwood and B. R. Rosen (eds.). Biology and Systematics of Colonial Organisms. Academic Press, New York, pp. 39–48.

Curtis, A. S. G., and Van de Vyver, G. 1971. The control of cell adhesion in a morphogenetic system. J. Embryol. Exp. Morph., *26*: 295–312.

D'Ambrosio, M., Guerriero, P., Traldi, P., and Pietra, F. 1982. Cavernicolin-1 and cavernicolin-2, two epimeric dibromolactams from the mediterranean sponge *Aplysina* (*Verongia*) *cavernicola*. Tetrah. Lett., *23*: 4403–4406.

Davie, E. I., Simpson, T. L., and Garrone, R. 1983. Experimental germanium incorporation into siliceous sponge spicules. Biol. Cell., *48*: 191–202.

Dayton, P. K. 1979. Observations of growth, dispersal and population dynamics of some sponges in McMurdo Sound, Antarctica. In: C. Lévi and N. Boury-Esnault (eds.). Biologie des Spongiaires. Colloq. Internat. C.N.R.S., Paris, *291*: 271–282.

De Laubenfels, M. W. 1936. A discussion of the sponge fauna of the Dry Tortugas in particular and the West Indies in general with material for a revision of the families and orders of the Porifera. Carnegie Inst. Wash. Publ. No. 467, Pap. Tortugas Lab., *30*: 1–225.

De Laubenfels, M. W. 1948. The order Keratosa of the phylum Porifera: A monographic study. Occ. Pap. Allan Hancock Found., *3*: 1–217.

Dendy, A. 1915. Observations on the gametogenesis of *Grantia compressa*. Quart. J. Micros. Sci., *60*: 313–376.

Dendy, A. 1921. The tetraxonid sponge spicule: A study in evolution. Acta. Zool. Stockh., *2*: 95–152.

De Pomar, B. 1973. Acerca del canículo axial en espongolitos siliceus. Rev. Asoc. Cien. Nat. Lit., *4*: 167–176.

De Sutter, D., and Buscema, M. 1977. Isolation of a highly pure archeocyte fraction from the fresh-water sponge *Ephydatia fluviatilis*. Wilhelm Roux's Arch., *183*: 149–153.

De Sutter, D., and Tulp, A. 1981. A method for large scale sponge cell separation: 1 g sedimentation (Cellular composition of the fractions obtained). Biol. Cell., *40*: 63–68.

De Sutter, D., and Van de Vyver, G. 1977. Aggregation properties of different cell types of the fresh-water sponge *Ephydatia fluviatilis*. Wilhelm Roux's Arch., *181*: 151–161.

De Sutter, D., and Van de Vyver, G. 1979a. Isolation and recognition properties of some definite sponge cell types. Devel. Comp. Immunol., *3*: 389–397.

De Sutter, D., and Van de Vyver, G. 1979b. Cell recognition properties of isolated sponge cell fractions. In: C. Lévi and N. Boury-Esnault (eds.). Biologie des Spongiaires. Colloq. Internat. C.N.R.S., Paris, *291*: 217–224.

De Vos, C. 1965. Le bourgeonnement externe de l'éponge *Mycale contarenii*. Bull. Mus. Nat. Hist. Natur. (Paris), *37*: 548–555.

De Vos, L. 1971. Étude ultrastructurale de la gemmulogenèse chez *Ephydatia fluviatilis*. J. Micros., *10*: 283–304.

De Vos, L. 1972. Fibres géantes de collagène chez l'éponge *Ephydatia fluviatilis*. J. Micros., *15*: 247–252.

De Vos, L. 1974. Étude ultrastructurale de la formation et de l'eclosion gemmules d'*Ephydatia fluviatilis*. Thèse. Univ. Bruxelles.

De Vos, L. 1977. Morphogenesis of the collagenous shell of the gemmules of a fresh-water sponge *Ephydatia fluviatilis*. Arch. Biol., *88*: 479–494.

De Vos, L. 1979. Structure tridimensionelle de l'éponge *Ephydatia fluviatilis*. In: C. Lévi and N. Boury-Esnault (eds.). Biologie des Spongiaires. Colloq. Internat. C.N.R.S., Paris, *291*: 159–164.

De Vos, L., and Rozenfeld, F. 1974. Ultrastructure de la coque collagène des gemmules d'*Ephydatia fluviatilis* (Spongillides). J. Micros., *20*: 15–20.

De Vos, L., and Van de Vyver, G. 1981. Étude de la contraction spontanée chez l'éponge d'eau douce *Ephydatia fluviatilis* cultivée in vitro. Ann Soc. Roy. Zool. Belg., *111*: 21–31.

De Vos, L., Boury-Esnault, N., Vacelet, J., and Donadey, C. 1981. Morphologie comparée des choanocytes des Spongiaires. Etude aux microscope électronique à transmission et à balayage. Biol. Cell, *41*: 8a.

Diaz, J.-P. 1973. Cycle sexuel de deux demosponges de l'etang de Thau: *Suberites massa* Nardo et *Hymeniacidon caruncula* Bowerbank. Bull. Soc. Zool. France, *98*: 145–156.

Diaz, J.-P. 1977. Transformation histologiques et cytologiques post-traumatiques chez la demosponge *Suberites massa* Nardo. Bull. Mus. Nat. Hist. Natur. (Paris), 3rd Ser., No. 445 (Zoologie *308*): 375–396.

Diaz, J.-P. 1979a. Variations, differenciations et fonctions des categories cellulaire de la demosponge d'eau saumaitres, *Suberites massa* Nardo, au cours du cycle biologique annuel et dans des conditions experimentales. Thèse. Univ. Sci. Tech. Languedoc., pp. 1–332.

Diaz, J-P. 1979b. La degenerescence ovocytaire chez la demosponge *Suberites massa*. In: C. Lévi and N. Boury-Esnault (eds.). Biologie des Spongiaires. Colloq. Internat. C.N.R.S., Paris, *291*: 79–86,

Diaz, J-P., and Connes, R. 1980. Étude ultrastructurale de la spermatogenèse d'une démosponge. Biol. Cell., *38*: 225–230.

Diaz, J-P., Connes, R., and Paris, J. 1973. Origine de la lignée germinale chez une démosponge de l'etang de Thau: *Suberites massa* Nardo. C.R. Acad. Sci., Paris, *277*: 661–663.

Diaz, J-P., Connes, R., and Paris, J. 1975. Étude ultrastructurale de l'ovogenèse d'une demosponge: *Suberites massa* Nardo. J. Micros., *24*: 105–116.

Donadey, C. 1978. Origine choanocytaire des cellules à inclusions de l'éponge *Plakina trilopha* Schulze (Démosponge Homosclerophoide). C.R. Acad. Sci. Paris, *278*: 519–521.

Donadey, C. 1979. Contribution a l'étude cytologique de deux démosponges Homosclerophorides: *Oscarella lobularis* (Schmidt) et *Plakina trilopha* Schulze. In: C. Lévi and N. Boury-Esnault (eds.). Biologie des Spongiaires. Colloq. Internat. C.N.R.S., Paris, *291*: 165–172.

Donadey, C. 1982. Les cellules pigmentaires et les cellules à inclusions de l'éponge *Cacospongia scalaris* (Demosponge Dictyoceratide). Vie marine, *4*: 67–74.

Donadey, C., and Vacelet, J. 1977. Les cellules à inclusions de l'éponge *Pleraplysilla spinifera* (Schulze) (Démosponges, Dendroceratides). Arch. Zool. Exp. Gén., *118*: 273–284.

Drum, R. 1968. Electron microscopy of siliceous spicules from the freshwater sponge *Heteromeyenia*. J. Ultrastruc. Res., *22*: 12–21.

Drumm, P. J., O'Connor, W. F., and Renouf, L. P. 1945. The pigments of sponges. I. The lipid pigments of the sponge *Hymeniacidon sanguineum* (Grant). Biochem. J., *39*: 208–210.

Duboscq, O., and Tuzet, O. 1936. Les amebocytes et les cellules germinales des eponges calcaires. Mem. Mus. Hist. Nat. Belg., *3*: 209–226.

Duboscq, O., and Tuzet, O. 1937. L'ovogènese, la fécondation et les premiers stades du développement des éponges calcaires. Arch. Zool. Exp. Gén., *79*: 157–316.

Duboscq, O., and Tuzet, O. 1939. Les divers formes des choanocytes des éponges calcaires hétérocoeles et leur signification. Arch. Zool. Exp. Gén., *80*: 353–388.

Duboscq, O., and Tuzet, O. 1941. Sur les cellules en croix des *Sycon* (*Sycon ciliatum* Fabr., *Sycon coronatum* Ellis et Soll., *Sycon elegans* Bower.) et leur signification. Arch. Zool. Exp. Gén., *81*: 151–163.

Duboscq, O., and Tuzet, O. 1942. Recherches complementaires sur l'ovogenèse, la fécondation et les premiers stades du developpement des éponges calcaires. Arch. Zool. Exp. Gén., *81*: 395–466.

Duboscq, O., and Tuzet, O. 1944. L'ovogenèse, la fécondation, et les premiers stades du développement du *Sycon elegans* Bower. Arch. Zool. Exp. Gén., *83*: 445–459.

Efremova, S. M. 1967. The cell behavior of the fresh-water sponge *Ephydatia fluviatilis*. Acta Biol. Hung., *18*: 37–46.

Efremova, S. M. 1970. Proliferation activity and synthesis of protein in the cells of fresh-water sponges during development after dissociation. In: W. G. Fry (ed.). The Biology of the Porifera. Academic Press, London. Sym. Zool. Soc. Lond., *25*: 399–413.

Efremova, S., and Efremov, V. 1979. Prolifération cellulaire dans l'embryogenèse de *Baikalospongia bacillifera*. In: C. Lévi and N. Boury-Esnault (eds.). Biologie des Spongiaires. Colloq. Internat. C.N.R.S., Paris, *291*: 59–65.

Egami, N., and Ishii, S. 1956. Differentiation of sex cells in united heterosexual halves of the sponge *Tethya serica*. Ann. Zool., Japan, *29*: 199–201.

Elvin, D. W. 1971. Growth rates of the siliceous spicules of the fresh-water sponge *Ephydatia mulleri* (Lieberkuhn). Trans. Amer. Micros. Soc., *90*: 219–224.

Elvin, D. W. 1972. Effect of germanium upon development of siliceous spicules of some fresh-water sponges. Expt. Cell Res., *72*: 551–553.

Elvin, D. W. 1976. Seasonal growth and reproduction of an intertidal sponge, *Haliclona permolis* (Bowerbank). Biol. Bull., *151*: 108–125.

Elvin, D. W. 1979. The relationship of seasonal changes in the biochemical components to the reproductive behavior of the intertidal sponge, *Haliclona permolis*. Biol. Bull. *156*: 47–61.

Emson, R. H. 1966. The reactions of the sponge *Cliona celata* to applied stimuli. Comp. Biochem. Physiol., *18*: 805–827.

Endo, Y., Watanabe, Y., and Tamura-Hiramoto, S. 1967. Fertilization and development of *Tetilla serica*, a tetraxonian sponge. Jap. J. Exp. Morph., *21*: 40–60.

Evans, C. W. 1977. The ultrastructure of larvae from the marine sponge *Halichondria moorei* Bergquist (Porifera, Demospongiae). Cah. Biol. Mar., *18*: 427–433.

Evans, C. W., and Bergquist, P. R. 1974. Initial cell contact in sponge aggregates. J. Micros., *21*: 185–188.

Evans, C. W., and Bergquist, P. R. 1977. A re-evaluation of the relevance of acid mucopolysaccharides in sponge taxonomy. Cah. Biol. Mar., *18*: 191–199.

Evans, C. W., and Curtis, A. S. G. 1979. Graft rejection in sponges: Its relation to cell aggregation studies. In: C. Lévi and N. Boury-Esnault (eds.). Biologie des Spongiaires. Colloq. Internat. C.N.R.S., Paris, *291*: 211–215.

Evans, C. W., Kerr, J., and Curtis, A. S. G. 1980. Graft rejection and immune memory in marine sponges. In: M. J. Manning (ed.). Phylogeny of Immunological Memory. Elsevier North-Holland Biomed. Press, pp. 27–34.

Evans, R. 1899. The structure and metamorphosis of the larva of *Spongilla lacustris*. Quart. J. Micros. Sci., *43*: 363–477.

Evans, R. 1901. A description of *Ephydatia blembingia*, with an account of the formation and structure of the gemmule. Quart. J. Micros. Sci., *44*: 71–109.

Fauré-Frémiet, E. 1931. Étude histologique de *Ficulina ficus* L. (Demospongia). Arch. Anat. Micros., *27*: 421–448.

Fauré-Frémiet, E. 1932a. Morphogenèse expérimentale (reconstitution) chez *Ficulina ficus* L. Arch. Anat. Micros., *28*: 1–80.

Fauré-Frémiet, E. 1932b. Involution expérimentale et tension de structure dans les cultures de *Ficulina ficus*. Arch. Anat. Micros., *28*: 121–157.

Feige, N. W. 1969. Die feinstruktur der epithelien von *Ephydatia fluviatilis*. Zool. Jb. Anat., *86*: 177–237.

Fell, P. E. 1969. The involvement of nurse cells in oogenesis and embryonic development in the marine sponge, *Haliclona ecbasis*. J. Morph., *127*: 133–150.

Fell, P. E. 1970. The natural history of *Haliclona ecbasis* de Laubenfels, a siliceous sponge of California. Pac. Sci., *24*: 381–386.

Fell, P. E. 1974a. Porifera. In: A. C. Giese and J. S. Pearse (eds). Reproduction of Marine Invertebrates. Academic Press, New York, *I*: 51–132.

Fell, P. E. 1974b. Diapause in the gemmules of the marine sponge, *Haliclona loosanoffi*, with a note on the gemmules of *Haliclona oculata*. Biol. Bull., *147*: 333–351.

Fell, P. E. 1975. Salinity tolerance and desiccation resistance of the gemmules of the brackish-water sponge, *Haliclona loosanoffi*. J. Exp. Zool. *194*: 409–412.

Fell, P. E. 1976a. Analysis of reproduction in sponge populations: An overview with specific information on the reproduction of *Haliclona loosanoffi*. In: F. W. Harrison and R. R. Cowden (eds.). Aspects of Sponge Biology. Academic Press, New York, pp. 51–67.

Fell, P. E. 1976b. The reproduction of *Haliclona loosanoffi* and its apparent relationship to water temperature. Biol. Bull., *150*: 200–210.

Fell, P. E. 1983. Porifera. In: K. G. Adiyodi and R. G. Adiyodi (eds.). Reproductive biology of invertebrates. Vol. I: Oogenesis, oviposition, and oosorption. John Wiley and Sons, Ltd., Chichester, pp. 1–29.

Fell, P. E. *in press*. Porifera. In: K. G. Adyodi and R. G. Adyodi (eds.). Reproductive Biology of Invertebrates, Vol. IV: Fertilization and Larval Development. John Wiley & Sons, Chichester.

Fell, P. E., and Jacob, W. F. 1979. Reproduction and development of *Halichondria* sp. in the mystic estuary, Connecticut. Biol. Bull., *156*: 62–75.

Fell, P. E., and Lewandrowski, K. B. 1981. Population dynamics of the estuarine sponge, *Halichondria* sp., within a New England eelgrass community. J. Exp. Mar. Biol. Ecol., *55*: 49–63.

Fell, P. E., Lewandrowski, K., and Lovice, M. 1979. Postlarval reproduction and reproductive strategy in *Haliclona loosanoffi* and *Halichondria* sp. In: C. Lévi and N. Boury-Esnault (eds.). Biologie des Spongiaires. Colloq. Internat. C.N.R.S., Paris, *291*: 113–119.

Fincher, J. A. 1940. The origin of the germ cells in *Stylotella heliophila* Wilson (Tetraxonida). J. Morph., *67*: 175–192.

Finks, R. M. 1970. The evolution and ecological history of sponges during Palaeozoic Times. In: W. G. Fry (ed.). The Biology of the Porifera. Academic Press, London. Sym. Zool. Soc. Lond., *25*: 3–22.

Fjerdingstad, E. J. 1961. The ultrastructure of choanocyte collars in *Spongilla lacustris* (L.). Zeit. Zellforsch., *53*: 645–657.

Fjerdingstad, E. J. 1970. Ultrastructure of the spicules of *Spongilla lacustris* (L.). In: W. G. Fry (ed.). The Biology of the Porifera. Academic Press, London. Sym. Zool. Soc. Lond., *25*: 125–133.

Florkin, M. 1968. Skeletal structures of Porifera. In: M. Florkin and B. T. Scheer (eds.). Chemical Zoology. Academic Press, New York, *II*: 31–35.

Fox, D. L. 1976. Animal biochromes and structural colors. 2nd ed. Univ. Calif. Press, pp. 1–433.

Francis, J. C., Poirrier, M. A., and LaBiche, R. A. 1982. Effects of calcium and salinity on the growth rate of *Ephydatia fluviatilis* (Porifera: Spongillidae). Hydrobiol., *89*: 225–229.

Frincke, J. M., and Faulkner, D. J. 1982. Antimicrobial metabolites of the sponge *Reniera* sp. J. Amer. Chem. Soc., *104*: 265–269.

Frost, T. M. 1976a. Sponge feeding: A review with a discussion of some continuing research. In: F. W. Harrison and R. R. Cowden (eds.). Aspects of Sponge Biology. Academic Press, New York, pp. 283–298.

Frost, T. M. 1976b. Investigations of the aufwuchs of freshwater sponges. I. A quantitative comparison between the surfaces of *Spongilla lacustris* and three aquatic macrophytes. Hydrobiol., *50*: 145–149.

Frost, T. M. 1978a. The ecology of the freshwater sponge *Spongilla lacustris*. Thesis. Dartmouth College, Hanover, N.H., pp. 1–196.

Frost, T. M. 1978b. In situ measurements of clearance rates for the freshwater sponge *Spongilla lacustris*. Limnol. Oceanogr., *23*: 1034–1039.

Frost, T. M. 1980a. Clearance rate determinations for the freshwater sponge *Spongilla lacustris*. Effect of temperature, particle type and concentration, and sponge size. Arch. Hydrobiol., *90*: 330–356.

Frost, T. M. 1980b. Selection in sponge feeding processes. In: D. C. Smith and Y. Tiffon (eds.). Nutrition in the Lower Metazoa. Pergamon Press, Oxford, pp. 33–44.

Frost, T. M. 1981. Analyses of ingested particles within a fresh-water sponge. Trans. Amer. Micros. Soc., *100*: 271–277.

Frost, T. M., and Williamson, C. E. 1980. In situ determination of the effect of symbiotic algae on the growth of the freshwater sponge *Spongilla lacustris*. Ecology, *61*: 1361–1370.

Fry, W. G. 1971. The biology of larvae of *Ophlitaspongia seriata* from two North Wales populations. In: D. J. Crisp (ed.). Fourth Europ. Mar. Biol. Sym., Cambridge Univ. Press, pp. 155–178.

Fry, W. G., and Fry, P. D. 1979. Aspects of functional anatomy and ecological physiology of *Disyringa* and some other infaunal tetractinomorph sponges. In: C. Lévi and N. Boury-Esnault (eds.). Biologie des Spongiaires. Colloq. Internat. C.N.R.S., Paris, *291*: 335–341.

Fusetani, N., Matsunaga, S., and Konosu, S. 1981. Bioactive marine metabolites—II. Halistanol sulfate, an antimicrobial novel steroid sulfate from the marine sponge *Halichondria* CF *moorei* Bergquist. Tetrahed. Lett., *22*: 1985–1988.

Gaino, E. 1980. Indagine ultrastrutturale sugli ovociti maturi di *Chondrilla nucula* Schmidt (Porifera, Demospongiae). Cah. Biol. Mar., *21*: 11–22.

Gallissian, M-F. 1980. Étude ultrastructurale de la fécondation chez *Grantia compressa*. Internat. J. Invert. Reprod., *2*: 321–329.

Gallissian, M-F. 1981. Étude ultrastructurale de l'ovogenèse chez quelques éponges calcaires (Porifera, Calcarea). Arch. Zool. Exp. Gén., *122*: 329–340.

Gallissian, M-F., and Vacelet, J. 1976. Ultrastructure de quelques stades de l'ovogenèse de spongiaires du genre *Verongia* (Dictyoceratida). Ann. Sci. Natur. Zool., Paris, *18*: 381–404.

Galtsoff, P. S. 1925a. Regeneration after dissociation (an experimental study of sponges). I. Behavior of dissociated cells of *Microciona prolifera* under normal and altered conditions. J. Exp. Zool., *42*: 183–221.

Galtsoff, P. S. 1925b. Regeneration after dissociation (an experimental study on sponges). II. Histogenesis of *Microciona prolifera,* Verr. J. Exp. Zool., *42*: 223–251.

Ganguly, B. 1960. The differentiation capacity of dissociated sponge cells. Wilhelm Roux's Arch. Entwicklungs Mechanik, *152*: 22–34.

Garrone, R. 1969a. Collagène, spongine et squelette mineral chez l'éponge *Haliclona rosea* (O. S.). J. Micros., *8*: 581–598.

Garrone, R. 1969b. Une formation parcristalline d'ARN intranucléaire dans les choanocytes de l'éponge *Haliclona rosea* O. S. (Démosponge, Haploscleride). C.R. Acad. Sci., Paris, *269*: 2219–2221.

Garrone, R. 1971. Fibrogenese du collagène chez l'éponge *Chondrosia reniformis* Nardo (Démosponge Tétractinellide). Ultrastructure et fonction des lophocytes. C.R. Acad. Sci., Paris, Ser. D, *273*: 1832–1835.

Garrone, R. 1974. Ultrastructure d'une "gemmule armée" planctonique d'éponge clionidae. Arch. Anat. Micros. Morph. Exper., *63*: 163–182.

Garrone, R. 1975. Collagen resorption in sponges: Involvement of bacteria and macrophages. In: Peeters Protides of the Biological Fluids. 22nd Colloq., Pergamon Press, Oxford, pp. 59–63.

Garrone, R. 1978. Phylogenesis of Connective Tissue. Morphological Aspects and Biosynthesis of Sponge Intercellular Matrix. S. Karger, pp. 1–250.

Garrone, R., and Pottu, J. 1973. Collagen biosynthesis in sponges: Elaboration of spongin by spongocytes. J. Submicros. Cytol., *5*: 199–218.

Garrone, R., and Pottu-Boumendil, J. 1976. Mouvements cellulaire, biosynthese et structuration du collagène chez les spongiaires. Bull Soc. Zool. France, *101*: 23–29.

Garrone, R., and Rozenfeld, F. 1981. Electron microscope study of cell differentiation and collagen synthesis in hydroxyurea-treated fresh-water sponges. J. Submicros. Cytol., *13*: 127–134.

Garrone, R., Thiney, Y., and Pavans de Ceccatty, M. 1971. Electronmicroscopy of a mucopolysaccharide cell coat in sponges. Experientia, *27*: 1324–1329.

Garrone, R., Vacelet, J., Pavans de Ceccatty, M., Junqua, L., Robert, L., and Huc, A. 1973. Une formation collagène particulière: Les filaments des éponges cornées *Ircinia*. Étude ultrastructurale, physio-chimique et biochimique. J. Micros., *17*: 241–260.

Garrone, R., Huc, A., and Junqua, S. 1975. Fine structure and physiochemical studies on the collagen of the marine sponge *Chondrosia reniformis*. J. Ultrastruc. Res., *52*: 261–275.

Garrone, R., Lethias, C., and Escaig, J. 1980. Freeze fracture study of sponge cell membranes and extracellular matrix. Preliminary results. Biol. Cellulaire, *38*: 71–74.

Garrone, R., Simpson, T. L., and Pottu-Boumendil, J. 1981. Ultrastructure and deposition of silica in sponges. In: T. L. Simpson and B. E. Volcani (eds.). Silicon and Siliceous Structures in Biological Systems. Springer-Verlag, New York, pp. 495–525.

Gasic, G. J., and Galanti, N. L. 1966. Proteins and disulfide groups in the aggregation of dissociated cells of sea sponges. Science (USA), *151*: 203–205.

Gatenby, J. B. 1927. Further notes on the gametogenesis and fertilization of sponges. Quart. J. Micros. Sci., *71*: 173–188.

Gatenby, J. B., Dalton, A. J., and Felix, M. D. 1955. The contractile vacuole of parazoa and protozoa and the Golgi apparatus. Nature (London), *176*: 301–302.

Gilbert, J. J. 1974. Field experiments on sexuality in the freshwater sponge

Spongilla lacustris. Control of oocyte production and the fate of unfertilized oocytes. J. Exp. Zool., *188*: 165–178.

Gilbert, J. J. 1975. Field experiments on gemmulation in the fresh-water sponge *Spongilla lacustris.* Trans. Amer. Micros. Soc., *94*: 347–356.

Gilbert, J. J., and Allen, H. L. 1973a. Studies on the physiology of the green freshwater sponge *Spongilla lacustris:* Primary productivity, organic matter, and chlorophyll content. Verh. Internat. Verein. Limnol., *18*: 1413–1420.

Gilbert, J. J., and Allen, H. L. 1973b. Chlorophyll and primary productivity of some green, freshwater sponges. Int. Rev. Ges. Hydrobiol., *58*: 633–658.

Gilbert, J. J., and Hadzisce, S. 1977. Life cycle of the freshwater sponge *Ochridaspongia rotunda* Arndt. Arch. Hydrobiol., *79*: 285–318.

Gilbert, J. J., and Simpson, T. L. 1976a. Sex reversal in a freshwater sponge. J. Exp. Zool., *195*: 145–151.

Gilbert, J. J., and Simpson, T. L. 1976b. Gemmule polymorphism in the freshwater sponge *Spongilla lacustris.* Arch. Hydrobiol., *78*: 268–277.

Gilbert, J. J., Simpson, T. L., and De Nagy, G. S. 1975. Field experiments on egg production in the fresh-water sponge *Spongilla lacustris.* Hydrobiol., *46*: 17–27.

Gold, R., Phelps, C. F., Khalap, S., and Balding, P. 1974. Observations on *Axinella* sp. hemagglutinin. Ann. N.Y. Acad. Sci., *234*: 122–127.

Goodwin, T. W. 1968. Pigments of Porifera. In: M. Florkin and B. T. Scheer (eds.). Chemical Zoology, Academic Press, New York, *II*: 37–41.

Goreau, T. F., and Hartman, W. D. 1963. Boring sponges as controlling factors in the formation and maintenance of coral reefs. In: Mechanisms of Hard Tissue Destruction. AAAS Publ. No. 75, Washington, D.C., pp. 25–54.

Greenberg, M. J., Reed, C., and Pierce, S. K. 1977. Dissociated cells of *Microciona prolifera* (Porifera) are inhibited from reaggregating by cytochalasins A, B and E. Comp. Biochem. Physiol., *56C*: 95–102.

Gross, J., Sokal, Z., and Rougvie, M. 1956. Structural and chemical studies on the connective tissue of marine sponges. J. Histochem. Cytochem., *4*: 227–246.

Guida, V. G. 1976. Sponge predation in the oyster reef community as demonstrated with *Cliona celata* Grant. J. Exp. Mar. Biol. Ecol., *25*: 109–122.

Gureeva, M. A. 1972. Sorties and oogenesis in the Baikal endemic sponges. Tsitologiya, *14*: 32–45 (in Russian).

Haeckel, E. 1871. Ueber die sexuelle fortpflanzung und das naturliche system der Schwämme. Jena Zer., *6*: 641–651.

Haeckel, E. 1872. Die kalksschwämme. Berlin, *1*: 1–418; *2*: 1–484; *3*: 60 plates.

Hammen, C. S., and Florkin, M. 1968. Chemical composition and intermediary metabolism–Porifera. In: M. Florkin and B. T. Scheer (eds.). Chemical Zoology, Academic Press, New York, *II*: 53–64.

Harrison, F. W. 1972a. The nature and role of the basal pinacoderm of *Corvomeyenia carolinensis* Harrison (Porifera: Spongillidae). Hydrobiol., *39*: 495–508.

Harrison, F. W. 1972b. Phase contrast photomicrography of cellular behavior in spongillid porocytes (Porifera: Spongillidae). Hydrobiol., *40*: 513–717.

Harrison, F. W. 1974a. The localization of nuclease activity in spongillid gemmules by substrate film enzymology. Acta Histochem., *51*: 157–163.

Harrison, F. W. 1974b. Histology and histochemistry of developing outgrowths of *Corvomeyenia carolinensis* Harrison (Porifera: Spongillidae). J. Morph., *144*: 185–194.

Harrison, F. W., and Cowden, R. R. 1975a. Cytochemical observations of gemm-ule development in *Eunapius fragilis* (Leidy): Porifera; Spongillidae. Dif-feren., *4*: 99–109.

Harrison, F. W., and Cowden, R. R. 1975b. Cytochemical observations of larval development in *Eunapius fragilis* (Leidy): Porifera; Spongillidae. J. Morph., *145*: 125–142.

Harrison, F. W., and Cowden, R. R. 1975c. Feulgen microspectrophotometric analysis of deoxyribonucleoprotein organization in larval and adult freshwater sponge nuclei. J. Exp. Zool., *193*: 131–136.

Harrison, F. W., and Cowden, R. R. 1976. Feulgen microspectrophotometric analysis of deoxyribonucleoprotein in sponge nuclei. In: F. W. Harrison and R. R. Cowden (eds.). Aspects of Sponge Biology. Academic Press, New York, pp. 141–152.

Harrison, F. W., and Davis, D. A. 1982. Morphological and cytochemical pat-terns during early stages of reduction body formation in *Spongilla lacustris* (Porifera-Spongillidae). Trans. Amer. Micros. Soc., *101*: 317–324.

Harrison, F. W., Dunkelberger, D., and Watabe, N. 1974. Cytological definition of the poriferan stylocyte: A cell type characterized by an intranuclear crystal. J. Morph., *142*: 265–276.

Harrison, F. W., Dunkelberger, D., and Watabe, N. 1975. Cytological examina-tion of reduction bodies of *Corvomeyenia carolinensis* Harrison (Porifera: Spongillidae). J. Morph., *145*: 483–492.

Harrison, F. W., Simpson, T. L., and Rosenberg, E. 1979. Immunofluorescent localization of cyclic AMP and cyclic GMP during dormancy release and devel-opment from gemmules of *Spongilla lacustris* L. (Porifera: Spongillidae). In: C. Lévi and N. Boury-Esnault (eds.). Biologie des Spongiaires. Colloq. Internat. C.N.R.S., Paris, *291*: 47–51.

Harrison, F. W., Rosenberg, E., Davis, D., and Simpson, T. L. 1981. Correlation of cyclic GMP and cyclic AMP immunofluorescence with cytochemical pat-terns during dormancy release and development from gemmules in *Spongilla lacustris* L. (Porifera: Spongillidae). J. Morph., *67*: 53–63.

Hartman, W. D. 1957. Ecological niche differentiation in the boring sponges (Clionidae). Evol., *11*: 294–297.

Hartman, W. D. 1958a. Natural history of the marine sponges of southern New England. Bull. Peabody Mus. Natur. Hist. (Yale Univ.), *12*: 1–155.

Hartman, W. D. 1958b. A re-examination of Bidder's classification of the Calca-rea. Sys. Zool., *7*: 97–110.

Hartman, W. D. 1969. New genera and species of coralline sponges (Porifera) from Jamaica. Postilla (Yale Univ.), *137*: 1–39.

Hartman, W. D. 1979. A new sclerosponge from the Bahamas and its relationship to mesozoic stromatoporoids. In: C. Lévi and N. Boury-Esnault (eds.). Biolo-gie des Spongiaires. Colloq. Internat. C.N.R.S., Paris, *291*: 467–474.

Hartman, W. D. 1981. Form and distribution of silica in sponges. In: T. L. Simpson and B. E. Volcani (eds.). Silicon and Siliceous Structures in Biological Systems. Springer-Verlag, New York, pp. 453–493.

Hartman, W. D. 1982. Porifera. In: Parker, S. P. (ed.). Synopsis and Classifica-tion of Living Organisms. McGraw–Hill, New York, *1*: 640–666.

Hartman, W. D., and Goreau, T. 1970. Jamaican coralline sponges: Their morphology, ecology and fossil relatives. In: W. G. Fry (ed.). Biology of the Porifera. Academic Press, London. Sym. Zool. Soc. Lond., *25*: 205–243.

Hartman, W. D., and Goreau, T. 1972. *Ceratoporella* (Porifera: Sclerospongiae) and the chaetetid "corals." Conn. Acad. Arts Sci., Trans., *44*: 133–148.

Hartman, W. D., and Goreau, T. 1975. A Pacific tabulate sponge, living representative of a new order of sclerosponges. Postilla (Yale Univ.), *167*: 1–21.

Hartman, W. D., and Reiswig, H. 1973. The individuality of sponges. In: R. S. Boardman, A. H. Cheetham, and W. A. Oliver (eds.). Animal Colonies. Dow. Hutch. Ross, Stroudsburg, pp. 567–584.

Hartman, W. D., Wendt, J. W., and Wiedenmayer, F. 1980. Living and fossil sponges. Comp. Sedimen. Lab., Univ. Miami, Sedimentia, *VIII*: 1–274.

Hatch, W. I. 1980. The implication of carbonic anhydrase in the physiological mechanism of penetration of carbonate substrata by the marine burrowing sponge *Cliona celata* (Demospongiae). Biol. Bull., *159*: 135–147.

Hechtel, G. J. 1965. A systematic study of the Demospongiae of Port Royale, Jamaica. Bull. Peabody Mus. Natur. Hist. (Yale Univ.), *20*: 1–94.

Henkart, P., Humphreys, S., and Humphreys, T. 1973. Characterization of sponge aggregation factor. A unique proteoglycan complex. Biochemistry, *12*: 3045–3050.

Herlant-Meewis, H. 1948a. Contribution a l'étude histologique des spongiaires. Ann. Soc. Roy. Zool. Belg., *79*: 5–36.

Herlant-Meewis, H. 1948b. La gemmulation chez *Suberites domuncula*. Arch. Anat. Micros., *37*: 289–322.

Hildemann, W. H., and Linthicum, D. S. 1981. Transplantation immunity in the Palaun sponge *Xestospongia exigua*. Transplant., *32*: 77–80.

Hildemann, W. H., Johnston, I. S., and Jokiel, P. L. 1979. Immunocompetence in the lowest metazoan phylum: Transplantation immunity in sponges. Science (USA), *204*: 420–422.

Hildemann, W. H., Bigger, C. H., Johnston, I. S., and Jokiel, P. L. 1980. Characteristics of transplantation immunity in the sponge *Callyspongia diffusa*. Transplant., *30*: 362–367.

Höhr, D. 1977. Differenzierungavorgange in der keimenden gemmula von *Ephydatia fluviatilis*. Wilhelm Roux's Arch., *182*: 329–346.

Hoshino, T. 1976. Demosponges from the western coast of KII Peninsula Japan. Zool. Mag., *85*: 248–261.

Hoshino, T. 1977. Demosponges from the KII Channel and environs, western Japan. Proc. Jap. Soc. Syst. Zool., *13*: 5–15.

Huc, A., and De Vos, L. 1972. La nature collagène de la coque des gemmules des eponges d'eau douc. C.R. Acad. Sci., Paris, *275*: 1399–1401.

Humphreys, T. 1963. Chemical dissociation and *in vitro* reconstruction of sponge cell adhesions. I. Isolation and functional demonstration of the components involved. Devel. Biol., *8*: 27–47.

Humphreys, T. 1965. Aggregation of chemically dissociated sponge cells in the absence of protein synthesis. J. Exp. Zool., *160*: 235–240.

Humphreys, T. 1970. Biochemical analysis of sponge cell aggregation. In: W. G. Fry (ed.). The Biology of the Porifera. Academic Press, London, Sym. Zool. Soc. Lond., *25*: 325–334.

Huxley, J. S. 1911. Some phenomena of regeneration in *Sycon;* with a note on the structure of its collar-cells. Phil. Trans. Roy. Soc. Lond., Ser. B, *220*: 165–189.

Huxley, J. S. 1921. Further studies on restitution bodies and free tissue culture in *Sycon*. Quart. J. Micros. Sci., *65*: 293–322.

Hyman, L. H. 1940. The Invertebrates. Vol. 1. McGraw–Hill, New York.

Ijima, I. 1901. Studies on the Hexactinellida. Contribution i. (Euplectellidae). J. Coll. Sci. Imp. Univ. Tokyo, Jap., *15*: 1–299.

Ijima, I. 1903. Studies on the Hexactinellida. Contribution iii. J. Coll. Sci. Imp. Univ. Tokyo, Jap., *18*: 1–124.

Jackson, J. B. C. 1977. Competition on marine hard substrata: The adaptive significance of solitary and colonial strategies. Amer. Natur., *111*: 743–767.

Jackson, J. B. C., and Palumbi, S. R. 1979. Regeneration and partial predation in cryptic coral reef environments: Preliminary experiments on sponges and ectoprocts. In: C. Lévi and N. Boury-Esnault (eds.). Biologie des Spongiaires. Colloq. Internat. C.N.R.S., Paris, *291*: 303–308.

Jaffe, G. 1912. Die entwicklung von *Spongilla lacustris* (L.) und *Ephydatia fluviatilis* L. aus der gemmula. Zool Anz., *39*: 705–719.

Jepps, M. W. 1947. Contribution to the study of the sponges. Proc. Roy. Soc. Lond., Ser. B, *134*: 408–417.

Jeuniaux, C. 1963. Chitine et chitinolyse. 1st ed., Masson, Paris, pp. 1–182.

Jewell, M. E. 1935. An ecological study of the fresh-water sponges of northern Wisconsin. Ecol. Monogr., *5*: 461–504.

John, H. A., Campo, M. S., Mackenzie, A. M., and Kemp, R. B. 1971. Role of different sponge cell types in species specific cell aggregation. Nature New Biol. (London), *230*: 126–128.

Johnson, M. F. 1976. Conspecificity in calcareous sponges: *Clathrina coriacea* (Montagu, 1818) and *Clathrina blanca* (Miklucho-Maclay, 1868). Thesis. Univ. South. Calif., pp. 1–442.

Johnson, M. F. 1978a. A comparative study of the external form and skeleton of the calcareous sponges *Clathrina coriacea* and *Clathrina blanca* from Santa Catalina Island, California. Can. J. Zool., *56*: 1669–1677.

Johnson, M. F. 1978b. Studies on the reproductive cycles of the calcareous sponges *Clathrina coriacea* and *C. blanca*. Mar. Biol., *50*: 73–79.

Johnson, M. F. 1979a. Gametogenesis and embryonic development in the calcareous sponges *Clathrina coriacea* and *C. blanca* from Santa Catalina Island, California. Bull. South. Calif. Acad. Sci., *78*: 183–191.

Johnson, M. F. 1979b. Recruitment growth, mortality and seasonal variations in the calcareous sponges *Clathrina coriacea* (Montagu) and *C. blanca* (M.-M.) from Santa Catalina Island, California. In: C. Lévi and N. Boury-Esnault (eds.). Biologie des Spongiaires. Colloq. Internat. C.N.R.S., Paris, *291*: 325–334.

Johnston, I. S., and Hildemann, W. H. 1982. Cellular organization in the marine demosponge *Callyspongia diffusa*. Mar. Biol., *67*: 1–7.

Johnston, I. S., Jokiel, P. I., Bigger, C. H., and Hildemann, W. H. 1981. Influence of temperature on the kinetics of allograft reactions in a tropical sponge and a reef coral. Biol. Bull., *160*: 280–291.

Jones, W. C. 1954a. The orientation of the optic axis of spicules of *Leucosolenia complicata*. Quart. J. Micros. Sci., *95*: 33–48.

Jones, W. C. 1954b. Spicule formation in *Leucosolenia complicata*. Quart. J. Micros. Sci., *95*: 191–203.

Jones, W. C. 1955a. Crystalline properties of spicules of *Leucosolenia complicata*. Quart. J. Micros. Sci., *96*: 129–149.

Jones, W. C. 1955b. The sheath of spicules of *Leucosolenia complicata*. Quart. J. Micros. Sci., *96*: 411–421.

Jones, W. C. 1956. Colloidal properties of the mesoglea in species of *Leucosolenia*. Quart. J. Micros. Sci., *97*: 269–285.

Jones, W. C. 1957. The contractility and healing behavior of pieces of *Leucosolenia complicata*. Quart. J. Micros. Sci., *98*: 203–217.

Jones, W. C. 1958. The effect of reversing the internal water-current on the spicule orientation in *Leucosolenia variabilis* and *L. complicata*. Quart. J. Micros. Sci., *99*: 263–278.

Jones, W. C. 1959. Spicule growth rates in *Leucosolenia variabilis*. Quart. J. Micros. Sci., *100*: 557–570.

Jones, W. C. 1961a. Properties of the wall of *Leucosolenia variabilis*. II. The choanoderm and the porocyte epithelium. Quart. J. Micros. Sci., *102*: 543–550.

Jones, W. C. 1961b. Properties of the wall of *Leucosolenia variabilis*. I. The skeletal layer. Quart. J. Micros. Sci., *102*: 531–542.

Jones, W. C. 1962. Is there a nervous system in sponges? Biol. Rev., *37*: 1–50.

Jones, W. C. 1964a. Photographic records of living oscular tubes of *Leucosolenia variabilis*. I. The choanoderm boundary, the choanocytes and the pore arrangement. J. Mar. Biol. Assoc. U.K., *44*: 67–85.

Jones, W. C. 1964b. Photographic records of living oscular tubes of *Leucosolenia variabilis*. II. Spicule growth, form and displacement. J. Mar. Biol. Assoc. U.K., *44*: 311–331.

Jones, W. C. 1965. Photographic records of living oscular tubes of *Leucosolenia variabilis*. III. Irregular growth of the oscular tube. J. Mar. Biol. Assoc. U.K., *45*: 1–28.

Jones, W. C. 1966. The structure of the porocytes in the calcareous sponge *Leucosolenia complicata* (Montagu). J. Roy. Micros. Soc., *85*: 53–62.

Jones, W. C. 1967. Sheath and axial filament of calcareous sponge spicules. Nature (London), *214*: 365–368.

Jones, W. C. 1970. The composition, development, form and orientation of calcareous sponge spicules. In: W. G. Fry (ed.). The Biology of the Porifera. Academic Press, London. Sym. Zool. Soc. Lond., *25*: 91–123.

Jones, W. C. 1971. Spicule formation and corrosion in recently metamorphosed *Sycon ciliatum* (O. Fabricius). In: D. J. Crisp (ed.). Fourth Europ. Mar. Biol. Symp., Cambridge Univ. Press, pp. 301–320.

Jones, W. C. 1979a. Spicule growth and production in juvenile *Sycon ciliatum*. In: C. Lévi and N. Boury-Esnault (eds.). Biologie des Spongiaires. Colloq. Internat. C.N.R.S., Paris., *291*: 67–77.

Jones, W. C. 1979b. The microstructure and genesis of sponge biominerals. In: C. Lévi and N. Boury-Esnault (eds.). Biologie des Spongiaires. Colloq. Internat. C.N.R.S., Paris, *291*: 425–447.

Jones, W. C., and James, D. W. F. 1969. An investigation of some calcareous sponge spicules by means of electron probe micro-analyses. Micron, *1*: 34–39.

Jones, W. C., and James, D. W. F. 1972. Examination of the large triacts of the calcareous sponge *Leuconia nivea* Grant by scanning electron microscopy. Micron, *3*: 196–210.

Jones, W. C., and Jenkins, D. A. 1970. Calcareous sponge spicules: A study of magnesium calcites. Calc. Tiss. Res., *4*: 314–329.

Jorgensen, C. B. 1944. On the spicule-formation of *Spongilla lacustris* (L.). 1. The dependence of the spicule-formation on the content of dissolved and solid silicic acid of the milieu. Det. Kgl. Danske. Vidensks. Selsk. Biol. Medd., *19*: 2–45.

Jorgensen, C. B. 1946. On the gemmules of *Spongilla lacustris* auct. together with some remarks on the taxonomy of the species. Vid. Med. Dansk. Nat. Foren., *109*: 69–79.

Jorgensen, C. B. 1947. On the spicule-formation of *Spongilla lacustris* (L.). 2. The rate of growth of the spicules. Det. Kgl. Danske. Vidensks. Selsk. Biol. Medd., *20*: 3–21.

Jorgensen, C. B. 1949. Feeding rates of sponges, lamellibranchs and ascidians. Nature (London), *163*: 912.

Jumblatt, J. E., Schulp, V., and Burger, M. M. 1980. Cell-cell recognition: Specific binding of *Microciona* sponge aggregation factor to homotypic cells and the role of calcium ions. Biochemistry, *19*: 1038–1042.

Junqua, S., and Garrone, R. 1982. Sponge glycoconjugates: Immunological properties and localization by fluorescent antibodies and lectins. J. Histochem. Cytochem., *30*: 445–450.

Junqua, S., Robert, L, Garrone, R., Pavans de Ceccatty, M., and Vacelet, J. 1974. Biochemical and morphological studies on collagens of horny sponges. *Ircinia* filaments compared to spongines. Connect. Tiss. Res., *2*: 193–203.

Junqua, S., Fayolle, J., and Robert, L. 1975a. Structural glycoproteins from sponge intercellular matrix. Comp. Biochem. Physiol., *50B*: 305–309.

Junqua, S., Fayolle, J., and Robert, L. 1975b. Isolation and characterization of structural glycoproteins from sponges. In: Peeters Protides of the Biological Fluids, 22nd Colloq., pp. 337–341.

Junqua, S., Lemonnier, M., Garrone, R., and Robert, L. 1979. Les glycoconjugues de la matrice intercellulaire de *Spongia officinalis*. In: C. Lévi and N. Boury-Esnault (eds.). Biologie des Spongiaires. Colloq. Internat. C.N.R.S., Paris, *291*: 407–411.

Kamatani, A. 1971. Physical and chemical characteristics of biogenous silica. Mar. Biol., *8*: 89–95.

Kanazawa, A., Teshima, S., and Hyodo, S. 1979. Sterols of the sponges (Porifera, Class Demospongiae). Comp. Biochem. Physiol., *62B*: 521–525.

Karrer, P., and Solmssen, U. 1935. Uber das vorkommen von carotenoiden bei einige meerestieren. Helvitica Chim. Acta, *18*: 915–921.

Kartha, S., and Mookerjee, S. 1978a. Cell aggregation and macromolecular synthesis in sponge cells. Indian J. Exp. Biol., *16*: 1123–1125.

Kartha, S., and Mookerjee, S. 1978b. Reaggregation of sponge cells: Specificity and recovery of adhesion. Wilhelm Roux's Arch., *185*: 155–165.

Kartha, S., and Mookerjee, S. 1979. Cell contact in aggregating sponge cells. An ultrastructural study. Mikroskopie (Wien), *35*: 213–220.

Katzman, R. L., Lisowska, E., and Jeanloz, R. W. 1970. Invertebrate connective tissue. Isolation of D-arabinose from sponge acidic polysaccharides. Biochem. J., *119*: 17–19.

Kauffold, P., and Spannhof, L. 1963. Histochemische untersuchungen an den reservestoffen der archaeocyten in gemmulen von *Ephydatia mulleri* Lbk. Naturwiss., *50*: 384–385.

Kennedy, G. Y. 1979. Pigments of marine invertebrates. In: F. S. Russell and M. Younge (eds.). Advances in Marine Biology, Academic Press, New York, *16*: 314–381.

Kennedy, G. Y., and Vevers, H. G. 1954. The occurrence of porphyrins in certain marine invertebrates. J. Mar. Biol. Assoc. U.K., *33*: 663–676.

Kilian, E. F. 1952. Wasserströmmung und nahrungsaufnahme beim süsswasserschämmen *Ephydatia fluviatilis*. Zeit. Vergl. Physiol., *34*: 407–447.

Kilian, E. F. 1954. Die feinstruktur des kragens bei den choanocyten der spongilliden. Ber. Oberhess. Gesellsch. Natur. Heilk. Giessen, N. F. Naturw, Abt., *27*: 85–89.

Kilian, E. F. 1964. Zur bioligie der einheimischen spongilliden ergebnisse und probleme. Zool. Beitrage, *10*: 85–159.

Kilian, E. F., and Wintermann-Kilian, G. 1979. Mouvement cellulaire et contraction chez *Spongilla lacustris* et *Ephydatia fluviatilis*. In: C. Lévi and N. Boury-Esnault (eds.). Biologie des Spongiaires. Colloq. Internat. C.N.R.S., Paris, *291*: 137–143.

Korotkova, G. P. 1963. On the types of restoration processes in sponges. Acta Biol. Acad. Sci. Hung., *13*: 389–406.

Korotkova, G. P. 1970. Regeneration and somatic embryogenesis in sponges. In: W. G. Fry (ed.). The Biology of the Porifera. Academic Press, London. Sym. Zool. Soc. Lond., *25*: 423–436.

Korotkova, G. P., and Aisenstadt, T. B. 1976. A study of the oogenesis of the marine sponge *Halisarca dujardini*. I. The origin of the oogonia and early stages of oocyte development. Tsitologiya, *18*: 549–555 (in Russian).

Korotkova, G. P., and Apalkova, L. V. 1975. Oogenesis of the Barentz Sea sponge *Halisarca dujardini* Johnston. In: Comparative and Experimental Morphology of the Sea Organisms. Kolske Filial Acad. Sci., U.S.S.R., pp. 9–26 (in Russian).

Korotkova, G. P., and Tonkin, B. P. 1968. Stimulation of the process of somatic embryogenesis in some porifera and coelenterata. Acta Biol. Acad. Sci. Hung., *19*: 465–474.

Kuhns, W. J., Weinbaum, G., Turner, R., and Burger, M. M. 1973. Aggregation factors of marine sponges. In: J. Lobue (ed.). Humoral Control of Growth and Differentiation. Academic Press, New York, *II*: 59–79.

Kuhns, W. J., Weinbaum, G., Turner, R., and Burger, M. M. 1974. Sponge aggregation: A model for studies on cell-cell interactions. Ann. N.Y. Acad. Sci., *234*: 58–74.

Kuhns, W. J., Bramson, S., Simpson, T. L., Burkart, W., Jumblatt, J., and Burger, M. M. 1980. Fluorescent antibody localization of *Microciona prolifera* aggregation factor and its baseplate component. Europ. J. Cell Biol., *23*: 73–79.

Langenbruch, P-F. 1981. Zur entstehung der gemmulae bei *Ephydatia fluviatilis* L. (Porifera). Zoomorph., *97*: 263–284.

Langenbruch, P-F. 1982. Die enstehung der gemmula-schalen bei *Spongilla fragilis* Leidy (Porifera). Zoomorph., *99*: 221–234.

Langenbruch, P-F. 1983. Body structure of marine sponges. 1. Arrangement of the flagellated chambers in the canal system of *Reniera* sp. Mar. Biol., *75*: 319–325.

Laseter, J. L., and Poirrier, M. A. 1970. Free fatty acids in the protective coats of *Spongilla wagneri* gemmules. Lipids, *5*: 722–724.

Lawn, I. D. 1982. Porifera. In: G. A. B. Shelton (ed.). Electrical Conduction and Behavior in "Simple" Invertebrates. Clarendon Press, Oxford, pp. 49–72.

Lawn, I. D., Mackie, G. O., and Silver, G. 1981. Conduction system in a sponge. Science (USA), *211*: 1169–1171.

Lederer, E. 1938. Recherches sur les caroténoids des invertébrés. Bull Soc. Chimie Biol., *20*: 567–610.

Ledger, P. 1974. Types of collagen fibers in the calcareous sponge *Sycon* and *Leucandra*. Tiss. Cell, *6*: 385–389.

Ledger, P. 1975. Septate junctions in the calcareous sponge *Sycon ciliatum*. Tiss. Cell, *7*: 13–18.

Ledger, P. W. 1976. Aspects of the secretion and structure of calcareous sponge spicules. Thesis. Univ. College N. Wales, pp. 1–125.

Ledger, P., and Jones, W. C. 1977. Spicule formation in the calcareous sponge *Sycon ciliatum*. Cell Tiss. Res., *181*: 553–567.

Leith, A. G., and Steinberg, M. S. 1972. Sponge cell adhesion: Velocity sedimentation separation and aggregative specificity of discrete cell types. Biol. Bull., *143*: 468.

Lemche, H., and Tendal, O. S. 1977. An interpretation of the sex cells and the early development in sponges, with a note on the terms acrocoel and spongocoel. Zeit. Zool. Syst. Evol-forsch., *15*: 241–252.

Lentz, T. L. 1966. Histochemical localization of neurohumors in a sponge. J. Exp. Zool., *162*: 171–180.

Lethias, C., Garrone, R., and Mazzorana, M. 1983. Fine structure of sponge cell membranes: Comparative study with freeze-fracture and conventional thin section methods. Tiss. Cell, *15*: 523–535.

Leveaux, M. 1939. La formation des gemmules chez les spongillidae. Ann. Soc. Roy. Zool. Belg., *70*: 53–96.

Leveaux, M. 1941. Contribution à l'étude histologique de l'ovogénèse et de la spermatogénèse des spongillidae. Ann. Soc. Roy. Zool. Belg., *72*: 251–269.

Leveaux, M. 1942. Contribution à l'étude histologique de l'ovogénèse et de la spermatogénèse des spongillidae. Ann. Soc. Roy. Zool. Belg., *73*: 33–50.

Lévi, C. 1956. Étude des *Halisarca* de Roscoff. Embryologie et systematique des demosponges. Arch. Zool. Exp. Gén., *93*: 1–181.

Lévi, C. 1957. Ontogeny and systematics in sponges. Sys. Zool., *6*: 174–183.

Lévi, C. 1960. Reconstitution de l'éponge *Ophlitaspongia seriata* (Grant) à partir de suspensions cellulaires. Cah. Biol. Mar., *1*: 353–358.

Lévi, C. 1963a. Gastrulation and larval phylogeny in sponges. In: E. C. Dougherty (ed.). The Lower Metazoa. Comparative Biology and Phylogeny. Univ. Calif. Press, Berkeley, pp. 375–382.

Lévi, C. 1963b. Scleroblastes et spiculogenèse chez une éponge siliceuse. C.R. Acad. Sci., Paris, *256*: 497–498.

Lévi, C. 1964. Ultrastructure de la larva parenchymella de démosponge. I. *Mycale contarenii* (Martens). Cah. Biol. Mar., *5*: 97–104.

Lévi, C. 1965. La microscopie electronique et l'étude des éponges. Atti Sem. Stud. Biol., Bari, *II*: 109–121.

Lévi, C. 1966. Le glycogene chez les spongiaires. C.R. Soc. Biol., *160*: 651–652.

Lévi, C. 1967. Les fibre segmentée intracellulaires d'*Haliclona elegans* Bow. (Démosponge Haploscléride). Arch. Zool. Exp. Gén., *108*: 611–616.

Lévi, C. 1970. Les cellules des éponges. In: W. G. Fry (ed.). The Biology of the Porifera. Academic Press, London. Sym. Zool. Soc. Lond., *25*: 353–364.

Lévi, C. 1973. Systématique de la class des Démospongiaria (Démosponges). In: P-P. Grassé (ed.). Traité de Zoologie, Vol. III, Fasc. 1. Mason et Cie, Paris, pp. 577–631.

Lévi, C., and Lévi, P. 1976. Embryogenèse de *Chondrosia reniformis* (Nardo), démosponge ovipare, et transmission des bactéries symbiotiques. Ann. Sci. Nat. Zool., *18*: 367–380.

Lévi, C., and Porte, A. 1962. Étude au microscope électronique de l'éponge *Oscarella lobularis* Schmidt et de sa larvae amphiblastula. Cah. Biol. Mar., *3*: 307–315.

Lewandrowski, K. B., and Fell, P. E. 1981. Sequential reproduction by different types of specimens of the estuarine sponge, *Halichondria* sp., with an emphasis on reproduction of postlarval specimens. Internat. J. Invert. Reprod., *3*: 227–236.

Liaci, L. 1962. Natura e localizzazione di un pigmento fluorescente in *Aaptos aaptos* O. S. (Demospongiae). Boll. Zool., *29*: 425–431.

Liaci, L. 1963a. Ricerche morfologiche e citochemiche sui tesocite di *Aaptos aaptos* O. S. (Demospongiae). Atti Soc. Pelorit. Sci. Fisc. Matem. Natur., *9*: 189–197.

Liaci, L. 1963b. Osservazioni sulle porfirne e sui lipocromi presenti in alcune demospongie marine. Boll. Zool., *30*: 33–43.

Liaci, L. 1963c. Natura dei pigmenti e clorazioni di alcune demospongie marine. Ann Pont. Inst. Sci. Lett. Santa Chiara, Napoli, *13*: 1–8.

Liaci, L. 1964a. Pigmenti e steroli negli invertebrati marini. Arch. Zool. Ital., *49*: 281–300.

Liaci, L. 1964b. I pigmenti di alcune demospongiae marine in rapporto alle associazioni con alghe unicellulari. Boll. Zool., *33*: 367–378.

Liaci, L. 1964c. Differenze nellia pigmentazione di une forme di *Tethya aurantium* (Pallas) Gray (Porifera). Atti Soc. Pelorit. Sci. Fisic. Matem. Natur., *10*: 569–572.

Liaci, L., and Sciscioli, M. 1967. Osservazioni sulla maturazione sessuale di un tetractinellide: *Stelleta grubii* O. S. (Porifera). Arch. Zool. Ital., *52*: 169–176.

Liaci, L., and Sciscioli, M. 1969. La riproduzione sessuale di alcuni tetractinellidi (Porifera). Boll. Zool., *36*: 61–70.

Liaci, L., and Sciscioli, M. 1970. Il ciclo sessuale di *Erylus discophorus* (Schmidt) (Porifera Tetractinellida). Riv. Biol., *63*: 255–263.

Liaci, L. Scalera-, and Sciscioli, M. 1975a. Sexual cycles of some marine Porifera. Pubbl. Staz. Zool. Napoli, *39* (Suppl.): 307–316.

Liaci, L., and Sciscioli, M. 1975b. Modalita di riproduzione sessuale di alcune poecilosclerina (Porifera). Atti Soc. Pelorit. Sci. Fisic. Matem. Natur., *21*: 109–114.

Liaci, L. Scalera-, and Sciscioli, M. 1979. La riproduzione sessuale in *Suberites carnosus* (Johnson) (Porifera). In: C. Lévi and N. Boury-Esnault (eds.). Biologie des Spongiaires. Colloq. Internat. C.N.R.S., Paris, *291*: 87–94.

Liaci, L. Scalera-, Sciscioli, M., and Matarrese, A. 1971a. La riproduzione sessuale di alcuni tetractinomorpha (Porifera). Atti Soc. Pelorit. Sci. Fisic. Matem. Natur., *17*: 235–245.

Liaci, L. Scalera-, Sciscioli, M., Matarrese, A., and Giove, C. 1971b. Osservazioni sui cicli sessuali di alcune keratosa (Porifera) e loro interesse megli studi filogenetici. Atti. Soc. Pelorit. Sci. Fisic. Matem. Natur., *17*: 33–52.

Liaci, L. Scalera-, Sciscioli, M., Papa, O., and Lepore, E. 1971c. Raffronto tra i cicli sessuali di *Tethya aurantium* (Pallas) Gray e *Tethya citrina* Sara, Melone (Porifera, Hadromerina). Atti Soc. Pelorit. Sci. Fisic. Matem. Natur., *17*: 287–298.

Liaci, L. Scalera-, Sciscioli, M., and Matarrese, A. 1973. Raffronto tra il comportamento sessuale di alcune ceractinomorpha. Riv. Biol., *66*: 135–153.

Liaci, L. Scalera-, Sciscioli, M., and Piscetelli, G. 1976. La riproduzione sessuale di *Tetilla* sp. (Tetractinellida-Porifera). Riv. Biol., *69*: 331–337.

Litchfield, C., and Liaaen-Jansen, S. 1980. Carotenoids of the marine sponge *Microciona prolifera*. Comp. Biochem. Physiol., *66B*: 359–365.

Lufty, R. G. 1956. XI. On the relation between dictyosome and contractile vacuoles in sponges. Trans. Roy. Micros. Soc., *76*: 141–145.

Lufty, R. G. 1957a. On the placental membrane of calcareous sponges. La Cellule, *58*: 239–246.

Lufty, R. G. 1957b. On the origin of the so-called mesoblast cells in the amphiblastula larva of calcareous sponge. La Cellule, *58*: 231–236.

Lufty, R. G. 1960. Histochemical studies on glycogen in the cells of the fresh water sponge. La Cellule, *61*: 145–149.

Maas, O. 1906. Über die einwirkung karbonatfreier und kalkfreier salzlösungen auf erwachsene kalkschwämme und auf entwicklungsstadien derselben. Arch. Entwicklungsmech. Organ., *22*: 581–599.

Maas, O. 1910. Ueber involutionserscheinungen bei schwämmen und ihre bedeutung für die affassung des spongienkörpers. Festschr. H. Hertwig, *3*: 93–130.

Mackie, G. O. 1979. Is there a conduction system in sponges? In: C. Lévi and N. Boury-Esnault (eds.). Biologie des Spongiaires. Colloq. Internat. C.N.R.S., Paris, *291*: 145–151.

Mackie, G. O., and Singula, C. L. 1983. Studies on hexactinellid sponges. I. Histology of *Rhabdocalyptus dawsoni* (Lambe, 1873). Phil. Trans. Roy. Soc. (Lond.), *301*: 365–400.

Mackie, G. O., Lawn, I. D., and Pavans de Ceccatty, M. 1983. Studies on hexactinellid sponges. II. Excitability, conduction and coordination of responses in *Rhabdocalyptus dawsoni* (Lambe, 1873). Phil. Trans. Roy. Soc. (Lond.), *301*: 401–418.

MacLennan, A. P. 1969. An immunochemical study of the surfaces of sponge cells. J. Exp. Zool., *172*: 253–266.

MacLennan, A. P. 1970. Polysaccharides from sponges and their possible significance in cellular aggregation. In: W. G. Fry (ed.). The Biology of the Porifera. Academic Press, London. Sym. Zool. Soc. Lond., *25*: 299–324.

MacLennan, A. P. 1974. The chemical basis of taxon-specific cellular reaggregation and "self"–"not self" recognition in sponges. Arch. Biol. (Brux.), *85*: 53–90.

MacLennan, A. P., and Dodd, R. Y. 1967. Promiting activity of extracelluar materials on sponge cell reaggregation. J. Embryol. Exp. Morph., *18*: 473–480.

MacMunn, C. A. 1890. Contributions to animal chromatology. Quart. J. Micros. Soc., *30*: 51–96.

Madri, P. P., Claus, G., Kunen, S. M., and Moss, E. E. 1967. Preliminary studies on the *Escherichia coli* uptake of the redbeard sponge (*Microciona prolifera* Verrill). Life Sci., *6*: 889–894.

Margoliash, E., Schenck, J. R., Hargie, M. P., Burokas, S., Richter, W. R., Barlow, G. H., and Moscona, A. A. 1965. Characterization of specific cell aggregating materials from sponge cells. Biochem. Biophys. Res. Comm., *20*: 383–388.

Marks, M. H., Bear, R. S., and Blake, C. H. 1949. X-ray diffraction evidence of collagen type protein fibers in the Echinodermata, Coelenterata, and Porifera. J. Exp. Zool., *111*: 55–78.

Masterman, A. T. 1894. On the nutritive and excretory processes in Porifera. Ann. Mag. Natur. Hist., *13*: 48–49; 485–496.

Mawet, A., and Rasmont, R. 1971. L'éjection de spicules par des éponges au cours de leur morphogenèse. Arch. Biol., *82*: 543–565.

Mazzorana, M. 1982. Contribution à l'étude de la biosynthèse du collagène chez l'éponge d'eau douce *Ephydatia mulleri* Lieb. Thèse. Université Claude Bernard (No. d'ordre: 1215), 74 pp.

McClay, D. R. 1971. An autoradiographic analysis of the species specificity during sponge cell reaggregation. Biol. Bull., *141*: 119–130.

McClay, D. R. 1974. Cell aggregation: Properties of cell surface factors from five species of sponge. J. Exp. Zool., *188*: 89–102.

McIntyre, D. E., Faulkner, D. J., Engen, D. V., and Clardy, J. 1979. Renierone, an antimicrobial metabolite from a marine sponge. Tetrahed. Lett., No. *43*: 4163–4166.

McNair, G. T. 1923. Motor reactions of the fresh-water sponge *Ephydatia fluviatilis*. Biol. Bull., *44*: 153–166.

Meewis, H. 1936. Contribution à l'étude histologique des éponges d'eau douce. *Spongilla lacustris, Ephydatia fluviatilis*. Mém. Mus. Roy. Hist. Natur. Belg., *3*: 519–537.

Meewis, H. 1938. Contribution à l'embryogenèse des myxospongidae: *Halisarca (Oscarella) lobularis,* Schmidt. Arch. Biol., *50*: 1–66.

Meewis, H. 1939a. Étude comparative des larves d'eponges siliceuses. Assoc. Franc. Adv. Sci., Liege, Compte Rendu, pp. 659–669.

Meewis, H. 1939b. Contribution a l'étude de l'embryogenèse des Chalinidae: *Haliclona limbata* (Mont.). Ann Soc. Roy. Zool. Belg., *70*: 201–243.

Meewis, H. 1941. Contribution à l'étude de l'embryogenèse des éponge siliceuse. Ann. Soc. Roy. Zool. Belg., *72*: 126–149.

Mergner, H. 1970. Ergebnisse der entwicklingsphysiologie bei spongilliden. In: W. G. Fry (ed.). The Biology of the Porifera. Academic Press, London. Sym. Zool. Soc. Lond., *25*: 365–397.

Metschnikoff, E. 1879. Spongiologische studien. Zeit. Wissench. Zool., *32*: 349–387.

Minale, L. 1978. Terpenoids from marine sponges. In: P. J. Scheuer (ed.). Marine Natural Products. Academic Press, New York, *I*: 231–240.

Minchin, E. A. 1900. In: E. Ray Lankester (ed.). The Porifera and Coelenterata. A Treatise on Zoology, Part II. Adam and Charles Black, London, pp. 1–178.

Minchin, E. A. 1909. Sponge spicules. A summary of present knowledge. Ergeb. Fortsch. Zool., *2*: 171–274.

Moore, H. F. 1910a. The commercial sponges and the sponge fisheries. Bull. U.S. Bur. Fish., *28* (1908, Pt. I): 399–511.

Moore, H. F. 1910b. A practical method of sponge culture. Bull U.S. Bur. Fish., *28* (1908, Pt. I): 545–585.

Mori, K. 1976. A new recent sclerosponge from Ngargol Palau Islands and its fossil relatives. Tohoku. Univ. Sci. Rep. (Geol.), *46*: 1–9.

Mori, K. 1977. A calcitic sclerosponge from the Ishigake-shima coast, Ryukyu Island, Japan. Tohoku. Univ. Sci. Rep. (Geol.), *47*: 1–5.

Moscona, A. A. 1963. Studies on cell aggregation: Demonstration of materials with selective cell-binding activity. Proc. Nat. Acad. Sci. (USA), *49*: 742–747.

Moscona, A. A. 1968. Cell aggregation: Properties of specific cell-ligands and their role in the formation of multicellular systems. Devel. Biol., *18*: 250–277.

Mukai, H. 1980. Notes on the freshwater sponges of Tatara-numa (Gunma-ken, central Japan), with review of literature on some developmental aspects of gemmules. Sci. Rep. Fac. Educ., Gunma Univ., *29*: 35–71.

Müller, K. 1911a. Reductionserscheinumgen bei süsswasserschwämmen. Arch. Entwicklungs-mechanik, *32*: 557–607.

Müller, K. 1911b. Das regenerationsvermogen des süsswasserschämmen. Untersuchungen uber die bei ihnen vorkommende regeneration nach dissociation und reunition. Arch. Entswickslungs-mechanik, *32*: 397–446.

Müller, K. 1914. Gemmula-studien und allgemein-biologische untersuchungen an *Ficulina ficus* Linne. Wiss. Meeresuntersuch., Kiel, *16*: 287–313.

Müller, W. E. G. 1982. Cell membranes in sponges. In: G. H. Bourne and J. F. Danielli (eds.). International Review of Cytology, Academic Press, New York, *77*: 129–181.

Müller, W. E. G., and Zahn, R. K. 1973. Purification and characterization of a species-specific aggregation factor in sponges. Exp. Cell Res., *80*: 95–104.

Müller, W. E. G., Müller, I., and Zahn, R. K. 1976. Species-specific aggregation factor in sponges. V. Influence on programmed synthesis. Biochim. Biophys. Acta, *418*: 217–225.

Müller, W. E. G., Müller, I., Pondejak, V., Kurelec, B., and Zahn, R. K. 1978a. Species-specific aggregation factor in sponges. Isolation, purification and characterization of the aggregation factor from *Suberites domuncula*. Differen., *10*: 45–53.

Müller, W. E. G., Zahn, R. K., Kurelec, B., and Müller, I. 1978b. Species specific aggregation factor in sponges. Transfer of a species specific aggregation receptor from *Suberites domuncula* to cells of *Geodia cydonium*. Differen., *10*: 55–60.

Müller, W. E. G., Zahn, R. K., Arendes, J., Kurelec, B., Steffen, R., and Müller, I. 1979. Aggregation of sponge cells. XX. Self-aggregation of the circular proteid particle. Biochim. Biophys. Acta, *551*: 363–367.

Müller, W. E. G., Zahn, R. K., Kurelec, B., Müller, I., Vaith, P., and Uhlenbruck, G. 1980. Aggregation of sponge cells: 22. Species-specific reactivity of a lectin from the sponge *Geodia cydonium*. Int. J. Biol. Macromol., *2*: 297–301.

Müller, W. E. G., Zahn, R. K., Kurelec, B., Lucu, C., Müller, I., and Uhlenbruck, G. 1981. Lectin, a possible basis for symbiosis between bacteria and sponges. J. Bact., *145*: 548–558.

Muscatine, L., Karakashian, S. J., and Karakashian, M. W. 1967. Soluble extracellular products of algae symbiotic with a ciliate, a sponge and a mutant Hydra. Comp. Biochem. Physiol., *20*: 1–12.

Nassonow, N. 1883. Zur biologie und anatomie der *Clione*. Zeit. Wissensch. Zool., *39*: 295–308.

Nassonov, N. 1924. Sur l'eponge perforante *Clione stationis* Nason. et le procede du creusement des galleries dans les valves des huitre. C.R. Acad. Sci., USSR, Ser. A: 113–115.

Neumann, A. C. 1966. Observations on coastal erosion in Bermuda and measurements of the boring rate of the sponge, *Cliona lampa*. Limnol. Oceanogr., *11*: 92–108.

Okada, Y. 1928. On the development of a hexactinellid sponge, *Farrea sollasii*. J. Fac. Sci. Tokyo Univ., Sect. 4, Zool., *2*: 1–27.

Okukado, N. 1975. The structure of tedanin, a new carotenoid of *Tedania digitata* (O. Schmidt). Bull. Chem. Soc. Jap., *48*: 1061–1062.

Ostrom, K. M., and Simpson, T. L. 1978. Calcium and the release from dormancy of freshwater sponge gemmules. Devel. Biol., *64*: 332–338.

Ostrom, K. M., and Simpson, T. L. 1979. A recent study of calcium and other divalent cations in the release from dormancy of freshwater sponge gemmules. In: C. Lévi and N. Boury-Esnault (eds.). Biologie des Spongiaires. Colloq. Internat. C.N.R.S., Paris, *291*: 39–46.

Pang, R. K. 1973. The systematics of some Jamaican excavating sponges (Porifera). Postilla (Yale Univ.), No. *161*: 1–75.

Paris, J. 1961. Contribution a la biologie des éponges siliceuses *Tethya lyncurium* Lmck. et *Suberites domuncula* O.: Histologie des greffes et sérologie. Vie Milieu, *11* (Suppl.): 1–74.

Parker, G. H. 1910. The reactions of sponges, with a consideration of the origin of the nervous system. J. Exp. Zool., *8*: 765–805.

Parker, G. H. 1914. On the strength and the volume of the water currents produced by sponges. J. Exp. Zool., *16*: 443–446.

Pavans de Ceccatty, M. 1955. Le système nerveux des éponges calcaires et siliceuses. Thèse, Univ. Paris. Mason Cie, Paris, pp. 203–288.

Pavans de Ceccatty, M. 1957. La nature secretoire des lophocytes de l'éponge siliceuse *Chondrosia reniformis* Nardo. C.R. Herbd. Seanc. Acad. Sci., Paris *244*: 2103–2105.

Pavans de Ceccatty, M. 1958. La melanisation chez quelques éponges calcaires et siliceuses: Ses rapports avec le systéme reticulo-histocytaire. Arch. Zool. Exp. Gén., *96*: 1–51.

Pavans de Ceccatty, M. 1959. Les structures cellulaires de type nerveux chez *Hippospongia communis* Lmk. Ann Sci. Natur. Zool., 12th Ser., *1*: 105–112.

Pavan de Ceccatty, M. 1960. Les structures cellulaires de type nerveux et de type musculaire de l'éponge siliceuse *Tethya lyncurium* Lmk. C.R. Acad. Sci., Paris, *251*: 1818–1819.

Pavans de Ceccatty, M. 1966. Ultrastructures et rapports des cellules mesenchymateuses de type nerveux de l'éponge *Tethya lyncurium* Lmk. Ann. Sci. Natur. Zool. Biol. Anim., *8*: 577–614.

Pavans de Ceccatty, M. 1969. Les systemes activités motrices, spontanées et provoquées, des éponges. C.R. Acad. Sci., Paris, *269*: 596–599.

Pavans de Ceccatty, M. 1971. Effects of drugs and ions on a primitive system of spontaneous contractions in a sponge (*Euspongia officinalis*). Experientia, *27*: 57–59.

Pavans de Ceccatty, M. 1973. Les activites cellulaires de type fibroblastique chez les invertebres; dans differenciation des cellules eucaryotes en culture. Colloq. INSERM, *19*: 147–152.

Pavans de Ceccatty, M. 1974a. Coordination in sponges. The foundations of integration. Amer. Zool., *14*: 895–903.

Pavans de Ceccatty, M. 1974b. The origin of the integrative systems: Change in view derived from research on coelenterates and sponges. Perspect. Biol. Med., *17*: 379–390.

Pavans de Ceccatty, M. 1979. Cell correlations and integration. In: C. Lévi and N. Boury-Esnault (eds.). Biologie des Spongiaires. Colloq. Internat. C.N.R.S., Paris, *291*: 123–135.

Pavans de Ceccatty, M. 1981. Demonstration of actin filaments in sponge cells. Cell Biol. Internat. Repts., *5*: 945–952.

Pavans de Ceccatty, M. 1982. In vitro aggregation of syncytia and cells of a hexactinellid sponge. Develop. Comp. Immunol., *6*: 15–22.

Pavans de Ceccatty, M., and Garrone, R. 1971. Fibrogenèse du collagène chez l'éponge *Chondrosia reniformis* Nardo (Demosponge Tetractinellide). Origine et évolution des lophocytes. C.R. Acad. Sci., Paris, *273*: 1957–1959.

Pavans de Ceccatty, M., and Mackie, G. O. 1982. Génèse et évolution des interconnexions syncytiales et cellulaires chez une éponge hexactinellide en cours de réaggrégation après dissociation *in vitro*. C.R. Acad. Sci., Paris, *294*: 939–944.

Pavans de Ceccatty, M., and Thiney, Y. 1963. Microscopie électronique de la fibrogenèse cellulaire du collagène chez l'éponge *Tethya lyncurium* (Lmk.). C.R. Hebd. Séanc. Acad. Sci., Paris, *256*: 5406–5408.

Pavans de Ceccatty, M., and Thiney, Y. 1964. Essai d'interprétation de la fibrogenèse cellulaire du collagène chez l'éponge *Tethya lyncurium* Lmck. Vie Milieu (Suppl.), *17*: 129–145.

Pavans de Ceccatty, M., Cargouil, M., and Coraboeuf, E. 1960. Les réactions motrice de l'éponge *Tethya lyncurium* (Lmk.) à quelques stimulations experimentales. Vie Milieu, *11*: 594–600.

Pavans de Ceccatty, M., Thiney, Y., and Garrone, R. 1970. Les bases ultrastructurales des communications intercellulaires dans les oscules des quelques eponges. In: W. G. Fry (ed.). The Biology of the Porifera. Academic Press, London. Sym. Zool. Soc. Lond., *25*: 449–466.

Pé, J. 1973. Étude quantitative de la régulation du squelette chez une éponge d'eau douce. Arch. Biol. (Brux.), *84*: 147–173.

Peetermans-Pé, J., De Vos, L., and Rasmont, R. 1975. Reproduction asexuee de l'éponge siliceuse *Ephydatia fluviatilis* L. dans un milieu fortement apauv rien silice. Vie Milieu, *25*: 187–196.

Penney, J. T. 1933. Reduction and regeneration in fresh water sponges (*Spongilla discoides*). J. Exp. Zool., *65*: 475–496.

Penney, J. T., and Racek, A. A. 1968. Comprehensive revision of a worldwide collection of freshwater sponges (Porifera: Spongillidae). U.S. Nat. Mus. Bull., *272*: 1–184.

Piez, K. A., and Gross, J. 1959. The amino acid composition and morphology of some invertebrate and vertebrate collagen. Biochim. Biophys. Acta, *34*: 24–39.

Poirrier, M. A. 1969. Louisiana fresh-water sponges: ecology, taxonomy, and distribution. Thesis, Univ. Microfilms, No. 70-9083, pp. 1–173.

Poirrier, M. 1976. A taxonomic study of the *Spongilla alba, S. cenota, S. wagneri,* species group (Porifera: Spongillidae) with ecological observations of *S. alba.* In: F. W. Harrison and R. R. Cowden (eds.). Aspects of Sponge Biology. Academic Press, New York, pp. 203–213.

Pomponi, S. A. 1974. A cytological study of the Haliclonidae and the Callyspongiida (Porifera, Demospongiae Haplosclerida). Thesis. Univ. Miami, pp. 1–90.

Pomponi, S. A. 1976. An ultrastructural study of boring sponge cells and excavated substrata. Proc. Wkshop. Zool. Appl. SEM, IIT Res. Inst. Scann. Elect. Micros., Pt. *VIII*: 569–575.

Pomponi, S. A. 1977. Etching cells of boring sponges: An ultrastructural analysis. Proc. Third Internat. Coral Reef Sym., Univ. Miami, pp. 485–490.

Pomponi, S. A. 1979a. Ultrastructure of cells associated with excavation of calcium carbonate substrates by boring sponges. J. Mar. Biol. Assoc. U.K., *59*: 777–784.

Pomponi, S. A. 1979b. Ultrastructure and cytochemistry of the etching area of boring sponges. In: C. Lévi and N. Boury-Esnault (eds.). Biologie des Spongiaires. Colloq. Internat. C.N.R.S., Paris, *291*: 317–323.

Pomponi, S. A. 1979c. Cytochemical studies of acid phosphatase in etching cells of boring sponges. J. Mar. Biol. Assoc. U.K., *59*: 785–789.

Pomponi, S. A. 1980. Cytological mechanisms of calcium carbonate excavation by boring sponges, Internat. Rev. Cytol., *65*: 301–319.

Pottu-Boumendil, J. 1975. Ultrastructure, cytochemie, et comportements morphogénétiques des cellules de l'éponge *Ephydatia mulleri* (Lieb.). Thèse. Univ. Claude Bernard, pp. 1–101.

Pottu-Boumendil, J., and Pavans de Ceccatty, M. 1976. Mouvements cellulaires et morphogenèse de l'éponge *Ephydatia mulleri* Lieb. Bull. Soc. Zool. France, *101*: 31–38.

Pouliquen, L. 1972. Les spongiaires des grottes sous marine de la région de Marseille. Tethys, *3*: 717–758.

Pouliquen, L., and Vacelet, J. 1970. Nouvelles observations sur des éponges pharetronides, Minchinellidae de Mediterranée. Tethys, *2*: 437–442.

Pourbaix, N. 1933. Mecanisme de la nutrition chez les Spongillidae. Ann. Soc. Roy. Zool. Belg., *64*: 11–20.

Pourbaix, N. 1934. Étude histochimique des substances de reserve au cours de la reproduction asexuee. Ann. Soc. Roy. Zool. Belg., *65*: 41–58.

Pourbaix, N. 1935. Formation histochiminique des gemmules d'éponges. Ann. Soc. Roy. Zool. Belg., *66*: 33–37.

Prell, H. 1915. Sur kenntnis der gemmulae bei marinen schwämmen. Zool. Anz., *46*: 97–116.

Prenant, M. A. 1925. Les porocytes de *Clathrina.* Trav. Stat. Zool. Wimereux, *9*: 198–204.

Prosser, C. L. 1967. Ionic analyses and effects of ions on contractions of sponge tissue. Zeit. vergleich. Physiol., *54*: 109–120.

Prosser, C. L., Nagai, T., and Nystrom, R. A. 1962. Oscular contractions in sponges. Comp. Biochem. Physiol, *6*: 69–74.

Pütter, A. E. 1908. Studien zur vergleichenden physiologie des stoffwechsels. Abh. Ges. Ws. Gottingen (Math-Phys), *6*: 1–79.

Pütter, A. E. 1909. Die ernährung der wassertiere und der stoffhanshalt der gewässer. Fischer, Jena, pp. 1–323.

Pütter, A. E. 1914. Der stoffwechsel der kieselschwämme. Zeit. Allg. Physiol., *16*: 65–114.

Rasmont, R. 1954. La diapause chez les spongillides. Bull. Acad. Roy. Belg., *40*: 288–304.

Rasmont, R. 1955a. La gemmulation des spongillides. II. Modalités de la diapause gemmulaire. Bull Acad. Roy. Belg., *41*: 214–223.

Rasmont, R. 1955b. La gemmulation des spongillides. Rupture de la diapause par des agents chimiques. Ann Soc. Roy. Zool. Belg., *85*: 173–181.

Rasmont, R. 1956. La gemmulation des spongillides. IV. Morphologie de la gemmulation chez *Ephydatia fluviatilis* et *Spongilla lacustris*. Ann. Soc. Roy. Zool. Belg., *86*: 349–387.

Rasmont, R. 1959. L'ultrastructure des choanocytes d'éponges. Ann. Sci. Natur. Zool., 12th Ser., *1*: 253–262.

Rasmont, R. 1961a. Physiologie de la reproduction asexuee des spongillides. Bull. Soc. France, *86*: 630–645.

Rasmont, R. 1961b. Une technique de culture des éponges d'eau douce en milieu controlé. Ann. Soc. Roy. Zool. Belg., *91*: 147–156.

Rasmont, R. 1962. The physiology of gemmulation in fresh-water sponges. Soc. Stud. Develop. Growth, *20*: 1–25.

Rasmont, R. 1963. Le rôle de la taille et de la nutrition dans le déterminisme de la gemmulation chez les spongillides. Devel. Biol., *8*: 243–271.

Rasmont, R. 1965. Existence d'une regulation biochimique de l'eclosion des gemmules chez les spongillides. C.R. Acad. Sci., Paris, *261*: 845–847.

Rasmont, R. 1968a. Nutrition and digestion. In: M. Florkin and B. T. Scheer (eds.). Chemical Zoology, Academic Press, New York, *II*: 43–51.

Rasmont, R. 1968b. Chemical aspects of hibernation. In: M. Florkin and B. T. Scheer (eds.). Chemical Zoology, Academic Press, New York, *II*: 65–77.

Rasmont, R. 1970. Some new aspects of the physiology of fresh-water sponges. In: W. G. Fry (ed.). The Biology of the Porifera. Academic Press, London. Sym. Zool. Soc. Lond., *25*: 415–422.

Rasmont, R. 1974. Stimulation of cell aggregation by theophylline in the asexual reproduction of fresh-water sponges (*Ephydatia fluviatilis*). Experientia, *30*: 792–794.

Rasmont, R. 1975. Freshwater sponges as a material for the study of cell differentiation. In: A. Moscona and A. Monroy (eds.). Current Topics in Developmental Biology. Academic Press, New York, *10*: 141–159.

Rasmont, R., and De Vos, L. 1974. Étude cinématographique de la gemmulation d'une éponge d'eau douce: *Ephydatia fluviatilis*. Arch. Biol., *85*: 329–341.

Rasmont, R., and Schmidt, I. 1967. Mise en evidence du caractere photo-sensible de la respiration des gemmules de spongillidae (Porifera). Comp. Biochem. Physiol., *23*: 959–967.

Reid, R. E. H. 1970. Tetraxons and demosponge phylogeny. In: W. G. Fry (ed.). The Biology of the Porifera. Academic Press, London. Sym. Zool. Soc. Lond., *25*: 63–89.

Reed, C., Greenberg, M. J., and Pierce, S. K. 1976. The effects of cytochalasins on sponge cell aggregation: New insights through the scanning electron microscope. In: F. W. Harrison and R. R. Cowden (eds.). Aspects of Sponge Biology. Academic Press, New York, pp. 153–169.

Reiswig, H. 1970. Porifera: Sudden sperm release by tropical demospongiae. Science (USA), *170*: 538–539.

Reiswig, H. 1971a. In situ pumping activities of tropical demospongiae. Mar. Biol., *9*: 38–50.

Reiswig, H. 1971b. Particle feeding in natural populations of three marine demosponges. Biol. Bull., *141*: 568–591.

Reiswig, H. 1971c. The axial symmetry of sponge spicules and its phylogenetic significance. Cah. Biol. Mar., *12*: 505–514.

Reiswig, H. 1973. Population dynamics of three Jamaican demospongiae. Bull. Mar. Sci., *23*: 191–226.

Reiswig, H. 1974. Water transport, respiration and energetics of three tropical marine sponges. J. Exp. Mar. Biol. Ecol., *14*: 231–249.

Reiswig, H. 1975a. The aquiferous systems of three marine demospongiae. J. Morph., *145*: 493–502.

Reiswig, H. 1975b. Bacteria as food for temperate-water marine sponges. Can. J. Zool., *53*: 582–589.

Reiswig, H. M. 1976. Natural gamete release and oviparity in Caribbean demospongiae. In: F. W. Harrison and R. R. Cowden (eds.). Aspects of Sponge Biology. Academic Press, New York, pp. 99–112.

Reiswig, H. 1979. Histology of Hexactinellida (Porifera). In: C. Lévi and N. Boury-Esnault (eds.). Biologie des Spongiaires. Colloq. Internat. C.N.R.S., Paris, *291*: 173–180.

Reiswig, H. M. *in press*. Porifera. In: K. G. Adiyodi and R. G. Adiyodi (eds.). Reproductive Biology of Invertebrates. John Wiley and Sons, Inc., Chichester.

Reiswig, H., and Brown, M. 1977. The central cells of sponges. Zoomorph., *88*: 81–94.

Reiswig, H., and Mackie, G. O. 1983. Studies on hexactinellid sponges. III. The taxonomic status of Hexactinellida within the Porifera. Phil. Trans. Roy. Soc. (Lond.). *301:* 419–428.

Robert, J. Labat-, Robert, L., Auger, C., Lethias, C., and Garrone, R. 1981. Fibronectin-like protein in Porifera: Its role in cell aggregation. Proc. Natl. Acad. Sci., USA, *78*: 6261–6265.

Rozenfeld, F. 1970. Inhibition du développement des gemmules de spongillides: Spécificité et moment d'action de la gemmulostasine. Arch. Biol., *81*: 193–214.

Rozenfeld, F. 1971. Effets de la perforation de la coque de gemmules d'*Ephydatia fluviatilis* (spongillides) sur leur developpement ulterieur en presence de gemmulostasine. Arch. Biol., *82*: 103–113.

Rozenfeld, F. 1974. Biochemical control of fresh-water sponge development: Effect on DNA, RNA and protein synthesis of an inhibitor secreted by the sponge. J. Embryol. Exp. Morph., *32*: 287–295.

Rozenfeld, F. 1980. Effects of puromycin on the differentiation of the freshwater sponge *Ephydatia fluviatilis*. Differen., *17*: 193–198.

Rozenfeld, F., and Rasmont, R. 1976. Hydroxyurea: An inhibitor of the differentiation of choanocytes in fresh-water sponges and a possible agent for the isolation of embryonic cells. Differen., *7*: 53–60.

Rozenfeld, F., Masson, H., and Rasmont, R. 1979. Analyse statistique du mouvement des cellules amiboide au cours de la gemmulation d'une eponge d'eau douce. In: C. Lévi and N. Boury-Esnault (eds.). Biologie des Spongiaires. Colloq. Internat. C.N.R.S., Paris, *291*: 31–37.

Ruthmann, A. 1965. The fine structure of RNA-storing archaeocytes from gemmules of fresh-water sponges. Quart. J. Micros. Sci., *106*: 99–114.

Rützler, K. 1971. Burrowing sponges, genus *Siphonodictyon* Bergquist, from the Caribbean. Smith. Contrib. Zool., No. *77*: 1–37.

Rützler, K. 1974. The burrowing sponges of Bermuda. Smith. Contrib. Zool., No. *165*: 1–32.

Rützler, K. 1975. The role of burrowing sponges in bioerosion. Oecol. (Berl.), *19*: 203–216.

Rützler, K. 1978. Results of the Austrian-Indian hydrobiological mission 1976 to the Andaman Islands—Part II. Aquatic Biol., *3*: 142–147.

Rützler, K. 1981. An unusual bluegreen alga symbiotic with two new species of *Ulosa* (Porifera: Hymeniacidonidae) from Carrie Bow Cay, Belize. P.S.Z.N.I.: Mar. Ecol., *2*: 35–50.

Rützler, K., and Bromley, R. G. 1981. *Cliona rhodensis,* new species (Porifera: Hadromerida) from the Mediterrean. Proc. Biol. Soc. Wash., *94*: 1219–1225.

Rützler, K., and Macintyre, I. G. 1978. Siliceous sponge spicules in coral reef sediments. Mar. Biol., *49*: 147–159.

Rützler, K., and Rieger, G. 1973. Sponge burrowing: Fine structure of *Cliona lampa* penetrating calcareous substrata. Mar. Biol., *21*: 144–162.

Sara, M. 1955a. Osservazioni sulgi amebociti esosinofili di *Clathrina* e *Leucosolenia* (Calcispongiae) e sulla loro colorazione vitale con blu trypan. Boll. Zool., *22*: 43–50.

Sara, M. 1955b. La nutrizione dell'ovocita in Calcispongie omoceli. Ann. Ist. Mus. Zool. Univ. Napoli, *7*: 1–30.

Sara, M. 1961. Ricerche sul gonocorismo ed ermafroditismo nei Poriferi. Boll. Zool., *28*: 47–59.

Sara, M. 1963. Una nuova specie di faretronidi (*Petrobiona incrustans*) dal Mediterraneo e considerazioni sulla sistematica delle Calcispongie. Mont. Zool. Ital., *71*: 229–237.

Sara, M. 1964. Simbiosi fra alghe unicellulari e invertebrati marini. Atti Semin. Stud. Biol., Bari, *1*: 3–24.

Sara, M. 1966. Associazione fra poriferi e alghe in acque superficiali del litorale marino. Ricerca Scient., *36*: 277–282.

Sara, M. 1970. Competition and cooperation in sponge populations. In: W. G. Fry (ed.). The Biology of the Porifera. Academic Press, London. Sym. Zool. Soc. Lond., *25*: 273–284.

Sara, M. 1971. Ultrastructural aspects of the symbiosis between two species of the genus *Aphanocapsa* (Cyanophyceae) and *Ircinia* (Demospongiae). Mar. Biol., *11*: 214–221.

Sara, M. 1974. Sexuality in the Porifera. Boll. Zool., *41*: 327–348.

Sara, M. *in press*. Porifera. In: K. G. Adiyodi and R. G. Adiyodi (eds.). Reproductive Biology of Invertebrates. John Wiley and Sons, Chichester.

Sara, M., and Liaci, L. 1964a. Associazione fra la cianoficea *Aphanocapsa feldmanni* e alcune demospongie marine. Boll. Zool., *31*: 55–65.

Sara, M., and Liaci, L. 1964b. Symbiotic association between zooxanthellae and two marine sponges of the genus *Cliona*. Nature (London), *203*: 321.

Sara, M., and Rellini-Orsi, L. 1975. Sex differentiation in *Sycon* (Porifera Calcispongiae). Pubbl. Staz. Zool. Napoli, *39* (Suppl.): 618–634.

Sara, M., and Vacelet, J. 1973. Ecologie des démosponges. In: P-P. Grassé (ed.). Traité de Zoologie, Vol. III, Fasc. 1. Mason Cie, Paris, pp. 462–576.

Sara, M., Gaino, E., and Valentini, F. 1973. Nouvelles donneés sur les associations entre éponges et bactéries. Rapp. Comm. Internat. Mer. Medit., *22*: 97–98.

Sara, M., Gaino, E., and Valentini, F. 1974a. Cell behavior in the reaggregation of sponges. Boll. Mus. Ist. Univ. Genova, *42*: 11–16.

Sara, M., Gaino, E., and Valentini, F. 1974b. Olynthus formation by cell aggregation in *Sycon vigilans* (Porifera, Calcispongiae). Vie Milieu, *24*: 225–234.

Schmidt, E. O. 1870. Beitrage zur descendenztheorie und zur systematik der spongien. Ausland, *43*: 30–35; 179–181; 246–247.

Schmidt, E. O. 1879. Die spongien des meerbusen von Mexico. Heft. I. Lithistiden. Gustav Fischer, Jena, pp. 1–32.

Schmidt, I. 1970a. Phagocytose et pinocytose chez les spongillidae. Zeit. Vergl. Physiol., *66*: 398–420.

Schmidt, I. 1970b. Étude preliminaire de la différenciation des thésocytes d'*Ephydatia fluviatilis* L. extraits mécaniquement de la gemmule. C.R. Acad. Sci., Paris, *271*: 924–927.

Schmidt, W. J. 1926. Über das wesen der lamellierung und das gegenseitige verhalten von organischer und anorgnischer substanz bei den keiselschwammnadeln. Zool. Zb. Anat. Ont. Tiere, *48*: 311–364.

Schröeder, K. 1936. Beitrage zur kenntnis der spiculabildung der larven-spiculation und der variationsbreite der gerüstnadeln von süsswasserschwämmen. Zeit. Morph. Oekol. Tiere, *31*: 245–267.

Schulze, F. E. 1887. Report on the Hexactinellida collected by H. M. S. Challenger during the years 1873–1876. Rep. Scient. Res. Challenger, Zool., *21*: 1–514.

Schulze, F. 1904. Hexactinellida. Wiss. Ergebn. D. Tiefsee-Exp. Valdivia, *4*: 1–226.

Schulze, P. 1925. Zur morphologischen feinbau der keiselschwammnadeln. Zeit. Morph. Okol. Tiere, *4*: 615–625.

Schwab, D. W., and Shore, R. E. 1971a. Mechanism of internal stratification of siliceous sponge spicules. Nature (London), *232*: 501–502.

Schwab, D. W., and Shore, R. E. 1971b. Fine structure and composition of a siliceous sponge spicule. Biol. Bull., *140*: 125–136.

Schwarz, K. 1973. A bound form of silicon in glycosaminoglycans and polyuronides. Proc. Nat. Acad. Sci., USA, *70*: 1608–1612.

Sciscioli, M. 1966. Associazione tra la demospongia *Stelletta grubii* (O. Schmidt) e la rodoficea *Phyllophora palmettoides* Ag. Atti. Soc. Pelorit. Sci. Fisc. Matem. Natur., *12*: 555–560.

Shore, R. E. 1971. Growth and renewal studies of the choanocyte population in *Hymeniacidon sinapium* (Porifera: Demospongiae) using colcemid and ^{3}H thymidine. J. Exp. Zool., *177*: 359–364.

Shore, R. E. 1972. Axial filament of siliceous sponge spicules, its organic components and synthesis. Biol. Bull., *143*: 689–698.

Simons, J., and Müller, L. 1966. Ribonucleic acid-storage inclusions of freshwater sponge archaeocytes. Nature (London), *210*: 847–848.

Simpson, T. L. 1963. The biology of the marine sponge *Microciona prolifera* (Ellis and Solander). I. A study of cellular function and differentiation. J. Exp. Zool., *154*: 135–147.

Simpson, T. L. 1966. A new species of clathriid sponge from the San Juan Archipelago. Postilla (Yale Univ.), *103*: 1–7.

Simpson, T. L. 1968a. The structure and function of sponge cells. Bull. Peabody Mus. Natur. Hist., (Yale Univ.) *25*: 1–141.

Simpson, T. L. 1968b. The biology of the marine sponge *Microciona prolifera* (Ellis and Sollander). II. Temperature-related annual changes in functional and reproductive elements with a description of larval metamorphosis. J. Exp. Mar. Biol. Ecol., *2*: 252–277.

Simpson, T. L. 1973. Coloniality among the porifera. In: R. S. Boardman, A. H. Cheetham, and W. A. Oliver (eds.). Animal Colonies. Dowden Hutch. Ross, Stroudsburg, pp. 549–565.

Simpson, T. L. 1978. The biology of the marine sponge *Microciona prolifera* (Ellis and Sollander). III. Spicule secretion and the effect of temperature on spicule size. J. Exp. Mar. Biol. Ecol., *35*: 31–42.

Simpson, T. L. 1980. Reproductive processes in sponges: A critical evaluation of current data and views. Internat. J. Invert. Reprod., *2*: 251–269.

Simpson, T. L. 1981. Effects of germanium on silica deposition in sponges. In: T. L. Simpson and B. E. Volcani (eds.). Silicon and Siliceous Structures in Biological Systems. Springer-Verlag, New York, pp. 527–550.

Simpson, T. L. *in press*. Porifera. In: K. G. Adiyodi and R. G. Adiyodi (eds.). Reproductive Biology of Invertebrates. John Wiley and Sons, Chichester.

Simpson, T. L., and Fell, P. E. 1974. Dormancy among the Porifera: Gemmule formation and germination in freshwater and marine sponges. Trans. Amer. Micros. Soc., *93*: 544–577.

Simpson, T. L., and Gilbert, J. J. 1973. Gemmulation, gemmule hatching and sexual reproduction in fresh-water sponges. I. The life cycle of *Spongilla lacustris* and *Tubella pennsylvanica*. Trans. Amer. Micros. Soc., *92*: 422–433.

Simpson, T. L., and Gilbert, J. J. 1974. Gemmulation, gemmule hatching, and sexual reproduction in fresh-water sponges. II. Life cycle events in young, larva-produced sponges of *Spongilla lacustris* and an unidentified species. Trans. Amer. Micros. Soc., *93*: 39–45.

Simpson, T. L., and Rodan, G. A. 1976a. Recent investigations of the involvement of 3′, 5′ cyclic AMP in the developmental physiology of sponge gemmules. In: F. W. Harrison and R. R. Cowden (eds.). Aspects of Sponge Biology. Academic Press, New York, pp. 83–97.

Simpson, T. L., and Rodan, G. A. 1976b. Role of cAMP in the release from dormancy of freshwater sponge gemmules. Devel. Biol., *49*: 544–547.

Simpson, T. L., and Vaccaro, C. A. 1974. An ultrastructural study of silica deposition in the freshwater sponge *Spongilla lacustris*. J. Ultrastr. Res., *47*: 296–309.

Simpson, T. L., and Volcani, B. E. (eds.). 1981. Silicon and Siliceous Structures in Biological Systems. Springer-Verlag, New York.

Simpson, T. L., Vaccaro, C. A., and Sha'afi, R. I. 1973. The role of intragemmular osmotic pressure in cell division and hatching of gemmules of the freshwater sponge *Spongilla lacustris* (Porifera). Zeit. Morph. Tiere, *76*: 339–357.

Simpson, T. L., Refolo, L. M., and Kaby, M. 1979. Effects of germanium on the morphology of silica deposition in a freshwater sponge. J. Morph., *159*: 343–354.

Sinsheimer, R. L. 1957. First steps toward a genetic chemistry. Science (USA), *125*: 1123–1128.

Siribelli, L. 1962. Differenze nel ciclo sessuale di popolazioni conviventi di *Axinella damicornis* (Esper.) ed *Axinella verrucosa* O. S. (Demospongiae). Ann. Ist. Mus. Zool. Univ. Napoli, *14*: 1–8.

Sivaramakrishnan, V. R. 1951. Studies on early development and regeneration in some Indian marine sponges. Proc. Ind. Acad. Sci., *34*: 273–310.

Smith, V. E. 1968. Comparative cytology and biochemistry of two marine sponges. Thesis. Univ. Calif., San Diego, pp. 1–175.

Smith, V. E., and Lauritis, J. A. 1969. Cellular origin and fine structure of mesoglea in a marine sponge, *Cyamon neon* de Laubenfels. J. Micros., *8*: 179–188.

Sollas, W. J. 1888. Report on the Tetractinellida collected by H. M. S. Challenger during the years 1873–1876. Rep. Challenger, Zool., *25*: 1–458.

Sollas, I. B. J. 1909. Porifera. In: S. R. Harmer and A. E. Shipley (eds.). Cambridge Natural History. MacMillian, London, *VI*: 165–242.

Spiegel, M. 1955. The reaggregation of dissociated sponge cells. Ann. N.Y. Acad. Sci., *60*: 1056–1076.

Stone, A. R. 1970a. Growth and reproduction of *Hymeniacidon perleve* (Montagu) (Porifera) in Langstone Harbour, Hampshire, J. Zool. Lond., *161*: 443–459.

Stone, A. R. 1970b. Seasonal variation in the gross biochemical composition of *Hymeniacidon perleve* (Montagu). J. Exp. Mar. Biol. Ecol., *5*: 265–271.

Stone, A. R. 1970c. Seasonal variations of spicule size in *Hymeniacidon perleve*. J. Mar. Biol. Assoc. U.K., *50*: 343–348.

Storr, J. F. 1964. Ecology of the Gulf of Mexico commercial sponges and its relation to the fishery. U.S. Fish Wildlife Serv. Spec. Sci. Rep., No. *466*: 1–73.

Storr, J. F. 1976. Field observations of sponge reactions as related to their ecology. In: F. W. Harrison and R. R. Cowden (eds.). Aspects of Sponge Biology. Academic Press, New York, pp. 277–282.

Strekal, T., and McDiffett, W. 1974. Factors affecting germination, growth and distribution of the freshwater sponge, *Spongilla fragilis* Leidy (Porifera). Biol. Bull., *146*: 267–278.

Sullivan, B., and Faulkner, D. J. 1982. An antimicrobial sesterterpene from a palauan sponge. Tetrahed. Lett., *23*: 907–910.

Tanaka, Y., Soejima, T., and Katayama, T. 1978. Biochemical studies of the carotenoids in Porifera. Distribution of the carotenoids in Porifera. Bull. Jap. Soc. Scient. Fish., *44*: 1283–1285.

Tessenow, W. 1968. Intrazelluläre verdauung der reservesubstanzen in vakuolen der blastenzellen von *Ephydatia mulleri*. Naturwissen., *55*: 300.

Tessenow, W. 1969. Lytic processes in development of fresh-water sponges. In: J. T. Dingle and H. B. Fell (eds.). Lysosomes in Biology and Pathology. North-Holland, London, *1*: 392–405.

Tessenow, W., and Kreutzmann, H-L. 1969. Saure phosphatase und differzierung der archäozyten bei susswasserschwämmen (Spongillidae). Biol. Rund., *7*: 180–181.

Tessenow, W., and Kreutzmann, H-L. 1970. Unspezifische esterase und differenzierung der archäozyten bei susswasserschwämmen (Spongillidae). Biol. Runds., *8*: 354–355.

Thiney, Y. 1972. Morphologie et cytochimie ultrastructurale de l'oscule d'*Hippospongia communis* LMK et de sa régénération. Thèse, Univ. Claude Bernard, pp. 1–63.

Thiney, Y., and Garrone, R. 1970. Association des mucopolysaccharides et des fibres de collagène dans le tissu conjonctif spongiaires. 7th Congr. Internat. Micros., Grenoble, pp. 589–590.

Thompson, J. E., Barrow, K. D., and Faulkner, D. J. 1984. Localization of two brominated metabolites, aerothionin and homoaerothionin, in spherulous cells of a marine demosponge, *Aplysina fistularis* (*Verongia thiona*). Acta Zool., in press.

Topsent, M. E. 1888. Sur les gemmules de quelques silicisponges marines. C.R. Acad. Sci., Paris, *106*: 1298–1300.

Topsent, E. 1928. Spongiaires de l'Atlantique et de la Mediterranée provenant des croisieres du Prince Albert Ier de Monaco. Result. Camp. Scient. Prince Albert I Monaco, *74*: 1–376.

Towe, K. M., and Rützler, K. 1968. Lepidocrocite iron mineralization in keratose sponge granules. Science (USA), *162*: 268–269.

Travis, D. F. 1970. The comparative ultrastructure and organization of five calcified tissues. In: H. Schraer (ed.). Biological Calcification: Cellular and Molecular Aspects. Appleton–Century–Crofts, New York, pp. 203–311.

Travis, D., Francois, C., Bonar, L., and Glimcher, M. 1967. Comparative studies of the organic matrices of invertebrate mineralized tissues. J. Ultrastruc. Res., *18*: 519–550.

Tregouboff, G. 1942. Contribution a la connaissance des larves planctonique d'éponges. Arch. Zool. Exp. Gén., *82*: 357–399.

Tregouboff, G., and Rose, M. 1957. Gemmules armees d'*Alectona millari* Carter. In: Manuel de planctunologie Mediterraneene, C.N.R.S., Paris, *1*: 260–263.

Turner, R. S. 1978. Sponge cell adhesions. In: D. R. Garrod (ed.). Specificity of Embryological Interactions. Receptors and Recognition, Ser. B, *4*: 201–232.

Turner, R. S., and Burger, M. M. 1973. Involvement of a carbohydrate group in the active site for surface guided reassociation of animal cells. Nature (London), *244*: 509–510.

Turner, R. S., Weinbaum, G., Kuhns, W. J., and Burger, M. M. 1974. The use of lectins in the analysis of sponge aggregation. Arch. Biol. (Brux.), *85*: 35–51.

Tuzet, O. 1932. Recherches sur l'histologie des éponges. Arch. Zool. Exp. Gén., *74*: 169–192.

Tuzet, O. 1947. L'ovogenèse et la fecondation de l'éponge calcaire *Leucosolenia* (*Clathrina*) *coriacea* Mont. et de l'éponge siliceuse *Reniera elegans* Bow. Arch. Zool. Exp. Gén., *85*: 127–148.

Tuzet, O. 1948. Les premieres stades du developpement de *Leucosolenia botryoides* Ellis et Solander et de *Clathrina* (*Leucosolenia*) *coriacea* Mont. Ann. Sci. Natur., *10*: 103–114.

Tuzet, O. 1963. The phylogeny of sponges according to embryological, histological, and serological data, and their affinities with the protozoa and the Cnidaria. In: E. C. Dougherty (ed.). The Lower Metazoa. Comparative Biology and Phylogeny. Univ. Calif. Press, Berkeley, pp. 129–148.

Tuzet, O. 1964. L'origine de la lignée germinale et la gametogénèse chez les spongiaires. In: E. Wolff (ed.). L'Origine de la Lignée Germinale. Hermann, Paris, pp. 79–111.

Tuzet, O. 1970. La polarité de l'oeuf et la symétrie de la larve des éponges calcaires. In: W. G. Fry (ed.). The Biology of the Porifera. Academic Press, London, Sym. Zool. Soc. Lond., *25*: 437–448.

Tuzet, O. 1973a. Éponges calcaires. In: P-P. Grassé (ed.). Traité de Zoologie, Vol. III, Fasc. 1. Mason Cie, Paris, pp. 27–132.

Tuzet, O. 1973b. Hexactinellides or Hyalosponges. In: P-P. Grassé (ed.). Traité de Zoologie, Vol. III, Fasc. 1. Mason Cie, Paris, pp. 633–690.

Tuzet, O., and Connes, R. 1963. Recherches histologiques sur la reconstitution de *Sycon raphanus* O. S. à partir des cellules dissociées. Vie Milieu, *13*: 703–710.

Tuzet, O., and Connes, R. 1964. Sur la presence de lophocytes chez le *Sycon*. C.R. Acad. Sci., Paris, *258*: 4142–4143.

Tuzet, O., and Paris, J. 1957. Les lophocytes de l'éponge siliceuse *Tethya lyncurium* Lamark et leur evolution. C.R. Acad. Sci., Paris, *244*: 3088–3090.

Tuzet, O., and Paris, J. 1963a. *Octavella galangaui* n. g. n. sp. Demospongiae, Oscarellidae de Banyuls-sur-Mer. Vie Milieu, *14*: 71–89.

Tuzet, O., and Paris, J. 1963b. Recherches sur la régénération de *Sycon raphanus* O. S. Vie Milieu, *14*: 285–298.

Tuzet, O., and Paris, J. 1964. La spermatogenèse, l'ovogenèse, la fécondation et les premires stades du developpement chez *Octavella galangaui,* Vie et Milieu, *15*: 309–327.

Tuzet, O., and Paris, J. 1966. Lophocytes et fibroblastes chez *Suberites domuncula*. Arch. Zool. Exp. Gén., *106*: 522–529.

Tuzet, O., and Pavans de Ceccatty, M. 1953. Les lophocytes de l'éponge *Pachymatisma johnstonni* Bow. C.R. Acad. Sci., Paris, *273*: 1447–1449.

Tuzet, O., and Pavans de Ceccatty, M. 1955. La mobilisation en amoebocytes des cellules des *Halisarca* (Eponges siliceuses). Les polyblastes chez les Eponges. C.R. Soc. Biol., *149*: 799–801.

Tuzet, O., and Pavans de Ceccatty, M. 1958. La spermatogenèse, l'ovogenèse, la fécondation et les premiers stades du développement d'*Hippospongia communis* Lmk. Bull. Biol., *92*: 331–348.

Tuzet, O., Garrone, R., and Pavans de Ceccatty. M. 1970a. Observations ultra-structurales sur la demosponge *Aplysilla rosea* Schulze (Dendroceratide): Une metaplasie exemplaire. Ann. Sci. Natur. Zool., Paris, *12*: 27–50.

Tuzet, O., Garrone, R., and Pavans de Ceccatty, M. 1970b. Origine choanocytaire de la lignée germinale mâle chez la démosponge *Aplysilla rosea* Schulze (Dendroceratides). C.R. Acad. Sci., Paris, *270*: 955–957.

Urban, F. 1910. Zur kenntnis der biologie und cytologie der kalkschwämme (Familie Clathrinidae Minchin). Internat. Rev. Ges. Hydrobiol., *3*: 37–43.

Vacelet, J. 1962. Existence de formations de réserve chez une éponge calcaire pharétronide. C.R. Acad. Sci., Paris, *254*: 2425–2426.

Vacelet, J. 1963. Acide désoxyribonucléique dans le cytoplasme de cellules à réserves d'une éponge calcaire pharétronide. Arch. Anat. Micros. Morph. Exp., *52*: 591–599.

Vacelet, J. 1964. Étude monographique de l'éponge calcaire pharétronide de Mediterranée, *Petrobiona massiliana* Vacelet et Lévi. Les pharétronides actuelles et fossiles. Thèse. Univ. D'Aix Marseille, pp. 1–125.

Vacelet, J. 1966. Les cellules contractiles de l'éponge cornée *Verongia caverni-cola* Vacelet. C.R. Acad. Sci., Paris, *263*: 1330–1332.

Vacelet, J. 1967a. Quelques eponges pharétronides et "silico-calcaires" de grottes sous-marine obscures. Rec. Trav. St. Mar. Endoume Bull., *42*: 121–132.

Vacelet, J. 1967b. Les cellules à inclusions de l'éponge cornée *Verongia caverni-cola* Vacelet. J. Micros., *6*: 237–240.

Vacelet, J. 1970a. Les eponges pharétronides actuelles. In: W. G. Fry (ed.). The Biology of the Porifera. Academic Press, London. Sym. Zool. Soc. Lond., *25*: 189–204.

Vacelet, J. 1970b. Description de cellules à bactéries intranucléaires chez des éponges *Verongia*. J. Micros., *9*: 333–346.

Vacelet, J. 1971a. Ultrastructure et formation des fibres de spongine d'éponges cornees *Verongia*. J. Micros., *10*: 13–32.

Vacelet, J. 1971b. L'ultrastructure de la cuticule d'éponges cornées du genre *Verongia*. J. Micros., *10*: 113–116.

Vacelet, J. 1971c. Étude en microscopie électronique de l'association entre une cyanophycée chroococcale et une éponge du genre *Verongia*. J. Micros., *12*: 363–380.

Vacelet, J. 1975. Étude en microscopie électronique de l'association entre bacté-ries et spongiaires du genre *Verongia* (Dictyoceratida). J. Micros. Biol. Cell., *23*: 271–288.

Vacelet, J. 1977a. Éponges pharétronides actuelles et sclérosponges de polynésie francaise, de Madagascar et de la Réunion. Bull Mus. Nat. Hist. Natur. (Paris), 3rd Ser., No. 444 (Zool. *307*): 345–368.

Vacelet, J. 1977b. Une nouvelle relique du secondaire: Une represéntant actuel des éponge fossiles Sphinctozoaires. C.R. Acad. Sci., Paris, *285*: 509–511.

Vacelet, J. 1979a. Quelques stades de la reproduction sexuee d'une eponge sphinctozoaire actuelle. In: C. Lévi and N. Boury-Esnault (eds.). Biologie des Spongiaires. Colloq. Internat. C.N.R.S., Paris, *291*: 95–101.

Vacelet, J. 1979b. Description et affinites d'une eponge sphinctozoaire actuelle. In: C. Lévi and N. Boury-Esnault (eds.). Biologie des Spongiaires. Colloq. Internat. C.N.R.S., Paris, *291*: 483–493.

Vacelet, J. 1979c. La place des spongiaires dans les systems trophiques marin. In: C. Lévi and N. Boury-Esnault (eds.). Biologie des Spongiaires. Colloq. Internat. C.N.R.S., Paris, *291*: 259–270.

Vacelet, J. 1980. Squelette calcaire facultatif et corps de régénération dans le genre *Merlia*. Éponges apparentées aux chaetetides fossiles. C.R. Acad. Sci., Paris, *290*: 227–230.

Vacelet, J. 1981. Éponges hypercalcifées ("Pharétronides" "Sclérosponges") des cavités des récifs coralliens de Nouvelle-Calédonie. Bull. Mus. Nat. Hist. Natur., Paris (4th Ser., Sect. A, No. 2), *3*: 313–351.

Vacelet, J., and Donadey, C. 1977. Electron microscope study of the associa-tion between some sponges and bacteria. J. Exp. Mar. Biol. Ecol., *30*: 301–314.

Vacelet, J., and Gallissian, M-F. 1978. Virus-like particles in cells of the sponge *Verongia cavernicola* (Demospongiae) Dictyoceratida and accompaning tis-sue changes. J. Invert. Pathol., *31*: 246–254.

Vacelet, J., and Lévi, C. 1958. Un cas de survivance, en Méditerranée, du groupe d'éponges fossile des pharétronides. C.R. Hebd. Séan. Acad. Sci., Paris, *246*: 318–320.

Vacelet, J., and Vasseur, P. 1971. Éponges des récifs coralliens de Tulear (Madagascar). Tethys (Suppl.), *1*: 51–126.

Vaith, P., Müller, W. E. G., and Uhlenbruck, G. 1979a. On the role of D-glucuronic acid in the aggregation of cells from the marine sponge *Geodia cydonium*. Devel. Comp. Immunol., *3*: 259–275.

Vaith, P., Uhlenbruck, G., and Müller, W. E. G. 1979b. Sponge aggregation factor and sponge hemagglutinin: Possible relationships between two different molecules. Devel. Comp. Immunol., *3*: 399–416.

Van de Vyver, G. 1970. La non confluence intraspécifique chez les spongiaires et la notion d'individu. Ann. Embryol. Morph., *3*: 251–262.

Van de Vyver, G. 1971. Mise en evidence d'un facteur d'aggregation chez l'eponge d'eau douce *Ephydatia fluviatilis*. Ann. Embryol. Moph., *4*: 373–381.

Van de Vyver, G. 1975. Phenomena of cellular recognition in sponges. In: A. A. Moscona and A. Monroy (eds.). Current Topics in Developmental Biology. Academic Press, New York, *10*: 123–140.

Van de Vyver, G. 1979. Cellular mechanisms of recognition and rejection among sponges. In: C. Lévi and N. Boury-Esnault (eds.). Biologie des Spongiaires. Colloq. Internat. C.N.R.S., Paris, *291*: 195–204.

Van de Vyver, G. 1980. Second-set allograft rejection in two sponge species and the problem of an alloimune memory. In: M. J. Manning (ed.). Phylogeny of Immunological Memory. Elsevier North-Holland Biomed. Press, Amsterdam, pp. 15–26.

Van de Vyver, G., and Barbieux, B. 1983. Cellular aspects of allograft rejection in marine sponges of the genus *Polymastia*. J. Exp. Zool., *227*: 1–8.

Van de Vyver, G., and Buscema, M. 1976. Influence of trypsin and concanavalin A on sponge cell aggregation. Arch. Biol., *87*: 245–259.

Van de Vyver, G., and Buscema, M. 1977. Phagocytic phenomena in different types of fresh-water sponge aggregates. In: J. B. Solomon and J. D. Horton (eds.). Developmental Immunobiology. Elsevier North-Holland Biomed. Press, Amsterdam, pp. 3–8.

Van de Vyver, G., and Buscema, M. 1981. Capacités morphogènese des cellules d'éponges dissociéés. Ann. Soc. Roy. Zool. Belg., *111*: 9–19.

Van de Vyver, G., and De Vos, L. 1979. Structure of a non-merging front between two fresh-water sponges *Ephydatia fluviatilis* belonging to different strains. In: C. Lévi and N. Boury-Esnault (eds.). Biologie des Spongiaires. Colloq. Internat. C.N.R.S., Paris, *291*: 233–237.

Van de Vyver, G., and Willenz, Ph. 1975. An experimental study of the life cycle of the fresh-water sponge *Ephydatia fluviatilis* in its natural surroundings. Wilhelm Roux's Arch., *177*: 41–52.

Van Tright, H. 1919. Contribution to the physiology of the fresh-water sponges (Spongillidae). Tijdschr. Ned. Dierk. Ver (2) *17*: 1–220.

Van Weel, P. B. 1949. On the physiology of the tropical fresh-water sponge *Spongilla proliferans* (Annand). I. Ingestion, digestion and excretion. Physiol. Comp., *1*: 110–128.

Veizer, J., and Wendt, J. 1976. Mineralogy and chemical composition of recent and fossil skeletons of calcareous sponges. N. Jb. Geio. Paläont. Mh., *9*: 558–573.

Vicente, V. P. 1978. An ecological evaluation of the West Indian demosponge *Anthosigmella varians* (Hadromerida:Spirastrellidae). Bull. Mar. Sci., *28*: 771–777.

Vinogradov, A. P. 1953. The elementary chemical composition of marine organisms. Mem. Sears Found. Mar. Res. (Yale Univ.), No. II: 1–647.

Vogel, S. 1974. Current-induced flow through the sponge, *Halichondria*. Biol. Bull., *147*: 443–456.

Vogel, S. 1977. Current-induced flow through living sponges in nature. Proc. Nat. Acad. Sci (USA), *74*: 2069–2071.

Vogel, S. 1978. Evidence for one-way valves in the water-flow system of sponges. J. Exp. Biol., *76*: 137–148.

Vogel, S., and Bretz, W. 1972. Interfacial organisms: Passive ventilation in the velocity gradients near surfaces. Science (USA), *175*: 210–211.

Volcani, B. E. 1981. Cell wall formation in diatoms: Morphogenesis and biochemistry. In: T. L. Simpson and B. E. Volcani (eds.). Silicon and Siliceous Structures in Biological Systems. Springer-Verlag, New York, pp. 157–200.

Volkmer-Ribeiro, C., and Rosa-Barbosa, R. 1979. Neotropical freshwater sponges of the family Potamolepidae Brien, 1967. In: C. Lévi and N. Boury-Esnault (eds.). Biologie des Spongiaires. Colloq. Internat. C.N.R.S., Paris, *291*: 503–511.

Vosmaer, G. C. J. 1885. Porifera. In: H. G. Bronn (ed.). Die Klassen und Ordnungen des Thierreichs, *2*: 177–496.

Vosmaer, G. C. J. 1928. Bibliography of the sponges. Cambridge Univ. Press, London, pp. 1–234.

Vosmaer, G. C. J., and Pekelharing, C. A. 1898. Ueber die nahrungsaufnahme bei schwämmen. Arch. Anat. Physiol., Physiol. Abth., pp. 168–186.

Vosmaer, G. C. J., and Wijsman, H. P. 1905. On the structure of some siliceous spicules of sponges. I. The styli of *Tethya lyncurium*. Acad. Wet. Amsterdam, Porcl. *8*: 15–28.

Warburton, F. E. 1958a. The manner in which the sponge *Cliona* bores in calcareous objects. Can. J. Zool., *36*: 555–562.

Warburton, F. E. 1958b. The effects of boring sponges on oysters. Prog. Rep. Atl. Cst. Stat. Fish. Res. Bd. Can., *68*: 3–8.

Warburton, F. E. 1958c. Boring sponges, *Cliona* species of eastern Canada with a note on the validity of *C. lobata*. Can. J. Zool., *36*: 124–125.

Warburton, F. E. 1958d. Reproduction of fused larvae in the boring sponge, *Cliona celata* Grant. Nature (London), *181*: 493–494.

Warburton, F. E. 1961. Inclusion of parental somatic cells in sponge larvae. Nature (London), *191*: 1317.

Warburton, F. E. 1966. The behavior of sponge larvae. Ecology, *47*: 672–674.

Watanabe, Y. 1957. Development of *Tethya serica* Lebwohl, a tetraxonian sponge. I. Observations on external changes. Natur. Sci. Rep. Ochanomizu Univ., *8*: 97–104.

Watanabe, Y. 1960. Outline of morphological observation on the development of *Tethya serica*. Bull. Mar. Biol. Stat. Asamushi, *10*: 145–148.

Watanabe, Y. 1978a. The development of two species of *Tetilla* (Demosponge). Natur. Sci. Rep. Ochanomizu Univ., *29*: 71–106.

Watanabe, Y. 1978b. Structure and formation of the collar in choanocytes of *Tetilla serica* (Lebwohl), Demosponge. Devel. Growth, Differen., *20*: 79–91.

Webb, D. A. 1935. The histology, cytology, and embryology of sponges. Quart. J. Micros. Sci., *28*: 51–70.

Weinbaum, G., and Burger, M. M. 1973. Two component system for surface guided reassociation of animal cells. Nature (London), *244*: 511–512.

Weissenfels, N. 1974. Bau und funktion des süsswasserschwämms *Ephydatia fluviatilis*. I. Das nephridialsystem der pinacocyten. Cytobiol., *8*: 269–288.

Weissenfels, N. 1975. Bau und funktion des süsswasserschwämms *Ephydatia fluviatilis* L. (Porifera). II. Anmerkungen zum korperbau. Zeit. Morph. Tiere, *81*: 241–256.

Weissenfels, N. 1976. Bau und funktion des süsswasserschwämms *Ephydatia fluviatilis* L. (Porifera). III. Nahrungsaufnahme, verdauung und defäkation. Zoomorph., *85*: 73–88.

Weissenfels, N. 1978. Bau und funktion des süsswasserschwänns *Ephydatia fluviatilis* L. (Porifera). V. Das nadelskelet und seine entstehung. Zool. Jb. Anat. Bd., *99*: 211–223.

Weissenfels, N. 1980. Bau und funktion des süsswasserschwämms *Ephydatia fluviatilis* L. (Porifera). VII. Die porocyten. Zoomorph., *95*: 27–40.

Weissenfels, N. 1981. Bau und funktion des süsswasserschwämms *Ephydatia fluviatilis* L. (Porifera). VIII. Die entstehung und entwicklung der kragengeisselkammern und ihre verbindung mit dem aufuhrenden kanalsystem. Zoomorph., *98*: 35–45.

Weissenfels, N. 1982. Bau und funktion des süsswasserschwämms *Ephydatia fluviatilis* L. (Porifera). IX. Rasterelectronenmikroskopische histologie und cytologie. Zoomorph., *100*: 75–87.

Weissenfels, N. 1983. Bau und funktion des süsswasserschwämms *Ephydatia fluviatilis* (Porifera). X. Der nachweis des offenen mesenchyms durch verfütterung von bäckerhefe (*Saccharomyces cerevisiae*). Zoomorph., *103*: 15–23.

Weissenfels, N., and Landschoff, H-W. 1977. Bau und funktion des süsswasserschwämms *Ephydatia fluviatilis* L. (Porifera). IV. Die entwicklung der monaxialen SiO$_2$-nadeln in sandwich-kulturen. Zool. Jb. Anat. Bd., *98*: 355–371.

Weissenfels, N., and Striegler, B. 1979. Bau und funktion des süsswasserschwämms *Ephydatia fluviatilis* L. (Porifera). VI. Das individualitätsproblem. Zoomorph., *92*: 49–63.

Wells, H. W., Wells, M. J., and Gray, I. E. 1960. Marine sponges of North Carolina. J. Elisha Mitch. Sci. Soc., *76*: 200–245.

Wells, H. W., Wells, M. J., and Gray, I. E. 1964. Ecology of sponges in Hatteras Harbor, North Carolina. Ecol., *45*: 752–767.

Wendt, J. 1979. Development of skeletal formation, microstructure and mineralogy of rigid calcareous sponges from the late palaeozoic to recent. In: C. Lévi and N. Boury-Esnault (eds.). Biologie des Spongiaires. Colloq. Internat. C.N.R.S., Paris, *291*: 449–457.

Wierzejski, A. 1935. Stusswasserspongien. Monographische bearbeitung. Mem. Acad. Pol. Sci. Lett. (B), Sci. Natur., *9*: 1–242.

Wilkinson, C. R. 1978a. Microbial associations in sponges. I. Ecology, physiology and microbial populations of coral reef sponges. Mar. Biol., *49*: 161–167.

Wilkinson, C. R. 1978b. Microbial associations in sponges. II. Numerical analysis of sponge and water bacterial populations. Mar. Biol., *49*: 169–176.

Wilkinson, C. R. 1978c. Microbial associations in sponges. III. Ultrastructure of the in situ associations in coral reef sponges. Mar. Biol., *49*: 177–185.

Wilkinson, C. R. 1979a. Nutrient translocation from symbiotic cyanobacteria to coral reef sponges. In: C. Lévi and N. Boury-Esnault (eds.). Biologie des Spongiaires. Colloq. Internat. C.N.R.S., Paris, *291*: 373–380.

Wilkinson, C. R. 1979b. Nitrogen fixation in coral reef sponges with symbiotic cyanobacteria. Nature (London), *279*: 527–529.

Wilkinson, C. R. 1979c. Skeletal morphology of coral reef sponges: A scanning electron microscope study. Aust. J. Mar. Freshwater Res., *30*: 793–801.

Wilkinson, C. R. 1980. Cyanobacteria symbiotic in marine sponges. In: W. Schwemmler and H. E. A. Schenk (eds.). Endocytobiology, Endosymbiosis and Cell Biology. Walter de Gruyter, New York, *I*: 553–563.

Wilkinson, C. R., and Garrone, R. 1980a. Ultrastructure of siliceous spicules and microsclerocytes in the marine sponge *Neofibularia irata* N. Sp. J. Morph., *166*: 51–64.

Wilkinson, C. R., and Garrone, R. 1980b. Nutrition of marine sponges. Involvement of symbiotic bacteria in the uptake of dissolved carbon. In: D. C. Smith and Y. Tiffon (eds.). Nutrition in the Lower Metazoa. Pergamon Press, Oxford, pp. 157–161.

Wilkinson, C. R., and Vacelet, J. 1979. Transplantation of marine sponges to different conditions of light and current. J. Exp. Mar. Biol. Ecol., *37*: 91–104.

Wilkinson, C., Garrone, R., and Herbage, D. 1979. Sponge collagen degradation *in vitro* by sponge specific bacteria. In: C. Lévi and N. Boury-Esnault (eds.). Biologie des Spongiaires. Colloq. Internat. C.N.R.S., Paris, *291*: 361–364.

Willenz, Ph. 1980. Kinetic and morphological aspects of particle ingestion by the freshwater sponge *Ephydatia fluviatilis* L. In: D. C. Smith and Y. Tiffon (eds.). Nutrition in the Lower Metazoa. Pergamon Press, Oxford, pp. 163–178.

Willenz, Ph. 1983. Aspects cinetiques quantitatifs et ultrastructuraux de l'endocytose, la digestion, et l'exocytose chez les eponges. Thèse. Université Libre de Bruxelles. 107 pp. 108 Figs. in separate volume.

Willenz, Ph., and Rasmont, R. 1979. Mise au point d'une technique de measure de l'activité de filtration de jeune éponges cultivées *in vitro*. In: C. Lévi and N. Boury-Esnault (eds.). Biologie des Spongiaires. Colloq. Internat. C.N.R.S., Paris, *291*: 343–351.

Willenz, Ph., and Van de Vyver, G. 1982. Endocytosis of latex beads by the exopinacoderm in the freshwater sponge. *Ephydatia fluviatilis*: An *in vitro* and *in situ* study in SEM and TEM. J. Ultrastr. Res., *79*: 294–306.

Williamson, C. 1977. Fluorescence identification of zoochlorellae: A rapid method for investigating alga-invertebrate symbioses. J. Exp. Zool., *202*: 187–192.

Williamson, C. E. 1979. An ultrastructural investigation of algal symbiosis in white and green *Spongilla lacustris* (L.) (Porifera: Spongillidae). Trans. Amer. Micros. Soc., *98*: 59–77.

Wilson, H. V. 1894. Observations on the gemmule and egg development of marine sponges. J. Morph., *9*: 277–408.

Wilson, H. V. 1902. On the asexual origin of the ciliated sponge larva. Amer. Natur., *36*: 451–459.

Wilson, H. V. 1907. On some phenomena of coalescence and regeneration in sponges. J. Exp. Zool., *5*: 245–258.

Wilson, H. V. 1910. A study of some epithelioid membranes in monaxonid sponges. J. Exp. Zool., *9*: 537–577.

Wilson, H. V. 1935. Some critical points in the metamorphosis of the halichondrine sponge larva. J. Morph., *58*: 285–345.

Wilson, H. V., and Penney, J. T. 1930. The regeneration of sponges (*Microciona*) from dissociated cells. J. Exp. Zool., *56*: 73–147.

Wintermann, G. 1951. Entwicklungsphysiologishe untersuchungen an süsswasserschwämmen. Zool. Jb. (Anatomie), *71*: 427–486.

Wintermann-Kilian, G., and Ankel, W. E. 1954. Uber das verhalten der zellen bei der vereinigung isolierter epithelkugeln von *Ephydatia fluviatilis*. Wilhelm Roux's Arch. Entwicklungsmech., *147*: 171–200.

Wintermann-Kilian, G., Kilian, E. F., and Ankel, W. E. 1969. Musterbildung und entwicklungsphysiologie der epithelien beim süsswasserschwämm *Ephydatia fluviatilis*. Zool. Jb. Anat. Bd., *86*: 459–492.

Yamaguchi, M. 1957a. Chemical constitution of renieratene. Bull. Chem. Soc. Jap., *30*: 979–983.

Yamaguchi, M. 1957b. On carotneoids of a sponge *Reniera japonica*. Bull. Chem. Soc. Jap., *30*: 111–114.

Yamaguchi, M. 1958a. Chemical constitution of isorenieratene. Bull. Chem. Soc. Jap., *31*: 51–55.

Yamaguchi, M. 1958b. Renieratene, a new carotenoid containing benzen rings from a sea sponge. Bull. Chem. Soc. Jap., *31*: 739–742.

Yamaguchi, M. 1959. Total synthesis of isorenieratene. Bull. Chem. Soc. Jap., *32*: 1171–1173.

Yamaguchi, M. 1960. Total synthesis of renieratene and renierapurpurin. Bull. Chem. Soc. Jap., *33*: 1560–1562.

Yourassowsky, C., and Rasmont, R. 1983. The differentiation of sclerocytes in fresh-water sponges grown in a silicon-poor medium. Differn., in press.

Zeuthen, E. 1939. On the hibernation of *Spongilla lacustris* (L.). Zeit. vergl. Physiol., *26*: 537–547.

Zittel, K. A. 1878. Studien uber fossile spongien. Dritte abtheilung, Monactinellidae, Tetractinellidae und Calcispongiae. Abh. K. Bayer. Akad. Munchen, *13*: 91–148.

Index

Page numbers in boldface type refer to illustrations.

in bioelectric fields, 254
in buds, 221, 418, 422, **424**
in burrowing, 214
in Calcarea, 16
calcareous spicules associated with, 136
chemistry of, 219–220
concanavalin-A binding to, 219
contraction affected by, 254, 291
cross links between, **218,** 219
definition of, 220
degradation of, by symbiotic bacteria, 220
density of, compared to habitats, 133
in ectosome, 521
endopinacocytes associated with, 46
enzyme effect on, 219
exopinacocytes associated with, 46
in gemmule coats, 227
in gemmule germination, 477, 481
in gemmule hatching, 496
giant, 217, 450
glycoproteins in, 219, 235, 242, 245
glycosaminoglycans in, 220
in Hexactinellida, 65, **66,** 217, 219, 220
in inhalant organs, 261–262
in larvae, 221
localization of, 111–112, 216–217, 220
in lophocytes, 7
in mesohyl, 46, 70
occurrence of, 70
in oscules, 292
in parenchymella larvae, 399
periodicity of, 217, 219, 221, 227
phagocytosis of, 235
rough, 216–217, **218**
ruthenium red staining of, 219, 235
secretion of, 232–234
    by archeocytes, 242–243
    by basopinacocytes, 46–47
    cell types for, 235, 237–238, 240, **241,** 242, 243, **244**
    and choanocytes, 59
    colchicine affecting, 232–233
    by collencytes, 240–241
    cytochalasin B affecting, 232–233
    by endopinacocytes, 46, 242
    by exopinacocytes, 46–47, 242
    by gray cells, 422
    hydroxyurea affecting, 234, **241**
    by lophocytes, 80, 232, **233,** 234, **234**
    by oocytes, 221
    [³H]proline pathway in, 233–234, 242
    by sacculiferous cells, 243

siliceous spicules associated with, 163, 169
size of, 217, 219, 221
smooth, 216–217, **218**
in somatic growth, 514
sperm masses associated with, 221
in spongin fibers, 221
structure of, 10–12, 216–217, **218,** 219, 221
taxonomic distribution of, 10–11
Collagen microfibrils, *see* Spongin microfibrils
Collar bodies in hexactinellids, *see* Choanosyncytium of hexactinellids
Collar cells, *see* Choanocytes
Collar of choanocytes, *see* Choanocytes, collar of
Collencyte(s), 83, **84,** 88
    acid phosphatase in, 83
    buds containing, 418, 420, 421
    cell cords containing, 511
    collagen secretion by, 240, 512
    compared to
        histoblasts, 494
        other cell types, 86
    cortex containing, 112
    degeneration of, 512
    definition of, 83, 85
    description of, general, 7
    ectosome containing, 521
    elimination by, 339
    excurrent canals containing, 284
    in gemmule formation, 459, 461
    incurrent canals containing, 267
    ingestion by, 325
    inhalant organs containing, 262
    larval attachment involving, 407, 412
    larval reaggregates containing, 412
    movement of, 517, 519
    neuroid cells referred to as, 85
    organelles in, 83, 242
    parenchymella larvae containing, 396, 399, 401
    pigment in, 130, 131
    protein synthesis by, 570
    reduction bodies containing, 506
    in regeneration, 531
    remodeling involving, 284, 517, 519, 521
    in somatic growth, 511, 512, 514
    in tissue recognition, 545, 549, 550
    tissue regression involving, 503
    transformation into
        apendopinacocytes, 285

Index

18 320BEP 4224
09/99 BR
09-465-00 GBC